Fish Catching Methods of the World

Fish Catching Methods of the World

Andres von Brandt

Fishing News Books Ltd.

Farnham · Surrey · England

First published 1964
Revised and enlarged 1972
Revised and enlarged 1984

Brandt, Andres von
Fish Catching Methods of the World. — 3rd edition

1. Fisheries — Equipment and supplies
I. Title
639'.2'028 SH344

ISBN 0 85238 125 5

Printed in Great Britain by
Avon Litho Ltd., Stratford-upon-Avon, Warwickshire.

Contents

Foreword

Fishing is as old as hunting and the gathering of food. However, whereas livestock breeding replaced hunting and agriculture superseded food gathering, fishing is still basically conducted along the ancient patterns of hunting the wild living stocks in the water as nature provides them. Furthermore, the main components of fishing gear — netting, lines, hooks, floats and sinkers which can be traced back to the earliest times — are still in common use and provide the bulk of the world's fish catch. The progress in development of fishing methods and gear which has made possible the recent dramatic increase in the world fish production is for the most part therefore not based on completely new concepts. It is rather due to the ingenuity of the fishermen, backed by engineers and scientists, in improving the quality and effectiveness of these basic components and in inventing an impressive variety of fishing gear and techniques to meet different fishing conditions and socio-economic requirements.

Professor v. Brandt, having devoted a considerable amount of his work and extensive travel to the study of fishing gear and techniques, has established himself as a leading authority on this subject. He has not only collected a great number of characteristic examples from most parts of the world but has also developed a rational classification system for the multitude of fishing devices and techniques, thus permitting a much better understanding of historical, geographical, ethnological and technical aspects and their inter-relationship. The work presented in his book is unique in this respect and fills a gap in our knowledge which has long been felt.

While due emphasis is given to developments in commercial fisheries the author has devoted considerable effort to describing also fishing gear and methods used by small scale and subsistence level fishermen. These are of particular interest because of their efficient adaptation to certain fish species and environmental peculiarities. Even though they do not contribute significantly to global fish production, they are important for providing a complete picture of the "state of the art" and deserve inclusion to prevent their being overlooked in the face of sophisticated technical progress.

The value of this particular one of the many contributions of Professor v. Brandt to the literature on fishing lies in the scholarly treatment of the principles on which fishing and fishing technology are based. The comprehensive and thorough approach to its subject matter will no doubt ensure that this book will remain for many years to come an important source of information and inspiration for students, researchers, development workers, commercial and sport fishermen as well as for the interested layman.

Much of this could have been said about the first edition of 'Fish Catching Methods of the World' published in 1964. It is certainly even more true for this second enlarged and revised edition. Finding and catching the fish is the first indispensable step towards making available the aquatic protein sources to meet the increased demand, particularly in the developing world. This important activity is consequently a major concern of the FAO Department of Fisheries. I sincerely hope that this book will find the wide distribution it deserves so that it can contribute to education and progress to the advantage of all concerned.

ROY I. JACKSON
Assistant Director-General (Fisheries)
Food and Agriculture Organization of the United Nations

Rome,
October, 1971.

Preface

Nowadays the study of fishing gear and fishing methods is an integral part of fishery science. The biologists as well as the gear technologists are interested in the influence of fishing gear on the living resources of the waters; managers calculate the relationship between the costs of fishing equipment and the earnings that are secured; and administrators engaged in fisheries find they need to have knowledge of fishing gear and its action in order to keep in line with lawful fishing regulations.

This interest did not always exist. It was not till the 18th century that writers considered fishing gear and fishing methods were worthy of notice. French encyclopaedists were the first to give publicity to catching methods; their engravings were very decorative and are highly prized even today for that quality.

But they were not made for fishermen. The first more detailed discussions of catching methods for practical fishermen were written by zoologists interested in fisheries at the end of the last and the beginning of this century. These publications can be considered the first steps made in the field of gear research. But to be fully precise the current international and worldwide interest of fishery science in fishing gear and fishing methods were born on the occasion of the first international Fishing Gear Congress of F.A.O. held at Hamburg in 1957, whose papers and discussions were subsequently published in that fine volume 'Modern Fishing Gear of the World 1'. That interest was intensified by fishing Congresses held respectively in London in 1963 and at Reykjavik in 1970 and also by the Congress on Fish Behaviour in relation to fishing gear held in Norway in 1967. The books and publicity resulting from these meetings spread even more widely the available information, and stimulated the rate of progress and general application of improved methods of fishing operations.

In relation to the quantity of the total world catch only a few methods are of interest to the commercial fisheries. These are especially trawling and purse seining. But there are other methods, too, by which fishermen can earn money and which cannot be neglected even when used in local areas and for a limited time only. There are a number of these catching methods distributed all over the world as well as some less important, whose origin is based on the simple fishing techniques evolved from the old fishermen's knowledge of fish behaviour. To understand the philosophy of all these methods and the gear used in them the author set to work to collect the details of practices of catching techniques in many parts of the world. This collection of knowledge in text and picture was finally published in the form of the first edition of this book "Fish Catching Methods of the World" issued in 1964. That publication became recognized as the thesaurus of fishing gear and catching methods. Some institutions used it as a text book for lectures and the author has to confess — my publisher may forgive me — that it was a pleasure to see copies of this book in the hands of students far far away — even when those copies were printed without the editor's permission.

Other people used the book as a basis for writing and illustrating new books. By these developments it emerged that there were some gaps in the first edition and that improved fishing methods were not included for the desired and needed comprehensiveness; moreover, the development of fishing methods is still proceeding. Thus, hand operated gear has become replaced by mechanized devices and first steps are even being taken towards automatic operation of some gears.

This has led to new ideas and tendencies showing themselves. So much so, that a second edition of this work was called for in order to put on record the great progress made in gear technology since 1964 and so make available to teaching institutions and practical fishermen alike the latest advances. I have therefore incorporated new chapters in the book covering the new methods, have amplified others where sections were incomplete and, above all, have added many new illustrations and increased the number amply to illustrate the text by nearly half as many again.

I believe, as the author concerned, that this much expanded text and the many new illustrations will be considered a new and improved contribution and a sign of progress. Nevertheless the reader is still asked to be indulgent if, for instance, he cannot find all variations of a particular catching method recorded. It might even be that some reader might find his own valuable publication is not mentioned in the bibliography. For any such omission (if in fact it is true) please extend tolerance. For this edition too, the author desires to express his thanks to all colleagues who have given their assistance in acquiring desired information. Especially he has to thank those of his friends who have been kind enough to let him participate in practical fishing which remains always the basis for the understanding of catching methods. To those patient companions this book is dedicated.

A. v. BRANDT

Hamburg,
30 September, 1971.

Preface to the third edition

Methods of catching fish have been known since mankind's earliest days, and the improvement of existing techniques and the development of new ones has continued right up to the present day. Short periods of rapid development alternate with long periods in which progress seems slow, if indeed progress is made at all, and this has given rise to the widespread belief that fishermen are conservative by nature — reluctant to give up traditional methods in order to try new and better ones. And yet the history of fishery technology has many important milestones — such as the invention of net-making in the Stone Age; the development of distant-water whaling industries using explosive harpoons fired from guns; the mediaeval development in Europe of cod fishing with handlines, and herring fishing with drifting gillnets, and the major advances in net-making, first through mechanization in the last century and more recently with the introduction of a whole range of synthetic fibres.

Most of these developments sprang from economic stimuli — the need to operate larger gear in order to satisfy export as well as home markets; the need to fish in increasingly deep water in order to boost catches; the need to mechanize in the face of high labour costs and, in recent years, the need to keep pace with the growing potential of computers in the operation of fishing gear.

It is readily apparent that today a new period of rapid development is being caused by the high, and constantly rising, costs of fuel. More efficient engines may be developed, but major savings will only be achieved by more fuel-efficient fishing techniques, and for this reason much attention is now being paid to new techniques of using lines, traps, enmeshing nets and boat-seines.

These activities have had their impact on this new edition of *Fish Catching Methods of the World*. The second edition, published in 1972, was a revised and enlarged version of the original 1964 book; but in this third edition many chapters have been completely rewritten, and so much additional material has been incorporated that the book has now almost doubled in size.

This new edition, like its predecessors, would not have been possible without the help of fishermen and academic colleagues in many parts of the world. Many practical fishermen have kindly allowed me to accompany them to sea in order to learn something of their methods, and the problems they encounter. I must also thank many of my colleagues for their generous assistance when I have visited their countries. In this respect I would like to mention especially Dr. E Dahm of the Institute for Fishing Gear and Fishing Techniques, in Hamburg, who has been kind enough to write two important sections in the chapters covering trawling, in which he deals with bottom and midwater trawling in freshwater. Many other colleagues have helped me by providing information, collecting material, and answering innumerable questions. I offer my sincere thanks to them all, and in particular to the following: Prof. Dr K. J. Ang, Serdang, Malaysia; Prof. Dr V. Angelescu, Mar del Plata, Argentina; Prof. N. Bacalbasa, Galati, Rumania; F. Carré, Paris, France; C. C. Chen, Taipei, Taiwan; I. Hayashi, Tokyo, Japan; Capt. L. C. Hu, Christchurch, New Zealand; Dr G. Jens, Udenhausen, Germany; Prof. K. S. Ko, Pusan, South Korea; Dr LiGreci, Messina, Italy; A. R. Margetts, Lowestoft, England; Dr T. Mengi, Istanbul, Turkey; Prof. Dr N. Nishimura, Tokyo, Japan; Dr M. Nomura, Arazaki, Japan; Dr A. Percier, Biarritz, France; R. Piboubes, Brest, France; Dr J. Schärfe, Ansedonia, Italy; Dr E. Solymos, Baja, Hungary; Dr P. R. Todd, Christchurch, New Zealand; Dipl. Ing. R. Wawrowski, Launceston, Australia.

Last, but not least, I would like to thank the publishers of this book for having patience enough to listen to all my requests — despite the fact that my English must often have brought them close to despair!

ANDRES von BRANDT

Hamburg, Germany
1984

Chapter one

Catching methods in fisheries; an introduction

Fishing is a form of primary production. Older than agriculture, the history of fishing, including that of catching methods, is as old as mankind. It may be that fishing was already practised by prehominids before the advent of *Homo sapiens*. Their remains have been excavated, together with prehistoric bones of fish, and pebbles shaped in a simple manner, in Olduvai Gorge in northern Tanzania. These pebbles may have been used for killing fish: they may have been the fishing gear of the predecessors of modern man.

In prehistoric times, and sometimes even today, fishing is nothing more than gathering, one of the simplest forms of economy. Every object is taken that can be used in any way. It matters not whether it is taken from the water or gathered from the dry land.

When undisturbed and in natural balance the waters of the world provide a rich choice of suitable materials, mostly of vegetable or animal origin. Fish may be the most important product of fresh and sea waters, but there may be some doubt if in prehistoric times man was always able to catch them. In general they are too fast-moving to catch by hand. It is likely that prehistoric man had to look more for plants and their products, like seeds of waternuts or reeds rich in starch, or for sessile and slow-moving animals like molluscs, worms, coelenterates and crustaceans.

A great number of algae and other waterplants are, or have been, harvested for human food and animal fodder as well as for fertilizer and for the extraction of various chemicals. Today fish provide a high percentage of the animal albumen so necessary for the whole of mankind. Not only are fishes and water plants the subject of modern fishing methods in sea and fresh waters, but so too are other animals like sponges, coelenterates, molluscs, crustaceans, insects, amphibians, reptiles, birds and mammals. Even frogs, crocodiles and snakes are often considered in the laws of different countries as 'fish' even when not fish from the zoological point of view. In the following chapters of this book the term 'fish' may include many other products of the water. Not all of them are used for food, fodder or fertilizers. Some of these products are needed to obtain raw materials for different purposes including those from which pharmaceutical and cosmetic products are derived. Others are sought for decoration only, like vertebrae of fish, shells of mussels, corals or pearls, and as in old times, shells are collected by children as toys.[324] Clothes have been made of fish skin, as well as membranes for drums,[611] and even armour with the help of scales and spines. There are many other ways in which man has used products of fresh and sea water for making tools, for building houses and boats, and for meeting his everyday needs.

To obtain all these wanted products of fresh waters and of the seas, man originally had to rely solely on his hands, occasionally also using his feet and his teeth. It is understandable that these methods soon became inadequate for his growing needs. Simple tools were invented to improve man's catching ability. Some of these became so efficient that they are used even today. These simple tools were the basis of better gear, but thousands of years were to pass before specific fishing gear was developed.

The purpose of this book is to give a review of fishing methods all over the world. Discussed here are the basic concepts of how a fish – in the broadest sense – can be caught. It may seem impossible to review all fishing gears operated anywhere in the world, now or in earlier times (many of which may now be found only in museums) but when different gears are compared it is surprising to find that the methods of catching are limited to a relatively small number of basic techniques as will be explained in the following chapters. There are not so many ways in which a fish may be caught; perhaps a dozen and a half, maybe less. The basic ideas of how a fish or other prey can be caught are used for the classification of all fishing methods, given at the end of this book. A careful reader, comparing earlier editions of this book with this one, will find that there are some revisions in the gear classification. However, nothing of the former concept has been changed except for the addition of some more detailed subdivisions. The principles of classifying catching methods have remained unchanged for twenty years.

Fishing gear belongs to the material culture of most peoples, and fishing is a living occupation of men. Those who claim that fishermen are conservative people who do not change their fishing gear for generations should visit any modern fishing harbour. Within a month or so they will be surprised to find how much fishing gear has been changed or varied to increase efficiency or to improve handling, although the principles of the fishing methods may not have been altered. This is why no information about the *detailed* construction of fishing gear is given in this book. The book may be in demand for many years, during which time gear will undergo many alterations. Therefore, it is repeated that this book will explain the principles of catching only, and how they have come about. Other books on the construction of fishing gear, its material and size, are available (*eg* FAO Gear Catalogues).[160,417,547]

Some fishing methods may be more economically sound than others under special conditions, and these are therefore described in more detail. Nevertheless, the author does not wish to make any distinction between 'important' and 'unimportant' fishing gear. This can change very quickly, and for many reasons. Even a fishing method such as trawling can lose its 'importance' by increasing the price of oil! For a small-scale fisherman a simple gear can be more important than the sophisticated one of a large-scale fishery. Therefore, all fishing methods are considered of equal value in one fishery or another. Before discussing the different fishing methods and their catching principles some general remarks may be necessary about fishing, and these will be given in the following sections of this chapter.

1.1 Fisherman and hunter

For gathering, no specific fishing gear is needed and even today the simple tools used for gathering seafood cannot be considered as genuine fishing gear (Chapter 2). This can be said also for the beginnings of another old form of collecting economy – namely hunting.

Fishing and hunting can be traced to the same origin. Even today it is difficult to explain why harpooning a tunny is fishing and harpooning a swimming deer, often with exactly the same gear, is hunting: or to decide if catching waterborne but landliving crabs is fishing or hunting. Originally, hunting and fishing may have been one, using similar methods. Between them there have always been interchanging techniques as between the catcher of animals on land or of fish from the water. Often it is not possible to distinguish whether a spear has been designed and used for fishing, hunting, fighting, or only as a symbol for ceremonial purposes.

Many methods of catching are known in both fishing and hunting, such as spearing, harpooning and shooting (Chapter 6); catching with hooks (Chapter 9); by trapping with different types of mechanical (Chapter 14) or non-mechanical traps (Chapters 15 and 16). Some hunting is even done with the help of netting which is so important for most fishing methods. According to drawings in Egyptian tombs, some think that the use of netting is older in hunting than it is in fishing!

It is quite futile to discuss whether hunting is older than fishing or fishing older than hunting. The opinion is sometimes expressed that fishing must be younger because it is easier to catch an animal on land than to win a fish from the sea. This is not convincing. In primary and primitive lands there are many inundated parts in the interior and on the edges of the sea that would facilitate fishery rather than hamper it. Accordingly, there are some who strongly hold the contrary opinion; namely, that fishing is of older origin than the hunting of terrestrial animals because only simple tools are necessary for its practice. According to these opinions, hunting requires the use of much better gear; indeed, of equipment which sometimes resembles the weapons of war. Therefore it is understandable that some authorities consider hunting and making war as different forms of 'violent occupation of living creatures'[344] in contrast to the supposedly peaceful occupation of fishing.

In another view, hunters – through the use of their weapons – tend to become experienced warriors while the fishermen, having less need of aggressive action in their pursuits, would fall into second place. As a consequence of this reasoning the practice of fishing in some parts of the world is carried out by people of a socially lower standing.

But although their beginnings were undoubtedly essentially the same, hunting and fishing have developed down the centuries on very different lines. The prestige attached to 'royal' huntsmen can be contrasted with the lowlier plight and status of the 'poor' fisherman. According to the traditional view a huntsman (today sometimes replaced by a cowboy or trapper) is considered to live a free and untroubled life, and the man who practises the royal sport of hunting, even if he lives in a log house, cannot be deemed to be poor. But the fisherman is always considered 'poor': the adjective clings to him as does blue to the sky and green to the meadow. Nevertheless, it seems that there is one exception to this generalization and that is the sport fisherman who is usually considered to have the status of a hunter.

It is interesting to note that modern fishing with sophisticated methods is considered as a form of hunting by the fishery industry itself. In this case hunting is seen in contrast to stock breeding. The hunter is looking for single fish or small groups of wild animals – not tamed or domesticated, not controlled in their life history, nor influenced in their behaviour or properties, and which may be living over a wide area. The stock breeder manages more or less domesticated groups of well-known and numbered animals, bred according to some concept to get special bodily properties, and kept together in a more or less artificial limited area. These differences can be compared with fishing for wild fish populations in open fresh and sea waters on the one hand, and with fish culturing in artificial ponds or controlled waters on the other. Some think that the aim of all branches of fishery should be to replace hunting by the management of controlled stocks in natural waters and in artificial ones. We are still far away from this objective even though there are some stock assessments and calculations about the quantities which could be harvested. There may be some doubt as to whether it will ever be possible to manage fish populations in the oceans in the same way that cattle are herded on land.

Because the hunter and fisherman in ancient times had primitive gear only, some modern fishermen seem surprised to learn that it was possible for them to achieve any worthwhile result. But the ancient hunters and fishermen (and also some of the small-scale fishermen today) have, in comparison with modern people in industrial fisheries, a striking superiority that comes from their fundamental understanding of the behaviour of their prey. With this knowledge they are able to outwit the fish and catch it even with their simple gear. In highly developed industrial fisheries with many sophisticated machines to operate fishing gear nearly automatically, and with electronic equipment for searching and finding the prey, very often the knowledge of fish behaviour has fallen into oblivion.

1.2 From subsistence fishing to commercial fisheries

We do not know how long it was before a human being made a gear which proved no longer as effective in hunting but was much more efficient than any other gear for fishing. This may be the beginning of a clear division between hunter and fisher. At this stage of development, fishing with more or less specialized gear was pursued by man to provide food for his own needs and those of his family, community or tribe. Only single fish were caught, maybe one large one and a few small ones. Today this would be a form of subsistence fishery – a small-scale fishery for which only simple gear is needed. As already noted, the knowledge of the fisherman about the behaviour of his prey was a major factor in his success. Spearing, and trapping with plaited fences and baskets, may be the most important methods during this time. The art of net-making (Chapter 18) was not developed before the late Stone Age and because it was difficult to get the right material for net-making, the first fishing gear made of netting rather than crudely woven strips of wood, was probably very small.

Originally man was interested only in catching sufficient fish for his daily needs and we know from some north European hunters and fishermen that nothing was allowed to be wasted by catching more than was necessary. At some point, however, it became possible to barter fish against other things, and in this case it became desirable to catch more – especially when it was found that fish could be preserved and stored by drying, smoking, salting or by some simple processes of fermentation. This gave a strong impetus for more fishing, and for better fishing gear to facilitate the development of a permanent artisanal fishery. To catch more fish required not only more time, but also a larger quantity of fishing gear – more pots, more traps, or more lines with more hooks. But not only was the amount of the gear operated increased but also its efficiency and size in order to be capable of catching bigger quantities. Fishing for single fish or for small quantities, as in subsistence fishing, was replaced by an artisanal commercial fishery sometimes related to special markets. This gave new impetus to the improvement of fishing methods.

The artisanal fishery, mostly no longer in the old traditional form, has its importance even today in modern society. The trade in fish became more and more important and this gave rise to the development of large-scale fisheries based on bulk fishing. In the Middle Ages in Europe the first large-scale fisheries were already established, to supply the markets with salted cod, salted herring and whale oil. These were also the first of the distant fisheries, fishing off shallow-water coasts often of other continents. For their management, large quantities of gear were now needed as well as the material for making them by specialized undertakings. Lines and hooks had to be produced for linefishing for cod; large quantities of netting were needed for making driftnets (Chapter 29) for herring; and spears and harpoons had to be mass-produced for whaling.

With the increasing demand, especially in industrial areas, there came also another trend – the need for large-scale fishery to abandon shallow waters and penetrate into greater depths in order to find larger supplies of fish. Greater depth meant also bigger and heavier gear and greater manpower for its handling. Nevertheless it was a long time before mechanization was introduced into fisheries (Chapter 31). Deep water fishing also extended to large lakes; so they talk, for instance, of a 'deep sea fishery' on Lake Constance even today, in contrast to the beach fishery. The same thing happened on the sea coasts. Here the development from the shallow water fishery to the deep sea fishery is still going on, which not only means fishing over deep water but also fishing at great depth. This brought new developments in bulk fisheries with beam trawls and later large otterboard bottom trawls for demersal prey (Chapters 20 and 21); purse seines to catch large quantities of pelagic prey in the upper range of the waters (Chapter 25), and midwater trawls to fish in the area where neither purse seines nor bottom trawls could be operated (Chapter 22).

Both small-scale artisanal and large-scale industrial fisheries have an important place in the nutrition of people today and in the future; the one by its flexibility, even when sometimes only small quantities (but of higher quality) are landed, and the other by its large quantities of often cheaper products which are needed to satisfy large markets and to serve the needs of the fish processing industry, including the production of fish meal for cattle food. Both needs can give impetus to the development and improvement of fishing gear and fishing methods as can be seen in the following chapters.

1.3 Sport fishing and commercial fisheries

From the view-point of catching, sport fishing can be considered a form of small-scale fishery designed not to make a living from the catch but to concentrate skill for fun and pleasure (Chapter 10). Both the commercial fisherman, setting lines with hundreds of hooks or operating a hand-line with a few only in the hope of getting a good catch, and the sport fisherman waiting for strong fighting game fish with his simple or sophisticated (sometimes also expensive) tackle, are the descendants of the prehistoric hunter.

Originally, fishing with hook and line was the method used by everyone. With the increasing privileges of the landowners it became the sport of rich people well into the last century, but has changed completely now from a derided hobby of some strange people to an important form of human recreation. As already mentioned, sport fishermen were considered as hunters, living in supposedly unrestrained freedom like one of the last links between man and nature. There are few ideas that have changed so completely in so short a time as those held by the public in regard to sport fishing! Therefore it is regrettable that in the modern life of many countries, especially the highly developed industrial ones, the art and practice of fishing has been divided into two ostensibly diverse and even adverse fields – sport fishing and commercial fishing. It must not be forgotten that both have the same origin, and from the viewpoint of fishing techniques they represent only two variations of the same principle of catching fish with hook and line. It seems that now there will be some change. Both sport fishery and commercial fishery are concerned to preserve nature against the worst influences of civilization. Moreover, fishing waters cannot be managed solely with the methods of sport fishing. Other more effective methods, as operated in commercial fisheries, must support the aim of managing fishing waters in a biological equilibrium. Sport fishermen and commercial fishermen have to work together not only to preserve but also to defend nature. Each simply represents a different variation of a fishing method. For this reason in this book sport fishing is considered in a special chapter (Chapter 10), but is given neither more nor less importance than any other fishing method.

1.4 Active and passive fishing gear

As mentioned before, there are relatively few basic principles which can be used to catch fish, in spite of the enormous variety of fishing gear operated in the world. In the classification at the end of this book there are only 16 different groups of fishing principles, and maybe even some of these could be grouped together for simplicity. Sometimes the same gear can be used for two or even more fishing methods with virtually no alteration in construction but simply a change in the method of operation.

In this classification no account is taken of the fact that sometimes, in fishing laws, gear is grouped into 'active' and 'passive' equipment. In passive gear the fish has to come voluntarily, as in traps, gill nets, and also some types of fishing hooks. Therefore much experience is needed to construct a passive gear in such a manner that the prey will accept the gear and not be frightened by its construction, colour, visibility, smell or anything else. Knowledge of fish behaviour will help to make the most effective gear. The success of active gear, like dredges, trawls and cast nets, and also spears and harpoons and some gear used for drive-in fisheries (Chapter 26), depends more or less upon man's skill or perseverance. The fisherman can influence the success of an active fishing gear by leading the gear into the path of the fish, or by driving them into it by various methods. To influence the success of a passive gear is much more difficult, due to the fact that not all stimuli affecting the behaviour of fish or other prey opposite a fishing gear are known. It must also be considered that the behaviour of the fish can change with their age, or with the season of the year, or maybe also by learning. Pollution can also influence fish behaviour as can be demonstrated with electrical fishing (Chapter 5).

A grouping into passive and active gear has nothing to do with the basic principles of catching. In many groups of fishing methods examples of both types of fishing gear are present. It must be said, too, that sometimes not only the size but also the towing speed of an active gear is critical to its efficiency. Increased size and speed need more power for the operation of a gear and this was often not available in early fisheries. It can be supposed, therefore, that passive gear was more often operated in ancient times than active gear. Finally, it has to be stressed that active and passive fishing gear must not be confused with moving and stationary gear. A stationary set line and a towed troll line are both passive gear which have to be accepted by the fish. These are both passive fishing methods with hooks. On the other hand a ripping hook moved up and down is, in most cases, an active fishing gear, catching (in this case by fouling the fish) more or less at random by a special form of linefishing with hooks.

1.5 Basic ideas for fishing methods: their distribution and possible improvement

At first casual glance a great many different types of fishing gear seem to have been developed in fisheries. The history of their creation, growth and distribution is still rather obscure. But when the fishing gear of various nations is compared, it becomes evident that the fishing techniques have developed from only a very few basic ideas for capturing fish, either singly or in mass, for the benefit of man. Most of these basic ideas for the manner of capturing fish are somehow spread over the world and have become the common possession of mankind.

Ethnologists discovered a striking similarity in the fishing methods of traditional, sometimes called primitive, fisheries. This cannot be explained by cultural exchange but rather by the like reaction of man to like problems. This is not surprising for, from time immemorial, fishing has presented, again and again, similar problems; and everywhere those problems have been solved by men in the same or similar ways. An analogy is that an animal reacts in an experimental situation in rather the same way no matter whether the experiment is made in Tokyo or in Hamburg. Nevertheless, there may have been a more direct exchange of knowledge about fishing gear in olden times, not only between neighbouring areas but also between continents, especially in sea fisheries, in spite of all contradicting discussions in this respect.

In just a few cases the spread of a fishing method or a fishing gear is well-known, especially when this has come about in modern times. A good example is the design of the so-called 'Madeira trap', made in a typical form and manner (*Fig 319*) which can be traced from India via the Seychelles, Zanzibar Island, Madagascar, and Madeira to as far west as the Caribbean Sea. There is also good reason for supposing that the ancient Oceanic fishermen with their gear and vessels reached out on the one side to Madagascar and as far as South America on the other side. The ice-fishing methods of the Arctic are well known through all the polar regions. Cover pots (Chapter 28), well known in Asia as well as in Africa, were found also by the explorers of America. Therefore, it is possible that there were better contacts in olden times than are accepted today.

Nowadays, of course, the exchange of knowledge about fishing methods scarcely meets any difficulties. International fishing areas, and worldwide organizations like FAO, facilitate very close contacts. The Republic of South Africa has adopted purse seining from California, and in the eastern Baltic large pound nets of Japanese design have been used. Isolated fishing tribes of the southwest coast of Madagascar now make their netting of polyamide monofilaments, and a Stone Age tribe on a forgotten island like Lan Yü (Botel Tobago) off the east coast of South Taiwan know how to make netting from hard laid polypropylene. Knowledge of the importance of new fishing methods, or of new net materials, spreads quickly and their development and testing will be carried out simultaneously in many parts of the world. Considered on the whole, beside duplicate or multiple invention of fishing techniques there frequently occurs the often uncontrollable communication of fishing techniques from one country to another. This is a simple phenomenon of 'borrowed culture'.

In each fishing area, the known fishing methods have been improved and altered, sometimes by a single fisherman, according to local needs. Beginning with simple methods and primitive gear, the more complicated techniques soon begin to emerge. This development has been hastened and improved by various stimuli. Periods of explosive development have been followed by more stagnant times and this is so even today. Some of the impulses encouraging gear development have already been mentioned, like the endeavour to catch fish in larger quantities, or in deeper waters where more fish can be expected. In both cases alterations in the construction of fishing gear are needed. Another stimulant for developing fishing methods and gear is the desire to progress from the originally guarded or watched fishing gear needing many helping hands, to automatic unguarded gear which can be operated by limited man-power. To do this the gear must be designed in such a way that no special guard or watchman is required to observe when fish enter the gear and to close it in time to prevent the fish from escaping. Moreover, a watchman controlling the quantity of the catch in a gear can work only during daytime and when the water is clear (*Figs 272* and *277*). This narrows the time of operation for the gear.

More suitable, and independent of daytime, is another method for the control of the catch in a gear by attaching to the gear so-called 'feeler lines' held in the hand of the watching fisherman (*Fig 434*). Such lines have been used not only in fresh waters but also in sea waters with the aim of detecting fish entering the gear so as to close and haul it at the right time. To save time some gear was adapted to register the catch automatically, warning the fisherman to come and secure the catch. Bells were fixed to the gear to announce the catch as the Chinese have done and as some sport fishermen do also today (*Fig 132*). Of course such alarm devices help and in some large Japanese pound nets sonar buoys have been placed to allow remote control of the catch. On the other hand it may be better to construct the gear in such a manner that the fish can be held alive by the gear for some time so that they can be taken at any convenient time later. Especially in trapping (Chapter 15) automatic catching gears were devised like mechanical traps (Chapter 14) – known also from hunting – and traps with non-return devices (Chapter 16), which proved so effective that they have been used not only for traps but also for other gear.

This gives a hint of another interesting development in fishing gear. Apart from the principles of catching, a limited number of single elements in the physical construction of fishing gear can be found to crop up in many different fishing methods. The use of a non-return device such as the funnel is one of these single elements which can be found in many types of fishing gear.

1.6 Division of labour and collective fishing

Some fishing methods need little manpower and can be operated by a child: in others even the power of a strong man is not sufficient. This is why very often, in traditional fisheries, a clear division of labour on a sexual basis can be found. There are some fishing methods considered suitable for women (and children) while others are reserved for men only. This sex-based division of labour may be as old as mankind. In general, the more exhausting work needing more physical strength is done by men only; other work, requiring less bodily strength, is within the range of women. This has nothing to do with the quality of the status of women and men. This separation is based on the physical differences between men and women – often forgotten today with an increasing misunderstanding of man and nature. This old knowledge about the need to separate duties between men and women to overcome the physical demands of life is considered as one of the earliest recognitions of mankind.[317]

In general, women are responsible for the collecting of food such as vegetables or small animals; for food preparation; for bringing up and rearing the children; for tending the garden; for the home and similar things. The man is considered responsible for hunting; defending his family, his tribe or his living area; and for many types of hard work like grubbing, housebuilding (sometimes), and other work which needs more physical power. An analogous development can be seen in the operation of the different fishing methods. Gathering is done by women only (Chapter 2) in so far as this method of collecting is not combined with diving, but even here some exceptions are known (Chapter 3). Fishing by stupefying, in the original form of poisoning, shows no strong separation, although today electrical fishing is in general done by men only (Chapter 5). In line fishing (Chapters 8 and 9) small-scale methods with a limited number of hooks can be used by women and men, but large-scale fishing, *eg* with longlines, is typically a fishing method for men only. This cannot be said of trapping (Chapters 14 to 17) where small traps are also set mainly by men. In fishing with bagnets (Chapter 19) the small hand-operated gear is often used by women, while the operation of large-scale bagnets is a job for men. Fishing with dragged gear (Chapters 20 to 22), seine nets (Chapter 24), surrounding gear (Chapter 25) and generally also drive-in nets (Chapter 26) are fishing methods for men. With lift nets (Chapter 27) we see again that hand-operated smaller gear can be also used by women while large ones are operated by men only. Falling gear (Chapter 28), like cover pots, are operated by men as well as women, but cast-nets are operated by men only. Fishing with gillnets (Chapter 29), entangling nets (Chapter 30), and especially fishing with modern computerized systems or with harvesting machines (Chapter 31), seems to remain for men only, even when the physical power needed is very low. The conclusion can be that not many fishing methods are suitable for women. They operate small gear in most cases but there are no statistics available about the quantities of food taken by fishing women to feed their families day by day all over the world, especially in black Africa and Asia. Some people think that the quantity taken by women in this manner is not much less than that which the commercial fishermen land with their heavy gear all over the world.

When, in contrast to men, the work of women is considered on an individual basis,[414] it can be seen that very often the women do not fish alone, but in a group like a loose collective, each woman with her own gear (*Figs 1* and *645*). This is done not just to chat during fishing but to secure a better catch by driving the fish together, and to prevent their escape when only a single gear is operated. It is also

Fig 1 Collective fishing by women and children with cover pots and scoop nets. Mali, 1962. (*Photo: FAO, P Pittet.*)

used to stupefy the fishes to some extent (Chapter 5) as when many persons disturb the mud by trampling.

Fishing in a collective with a single large gear is more typically the work of men. In fisheries, co-operation is very often needed for the construction of gear, especially when larger ones are needed. It may be a large barrier made of heavy wood for catching fish, or a large net with thousands of meshes. Co-operation is also needed for the operation and maintenance of the gear, especially in trawling (Chapters 21 and 22), seining (Chapter 24) and purse seining (Chapter 25). As in hunting, sometimes dozens of fishermen had to work together to get and to secure the catch. It seems that the voluntary alliance of men, even when for a limited time only to do common work, is elementary to the behaviour of man.[317] Such voluntary collectives not controlled by anyone outside the group, or by the state, survive in some fisheries today. Often these communities are for large-scale trapping such as on the Isle of Rügen (GDR),[489] or in the Mediterranean for large tuna traps. Even when two fishermen with their vessels work together, *eg* in pair trawling, this can be considered as a survival of the old group hunting of ancient times. Often such co-operation is necessary because even today, in spite of mechanization, many fishing methods cannot be done by a single person. On the other hand, increasing mechanization progressively reduces the number of people working in a collective.

Increasing mechanization is also the reason why now women can become more engaged in fish catching. Until recently wives could help only by rowing and steering a small vessel while the husband set the gear. Nowadays they can also work in large-scale fisheries when physical work is replaced by machines. But it should not be forgotten that there are other sections of fisheries where women for a long time had a dominating and sometimes commanding position, such as in marketing the fishery products. This is especially so in Africa. Women have also dominated fish processing, not only in northern but also in many tropical countries. Only in a few cases are women engaged in net-making: often they are not allowed to do so for religious reasons (Chapter 23).

Speaking of manpower and catching methods, a third group of people must be mentioned who, sometimes, can have a special position in fishing. These are the older men who can no longer participate in the usual fishing methods, especially in sea fisheries. Sometimes they operate smaller gear, *eg* spears, as in northern Europe, with special permission because they are generally prohibited. The most important contribution of the old men of a fishing community may be net-making and mending. The very quick introduction of monofilaments for the making of gillnets in south and east Asia may be due to the ability of the old fishermen in thousands of villages knotting a more effective netting with the new material – despite the fact that this material is stiff and not easily knotted.

1.7 Manpower, mechanization and automation

The wish to improve the efficiency of the fishing gear stimulated the development of the known fishing methods and, as far as possible, the effort to find new fishing techniques. Many impulses pushed forward this tendency not only to catch more, but also to catch in deeper waters, and to replace labour-intensive attended fishing gear by those that catch automatically without anyone in attendance. It seems that since olden times fishermen considered physical manpower as unavoidable in fishing. When larger catches were needed, and the amount of gear was increased or enlarged, it meant that more men had to co-operate. The problem of reducing manpower with the help of machines in fisheries seems not to have been resolved before the eighteenth century, when capstans with a vertical axis were introduced in the large-scale herring driftnet fishery. The Chinese may have known of mechanical help in fisheries long before. Manpower winches with a horizontal axis came later, perhaps first in coastal fisheries for the operation of beach seines. At the turn of the last century, fishing vessels became motorized and the winches motor-driven, which reduced manpower requirements very much in gear operation. Originally the idea was to ease handling of the gear by winches, but with increasing catch value and the rising cost of manpower, powered machines also had to replace men without decreasing the yield. In this development, motors replaced oars and sails, and power-driven winches reduced the number of the crew while increasing profit and safety at the same time. The catch per man, per vessel or per tonnage of a vessel was increased rapidly and is still increasing. This development became very important in the increasing mechanization of large-scale and small-scale fisheries. The modern operation of gear in trawling with large stern trawlers; the handling of large purse seines with power blocks on modern seiners; the introduction of powered drums for netting and lines, and reels for ropes for seining, are all examples of successful methods not only to facilitate the work of many but also to decrease manpower.

To reduce the number of the crew by machines is especially important in industrial countries with lack of, or very expensive, manpower. Mechanization is not so much of interest to developing countries, which try to keep as many people as possible in fisheries to give them labour and food, and also not for industrial countries during periods of recession with high unemployment. In these cases the jobs may be more important than a fishing method made labour-extensive by mechanization.

The most recent tendency in gear development is to alter fishing methods in such a manner that they operate automatically with little effort by man. Especially in operating handlines the slogan became: 'push a button and let it fish'. In this case, computers are used to make decisions to steer the gear. In the new systems, the overall operation of the gear is divided into a number of different steps, and each step runs automatically. That does not mean robots are replacing fishermen; they help not only by doing the work, but also by 'thinking' quicker than men. In any case the fisherman has the final decision! The most advanced development seems to be in trawling, which could become useful in the future so long as other events (*eg* increasing oil prices) do not hamper its development (Chapter 22). In small-scale fisheries 'harvesting machines' have been developed (Chapter 31) which can provide a basis for computerizing in the future as has already been done with many agricultural machines. Nevertheless, these are ideas for the future. For the time being, in most fisheries of the world, manpower, experience and knowledge of fish behaviour are decisive in the construction and successful operation of fishing gear.

1.8 Fishing technology

One and the same fishing gear can be used in several different ways. When the method of fishing is not known it is hopeless to try to decide if, for example, a net is to be used for seining or dragging, for drive-in fishery, or even for gilling or entangling. This is one of the reasons why the classification of fishing gear and methods given at the end of this book is based not on the gear construction but on the principles of how the fishes or other prey are caught. These principles of catching can be used in different ways and sometimes the gear operation is supported by special fishing tactics, mostly based on methods of luring the prey, not so often on frightening them.

Gear construction, gear operation and fishing tactics are considered as parts of fishing technology and so are considered together in this book. But fishing technology also includes the materials used in gear construction and – as far as necessary – also the fishing vessels.[549] As regards net materials, it seems that the problem of replacing natural fibres by synthetic ones has been solved with the introduction of netting twines, *eg* polyamids (PA), polyesters (PE) and others with properties in accordance with the needs of the different fishing gear. There is no doubt that methods like mid-water trawling would not have been possible without the introduction of finer and stronger synthetic twines, apart from the invention of echo sounders. Also, the improvement in purse seining was not possible without these new fibres, quite apart from the introduction of the power block. A last example is the recent success of gillnetting, which was not possible without the use of twines made of fibres with low visibility, or even those that are transparent, like some monofilaments.

This is now known more or less all over the world, and no further sensational innovations can be expected in this direction with the exception of improvements in the properties of the fibres and also by the mixture of different fibres used for netting yarns and ropes. There must also be the hope that prices do not escalate! The development of fishing methods, especially in sea fisheries, would not have been possible unless there had been a parallel development of more and more specialized fishing vessels, from rafts and rowing boats to sailing vessels, to steamers and motor vessels with increasing power, and eventually, perhaps, to vessels driven by atomic power. Thus, parallel with the development of fishing techniques, the development of fishing craft is going on. This extends from the bamboo raft still much used in Asia for short-time fishing, to the factory vessel operating with a catcher fleet or the self-catching factory ship capable of staying at sea in far distant fisheries for many months and processing the catch immediately on board. The fishing vessel is therefore no longer an all-purpose vessel from which it was possible also to do some fishing, but a specialized vessel with many typical arrangements. Nowadays, in modern sea fisheries, the fishing vessel and the fishing gear have become one unit. The development of fishing gear and fishing methods cannot be seen as an isolated process. Success and progress in fisheries is based on the harmony between man, his surroundings and fish, all three influencing the construction and operation of fishing gear and fishing vessels.

Chapter two

Fishing by gathering

Long before any fishing gear was invented, men used their hands along the shores of lakes, rivers and seas to capture fish and other aquatic animals; to collect mussels or seaweed; and to harvest amber or minerals thrown up by tide and wind. In a word, they gathered everything useful to their needs, from the river banks and the beaches and from shallow waters or flooded areas now drying up. Some people think that gathering is the oldest and most important human activity and one to which we owe our present existence.[53] This old form of harvesting water products by walking along the dry beach looking for something that could be needed for food or working material, or wading for the same purpose in shallow waters, or diving in deeper ones, and doing this mostly without the help of boats or rafts, without tools, and using only the hands, has been known perhaps for millions of years, from the time of prehistoric man and his predecessors right up to the present day.

Today, gathering by hand is not only done in countries with a low level of economy but also in highly developed industrial countries, though sometimes for different reasons. Also, modern people gather by hand foodstuffs (*Fig 2*) or other apparently useful objects which can be brought home, not because of need but more for fun or for souvenirs. Today, at suitable places, holidaymakers and hobby fishermen have replaced the hunters and collectors of olden days. It may be that even today commercial fishermen continue to fish by simple collection especially in tropical countries.

In some areas the inducement to continue fishing by simple gathering by hand, and with nearly no tools, was created by new ideas like the so-called 'aesthetic' fishery[679] which does not aim to get foodstuff, but to collect nice-looking shells or corals for decoration, or to catch living animals for the aquarium at home. The animals are mostly tropical fish but also include crustaceans and other animals of the lower orders. In some countries of southern Asia beautiful little fish are collected for fighting contests for entertainment.[404] Many of these animals are found in small pools and are caught in

Fig 2 Sunday morning on the French Atlantic coast. Father and son digging for shells.

a simple manner without any typical fishing gear.

Another reason for fishing by gathering is to collect 'bait worms', the more northern and less valuable sandworm, *Nereis virens,* and the more expensive southern bloodworm, *Glycera dibranchiata*. It has been calculated that in the USA bloodworms bring the highest price for weight of any fishing product! Beside bait worms other types of bait are also sought for linefishing by commercial and sport fishermen. Such simple collecting can form the basis of a profitable job in centres of sport fishing all over the world, like the trade in fish and other animals for aquariums which has big centres in Hong Kong, Singapore, Djakarta, the Caribbean and Manila. Unfortunately this form of fishing, like other forms, shows symptoms of 'over-collecting' in some areas, especially on the seacoast.[283] So far stocks of the interesting living resources in shallow, coastal and fresh waters have not yet been diminished by increasing pollution.

2.1 Hand-picking

Gathering by hand can be considered the simplest form of fishing surviving the centuries and modern developments. Of course, what can be picked up is limited to some objects only and to the zones within the manual reach of man. The largest quantities are collected from animals which may be sessile or only slow moving. Therefore it is understandable that mussels and snails, echinoderms and some small crustaceans are the main animals caught by hand-picking. Most fish, even when trapped in small pools, but in good physiological condition, are too quick and sensitive to be caught by hand. So it is known from former inhabitants of Tasmania that because of their inefficient fishing technique their fishery was concentrated on snails, mussels and crayfish. There were only a few scaled fish which the Tasmanians could get, maybe in the same manner (by bare hand) as their neighbours, the Maoris, in New Zealand are catching eels even today.[39] Some fish may be grasped easily, as well as frogs, small alligators, crocodiles, turtles and other animals living in or near water. Fish roe is among the objects easy to collect by hand. So Alaska has an important 'herring-roe-on-kelp' fishery even today.

The objects that can be collected by hand also include plants, especially seaweeds, many of them used for human consumption or as fodder for cattle, or for the production of other products like iodine, agar from red algae, and alginic acid from brown algae, principally kelp. Last, but not least, seaweeds are also collected for agricultural fertilizer. Heavy gales at sea tear seaweed off the rocks and, when it drifts ashore, people need only to collect it (*Fig 3*). At some places the seaweeds can be harvested very easily from the rocks during ebb tide or in shallow water and brought ashore.[60] In such places the Icelanders brought or bring their sheep and horses to graze on the algae.[324]

The most interesting areas for hand-picking are those sea coasts which enjoy great differences in the rise and fall of tides, and where wide muddy areas are exposed twice a day. Here many species of shells can be collected or dug by hand from the sand or mud. Sometimes narrow populated mussel beds are hidden in the ground. In contrast to muddy areas, sandy beaches are of less interest. Nevertheless it is known that on nearly all sandy beaches, during the daytime, crabs can be dug out by hand. To catch them with the bare hand when they run over the beach during daytime or at night is difficult, but this is possible with the slower-moving hermit crab. In general, sandy beaches from which, during low tide, animals coming in with the flood can return unhampered with the ebb tide are not considered favourable for fishing by gathering by hand.[318] Rocky coasts with many small pools, areas prolific in seaweed growth, or caverns and cliffs favourable for the growth of aquatic plants and with hiding places for animals, are all ideal areas for gathering. Molluscs, mussels, as well as snails and sea urchins, are here the main objects harvested by hand-picking (*Fig 4*). Moreover, various species of crustaceans, even barnacles and fish, left behind in little pools or caverns, are secured when the water recedes. Mussels and snails are preferred, especially in low tide areas, because they move so slowly. Mussels are dug from the bottom, while snails are removed from the stones to which they adhere or are gathered from the ground.

Fig 3 To lengthen the reach in retrieving fish or seaweed came the spear and rake. These Breton fishermen harvest seaweed for fertilizer with long-handled rakes.

In France, with large areas of low tides off the Atlantic coast, a special term is used for this fishery:

Fig 4 Chinese women use simple implements to gather shellfish. In the foreground is the typical collector's basket.

this is the 'pêche à pied' (fishing by foot) which still plays a great part, not only for the benefit and interest of occasional visitors or poachers and beach-combers, but also for meeting the practical needs of commercial fishermen.[520] The phrase 'fishing by foot' is not to be confused with 'fishing by horse'. That too is practised as, for instance, where horses are used to frighten the fish by their movements in the water, or to drag a fishing gear. The term 'fishing by foot' is really thought of as a contrast to 'fishing from the boat', which method is obviously a step up in activity in the eyes of the poor. A restriction has to be made nowadays: 'pêche à pied' no longer means only hand-picking or gathering, it means nowadays any fishery operated without boat and this can be also catching with typical fishing gear, which will be shown later.[577, 578] On the other hand, hand-picking is also done from boats in the open sea, *eg* for catching garfish. In taking turtles by hand, care must be taken to avoid being bitten![110] It is easier to catch small fishes by hand. It has been suggested that survivors of a shipwreck on a raft or in a lifeboat can pick up such fish which nibble the nails of their fingers![526] According to the same author, sharks with a length of up to 1·50 metres can be taken without difficulty by their dorsal fins! To avoid being bitten a piece of wood or a rolled towel should be pushed into the mouth of the shark. (Unfortunately, it is not stated which type of shark can be caught by hand picking!)

Gathering by hand can be found on all sea coasts and also in freshwater areas. Here of particular interest are flooded territories adjoining rivers which regularly overflow after heavy rainfall. Like the sea, freshwaters offer many valuable products. To ensure their usefulness even more, many little artificial pools are constructed in which the animals or products desired are left behind when the water falls. The water may be bailed out in order to gather the fish, as is done even today in the small ponds which remain when rice fields are drained to permit the flowering and ripening of the paddy. Manual collecting is the method used where lagoons or annually flooded lands dry out, as along the great rivers of Asia, Africa, and tropical South America.[336] It has been said that the greatest of all tropical inland fisheries is that where, at the time of the floods, many fishes are caught by hand. But this fishery will be doomed in the future when the rivers are restrained between embankments and the land settled for intensive cultivation.

Areas of hand-picking can also include all shallow waters, and deeper ones as far as the fishermen can wade in (*Fig 5*). In water reaching up to the chest or higher the fisherman has to find his prey, *eg* clams, by feeling them with his feet. He can lift them from the bottom with one foot or by raking them with a foot into a basket held on the bottom (*Fig 400*). Sometimes the fisherman or woman dives briefly to pick up by hand what has been found with the feet. Of course, hand-picking in deeper water without a boat is also possible by a swimming and diving fisherman, as will be discussed later (Chapter 3).

Hand-picking along the beach, in sea waters and fresh waters, in shallow waters or by diving in deeper ones, is not only known all over the world

Fig 5 Women of the Zulu tribe collecting mussels on the coast of Natal near Durban, S. Africa. (*Photo: South African Panorama. 1979.)*

today but also since unknown times. The prehistoric importance of such collecting activities is revealed by the monuments left behind in the form of so-called kitchen middens 'kjökken möddinger' found at various points in Europe, east Asia, North Africa and both of the Americas. The heaps of garbage left behind by the fishermen and huntsmen of that later mesolithic period are primarily composed of shells of sea mussels gathered and eaten in those far distant times. The huge mounds of marine shells sometimes up to six metres in thickness represent the accumulated food-debris of centuries, of coastal fisher-collectors of maybe 6,000 to 7,000 years ago.[118] But not only from prehistoric times have shell mounds been found. Hills of shells up to 120 metres in length and 8 metres in height have been found near the old Phoenician town of Sidon,[321] but at this time the shells were gathered not for food but to gain the desired purple colour to dye the clothes of the dignitaries of this period. Hills of shells can be seen nowadays where large quantities of abalone are caught by modern diving food gatherers such as in California or southern Africa. However, not all abalone fishermen are as lucky as those of New Zealand, who collect an abalone with wonderfully coloured shells which fetch a high price on the world market.

Hand-picking was formerly considered an important method of catching fish and one demanding great skill. During the famous Nigerian fishing festival in the River Argungu (Nigeria), the contest between fishermen includes not only the usual boat racing but begins with fishing by hand. The first man to catch a fish is the winner, thereby honouring one of the oldest fishing methods.

Old European fishery books mention that this method of grasping the fish is the simplest method of fishing. But note this: a famous fish booklet of Nuremberg, dated 1758, comments rather disdainfully:' . . . that is a fishery of the poor common folk who sometimes wish to bring home a small meal'. The simplicity of hand-picking has the disadvantage that it is not only used all over the world but very often not by regular, authorized fishermen, but by big – and more often by smaller – poachers or fish thieves. If a Chinese philosopher failed to mention fishing as among those activities bestowing great happiness, it means certainly that he never roamed along brooks as a little boy tickling trout or grasping crayfish with his hand. This practice is universal; from Greenland, the Kuril Isles, and other northern areas it is known that even salmon can be caught by hand. 'Tickling' is the English expression for this method of fishing. To do this, the fisherman (or boy) dips his arm quite slowly into the water and tries very cautiously to approach a stationary salmon or trout. When he succeeds in touching it he moves his hand very carefully along the belly of the fish until he reaches the gills. Then, with thumb and middle finger grasping the gill openings, he endeavours quickly to whisk it on to the bank. He does not always succeed. The bigger the fish the more chance it has of freeing itself at the last moment by struggling and, not infrequently, the fisherman, in his excitement, finds himself in the water instead of seeing the salmon on land.[114] The Lengua Indians in the Gran Chaco guard against losing the fish by fixing around the hand a ribbon to which small vertebrae are fastened. This gives them a firm grip which prevents the fish from escaping.[322] Nowadays it is recommended to use gloves or a scouring clout in case there is some chance to catch fish by hand – especially conger!

In general, hand-picking is a small-scale fishery, but it can become big business when precious products are collected, like pearls and mother-of-pearl or corals. Marco Polo mentioned some Arabian islands where large quantities of ambergris had been collected along the coastlines and this valuable material must have also been collected by the Madagascans. Today there is big business in the field of fishing by gathering where the mass collection of seaweed or shell grit can be carried out from the shore. To do this economically, large-scale enterprises are developed. Large harvesting machines dredge tons of seaweed or shell debris from the low tide area or in shallow water, and so replace the human collector and his hand (see Chapter 31).

2.2 Stranded prey

It can happen that fishes or other water animals become stranded involuntarily on the beaches. Small fish can be seen jumping on shore when frightened by predators, or flying fish, attracted and disorientated by light, landing on the deck of a vessel. Then even quick-moving fishes are easily caught by hand. This can happen even with large fishes like salmon when they fail to jump over an obstacle during migration. It has been said of old Indian fisheries in North America that some tribes simply collected salmon which failed to jump over obstacles and thus fell on land or became stranded and exhausted after spawning.[625] Sometimes large schools of small fishes are driven by predators into shallow water and big quantities are washed up on shore. Maybe the next wave will wash them back into the water if they are not taken by birds or men. Here a strange fishery has to be mentioned although it is not strictly involuntary stranding on the beach. This is the fishery for grunion (*Leuresthes tenuis*) when, during the night, this strange fish comes on to land to spawn along the coast of California.[273, 643] In this case, catching with bare hands is the only method allowed by law. The use of nets is illegal. Not only fish can be stranded: this can happen also with swimming snails and squid. In northern New England and eastern Canada strandings of enormous quantities of living shortfin squid (*Illex illecebrosus*) have been noticed.[360] The causes of such mass strandings remain unknown. This is also the case with the ocean sunfish (*Mola*) and a few kinds of sea turtle which can be easily caught by hand after stranding.

Not so widely known is the fact that in Iceland well-known food fish like capelin (*Mallotus villosus*) and cod (*Gadus morhua*) can be washed up by the sea. In the 12th century the harvesting of this 'driftfood' was combined with special 'drift-fish rights' and could be important for surviving when, in late winter, food supplies often ran low and weather conditions made fishing impossible.[324] Beside capelin and cod, other fish have also been mentioned as swimming ashore – like spiny dogfish (*Squalus acanthias*), seithe (*Pollachius virens*) and even redfish (*Sebastes marinus*) and wolf-fish (*Anarhichas lupus*).

The Maoris of New Zealand know a form of artificial stranding of fish by damming up with stones some running water which can then flow only in a trench excavated at the side. The fish are guided into the channel, then the stone barrier is removed so that the water can run again the former way and the trench suddenly runs dry. The fish cannot escape, are stranded, and are gathered by hand.[39]

Finally, whales can also be 'gathered' on the beach when involuntarily stranded in shallow waters or when driven inshore by man, as formerly happened frequently on certain islands in the Pacific and is still practised with pilot whales in the Faeroes (*Fig 6*). The use of stranded whales is considered as the first form of whaling. From time to time news goes around the world that schools of whales or dolphins run themselves aground as an easy prey for men. The reasons for this behaviour are not known. Nowadays oil pollution is considered as a possible reason for the disorientation and stranding of whales, but such events were already known to Aristotle (394-322BC) and, like him, modern scientists can give no convincing answer for the stranding of large schools of these sea mammals even though men try to return them to the sea.

2.3 Catching by bailing out

Fully active fish are difficult to catch by hand even in small water areas. An old method of overcoming this difficulty is by bailing out the smaller pools until the fish can be caught by hand in the remaining water or until they strand themselves.[361, 590, 666] This is a simple fishing method without specific fishing gear. It is known all over the world, especially in

Fig 6 Stranded pilot whales in the Faeroe Islands. (*Photo: B Ulrich.*)

Africa and southern Asia. Smaller fish can also be drawn with the pot used for bailing. To get the fish, the water will be filtered through a basket or netting worked like a strainer. Such simple filters are also used when leading water in which fish are expected to be found from one field to another one. This also can be an effective fishing method without any specific fishing gear.

2.4 Implements for 'gathering' in fisheries

As can be seen by the examples of gathering quoted earlier, until now no special fishing gear has been needed. The main tool is the human hand. Everything that man can reach by hand, and which he considers as useful, can be taken. The term 'fishing by foot' simply means not only fishing without a boat but often also without gear, as far as this gear is considered as typical for fisheries in general. More important for success than the gear is the endurance and fitness of the collector. Of the French 'bassiers' (that means those who fish during low water, or 'basse mer'), it is said that the secret of their success lies in the way their legs have developed a resistance to cold, in their good eyes, and in their quick perceptive senses. A symbol of their collecting activity is the possession of a little basket or a bag of netting for taking home the collected products – and this is general the world over and not only characteristic of the French Atlantic coast (*Fig 7*). It is of interest to know that California imposes limits on the size of such bags to prevent overfishing of the shellfish stocks.

It must, however, be conceded that this collecting fishery is not carried out only by hand. Special auxiliary gear has been developed, usually quite individually, but of such a general nature that it cannot be recognized exclusively as fishing gear. To facilitate the work with the hand when digging out shells from the ground, or to loosen or cut some

Fig 7 Japanese women seeking shellfish from the sandy shore use a small hand tool.

sessile animals or plants from stones and rocks, or for bailing out small pools, simple individual selected tools can give some help.[171] Shovels, spades, scratchers and hoes (*Figs 7, 8* and *9*) are used for digging out mussels and also sand eels. These tools, well known to gardeners, are seldom made specially for this form of fishing. Seaweeds are gathered with rakes and forks. Knives, and even screwdrivers, crowbars, chisels and hammers or similar instruments are used to remove animals from the rocks. Tweezers, spoons and even sticks, originally used for fruit picking, can be seen in this fishery. Hooks and pokers are needed to dislodge octopi, crawfish and eel-like fish from their hiding places (*Fig 10*). Pokers can also be considered as small gaffs (Chapter 12). Some collectors also use, with or without permission, real fishing gear like spears, instruments of percussion, small stow nets, scoopnets and push nets, minute dip nets, and special lines with hooks, all of which will be described later.

It may also be mentioned that sometimes bleach, bluestone or even salt are used to drive octopi out of their holes, or even shells like razor-shells out

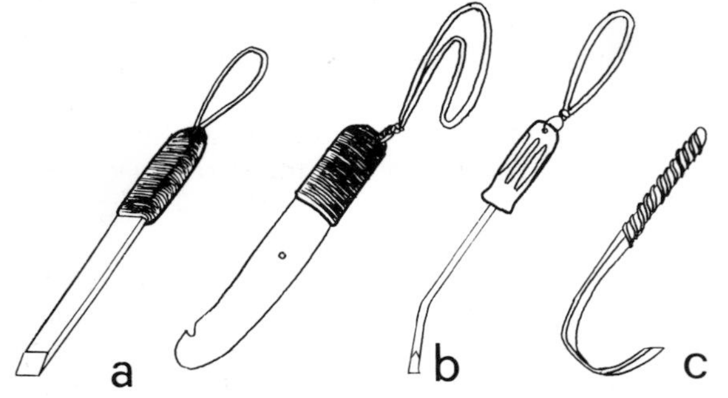

Fig 8 Simple tools for gathering molluscs, especially abalone: (*a*) California; (*b*) South Africa; (*c*) Japan.

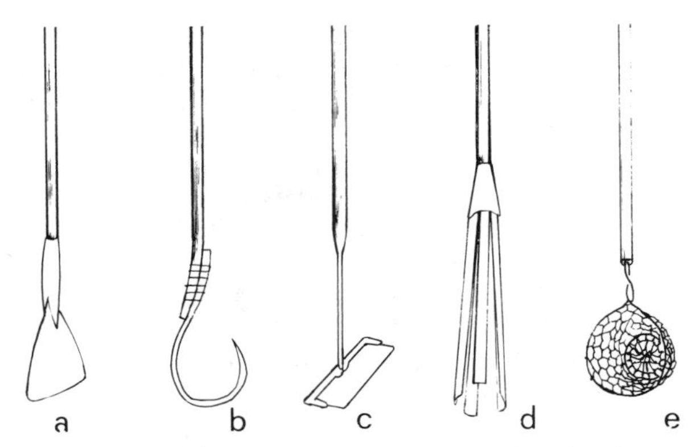

Fig 9 Long-handled tools to gather molluscs in deeper water: (*a*) Madagascar; (*b*) Japan; (*c*) USA; (*d*) Japan; (*e*) Thailand.

of, or off, the bottom mud.[415] In fishing by gathering, individuals have a wide field in which to invent useful tools, and very seldom are there regulations to control the quality or quantity of the gear used by collectors.

Fig 10 Note the hooks which French fishermen use for fetching octopi out of their holes.

2.5 Fishing with the feet

Some fish dig themselves not too deeply into the bottom mud in shallow water. Then the ground is searched with the feet or hands to find the fish. On the East Friesian (North Sea) coast, the taking of turbot from the pools which remain as the tide ebbs, is called 'Buttpetten' – treading or trampling to find flat fish like flounder, plaice and turbot. When a fish is found, it is held firmly by the feet till it can be grasped with the hand.[398] This method is known in many parts of the world; it has been used by the Indians of the Pacific coast of America and in many fisheries of Asia.[211, 212, 427, 632] Australian aborigines grope carefully along muddy shores and so secure with their feet a sort of catfish to be found there. In modern Egypt it is common for the fisherman to try to feel with his naked feet the spawning holes of breeding tilapia. When he finds such star-shaped holes he grasps the female with his hand.[157]

Fishing for sponges is now in the hands of divers with good diving equipment (Chapter 3). Nevertheless, it is known that the earliest and most primitive method of collecting sponges, which has been practised in parts of Tunisia, is by wading in the shallows and collecting sponges with the toes.[168]

In another fish catching method the feet are also needed. The true African lungfish (*Protoptorus*) and the catfish (*Clorias*) like to burrow into the mud as the waters dry up. Lungfish enclose themselves in a cocoon-like sheath made from the slime secreted by their own bodies. Their position in the dried mud is located by stamping with the foot on the hard-baked mud surfaces. When this is done in the right place, over a fish, a distinct rumble is heard as it wriggles and grunts at the disturbance. The fish thus found is dug out by hand or with a hoe.[82, 244] Digging out fish in the dry season without specific gear is also known in southeast Europe in the wide inundation area of the Danube.[13, 247] Here also some fish, loaches, hide in the mud during the dry season and are dug out by hand or with simple gear.

2.6 Mechanization of gathering

Fishing without gear but only by means of the hand was the very beginning of man's fishing activities. It is the purest form of gathering economy, although some people think that the fishery, considered as a whole, cannot be regarded as having passed beyond the lowest level of this appropriating form of economy. But from this primitive method of collecting by hand all other fishing techniques have developed. The basic ideas for progress have been to replace the hand by better manmade tools and to decrease manpower by mechanization – initially by hand-operated implements like winches, and later by machine-driven ones. The last stage is a fishing system automatically steered by computers which take over some human reasoning or, at least, make decisions more quickly and with more certainty.

Hand-picking may be a long way from such ideas because it is carried out by people who can be likened to gardeners in comparison to farmers who have to cultivate large areas in an economical manner. But there is no doubt that hand-picking can be replaced by mechanical methods. There are a few examples where mechanization can support hand-picking (especially hand-digging for shells and other bottom-hidden animals) by mechanically washing out and collecting the creatures. This can be done in a simple manner also in collecting bait

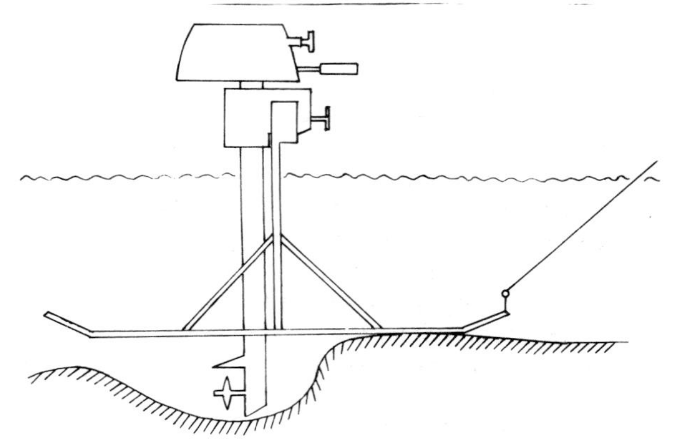

Fig 11 Washing baitworms out of the mud with the help of an outboard motor fixed on a tripod or towed on a sledge. (*Hutzfeld, 1977*)

worms (wanted by sport fishermen) with the help of a small out-board motor (*Fig 11*). The running motor stirs up the mud with the propeller and brings the worms to the surface where they can be collected by hand or in small scoop nets.[272] After the war a similar method was used in northern Germany for washing out clams with the help of the running motor of a cutter.[330, 438] Large quantities can be washed out by this system; far more than could be collected by hand or with scoopnets. Therefore, other 'wash-out' methods have been devised, combined with dredges and collecting bags, but these are not gathering as discusssed in this chapter, but a fishing method using dragged gear, which is considered later (Chapter 20).

Chapter three

Male and female divers

The 'gathering activity' of the fisherman who works with almost no gear, and without a boat, is not restricted to the beach or to shallow water. By adopting the practice of diving, particularly in the warmer regions of the world, he has been able to penetrate into deeper water to gather and grasp what he cannot secure from the shore. Long before the currently popular sport of scuba diving began, there existed underwater hunting wherein men moved, as one says today, 'as fish among the fishes'.

Even today divers are active in carrying out, by simple diving, a number of important fisheries. Diving for pearl oysters in Japan, Indonesia, Australia, Sri Lanka and south India is famous and important, but fishing for sponges by divers in the Mediterranean and Caribbean Sea is also well known. Diving for corals is also famous: the red one of the Mediterranean, the black one of the Red Sea and the Pacific Ocean (Hawaii), and last but not least the red and white ones of the Pescadores Islands in the Formosa Strait. Corals can be taken by divers without, or more thoroughly with, complicated equipment without destroying coral stocks which may happen when entangling gear is used (*Figs 696* and *697*).

Other marine products are also harvested by divers working in many areas of the tropical and sub-tropical seas. These products may be mussels, abalone or clams, not to forget also giant clams and pearl oysters, sponges for human and technical uses, octopi, sea urchins and sea cucumbers ('trepang' or 'bêche-de-mer'), several types of crustaceans (especially lobsters and spiny lobsters) and turtles. Also gathered are edible seaweeds found in shallow waters, and others used for a variety of industrial and agricultural purposes as mentioned in Chapter 2. Finally, as a sad symbol of the post-war period, fishermen (especially in the northern seas) have made a good business from diving for submerged ammunition and scrap. Even earlier fishermen dived in the harbour of Mindelo (Cape Verde Islands) to collect coal fallen overboard from the old steamers which bunkered there before leaving for South America.

3.1 Divers catching fish and supporting fishing operations

Divers can, under some circumstances, also catch fish (*Fig 12*). Of course it is much more difficult to catch very quick ones in their own surroundings than those hampered by physiological unfitness when spawning, or weakened by sickness or

Fig 12 That diving to catch fish is old-established is shown by this woodprint from the famous early Japanese sketch-book, *Manga*, by Hokusai, picturing divers at work.

exhausted by migrating. It is reported that the Indians of the northwest California coast, while operating as divers, sometimes grasped sturgeons weakened by spawning and guided them to the bank.[328] Catching carp by hand is sometimes referred to in old Japanese documents.[430] In the Japanese book *Chat about the southern islands* published nearly 150 years ago, it was mentioned that around the Ryukyu Islands some sea fish were caught by divers with the left hand whilst swimming with the other.[427] A strange story in this connection is also told from Easter Island. In the olden times there were so many fish in this area that swimmers could squash them between their legs. Even today a special place in these islands is called 'Fish-catching-with-thighs'.[164]

In addition to 'dive fishing' for molluscs, corals, sponges and other sea creatures the co-operation of divers can be helpful in other fisheries. There are many fishing methods in use, particularly in tropical areas, in which divers or swimming fishermen help to operate fishing gear. They can set and haul fishing gear like pots for rock lobsters in India and other places with small fisheries, where even a simple boat may be too expensive and the gear is operated only by divers. Divers can also drive fish into a gear, remove them from a net, frighten them from the bottom to the surface,[313] or collect stupefied fish from the bottom. Divers can also direct fishing gear to the right place, like plummets for sea cucumbers (*Fig 48*), or place handlines before fish as is done in Japan. When operating some types of drive-in gear in tropical waters (*Fig 589*) the co-operation of large groups of swimming divers may be necessary.

Diving fishermen can also examine artificial fish shelters and stationary gear. It has been reported from the fisheries in central and southern Africa that sometimes, when seining, a man dives to find out if there are enough fish in the gear and if the time is right for hauling. This may be the most reliable method of determining the quantity of the catch so urgently needed also in the modern large-scale fisheries of industrial countries.[361] Indonesian fishermen are known to dive to inspect their gigantic weirs. In northern Europe some fishermen operating large pound nets in the western Baltic are trained to dive to inspect the best working of their gear. It may also be remembered that in modern fisheries the help of divers is often needed for clearing netting from propellers, for retrieving lost fishing gear, and to make minor hull repairs from below the water level.[224] Moreover, one decisive reason for the co-operation with divers in fisheries is the fact that in some tropical countries, before the gear is set, they dive to listen to determine whether there are suitable fish in the neighbourhood. In Thailand, purse seiners are sometimes accompanied by a diver specializing in fish location by underwater listening. Listening for fish by divers is also known in Malaysia in the seine net fishery. A small sampan with low sides is used on which the swimming fisherman can hold fast. From time to time he dives his head underwater to look for fish but also to find them by listening. Experts affirm that by the noises caused by some fish they can determine not only the type of fish, but also their location and the size of a school. It has been declared that up to six types of fish can be distinguished by their different noises. According to Malaysian fishermen, fish noises vary when they are swimming near the water surface or on the bottom.

3.2 Diving equipment

Divers have been working since olden times completely without any auxiliary means for prolonging their stay under water. Nude diving is still undertaken all over the world today, even though the famous divers of the Arabian Gulf have exchanged their hard and dangerous job for the more attractive living of oil exploitation. Formerly pearl diving was done with dhows, 20 metres long, and with a crew of up to 30. Two men, a diver and a hauler, worked in teams of two. The diver descended on a weighted line, the end wound round his foot. Experienced divers could plunge 15 metres. Some divers stayed down for four minutes though some for only one and a half minutes. For hauling, the diver tugged on the rope and the hauler pulled him up. Some divers dived about 40 times a day.[177] The only external aid in the past has been that of diving spectacles, but these have been in use only in comparatively recent times – in Japan since the beginning of this century. They are, however, very desirable and the fishermen on even remote islands manufacture their own divers' spectacles (with wooden frames) if they can obtain plain glass (*Fig 13*). This is necessary because it is not possible for the human eye to see clearly under water without divers' spectacles.

Nose clips made of horn, as used by the Arabian divers of India, or any protection for the ears, like modern water-pressure regulation balloons combined with mask and glass window, were unknown to early diving fishermen and this remains so today in many parts of the world, particularly in south Asia where most divers have no equipment other than diving spectacles.

An important development in diving was the

Fig 13 Diver of the Taiwanese island Lan Yü, formerly called Botel Tobago, with hand-made wooden-framed diving goggles (1969).

introduction of a diving suit equipped with helmet and hose connected to a pump for respiration. Installed aboard small open boats, this equipment became popular with sponge and abalone fishermen both in the Far East and in the New World. Such diving apparatus is not new, but it was a long time before it was introduced into fisheries. Among others, Leonardo da Vinci (1452-1519) made a sketch of a diving suit for an Indian pearl diver (about 1488-1497). The suit was made of waterproofed leather. To protect the diver against attack by fishes, especially sharks, or other animals, the suit was designed to have long spines. The tube for breathing, reaching to the water surface, was stiffened with rings of metal to resist the compression of the water. The diver had diving spectacles with magnifying glasses.[165] Leonardo's proposal for a diving suit was not realized before the 19th century. The equipment is known as a 'scaphander' and is used today especially for technical work under water. The helmet is replaced by a mask for breathing connected to a hose up to 100m long. Due to similarity of this equipment and the Turkish water-pipe it is also called a 'hookah' in some fisheries.

At first, hand pumps only were used to supply air to the diver (*Fig 14*). Power compressors began to replace hand pumps about 1913. After the First World War, high-capacity compressors were introduced.[168] These improvements provided greater security for the divers, and their working time under water was prolonged. A diver can work under water for varying times depending on the depth of the water and his physical condition. As an example, on average a British diver-fisherman spends one and a half hours a day on the bottom for 350 scallops.[224] In Korea a diver can work for as long as 25 to 30 minutes in a depth of 30 metres. Generally he works eight hours a day, making eight to ten dives. Nowadays the safety of diving with air hose has been increased by winding a telephone cable around the hose. With this the diver can be in permanent speaking contact with his vessel.

As far as data is available, in the Mediterranean diving dress has been in use in the sponge fishery since 1860. In 1874 it was introduced into the

Fig 14 Korean diver with diving suit and air supply provided by hand pump. Korean South coast. (1972).

USA,[168] and since 1879 in the Swedish fishery (for oysters) off the western coast.[684] In Central America, diving suits have been in use since the beginning of this century, especially in the sponge fishery off Florida in the Gulf of Mexico.[600] Diving for abalone off California was established by Japanese divers when it became unlawful to fish for abalone in the shallow intertidal zone (1900). Before this law, abalone had been gathered by Chinese fishermen with the help of hooked poles – without diving. Japanese divers introduced diving suits to gather abalone in deeper water. The diving dress with its hose connection in modern form avoids many dangers which threaten the nude skin diver. On the other hand the disadvantages of this method are that the boat has to be anchored and that the diver's range is limited by the length of the air hose. Moreover, when more than one diver is working from the same vessel their air lines can entangle with each other.[224] Therefore the increased mobility gained ensured that when, after the Second World War, independent, autonomous, diving equipment such as scuba (Self-Contained Underwater Breathing Apparatus) was developed, it was immediately widely used – not only for submarine sport fishing but also for commercial fishing by professional fishermen (*Fig 15*).

Fig 15 Indonesian scuba divers in Flores, Lesser Sunda Islands. (*Photo: Kollmannsperger, 1975.*)

Autonomous deep-diving systems reduce costs considerably, and increase productivity. On the other hand, scuba diving needs expensive equipment. This is why older methods with suits are still practised beside modern scuba diving. Simple snorkels are also widely used around the world and it is known that Australian aborigines used long pieces of hollow reed as a means of approaching wildfowl under water.[224] Today, migrating Greek sponge divers use simple snorkels for searching, as well as breathing tubes with old compressors, but also with transportable modern scuba equipment with oxygen breathing. Skin divers can be seen as well as divers with helmets and air tubes. Often they have only a mask with a large glass visor and a connection tube to the air compressor.

Divers working as skin divers or in suits from boats usually now have a double rope connection with the boat. One rope is loaded with a weight by means of which the diver can descend by himself without any effort. The other rope serves as a signal line. The weighted line (usually attached to a stone or a heavy lead) is also useful for anchoring the boat. Moreover, this line provides a permanent connection to the boat so that the diver can easily find it or, by giving a signal on the second line slung round his body, he can be hauled up by means of a winch on the boat. This help is especially necessary for divers working in suits with rubber tube connections. By this means of facilitating his descent and ascent the diver is able to stay under water for a longer period. Nevertheless, the undersea activities of divers in diving suits are mostly limited to 60 metres with only 30 minutes of useful work. A scuba diver may dive 50 metres and even more, but once he dives more than 10 metres he already needs one or more pauses of 5 minutes each for decompression during ascending.

Before about 1917, divers in heavy diving dress and with breathing tubes walked along the seabed looking for shells *etc*. Later the method of 'working to windward' was used. In this method the diver is towed, by his vessel, a few feet from the bottom, while the vessel drifts at low speed, maybe under sail. When the diver sights the wanted shells he signals the surface and is lowered to collect. Where the water was warmer the diver did not use the full diving dress but often the helmet or the corselet only.

Generally speaking, diving is daytime work, but in Italy commercial divers catch big fish during the night by shooting with the aid of underwater lamps. Fish, as well as crustaceans and octopi, are worried by the light and mesmerised. The use of lights by divers is forbidden in some countries. Sometimes diving, at least free diving, is completely forbidden, or the length of the surface-connected hoses can have a legal minimum length to protect some stocks against overgathering, especially by sport divers.[168] In some countries, diving in one form or other is restricted or forbidden, as in New Zealand and

Australia where compressed air in diving for crawfish is banned.

The problem of how to protect the diver against attack, especially by sharks (considered earlier by Leonardo da Vinci) is still of topical interest. Australian divers operate from self-propelled shark cages; those of South Africa wear rugby boots to kick away sharks if they are disturbed while under water! Accidents caused by sharks, even in shallow waters, lead to a furious chase of them, whether they are of a dangerous species or not, especially off the Australian coast. On the other hand, commercial divers are blamed for the decreasing numbers of shark populations, while abalone divers are blamed for the decline in the catch of abalone in recent years because of their fear of shark attack. However, there are more accidents due to failure to observe the time needed for decompression in coming up from a dive of more than 10 metres than by shark attacks.

3.3 Female divers

Diving is mostly done by men, but there are famous female divers, particularly those of Japan, – the so-called 'ama' which means sea-women.[27] They also operate in Korea and this probably arises from the Japanese influence. The Korean female divers operate especially from the Isle of Cheju, situated off the south coast. They collect mainly abalone, trepang, seaweed and molluscs; also fish. The ama dive without any special equipment in shallow water (five to ten metres) and for a short time only – fifty seconds to one and a half minutes. Like sports swimmers they dive head first in contrast to the Arabian and Sri Lankan pearl divers who dive feet first.[28]

In the Japanese fishery it is plain that women are more suited to diving than men, because they have a better fat layer which insulates their bodies. It is quite understandable that economic conditions make it necessary for the women to undertake this diving for food because the men are frequently absent from their villages for a long time while fishing for tuna. The fact that, for practical purposes, only women undertake diving has led the not very prudish Japanese to invent stories of explanation that would not be appreciated by the puritanical inhabitants of the western world![261] On the other hand, diving fishermen off the Mauretanian coast use trousers of leather for protection against curious small sharks! Kuwait pearl divers use black trousers, three-quarter in length, possibly for the same reason.

Japanese women divers, when they are diving, work either independently ('kachido') or mother and daughters work from a boat with a male assistant, who is usually the husband. The Japanese call this group of sea women 'funando'.[519] But even the independent women divers seldom fish alone, but prefer to operate in groups. In Korea there are usually ten female divers working together. Anybody who has visited the submarine world would know that company is essential in order to have a feeling of safety. Sport divers customarily are not allowed to dive alone. If there is some fellowship or company, they can help each other. In tropical areas some dangerous marine organisms may cause many difficulties. Even small organisms, when they are poisonous and venomous to man (like some nice-looking cone shells) can cause accidents or even death. In these cases, divers working in groups can give that timely help which may avert disaster.

Regarding the sea women 'ama', it is said that their knowledge of the diving techniques is handed down from mother to daughter. Thus diver families and whole settlements are to be found who fish together. This highly desirable and necessary co-operation has led to the development of professional castes or caste-professions – depending on whether the profession has caused the group to combine with a caste or whether membership of a caste has led to the adoption of the profession of diving.[659] There are some suggestions that women divers also work in other parts of the world, *eg* in the Torres Strait between Australia and New Guinea.[369] In Taiwan women divers often work in shallow waters where diving is needed to pick up by hand what has been touched by foot as mentioned before. In Tasmania, the women of the extinct aborigines were said to have been strong swimmers and excellent divers, who procured most of their food (like shellfish and crayfish) by diving in rocky areas. On the Island of Santa Cruz (in the eastern corner of Melanesia) women are now beginning to dive equipped with rubber catapults (*Figs 18* and *59*) for underwater harpooning.[315]

3.4 Tools and collecting bags

Like the collectors on the beach or in shallow water, originally divers had no specific gear to scrape together shells, to loosen sessile animals, or to cut seaweed. Kuwaiti divers for pearl oysters used leather thimbles for finger protection only. They needed no other tools for hand-picking. Nevertheless, some types of more or less specialized gear have been introduced in other types of diving according to whatever is to be collected. A knife, a hook, tweezers or similar tools must suffice to remove mussels or sponges or to draw crayfish out of their holes. *Figure 16* shows some of the tools used by Korean women divers to loosen shells, to catch octopi and to fish them. There are also more specialized tools, *eg* sickles for seaweed, hook-like implements to loosen sponges (*Fig 17*), iron bars to prize off abalone fixed to rocks, and small hooks to draw animals out of their hiding places, as well as short hand-held rakes for dislodging sea urchins from the substrate.

As with the collectors of the beach, some divers like to use genuine fishing gear such as snares and also fishing spears and harpoons to catch fish. Even in some remote areas, submarine harpoons with elastic triggers, as originally invented by sports divers, can be found in use (*Fig 18*). Sometimes gear made of netting is operated by divers. In Lake Nyassa cyprinids are caught by two divers towing a small bag net of mosquito netting between them. The bag is held open by a spreading stake at either side of the opening and is folded up at the end of the dive.[361] When rising out of the depths, African divers are told to retain the catch with their teeth. Usually, however, like the collectors on the beach, they have bag nets fastened to their bodies or to a float or a barrel which rests nearby on the surface of the water. The bag net can be held open like a scoop net by a wooden ring; or, as can be seen in *Figure 19*, the bags are closable and have a small hole through which to put the prey into the bag. There may also be a container, usually a wooden tub floating on the surface. The diver keeps contact with the floating tub by a rope so that he may find it easily to deposit his collected products. The container also serves as a raft when he wants to rest. Formerly, the unprotected diver had to come to the surface at short intervals to breathe, and also to put the collected catch in the container or in the accompanying vessel. Modern divers using diving dress with piped air supply stay longer under water and do not need to come out of the water so often. They may also carry a basket or net bag for their

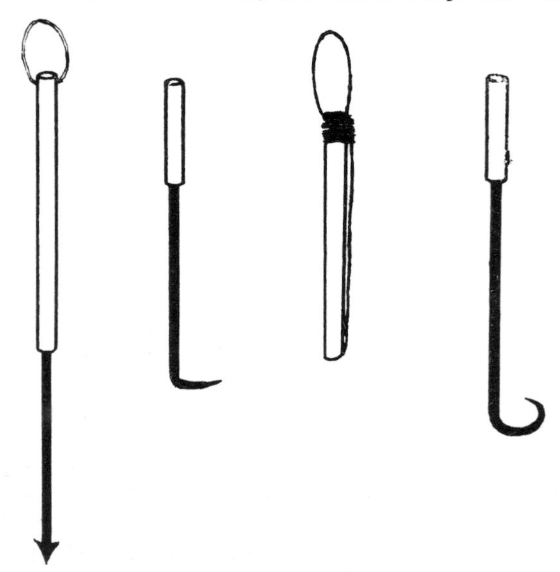

Fig 16 Small tools used by Korean women divers: spear for fishes, hook for shells, tool for loosening abalone, and hook for octopus. (*Courtesy of Mr. Lee, Chang Ki.*)

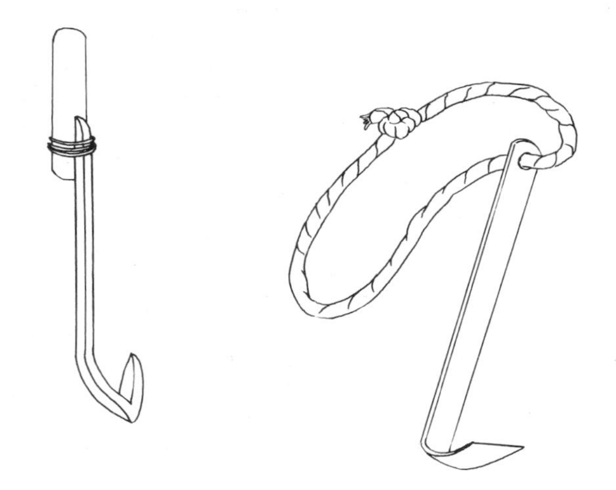

Fig 17 Tools for divers: (*left*) for loosening shells (Japan); (*right*) for loosening sponges. Greece. (1977).

Fig 18 Diver of Manila Bay with hand-made harpoon and collecting bag (1960).

Fig 19 The equipment of a Korean female diver near Pusan consists of a collecting bag with float, goggles and a sickle-shaped knife.

catch, which is hauled to the surface by their assistants. In this manner very effective harvesting systems have replaced the old forms of collecting foodstuff and other material under water. Modern Australian divers use plastic bags inflated from the diver's air supply to lift the full net to the surface.[454] When harvesting seaweed, Japanese divers tie 10 to 20 seaweeds together by a rope. When the stems are cut off, signals are sent and the seaweed is pulled up by the fishermen on the accompanying vessel. Other products, like sea urchins, are harvested in a similar way in California.[292]

3.5 Technological progress in diving

Progress in diving for fishing purposes is linked with the development of the techniques of diving, especially the diving suits and breathing devices. But there is also a desire to improve the tools used, especially in collected shells. Biologists claim that the usual clam forks and hoes used yield only about 60 per cent of the marketable sized clams of the dug-over soil, but kill almost half of all the clams left behind.[131] For this reason there have been investigations into how to increase the harvest of the shells collected by shore gatherers in tidal areas or by divers. One idea is to use water nozzles attached to a water hose with a pump staying on board the vessel attending the divers. These washout nozzles are helpful in digging out the larger clams which are usually deeply buried in the substrate. The diver grasps the clam siphon with one hand and washes the material away from the animal with the nozzle until it is free. Another idea is to use a hand-operated venturi dredge. This is a sucking device working on the principle of some vacuum pumps. An engine in the supporting vessel pumps water under high pressure through a water jet which creates a sucking action in a connected flexible pipe (*Fig 20*). By this means material, including clams, can be sucked off the bottom into a screen mesh container for separating and cleaning. The same system is also used for large harvesting machines which will be discussed later (Chapter 31).

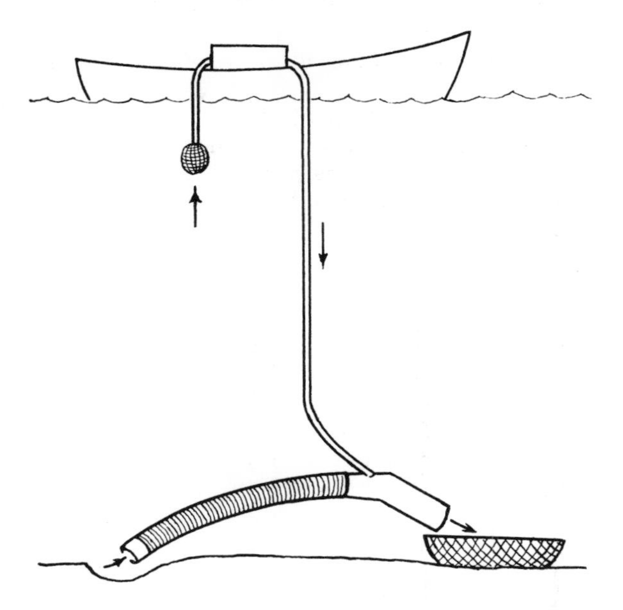

Fig 20 Operating principle of a venturi dredge.

Quite another problem of diving is to descend into deep water. It has been mentioned that divers with air-breathing apparatus can dive to depths of 60 or 70 metres. This depth is considered as a dangerous limit. At greater depths the diver can suffer intoxication sickness which can cause loss of consciousness. But corals, especially the more precious types, grow in deeper waters in the Pacific. Coral divers try to descend to 90 or even 100 metres. With a mixture of oxygen and helium, divers can attain more than 100 metres, and maybe even 200 metres is possible. But these depths invite accidents and it seems wiser to operate with small submarines in coral fishing at those depths (*Fig 21*). These can be small vessels of seven metres length with two or even three operators. The boat is driven by batteries and can work at depths of up to 200 or 250 metres. To cut off and collect corals, the submarine has a special mechanical grab arm (manipulator) with a striking mechanism to remove the precious 'loot'. The corals are collected in a bag of netting fixed to the outside of the submarine. Such submarines built for coral fishing may be less dangerous than diving with the usual equipment, especially with mixed gases. Moreover, such vehicles can dive to greater depths. Large ones can dive to 550 or 600 metres with an inside pressure of one atmosphere. Submersibles, mostly for two persons and with a 'launch-recovery-transport vehicle', are operated in the fishery for black corals off Hawaii (*Fig 22*).[198] Experiments have also been made with a small type to harvest red and white corals off the western coast of Taiwan. Nevertheless, the experiments in the Pescadores Islands (Penghu) in the Formosa Strait have shown that a strong current can hamper navigation of this type of diving vehicle, so that harvesting corals is nearly impossible. Navigation of the diving vehicles from the shore with the help of TV, as proposed recently by the Japanese, will not help to solve the problem.

Before finishing this chapter about diving it should be mentioned that in some countries non-commercial and commercial fishermen are antagonistic toward each other. This is because some irresponsible amateurs, as hobby fishermen, scoop up everything in sight including shellfish and fish at weekends, sell their harvest indiscriminately to the detriment of full-time fishermen – and return to their main jobs during the week. There are some discussions going on to see how the interests of full-time fishermen can be safeguarded. This includes also the problem of how to protect fishing gear against curious hobby divers who can cause considerable damage in addition to loss of catches.

Fig 21 Small submarine for coral fishing in Formosa Strait.

Fig 22 Modern deep-sea submersible operated in the coral fishery of Hawaii, transported on a special vehicle towed behind the mother ship. To launch the submersible, the transporter is sunk to about 18 metres where the submersible is launched under its own power. Procedure is reversed for recovery. (*Courtesy of Maui Divers of Hawaii Ltd. 1979*).

Chapter four

Animals as a help in fisheries

Man very soon learned to capture animals, to tame them and to use them for his own purposes. But the capacity and inherent ability to do this varied greatly between different tribes and nations. The ability of the Hindus, for example, to tame and handle animals is to be noted. They succeeded in taming young wild elephants much earlier than did the peoples of Africa. The African elephant is considered more difficult to tame[687] but nevertheless they became famous in the armies of north African potentates and even crossed the Alps with Hannibal's army.

There is a distinction between tamed and trained wild animals, and animals that are definitely domesticated. The first are to be seen in the circus or in a variety theatre. But domesticated animals in the real sense are not by any means those animals which live with man, either tolerated or unwanted, but those which man has tamed and bred for his own benefit or pleasure. By this practice of domestic breeding their characteristics may be deliberately changed. Through selecting special animals as parents, breeding is carried out with the specific purpose of developing special qualities in the offspring. Modern domesticated animals are simply the product of a long chain of animals that have been bred by man and used by man throughout many generations.

Animals have also been tamed and trained for use in fisheries. Training them to catch fish may not be as difficult as might be thought because many animals are known to do so normally. There are many mammals which catch fish – including cats, otters, bears, seals, and rats. It is known that there even exists a species of bat which can fish. There are also some animals which can be fed on fish but do not normally catch them, like reindeer and dogs. Many birds dive and fish, and some work in large flocks like cormorants, pelicans, darters and snakebirds. Reptiles and amphibians also fish – such as many water snakes, older crocodiles, turtles and frogs, not forgetting the many predatory fishes which catch others, or cannibalistic older fish which feed on the young of their own species. To complete the list, even some spiders and insects catch small fish, sometimes by quite complicated methods. There are a great number of fish-catching and fish-eating animals all over the world, but most of them are considered by man as competitors and predators. Only a few can be tamed and trained by men for direct fishing, although others can help indirectly in fisheries. Nevertheless, horses as well as dogs are engaged in fishing directly, along with otters and birds like cormorants and waterfowl. Moreover, man has learned how to fish even with suckerfish and octopi and also, by understanding the behaviour of many other animals, how to find the wanted prey by careful observation.

4.1 Horses and fishermen

Before the invention of motorized transport there were only a few animals, like donkeys, horses and cattle, to transport gear and the catch and to carry fishermen to their fishing grounds which may be some kilometres away.[270] In some cases animals are also used indirectly in fishing, like cattle towing boats in and out of the water on the Portuguese coast. Directly connected with fishing are the horses, which tow long seine nets in Argentine rivers as in the Rio de la Plata and the Rio Uruguay. Well known on the Belgian coast are the famous horses of Oost Duinkerke ridden by shrimp fishermen when fishing.[57] The heavy horses tow a small trawl-like gear for catching shrimp in shallow water (*Fig 490*). The net with the otter-boards can be towed either by a single horse or by two horses as in pair trawling (Chapter 21). It may be of interest to note that this fishery is prohibited from the beginning of November to prevent chilling the horses, and they fish only in about 30cm of water for the same reason.

The cooperation of horses in catching snappers has been recorded from the Maoris of New Zealand. The men would ride into shallow waters and when a snapper was spotted, they would follow the fish until the exhausted animal tried to find a hiding place in the mud stirred up by the horse. Then the Maori would dismount with his pitchfork and wait till the snapper tried to escape. As soon as the fish made its attempt it was speared by the waiting Maori with the fork.[140]

4.2 Dogs used in fisheries

The dog is a typical example of a domesticated animal. His association with man reaches back many centuries since first the wild dog was tamed, handled and began to develop into the useful companion he is today. In its original free life the dog was accustomed to unite in packs for hunting, and to follow a leader. That inherited characteristic makes the dog suited to accompany the huntsman. Pictures of Diana as the hunting goddess generally also show slender, quick, whippets accompanying her. Dogs help the huntsman by nosing out, scaring, encircling, chasing and retrieving the prey. But to the fisherman the dog is no natural companion. In general, such animals do not catch fish: even the ancestors of dogs, like wolves, catch fish only when they are ravenous. It is not just because the dog is afraid of water. He is a useful help in the hunting of waterfowl, but to use him for fishing seems to be against his nature. Nevertheless, it is sometimes reported that dogs have been known to retrieve living fish in shallow water and to help the sports fisherman to land fish taken by line.[208]

That dogs can be trained to drive fish into a fishing gear has been mentioned in many different parts of the world. The inhabitants of Tierra del Fuego used dogs to drive fish into nets placed on small beaches.[202] But dogs have also been trained to catch fish directly and to bring them to their masters. Dogs cannot take fishes with their claws, like bears and cats, because they are not pointed. They have to catch them by mouth. The Ainus, those mysterious European-like aborigines of north Japan and Sakhalin in the USSR, possessed the art of training dogs to the extent that by order and by swimming in packs, they could frighten fish into shallow water where they were caught and retrieved.[663] As a reward the dogs were given the fish heads. Similar observations are known in other countries like Ireland, Scotland, England and Wales as well as Normandy, in France. It has also been reported that even the dogs of Hungarian shepherds could be trained to catch single fish.[214] That dogs can be fed with fish is generally known. The Eskimos do so with their sledge-dogs. Dogs of the Kamchatkans in the USSR, which are fed in the winter with nothing but lightly salted and dried or smoked fish, are said to fish successfully in the summer on their own behalf. Half-wild dogs on the Turkish Black Sea coast feed on fish and porpoises left by the fishermen on the beach. From Malaysia it is even reported that crabs are caught by dogs.[92] In referring to dogs in fisheries we have to mention, too, the dogs which tow mud-sleds for transporting shrimps from the traps to the shore during low tide on the German Bay (*Figs 23* and *24*).

Fig 23 Dogs towing a mud sled for the transportation of shrimps from the traps to the shore during low tide on the German Bay in Wremen near Bremerhaven, (1965).

Fig 24 The catch of shrimps is reloaded from the mud sled to a small barrow, both towed by dogs.

4.3 Fishing with otters

Otters are also included among those animals which can be trained for frightening and sometimes even for retrieving fish. There are many species of otter in different parts of the world. Two of them may be used especially in fisheries. In India, Burma and southwest China, and as far south as Malaysia and

Sumatra, it is the 'smooth otter', *Lutra perspicillata* that has been used by fishermen to drive fish into nets. In more temperate Asia, in countries as far south as Sri Lanka, Burma, Thailand and Sumatra, the common otter, *Lutra lutra* is available for fishing as in Europe and in northern Africa.[379] Marco Polo, in his travels more than 600 years ago, saw Chinese fishing with otters in the Yangtse Kiang River. Other travellers have also reported this type of fishery being carried on today.[493] Fishing with otters seems to be especially restricted to the Yangtse area, where it was known before AD600. The Chinese are reputed to have developed commercial fishing with the aid of otters from the inhabitants of Indo-China and the Malaysian area. In India otters were used for fishing in the areas of the Rivers Indus, Ganga and elsewhere in Bengal. Their use was also known in southern India, particularly in the bays of the Cochin Coast. From there English sportsmen sometimes took such trained animals back to England with them. In early days people in many European countries kept otters for catching trout – for instance in Scandinavia. The famous book of Olaus Magnus: *De gentibus septentrionalibus,* (Rome, 1555), gives a sketch of a fishing otter in this area.[478] Fishing with otters was also known in Central Europe (Germany and Poland) and especially in England and Scotland. Here the otter for fishing was mentioned for the first time in 1480. Izaak Walton describes the training of otters for fishing in his book, *The Compleat Angler,* written in 1653. There he says that young animals of three to four months of age were caught and trained like dogs. The otter can become very tame and trusting and will stay with his master during some fifteen or sixteen years of active fishing. The normal practice was for the otter to be muzzled to prevent its eating the fish and to be fastened by a line to its master. Released into the water, it scared the fish and chased them into set nets, or else encircled them over dip nets set in the river, like a dog rounding up sheep. Then, when sufficient fish were over the net, it and the otter were hauled in together.[645] Very little information exists about the use of otters in the New World, but apparently otters were also used in Central and South America.[204, 669] The fishermen of British Guyana are said to use the otter as an indirect means of obtaining fish. By watching the place where the otter leaves its prey after capture, the fishermen can confiscate the booty for their own use.[244]

4.4 Fishing with birds

The method of obtaining fish not by catching them, but by stealing them out of the burrows and lairs of fishing animals such as otters, is also known in the case of birds. It was stated in 1827 that Hungarian poachers had taken fish out of the nests which eagles had built for their nestlings.[214] It seems that this method of 'indirect' fishing was widespread in olden times and is described also by the famous scientist Albertus Magnus (1193-1280).

It is known that many birds catch fish. These are powerful birds of prey such as eagles and hawks, but also small birds like halcyons and kingfishers. Well-known for fishing are herons and storks, as well as many types of waterfowl, and therefore they are very often unwanted in ponds and lakes. There are also fishing owls in Asia, Africa and Europe.

Nevertheless, there are not so many birds which have been tamed for direct fishing or which can give indirect help in fisheries. This seems to be also true for pelicans. These birds are known for their collective fishing system. Swimming in a semi-circle they can drive fish into shallow waters where they can be taken easily. However, pelicans are said never to have been domesticated or tamed to help men in fisheries. On the other hand the Sumerians, aware of the successful fishing activity of these birds, took the fish caught out of the throats of white pelicans. No details about Sumerian fishing are known but it may be that direct fishing with cormorants in Japan, the use of waterfowl in Lake Dojran in south eastern Europe, as well as the fishery with ducks known in one part of Indonesia as discussed in the following section, may be more successful than the method using pelicans.

4.5 Cormorant fishing

Far more is known about fishing with cormorants (*Fig 25*) than about fishing with any other bird. The Chinese knew and practised this fishery with cormorants practically from time immemorial.[203, 286, 613] Probably the Hindus, Indo-Chinese, Koreans and Japanese learnt this method of fishing from them.[3] For the Brahmins and all Buddhists this practice of fishing with cormorants, like that of fishing with otters, was and is very convenient because the first commandment of their religious laws prohibits the killing of living creatures which, of course, includes fish. Thus, when the killing was done by using animals and not by man, he was free of guilt.

The cormorant fishery in Japan is that which is best known.[205, 444] The year AD813 is reputed to be the historical beginning of the Japanese cormorant fishery. Nevertheless, nocturnal cormorant fishing seems to be much older; it is mentioned in a historical report, named *Kojiki,* completed in AD712. At any rate. that fishery was known in

Fig 25 Before the cormorants are released for fishing they are securely tied.

Japan before the Heian period which extends from the ninth to the twelfth century. A record from the year 1028 states that at Gifu the cormorant fishermen operated with twelve birds each – and that is how it is still done today. Europeans did not learn about cormorant fishing until the fourteenth century, but since the beginning of the seventeenth century they also have caught and used cormorants for fishing purposes. But for them its practice was more a sport like that of falconry. This has been particularly the case in Belgium, France and England. Like fishing with otters, it has there remained a hobby and has not become a general method. Fishing with cormorants became for some time a royal sport like hawking. A 'master of cormorants' was a member of the English Royal Courts of James I (1566-1626) and Charles I (1600-1649). Also Louis XIII of France (1610-1643) had, about the year 1625, some tame cormorants in Fontainebleau, which are said to have come from Flanders. This may be a hint that they came from China, because Jesuit priests from the Spanish Netherlands were sent as missionaries to that country. Cormorants used for fishing are not always of the same species. There are twenty-six species in the world. The Japanese use only four in their fishery, but principally the Chinese cormorants *Phalacrocorax capillatus* and *Phalacrocorax carbo* (*sinensis*). The latter is also the species most widely spread throughout Europe, and it was this species that was used here for fishing.

Unlike the practice of other countries which also know of and use cormorants for fishing, the Chinese have domesticated their birds in the real sense. Whereas in other countries young cormorants have been caught and trained, the Chinese actually breed them from eggs. In west and south China the cormorants that are held in captivity lay from three to ten eggs in a season and these are then hatched by hens because cormorants in captivity neglect their eggs. Captive Japanese cormorants very seldom lay eggs. They must therefore be caught as young birds and tamed and trained. In Japan, wild cormorants breed in the north of Hokkaido and on the Kurils. In winter (middle of October to the end of January) they migrate to central Japan. In earlier times young cormorants were only captured in the Ise Bay on the Pacific coast of central Japan, but since 1922 cormorants have also appeared during winter on the Ibaraki Prefecture north of Tokyo, and they have been caught there exclusively for fishing purposes since 1950. To catch them, the migrating cormorants are lured by means of living or stuffed birds to prepared places and there caught with twigs coated with bird lime.

Much effort and care is needed to satisfactorily tame and train the cormorants. The birds are inspected daily and nursed so that they get used to people. For that purpose the fisherman, in the beginning, tends them every two to three hours, talks to the birds, and rubs them gently so that they become more and more tame. Their beaks are filed so that they are unable to hurt their masters and their wings are clipped. This training takes seven to eight months. They are taught to sit on the edge of the boat and to fish by order. They also have to get used to the neck ring and line which are put on them. Cormorants can live many years in captivity and, according to some reports, often attain twenty to thirty years of age. From the age of three to eight years, however, they are at their best for fishing, although it is expected that they can be used for ten years. A Japanese fisherman possessing twenty to twenty two birds must reckon to lose three every year so that each year several new birds must be procured.

The principle of the cormorant fishery is that a string is tied around the base of the neck before the bird is released for fishing. This permits it to swallow only small fish. It is trained to deliver up to its master larger fish which it cannot gulp down. It is then rewarded with small fish. The birds may be taken to the river for fishing any day. In the case of bad weather caused by wind or snow, or when the water is turbid, they cannot fish, but still have to be fed and watered. This also applies, of course, in the period when fishing with cormorants is prohibited as it is in Japan during certain periods. At Gifu, this is from 15 March to 10 May. On the Takatsu River fishing is allowed only during three months in winter; during the other nine months the birds have to be fed and this is a heavy burden on the fisherman, as each cormorant needs 800 grams of fish per day.

As with many animals that live in a community, the cormorants have a strict order of precedence. The birds must always sit in the same order on the edge of the boats otherwise there is trouble. Only sociable or mutually friendly birds can be placed together in a transport basket. These are baskets which will carry two and sometimes four birds (*Fig 26*). The Chinese operate in daylight sometimes with completely free-swimming birds. This can be a single cormorant only. The bird has, on the right foot, a line one metre in length. If the cormorant does not return to the boat with its prey immediately after diving, the fisherman can catch this line with a hook on a long stick.[286]

Fig 26 The Japanese cormorant fisherman in his typical dress. In the foreground are the baskets in which the cormorants are transported.

In Japan, ten to twelve cormorants are fastened to lines and are directed by the fishermen in night fishing when the river is illuminated by torches or fire baskets to attract fishes. However, fishing by daylight with free-swimming cormorants from the bank or from the boat is also practised in Japan. The main centre of the Japanese cormorant fishery is on the Nagara River, notably around Gifu and Inugama in the Gifu Prefecture. This fishery is there only as an attraction for tourists, and the fishermen, who are members of certain long-established families, are paid for their work of attracting visitors. The cormorant fishermen wear an ancient traditional costume with a black pointed cap and a straw apron (*Fig 26*). It is said (and readily believed) that the cormorants know exactly who their keepers are. Usually several boats operate together in a certain formation. As the first boat takes the better catches, turns are taken in that position. Every year more than 100,000 visitors, Japanese as well as foreigners, travel to the Gifu Prefecture in order to see the nocturnal spectacle of the cormorant fishery under the light of the burning fire baskets. It is certainly an attractive and interesting sight.

Fishing with cormorants has become too complicated and unprofitable in modern times for the conduct of any large-scale fishing enterprise. However, it still pays to catch high-priced fish like the ayus, *Plecoglossus altivelis*, a trout-like fish famous for its annual anadromous migratory behaviour. Smoked or cooked the fish is considered a delicacy. The cormorants, of course, also catch other less valuable fish. According to Japanese experience, efficient cormorants are able to catch up to 150 fish in an hour. And that rate of catch easily explains why fishermen consider free-living cormorants one of the greatest menaces to their fisheries.

It is interesting to note that cormorant fishing was known not only in east and southeast Asia, but also on the other side of the Pacific Ocean. It was apparently developed and practised in Peru where ancient vases are known showing painted scenes wherein fishermen on rush rafts have birds with string round their necks, which suggest that they might have been trained exactly like the cormorants.[323, 669]

It seems that today fishing with cormorants is operated in commercial fishing in continental China only. In Japan it has become purely a tourist attraction. Japanese, and visitors from overseas, like to go out during the night with a pleasure boat to have a drinking party and to see the cormorants fishing in the light of open fires which attract the fish.

4.6 Driving fish with diving birds

Tamed and trained cormorants are, or have been, useful for fishermen in the Far East but in general wild cormorants are detested by all fishermen. This is understandable because cormorants and other diving birds are able to completely clear small lake areas of fish within a short time, or at least to thoroughly frighten away all the fish in those waters. Man recognized this fact very early and in some cases has applied it to his own purposes, for since olden times he has used diving birds to drive fish into fishing gear which he has erected to trap them. In such cases the birds so used are not persecuted as fish thieves but, on the contrary, are greatly valued.

In some areas of Finland and Sweden the goosander, *Mergus merganser,* has been protected only because the fish fled from them into artificial twig huts or shelters which were then encircled by fishing gear.[581, 612] The diving birds thus indirectly help the fishermen to scare various species of freshwater fish into these artificial shelters from which they can be taken from time to time. Apparently this method was formerly widely used, at least in some parts of Europe.

In this connection the fishery with birds on Dojran Lake,[15, 196, 389], situated between Yugoslavia and Greece, is very interesting. As early as the third century BC Herodotus praised this circular lake and its good fishery. The lake has a nearly uniform depth of ten metres and is therefore everywhere accessible to the diving birds which come from the north to winter there. The fish flee before the birds and that fact is utilized by the fishermen, especially on the Yugoslavian beaches, in order to drive the fish together and so concentrate them in traps. About 50 per cent of all fish, primarily roach, carp, perch and bleak are caught on the Dojran Lake through the agency and help of birds. For that purpose, certain areas of the beach are fenced in with mats before the migrating birds arrive, so that only one entrance remains open towards the lake. The fenced area is kept free from the birds by special watchmen so that the fish can retreat more and more to that area away from the birds which are then diving freely out on the lake. Meanwhile some of the birds are caught in special traps (*Figs 27* and *28*) and their wings are clipped. These birds, which are unable to fly, are called the 'working birds'. Particularly valued for this purpose are the mergansers *Mergellus albellus, Mergus merganser* and *Mergus serrator;* and of other diving species, particularly the crested grebe, *Podiceps cristatus;* of the cormorants, *Phalacrocorax carbo,* and of the loons, *Colymbus arcticus* and *C. seellatus.* These last, however, come to the Dojran Lake only in very cold winters. Other birds, such as Arctic diving ducks and also bald coots, are used only as 'emergency help'. Each working group of birds is composed of various species, the proper composition of which is essential for an efficient working team. *Mergellus albellus* is considered to be the most important working bird.

After several weeks, when sufficient fish have gathered within the protective fence, the entrances to these fishing areas are completely closed off by rush mats. Each area is then sub-divided into twenty or thirty chambers. Each chamber is separated from the next one by loose open mats through which the fish can pass but not the birds. When the now-

Fig 27 On the Dojran Lake in Yugoslavia, birds, after being lured into special traps as in the picture, are placed in a succession of chambers to drive fish into other chambers where they can be caught. (*Photo: B Drnkov*)

Fig 28 Working birds trapped at the Dojran Lake. (See previous and following figures). (*Apolstolski and Matvejev, 1955*).

hungry working birds are brought into an outer chamber they soon begin to dive after the fish, thus chasing them from that chamber through the mat into the next one. Only the fish that are too big to go through the mats are then left. These fish – which cannot be swallowed by the birds – (in particular large carp) are then speared by the fishermen (*Fig 29*). The loose mats are replaced by dense ones and the working birds are brought into the subsequent chamber. Here the hunt for the fish begins anew. The empty chamber is broken up and the mats are used at other places. In this way the

Fig 29 In this chamber not only are the working birds shown, but in the background there are fishermen with spears to catch the bigger fish. (*Apolstolski and Matvejev, 1955*).

fish are driven progressively towards and into the last chamber where all the remaining fish in the area are concentrated. From that last chamber the fish are taken by means of a fyke-net-like construction.

When the winter fishery is over, spring fishing for spawning fish begins using the same method. When that fishery, too, is finished the working birds are set free. It is reckoned that about 30 per cent of the birds will have died before this time. The working birds remain on the lake until their wings have grown again and they are once more able to leave their involuntarily prolonged winter abode.

There may be many more such tactics for catching fish with the help of birds in small-scale fisheries. It is reported from Indonesia (South Kalimantan) that in fishing for snakehead, *Ophiocephalus* sp. – an air-breathing fish in tropical inland waters – ducks have been trained to chase their fry. This causes the male and female snakeheads guarding the young fish to turn furiously on the duck which is then hauled aboard the canoe by a line at the end of a long bamboo pole attached to the boat. The fish follow the withdrawn bird, snapping in their rage at unbaited hooks, and are caught.[505]

Such fishing methods as those mentioned above are based on a great knowledge of the behaviour of fish and birds, and are a clear proof of how much, even today, fishing methods are first related to biology and only in the second place to engineering technique.

4.7 Sucker fish for catching turtles

This story about the use of animals for the scaring and capturing of fish and other aquatic animals is not yet finished. A rather strange method involves the use of the sucker fish or remora, *Echeneis* sp. These are fish of the perch family, in which the anterior dorsal fin is transformed into an adhesive disc. With that disc they attach themselves to large fish, for instance, pelagic sharks, tuna and swordfish, in order to be transported by them. This phenomenon occurs with aquatic animals and also with some living in the air – such as insects which are towed from place to place. The sucker fish are a well-known example of this phenomenon. They can attach themselves by suction, even to the bottom of ships, and it was believed in the ancient Mediterranean that large specimens could even stop or hinder vessels. Mark Antony is said to have lost the battle of Actium (31BC) when his vessel was stopped by these fishes, and Caligula was captured for the same reason on the voyage to Ostia – so it is claimed. This ability to adhere powerfully is used for catching turtles and even sharks.[261, 422, 436, 661] For that purpose remoras are caught with hook and line, fastened at the tail by a line, and set free from a boat when the sighted victim is near. The fastening is usually made by means of a rope bored through the peduncle or by a ring through or around the tail to which a line is attached. When the sucker fish have fastened themselves, for instance, to a turtle, a sort of drill begins until the victim is hauled alongside the boat, or at least so near that it can be speared. The attaching power of the sucker fish is considerable and the one mainly used, *Echeneis naucrates,* which is some 60cm in length, can easily stand a pull of 9-10kg.

It is most remarkable that fishing with sucker fish has been known in so many parts of the world. Columbus reported it as practised by the Indians in the Caribbean Sea[585] and Alexander v Humboldt reported that this method was used in Cuba for catching turtles. Today this fishing technique is unknown in the Caribbean. It was formerly probably known also in Venezuela and Columbia.[669] The Chinese are said to have known fishing with sucker fish, as did the dark native fishermen of Australia in the Torres Strait between Australia and New Guinea. On the east coast of Africa, fishing with sucker fish was carried out from Zanzibar, Kenya and the Comoro Islands. In earlier times sucker fish were also probably used for catching crocodiles in the estuaries of the Strait of Mozambique.

It may be added, that remoras have been mentioned, too, as fish which can be caught by wrecked survivors drifting on a raft, when the fish try to fix themselves onto the raft. But it must be remembered that these fish would change immediately from the raft to a passing quicker fish or turtle.[526]

4.8 Fishing with octopus

Certainly there are many other occasions when fishermen make use, directly or indirectly, of animals or their behaviour, although in a less demonstrative manner than has so far been described. Only one other strange fishing method has to be mentioned here, even though no fish are caught! It is related that Japanese fishermen used octopi as divers to collect porcelain from a wrecked ship which had a cargo of valuable porcelain bowls. This was in the Inland Sea, between the islands of Honshu and Shikoku. For this purpose an octopus was fastened to a line and lowered to the wreck. Because of its wish to seize hold, and so escape, the octopus became attached by suction to the porcelain in or near the wreck. When it was lifted out of the water it brought with it the cups and vases to which it had sought to cling. During the First World War the Cretans used tethered octopi in the same manner to retrieve coal which had fallen overboard from warships![337, 509] It can happen even today when fishermen in Japan and Korea are trolling for octopi (*Figs 217* and *218*). The hooked animal is hauled up with its hiding place: this can be an old teacup – unfortunately usually made of plastic today!

4.9 Using the friendly porpoise

In many cases animals help indirectly to catch fish. There is for instance, the detection of fish by observing the concentration of birds. Before the invention of our modern fish-detecting devices, this was the practical fisherman's most important method of finding fish shoals. Even today the observation of bird flocks is used for recognition and identification when airplotting shoals.[77, 538]

Not only birds but also porpoises are used to find tuna, since it was discovered that shoals of fish were very often accompanied by porpoises.[494] It is an old story that porpoises and fishermen are friends, especially in the Mediterranean. The Roman historian Pliny the Elder (AD23-79) stated that the fishermen of Gallia Narbonensis (that is, the Mediterranean coast of southern France) caught mackerel driven into their nets by porpoises near to the shore. The Greek poet Oppianos (second century AD) mentions with enthusiasm this unconscious aid of porpoises for the fishermen of Euboea in his didactic poem 'Halieutica' about fishing.[482] It has been stated that porpoises were first used to drive fish into nets thousands of years ago in India.[252] Even today, sardine fishermen like to see these animals near their boats when they are fishing with lights and surrounding gear. The porpoises are shy of light but, according to fishermen, they circle round in curiosity at a distance from the lamps, and thus help to round up and concentrate the sardine shoals. When they are concentrated the fishermen surround the sardine shoal with their nets.

The fishermen off the Turkish coast of the Black Sea believe that porpoises used to practice driving fish towards the coasts but, becoming frightened by fishermen using dynamite on shoals near the sea shore, now stay out in the open sea. The result is that the fish schools no longer come to the coast. This is quite understandable as porpoises are very sensitive to all kinds of noise. There is a story from the old fishery of Indo-China that their fishermen learned that porpoises fed on mullet in the morning and evening. To escape their persecutors the mullet swam near to the coast at those times and there the fishermen were waiting to catch them with cast nets. At the same time, boys set to work frightening the porpoises away and helped them to reach the open sea if they became stranded or entangled in the nets by accident.[37]

Something similar can be read in the old Norwegian king's book, *Konungsskuggsja.*[380] There it is reported that friendly relations existed between the fishermen and the fish-hunting whales. Such a whale, it is said, 'drives herring and other fish from the high sea towards the land, and it has such an admirable nature that it knows how to steer men and ships and drives herring and other fish towards them, as though God has sent it and ordered it to do so and as though it be his duty as long as the fishermen are fishing in a peaceful way. But when they are quarrelling and thrashing until blood runs, it appears that the whale is feeling it and it swims then between the land and the fish and drives them all away from the fishermen to the high seas . . .'. It was therefore forbidden to hunt that whale during the herring season. A similar story is told by the Indians in the Gulf of Mexico. In this case killer whales drive the fish to the beach.[350] In Oceanic myths, tuna drive fish towards the coast, and also in Tasmania similar stories are told.

More modern and realistic is the fishery for mullet with the help of dolphins, as done by the fishing tribe of Imraguan of the village of El Mahara on the Mauretanian coast. The fishermen beat the water to imitate the noise of jumping mullet by which the porpoises are attracted to catch them. By this means the mullet are driven towards the coast where they are caught in gillnets. Sometimes killer whales, *Orcinus orca,* hamper the porpoises in doing this valuable work which the fishermen need in order to have a successful catch of mullet. This is nearly the same tactic as mentioned before from Gallia Narbonensis and known to the early writers. The relationship between human and dolphin behaviour has been exploited for many centuries and it has been asked whether it may be possible to develop and extend this kind of fishing co-operation with the dolphins to other species of migrating fish.[101] With the last item, however, we exceed the theme of this chapter, which should really deal with animals used for helping in fishing. Moreover, the hunting and fishing folk of olden times had the imagination to believe that such animals that helped them were really ghosts of men hiding themselves in those bodies. They guided the booty to huntsmen or fishermen like the minke whale did with the herring. Such mythical concepts in connection with fisheries will be discussed in Chapter 23.

Chapter five

Fish harvesting after stupefying

The fisherman who collects from the beach or shallow water can secure only sedentary, stranded, or slowly moving organisms. Active living fish will seldom be caught in this manner. The collecting activity of the diver is scarcely different, and it must be admitted that such fish as are caught in that way represent only a small percentage of the whole. To prevent the escape of fish – which is possible even in small pools – man developed methods to paralyse or stun and stupefy the fish and thus ensure their capture.

5.1 Simple forms of mechanical stupefying

The simplest method of stupefying small game from a distance is by throwing a stone, provided the game is hit! Stones are considered as the first long-range weapon of prehistoric man and they are used, even today, in fisheries. The result may be that the game is stupefied, or that it is injured, hampering its escape, or even that it is killed. A similar result can be reached by striking the prey with a short stick, a club, the blunt side of an axe or even a quick kick. Seals are stupefied by a blow from a hard wooden club followed by stabbing through the heart with a sharp knife, which is considered a rapid, highly efficient and humane method of killing. Fish in the water are more or less protected by this element against the efficiency of a blow and may not be killed but stunned only. As the blow is made mechanically it is named 'mechanical narcosis'. Fishing by means of throwing stones can be observed all over the world. Children especially throw stones at fish in an effort to stun or stupefy them. The same result can be achieved by throwing clubs or other pieces of wood like those used by the native fishermen of Australia who threw boomerang-like wooden projectiles at fish. If the fisherman was lucky enough to hit it, the fish was stunned and could be caught by hand.[660] It must be remembered that most boomerangs used as missiles by native Australians in war and hunting do *not* return to the thrower. The famous returning boomerang of Australia was mostly a plaything. It was seldom used for hunting except for spinning above flocks of ducks which mistake the gear for a hawk and are driven down into nets strung from trees. It has to be added that boomerangs or other thrown wooden missiles were also known for hunting in Europe, India, ancient Egypt and Central America.

Widespread in some areas which have cold winters is another simple method of mechanical stupefying. Here burbot and pike are found to be spawning just beneath the ice in shallow water during the early spring. If the ice is transparent the fish can be seen through the ice. But any attempt to make a hole in the ice and capture the fish would be useless, for despite their laziness, occasioned by the low water temperature, they would escape immediately. In the fisheries of northeast Europe as well as in North America, however, it was discovered that the fish could be temporarily stunned or narcotized and prevented from escaping by beating heavily on the ice over them with clubs or mallets. Wooden hammers are used for this purpose even today by non-professionals.[690] To do this successfully, however, the ice must not be too thick and should already be slightly brittle and the fish should be located just below where the ice is struck.[528] It is through the vibrations caused by the blows on the ice that a temporary stupefaction is produced. It lasts long enough for the fish to be retrieved from below the ice. Sometimes, two persons fish together. One looks for the fish, to beat the ice above them with a wooden club or hammer. The other makes the holes with an ice-axe and takes the stunned fish by hand or with a scoopnet. This can also be done during the night using lights. Sometimes fish are also caught by children under the first ice of autumn. Children are not so heavy and can move over thin ice, crawling on feet and hands simultaneously. The ice will break with the first strike made to stupefy the fish which then has to be taken very quickly by hand without the catcher falling into the water![345] Fishing by beating the ice with the aim of stupefying the fish under it was mentioned by Olaus Magnus (1555). The technique is not only known in northern countries but also in the area of the Danube.[214] An equivalent method of mechanical stupefying was known in the ancient Chinese fishery in which one knocked with a hammer on the stones in a river to stupefy fish which might be hiding beneath them.[613] This method of catching is also known in southern Asia. In Nepal 'rockstriking' with a hammer is considered a very harmful practice, like poisoning and dynamiting.[576]

5.2 Stupefying fish with dynamite

Fishing by mechanical narcosis has also been developed in modern forms. When shooting at fish with rifles and shotguns the intent is not so much to hit the fish as to put a charge of bullet or shot just before its head so that the concussion caused in the water may temporarily stun or stupefy the fish. To aid the shooting of salmon in this way, for instance, a special small dam is often built so that the fish must come to the surface to leap over it. Before it leaps, a shot can be fired into the water near it and the stunned fish is then either caught by scoopnet or retrieved by dogs.

Mechanical narcosis is produced to a great extent by using explosives in fisheries. It has been said that explosives were used for fishing as early as around 1600! Fishing with dynamite is known all over the world and it is usually prohibited, unfortunately very often without success. Fishermen can obtain dynamite today often without difficulty, sometimes in exchange for fish, from people working in mines, quarries or in road-making. However, in some countries severe punishment can be imposed for using explosives. In the Philippines the penalty is imprisonment from 20 years to life. If the use of explosives results in the loss of human lives the penalty can even be death. This prohibition is based on the fact that the method is very dangerous and that young fish and fish fry are also destroyed by the explosion; and moreover, many useful fish sink to the bottom because their air-bladders are destroyed. They are then lost unless collected from the bottom by divers. We know now that fish stupefied by explosion for a short time only can swim away apparently undamaged only to die some days later through internal injuries.[391] Off the Black Sea coast, Turkish fishermen make dynamite bombs by pressing the dangerous material together, with a fuse, in the form of a great egg (*Fig 30*). The whole is held together by paper and twine. The fisherman with the bomb takes his place in the bow of a boat which is rowed very slowly and quietly. This man has constantly to smoke a cigarette

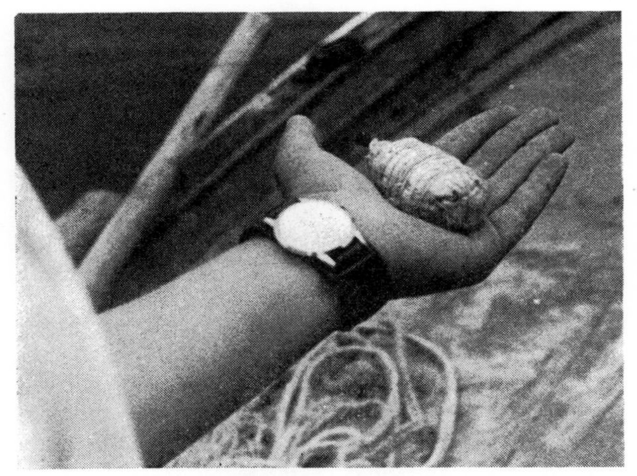

Fig 30 Home-made dynamite bomb for fishing off the Turkish Black Sea coast. (1963).

because as soon as one good school of fish is discovered the fuse must be ignited from the cigarette. The bomb must then be thrown immediately or accidents occur. Lost fingers on the right hand are typical defects of dynamite fishermen!

Fishing with hand grenades as practised during both World Wars was particularly damaging. The hand grenade was actually called the 'soldier's fish hook'. When a hand grenade was exploded in an experiment, a diver brought up from the depths ten times more fish than was gathered on the surface.[121] Fishing by dynamite in Greece became rather notorious, but there it has now also been prohibited for the reasons mentioned. It happens, however, that sharks are attracted by such explosions since they have learnt that the acoustic stimulant means that they can easily get fish for themselves. Dynamite explosions are therefore now used in some places to attract sharks.

Dynamite in small quantities, however, can be very useful for frightening the fish. Purse seiners in California use small bombs to frighten the fish away from the opening of the net before the gear is completely pursed and closed. These bombs are called 'cherry bombs' according to their original form. In the Philippines, where fishing with large dip nets called 'basnig' is practised, a small explosive charge is used to stun the encircled fish and so prevent their escape when the net is lifted. This too, however, is illegal as mentioned before, although it is well known that the use of dynamite may possibly determine whether any particular operation is a success or not.

5.3 Fish poisoning

The mechanically achieved narcosis of fish is,

however, far less important than that produced chemically by fish poisoning. For this purpose poisonous material from so-called ichthyotoxic plants is crushed, cut to pieces, or pulverized and sprinkled on the water or added to bait (*Fig 31*).

Fig 31 Aborigines of the Xingu area fishing with ichthyotoxic plants. (*Photo: E J Fittkau*).

The fish are thereby narcotized or at least so affected that they rise to the water surface for air and can be captured easily. It is necessary, however, that this fishery takes place in small areas of stagnant or slow-running water. Fish poisoning is generally used in small bodies of water, up to about 500 hectares, or in bays and arms of larger lakes.[524] Pools too large to be bailed out are treated with poison. In running water, barriers are installed downstream from the place where the poison is to be used in order to catch the more or less floating, helpless fish. To make this fishery more profitable the fish are driven together in certain sections of a brook or lake before the poison is applied. To catch larger fish in deeper waters, poisoned mixtures are put into the bellies of bait fish as is known in many tropical fisheries. The stomach of a dead squid, for example, is filled with a mixture of poison and the flesh of small fish.[93] As soon as the larger fish have taken this bait the poisoning effect makes them rise to the surface. In that way, or when divers take poisonous substances down as is done in Samoa, the practice of fishing with poison can be carried out in the deeper waters of the sea.

Fish poisoning with ichthyotoxic plants provides perhaps one of the most interesting chapters in the story of native fisheries. Plants containing saponin and those containing certain lactones are especially used in this method. These are very strong protoplasma poisons which have a stupefying effect on the peripheral, sensory and motor nerves and muscles of the fish caught. The fish suffer from cramp and suffocation because of the breakdown of the red blood cells. This is a very cruel method of fish catching. It is therefore understandable that in many countries this, as well as poisoning of fish in general, is prohibited or is only permitted under certain conditions.

It is difficult to explain how these ichthyotoxic plants with their specific poisonous effect on fish were first discovered. Probably their power was found by chance, perhaps during washing, because so many plants containing saponin were used for that purpose. As the primitive races, of course, could not comprehend the connection it will be readily understood how native 'magicians' effectively used poisons in their exercise of fishery 'magic'. It was their knowledge of poisonous plants which gave the magicians or medicine men the power to influence their tribesmen and appear to dominate the fish. Some stories exist about how fish poisoning was invented. A very nice one has been told by the Indians in Guyana.[332] A long time ago a father was going out with his little son to bathe. The father was astonished to see that the fish always died when the boy was swimming in the water. It was easy to collect the fish and they were found good to eat. Therefore the father practised this method of fish catching. But the fish decided to prevent the future death of members of their families so one day when the boy was sitting on a wooden block before jumping in the water, some sting-rays came and jumped together out of the water against the boy, wounding him with their hard spines. These wounds were very dangerous and the father was naturally anxious to carry home his dying son. As he did so the lad's blood dropped on the ground and each spot became an ichthyotoxic plant (*Loncho carpus*). That plant has been used by the Indians for fish poisoning in rivers ever since that time. Fishing with poison is particularly prevalent in tropical areas such as Asia and South America, but is also used in the temperate zones of Asia, Europe and North America. It has been a matter of discussion whether the absence or disappearance of some fishing methods from the fishery of the Indian tribes of North America could possibly be traced to their having discovered the substantially more successful and easier method of using poison.[528]

The number of ichthyotoxic plants useful for fishing, as far as they can be ascertained at all, is quite considerable.[631] The stupefying chemicals can be concentrated in the stems, roots, leaves, seeds or berries of these plants. A list of such names would, in fact, run into many hundreds – maybe even thousands. Only a few of them have become widely spread and some have been introduced even into European fisheries (*Fig 32*). Among these plants are kokkelseed. These are also called 'fish seeds' or 'lice seeds', as in the boiled form the liquid is used for exterminating vermin. Kokkelseeds are the fruit of *Anamirta cocolus,* a creeping shrub with cork-like bark which grows in Indo-China and Sri Lanka. The seeds contain picrotoxin, of which small doses cause narcosis. Black Sea fishermen roast the seeds before crushing. The powder is carefully mixed with dough. Small pellets are made and thrown into the water where fish are expected. This bait will stupefy the fish in a short time. The seeds have also been known in Europe for centuries and their use was prescribed for fishing in Brunswick in 1528. Fish are said to recover from this narcosis when brought into fresh water and, to assist that recovery and to provide good quality fish, it is reported from Bosnia that liquors were poured into the fish's mouth.[87] Also it is said by modern sports fishermen that when pike fishing it is very important that the bait be lively, even if it has to be enlivened from time to time by a nip of brandy,[626] so it is to be feared that this striving for the modern attainment of high quality was only an excuse for the fisherman to provide himself with the spirits he himself needed or desired!

Fig 32 'Fish-seeds' and 'crow's eyes' for fish poisoning.

The so-called 'crow's eyes' or *nux vomica* constitute another fish poison which is equally well known in European fishing practice. These are the flat seeds of a shrub growing in Indo-China and as far away as Australia. It is called *Strychnos nux vomica* and is sometimes even cultivated in order to produce the alkaloid brucinum and strychnine. The seeds contain up to five per cent of alkaloid, of which a little less than half is strychnine. Finally there is rotenone, a very important fish poison also known in Europe. Many plants contain this poison and are used in fishing, including the native fisheries of South America as well as those of southern Asia. In Malaysia it is especially the root of tuba or derris that is used.

Derris is a name applied to several tropical twining plants of the great family Leguminosae from southern Asia, particularly those found in India – *Derris elliptica* (Beuth), *D. uliginosa* (Beuth) and *D. lagensis* (Prein).[251] *Derris elliptica* is used especially to extract rotenone which is also known as a valuable insecticide. The roots of these plants contain up to ten per cent of rotenone, the greatest amount being found in the bark of the root.[502] Derris roots are called 'akar tuba' in Malay, therefore it is also known as tuba root. Rotenone has been used for fishing in southeast Asia from time immemorial as a fish poison for individual fishing, even when now forbidden – and also for festive occasions. (For the festival of 'Fish Drive' in Pahang, a state on the east coast of Malaysia, 'tons of tuba roots are crushed and pounded for a juice that intoxicates the fish, causing them to zig-zag merrily to the surface . . .'). It has to be added that rotenone, like other ichthyotoxic materials, is not only used for catching fish but also for the eradication of unwanted species, *eg* the piranhas, *Serrasalmus* sp. in Brazil,[654] and unwanted fishes in pond fisheries. Fish are extremely sensitive to this poison of rotenone, so that a very small amount is enough to stupefy them. Bundles of derris roots can be bought either fresh or dried in the south Asian markets. For fishing purposes the roots are crushed and pulverized in the water, when they exude a milky juice. This juice is also used by Chinese gardeners as an insecticide on plants. Dried roots must be soaked first. In British Guyana the bundles of roots are pounded with a stick or stone in water, when a thick milky juice comes out. The roots are wrung out in the water until all the juice has been extracted. The milky emulsion is then scattered over the water. In one or two hours' time, when the fish are swimming violently about near the surface, they can be caught by hand, with spears or with scoopnets. In some places in south Asia derris is cultivated for the production of rotenone. This is done in open ground and the derris is not allowed to grow into large plants. Related species of these plants in the forest grow into enormous lianes.[251] Nowadays rotenone can be produced synthetically. As it is a poison specifically affecting fish, and is relatively harmless to men and warm-blooded animals, it has become important in modern fishery practice in so far as it can be used when it becomes necessary to remove bad fish stocks or those of minor quality from certain waters or areas. Rotenone, as well as other poisons, can be used in circumstances where fishes have to be harvested very quickly *eg* when a stretch of water dries up.[17] The high efficiency of rotenone is proved by the fact that a dilution of 1 kilo per 100 cubic metres is quite sufficient to kill or facilitate the removal of all fish from a particular water.

Besides those plant poisons originating from tropical zones, there are quite a number of indigenous plants in Europe which have also been used for fishing. Of course, in the temperate zones there are not thousands of ichthyotoxic plants as there are in the tropics. There are lists in both old and modern literature of the plants used for fish poisoning in Europe, but very often many dubious names are included, and also plants attracting fish are mixed with ichthyotoxic ones. The best-known ichthyotoxic plants in Europe are the following:

1. Yews (Taxaceae)
   Common yew (*Taxus baccata*)
2. Spurges (Euphorbiaceae)
   Spurge (*Euphorbia esula*)
3. Daphne plants (Thymelaeaceae)
   Common daphne (*Daphne mezereum*)
4. Primroses (Primulaceae)
   Cyclamen (*Cyclamen europaeum*)
5. Borage (Borraginaceae)
   Ox tongue (*Anchusa officinalis*)
6. Shade (Solanaceae)
   Thorn apple (*Datura stramonium*)
   Tobacco (*Nicotina tabacum*)
   Common henbane (*Hyoscyamus niger*)
7. Scrophularia (Scrophulariaceae)
   Mullein (*Verbascum nigrum*)
   Mullein (*Verbascum undulatum*)

This list is far from being complete even for Europe. There are some ichthyotoxic plants more especially in southeastern Europe.[130, 213] Some of these plants, such as yew, daphne, cyclamen, thorn apple and henbane, are also dangerous to man. The effect of yew as a fish poison is disputed: in place of it, juniper and arborvitae, or the etheric oils contained in their leaves, are mentioned as being preferable for their poisoning effect on fish. Irish salmon fishermen used crushed roots of the Irish spurge (*E. hiberna*). These roots were dug up, allowed to decay and then crushed. The mass was then put into bags and trodden into the water of the river in which it was desired to kill salmon.[657] In the case of daphne the poison is produced by boiling the blossoms. According to tradition, daphne was used in China for fishing as long ago as 2200BC. The sap of cyclamen tubers is also used in poison fishing. This was known to the Romans – and their descendants are still aware of it. The leaves and roots of ox tongue can also be used, and it has been said that fish-thieves rubbed their feet with the leaves of this plant before wading into the forbidden water.[48] From Solanaceae particularly, the seeds are used for fish poisoning. In Romania the seeds of thorn apples were removed and mixed with the bile of pigs. This concoction was mixed into small balls of maize meal and then thrown into the water.[130] From daphne, and also mullein, the poison is obtained by boiling the blossoms. The poisoning effect of mullein blossoms (which contain saponin) was known to the Greeks, who learned it from the Phoenicians. Old fishery books give many formulae for the use of various poisonous plants in fishing. The object was always to stupefy the fish in such a way that they rose to the surface and could be easily captured by hand.

As in hunting, poisons of animal origin, as distinct from those made from plants, are rarely used for fishing. Occasionally gallic acid from various animals like sheep, cows, or carp is employed, *eg* in Egypt or, as mentioned before, in Romania. The effect is similar to that of saponin as it destroys the blood cells and affects the muscles and deadens the circulation and nervous system. In some cases water in which black trepang has been boiled is used for fish poisoning. Ryukyuan fishermen poison fish by throwing trepang pieces into the sea, and it has been claimed that then a large number of fish rise to the surface. This method has been well known in the fisheries of the Indian and Pacific Oceans since olden times. In small ponds it seems to be sufficient to hang such animals in the water or to use fluid squeezed from the intestines, or the secretion of the skin.

In many countries fish poisoning has been forbidden for a long time. In Germany the use of the fruits of yew and daphne for fish poisoning has been forbidden since 1212. Nowadays, more effective chemicals have replaced the ichthyotoxic plants. Nevertheless, in tropical areas fish poisoning may remain a very useful method of catching fish in a simple way, especially if the poison is used carefully and economically.

A special method of fishing must be mentioned here, and that is fishing with poisoned wounding gear (Chapter 6). Especially in whaling, poisoned heads of spears or arrows have been used in some areas. On the Aleutian Islands hunters planted poisoned spears in the whales and returned to the shore. In two or three days the infected whale died and was washed ashore where it was claimed by the owner of the spearhead, on which he had cut his mark. The points of arrows were also poisoned by these people with the help of the roots of aconite, *Aconitum* sp., a member of the family Ranunculaceae. For this purpose the roots were dried and pounded or grated, water was poured upon them and they were kept in a warm place until fermented. It was the German traveller G W Steller (1709-1747) who wrote the first report about whaling with poisoned arrows from the Kuril Islands but his work was not published before 1774. Poison whaling was carried out, as far as is known, not only on the coasts of the Aleutian Islands and Kuril Islands, but also on the Kodiak Islands and the coasts of Kamchatka and off Hokkaido in northern Japan.

Another special form of working with poisoned wounding gear is the infection of whales with a lethal bacteria. The Norwegians have known this method for at least 500 years in whaling practices. In one isolated district, shooting whales with poisoned – or better – infected bolts was used until the 1890s.[518] For this purpose the fjord with a whale in it was closed by netting and the animal was infected with bacteria from swine suffering from anthrax, with the help of arrows. The whale became sick after one or one and a half days, rose very often and could be killed easily.[84] Fishermen remembered this method during World War II, when whales could not be killed by shooting with rifles or other guns, and crossbows only were available to them.

5.4 Fishing with industrial chemicals

Spreading some industrial chemicals on the water is another way of getting fish. By this means the fish are not only stupefied but can also suffer irreversible damage. The so-called lime fishery is one of these methods of affecting fish by caustic substances. For this purpose quicklime, that is dry lime before it is slaked with water, is thrown into the water. As it slakes, the gills of the fish are cauterized and they rise to the surface. In a dictionary for hunting and fishing, published in 1772, the following direction for using lime is mentioned:[433] 'Two people drag a sack of lime to and fro in the water, thus all fish become blind, and rise to the surface so that they can be caught by hand'. This method, too, is prohibited in most countries. In Egypt lime is used to remove predatory fish like eel and catfish from fish ponds. After the ponds have been drained, the eels and catfish dig into the soft mud to about one metre depth. Burnt lime, about one ton for each hectare, is then spread over the mud. The predatory fish begin to appear on the surface of the mud within twenty-four hours and can be collected.

Another method of using unslaked lime for fishing is to use it to create an explosion. In this case a bottle is filled with quicklime and submerged. As water enters the bottle the lime is slaked and the bottle explodes. The fish are stupefied in a mechanical manner, but they are also damaged by the caustic chemical. A similar effect can be caused using carbide. Copper vitriol is another chemical used for killing fish in water, but it is mostly used to frighten animals like octopi out of their holes. In this case divers put a cloth bag containing copper sulphate crystals into a cave suspected of harbouring an octopus. The dissolving chemical contaminates the water, forcing the creature to come out into the open where it can be caught. Also mussels burrowing in tidal areas can be brought out with the help of this chemical. Sodium hypochlorite, bleach, is also used for scattering in the hiding places of some water animals. Nowadays so-called 'chemicals for collectors' are offered with different trade names for harvesting 'ichthyological specimens' during scientific expeditions. The chemical is spread in different concentrations over the water surface, or by divers, in the likely hiding places of fish. The chemicals are said to be of rapid stupefying power without toxic hazards to collectors, divers, or people who may eat fish gained by this method.

5.5 Deoxygenation or suffocation

Finally, another 'chemical' method has to be mentioned. It is well known that after a violent storm has caused deoxygenation through the stirring up of the bottom mud, fish die in great numbers. This principle is known in many parts of the world – even when the reason for this effect is not understood. The Indians in British Guyana trample the mud to stir it up until the fish are suffocated and can be caught easily. Australian aborigines muddy the water in the same way with their feet and then club or spear the half-stupefied fish.[529] Many African people undertake collective fishing by partially suffocating the fish by muddying up the water of small pools. It may be that this principle of suffocating the fish by stirring up the mud is at the back of many of the big communal fish drives, so much a feature of primitive tribal custom, especially in tropical countries.

This method is also known in temperate zones. It has been reported from Hungary that in some areas with small shallow waters full of plants and rich in fishes, where fishing with usual fishing gear is not possible, stupefying the fishes by deoxygenation is applied. For this reason the farmers with their whole family stir up the mud by trampling around in the water. Here as elsewhere muddying is also often produced by driving a herd of cattle or horses to and fro in the pool.[214, 244, 361] It may be added that during hauling purse seines for large tuna, some fishermen jump into the water inside the closed gear full of large fish to catch them by hand. It is possible only because the fish, being pressed together in the gear, are nearly half dead by deoxygenation.

5.6 Electrical fishing

In addition to stupefying fish by mechanical and chemical means, it is also possible to narcotize them with electricity. This is done by one of the most modern fishing methods – electrical fishing. In principle its aim is the same as the mechanical and chemical methods just described; fish otherwise unobtainable are narcotized so that they cannot escape and can thus be easily taken. That some fishes have the ability to produce electrical current has already been reported by writers of some thousand years ago. It was known that some rays like *Torpedo* sp. produce an electrical current for their partial orientation, for locating their prey, and for stupefying or even killing it. Although practical use of electrical fishing methods began after the First World War, it was not before the end of the Second World War that research work enabled man to imitate the technique of the electric ray to use electricity for fishing. Scientists interested in physiological problems studied the reaction of aquatic animals to direct and alternating currents and, since 1912, also to the so-called interrupted current discovered by the Frenchman Leduc in 1900. In the meantime it was found from the accidental breaking of an electrical cable which fell into a river, that fish could be caught very easily after stupefying by electricity. The result was that people, with or without permission, tried to catch fish with the help of electrical current. A report from Romania[130] gives an impression of how this has been done there and elsewhere. 'An electrical cable transmitted the electricity to a river, where it was turned around the shaft of a hay fork, touching the iron parts. In some villages a stick with a bread-basket made of wire fastened on one end is used like a scoop net for catching the stupefied fish.' This was of course a very dangerous technique of electrical fishing before the first transportable generators or powerful batteries were introduced as sources of energy.

Originally, practical fishing with electricity was applied only to fresh water. Its development required not only co-operation between fishermen and electrical engineers, but also the aid of physicians and neurologists. Nevertheless till now many questions have remained unanswered. The basic principle is that an electric field develops when both the anode (+) and the cathode (−) of an electrical system are put into the water. As soon as a fish enters that field two things may occur. If the conductivity of the water is low the current will use the fish as a better conductor and flow to a great extent through it: if the conductivity of the water is much better than that of the fish, the current will then flow around the fish. In the first case the current has a stupefying effect on the fish, but not in the second case (*Fig 33*). This also explains how it is that varying results are frequently obtained from electrical fishing and that difficulties must occur in sea water which happens to have a high conductivity. This conductivity depends also on the temperature. A low temperature increases the conductivity so that electrical fishing may not be successful in a certain water during summer but would be so in winter or in unexpected cool seasons when other methods are not successful. The fish to be caught, its type, its physiological condition, and its position in the electrical field would also influence the success of the operation. Direct current is used for this type of fishing, *ie* in the form of interrupted direct current as the so-called impulse current has a greater physiological effect. It was seen very soon by practical fishermen that the direct current interrupted by switching off and on had a greater effect than the uninterrupted current, but it was not before 1948 that impulse gear was introduced in practical fishery by C Kreutzer. Direct current has a really narcotizing effect, whereas alternating current produces only cramps in the muscles, possibly with the fish retaining full consciousness.[220, 386, 392, 638]

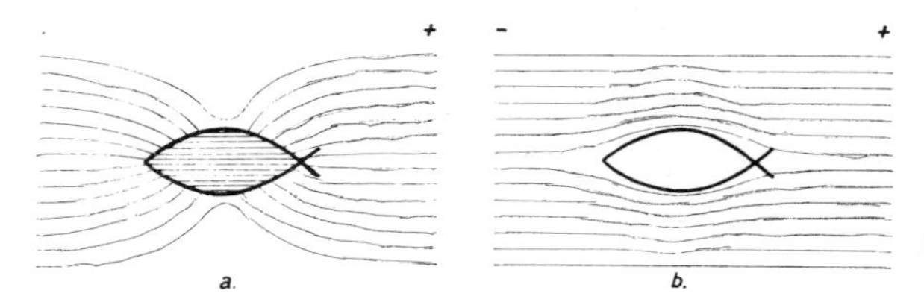

Fig 33 Figures show how electrical current introduced into water affects fish: (*a*) in water with low conductivity the current flows through the fish; (*b*) in water with good conductivity the current flows round the fish.

Four stages can be distinguished in the effect which direct current has on fish. When a fish enters the electrical field the first stage of agitation is felt by it. This, in the marginal zones of the field, may possibly have a frightening effect and thus let the fish escape. The second stage is the 'galvanotaxis'. In this stage the fish reacts anodically; that means it swims towards the anode. That is a great advantage because the fish is thereby guided to the desired spot. When the fish approaches the anode the third stage, that of narcosis, occurs ('galvanonarcosis'). The fish begins to sink and has to be caught quickly. The anode is therefore usually designed to be attached to a scoop net (*Fig 34*). Finally, the fourth and last stage occurs when the power used reaches the killing threshold. With alternating current the first stage is also a convulsion only. In the second stage, the so called 'oscillotaxis', the fish is turned vertical to the electrical field, and does not react anodically. In the third stage the fish will be stupefied ('electronarcosis') and may be killed. If the current is switched off at the right time, some fish are not killed but remain narcotized for some minutes before they recover and can swim away. The reaction of the fish in the pulse current is similar to the one for the interrupted direct current. The fish reacts anodically, but the physiological effect is much higher. By this it becomes possible to catch fish also under unfavourable conditions such as in waters with higher conductivity.

Fig 34 Team of men operating electrical fishing in fresh water. The fish are forced to congregate round the anode beneath which is suspended a scoop-like net with which they will be lifted out of the water. (*Meyer-Waarden, 1957*).

Hitherto electrical fishery as a fishing method has been carried out mainly in fresh water from the banks or from a boat. *Figure 35* shows examples of electrical fishing in small fresh waters. In each case a scoop net is an integral part of the anode. The cathode can be stationary or towed netting made of wire, or a sheet of metal, or netting with

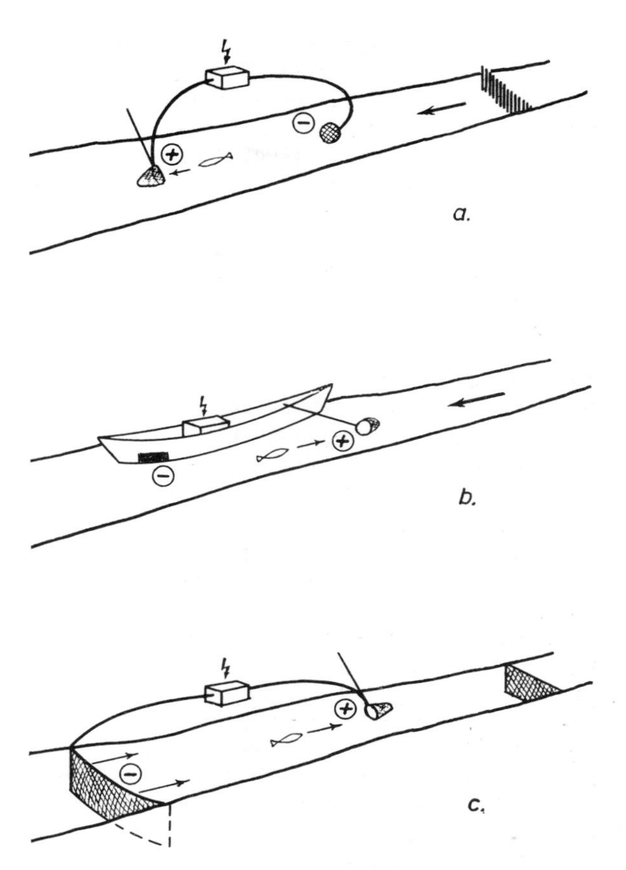

Fig 35 Different types of electrical fishing in fresh water: (*a*) from the shore; (*b*) by boat; (*c*) driving with electrified netting.

wires placed inside. *Figure 35a* shows a fishery from the shore, where the aggregate is set on shore. Electrical fishing with a boat is much more flexible (*Fig 35b*). The electrodes can be placed like those shown in the figure, or the anode is guided by hand and the cathode is towed at a distance of two or three metres behind the boat. A special form of shore fishery is shown in *Figure 35c*, where the fish are frightened into a scoop net or another gear is set on the end of the section to be fished.

Electrical fishing is often the only possible method of fishing waters which are otherwise inaccessible because of many obstacles and underwater growths. It is a method that is useful for controlling and ascertaining the extent of stocks of fish. Through it, fish regarded as vermin, as too old or sick, or of poor type, can easily be removed. Spawning fish can also be carefully procured and the fingerlings easily caught. In cases of emergency a fish population can quickly be saved or damage can be controlled immediately by the use of electricity. At present it is perhaps the only fishing method used in fresh water fisheries that permits the genuine management of a fish stock – at least in cases where it can be correctly applied. Electrical fishing in contrast to all other fishing methods does not disturb, drive or press the prey. It cannot be denied, however, that there are sometimes unexpected difficulties with electrical fishing. Therefore some experience is needed to understand why, in some cases, the method cannot work or in others why success at the beginning of an operation later diminishes. Unfortunately, these difficulties have increased in some countries due to the amount of pollution in fresh waters. The pollution influences the physiological behaviour of the fish in a manner disadvantageous for electrical fishing. With direct current the typical anodical effect can be lost in some cases due to the influence of pollution. This means the fish no longer swims under the influence of electrotaxis in the direction of the anode (*eg* a scoop net), but remains at a distance. Nevertheless, with the pulse current, the reaction of the fish influenced by polluted water has proved to be nearly normal under these conditions.[221]

5.7 Electrified gear in sea fisheries

The use of electrical fishing as discussed in the last section becomes difficult in the open water of fresh water lakes and in the seas. Here electrical fishing in the pure sense is not possible for the reasons mentioned before. But in sea fisheries electricity can often be combined with more usual fishing gear to improve its efficiency. This has been done with success with harpoons, stow nets, trawls (including beamtrawls), seine nets, and fish pumps as will be discussed in later chapters.

When, in sea fisheries, towed gear is combined with electricity the aim is to prevent the fish escaping from the opening of the gear and being lost. When harpoons or hooks are electrified the aim is to kill the prey to prevent struggling and fighting by which lines can be broken and the quality and appearance of the fish can be reduced. In many cases electricity can be helpful to stun or shock fishes already caught by other gear. In sea fisheries electricity can also be used in stirring up shrimps or fishes with the help of an electrical field. Very often this is referred to as electrical fishing. (See also *Fig 500* in Chapter 21).

In order to gain permission for electrical fishing in any form in most countries participation in a successful training course in electrical fishing techniques is needed. Moreover, the apparatus offered by factories for fishing, frightening or killing with electricity must have passed stringent safety regulations to exclude accidents during fishing, as far as possible.[217]

Chapter six

Spearing, harpooning and shooting fish

The range and capacity of man to seize living fish, or those that have been stunned or narcotized by some means from a distance, is limited by the length of his arm. By using a stick, the fisherman who is gathering or collecting his catch can reach more distant objects and possibly even secure them. The simplest implement for such purpose is a pointed stick – a kind of lance or spear by means of which fish and other aquatic animals further away than his arm can stretch may yet be touched or hooked, or even speared and caught. The spearhead has to be formed in a special manner to secure the prey. Japanese have compared the spear with the lengthened human arm and the spearhead with the nails of the fingers.[427] The range of a spear depends on the length of its shaft and this depends on its purpose. The range of a spear can be further extended when the spear is not only pushed but thrown as a 'manpower gear' or shot like a missile with the help of some device like a catapult. In this way the range of the fisherman can be doubled, tripled or extended even further.

Spears have been known since times immemorial. Unfortunately, in prehistoric finds as well as in collections of spears obtained from primitive people, it is often not clear if the object found is a fish spear or a weapon, a ceremonial implement, an agrarian fork, or a device for offering meat in a sacrifice. Even in European museums eel spears are, consciously or unconsciously, sometimes exhibited as candlesticks of the Middle Ages!

6.1 Spearing with pushed gear

The fishing spear in its simplest form is the fisherman's most primitive gear and is known from prehistoric times. Like the hunter's spear it was developed to satisfy the need to extend the range and reach of the human arm. It is the same development which led to the use of a club or hammer instead of the fist; the development from the cupped hand for lifting water to the creation of the bowl, the spoon and the shovel. Using a spear in water, however, is not as easy as it is on land. The refraction of light in the water has to be considered and allowed for, and it needs experience to calculate it exactly. This is all the more necessary when fishing is practised with spears under artificial light at night (*Fig 36*). In an old German book, printed about 90 years ago,[305] spear fishing in Lake Constance is described as not an easy method of fishing, and one which needed a lot of experience and power. Spearing should be done in calm and shallow waters and the large fish to be caught must stay still for some time at the same place if it cannot be found in a large school.

Fishing with spears has certainly been known for over 10,000 years[108, 689] and such spears are indeed to be found in all the fisheries of the world. Islamic fishermen sometimes hesitate to use fishing spears. On the Turkish Black Sea coast there is a legend told about a blasphemous pharaoh who wanted to kill the Lord of Abraham. When he was shooting an arrow, angels were ordered to keep a fish (*Zeus faber*) in the way of the missile and the fish was pierced instead of God. In gratitude for this service the Lord ordered that never more should a fish be pierced by a spear or arrow. This is one of the stories why the 'John Dory' has its characteristic spot. Today, objects of spearing in commercial fisheries in inland waters and off the coasts are primarily larger and more valuable fish like salmon, tuna, swordfish, sharks and eels. But this does not mean that other fish, especially when spawning, are not speared. Moreover, spears are also used by commercial fishermen to catch slow-moving octopus, sea cucumbers and sessile sponges. Spearing has also become a form of sport fishing (Chapter 10), but in many countries spearing, and the use of other instruments which penetrate or mutilate, is forbidden. (Sometimes this is not done to protect fish but because such spears can also be weapons of attack on human beings!). In some other countries special permission for spearing is needed. In Poland, older fishermen who can no

Fig 36 Hundreds of years ago it was found that fish were attracted by light. This engraving by the Frenchman, Duhamel Du Monceau, shows vigorous fishing by torchlight, with spears. (1776-79).

longer go out with a boat during wintertime are given special permission to use spears. This has also been done for social reasons in the Federal Republic of Germany in the Baltic Sea.

Spears range from the simple pointed hardwood stick, such as the Australian natives use even today, to the more complicated many-pronged spears. The wooden point of a lance was doubtless first replaced by a point made of bone, stone or some other hard natural material, and finally by metal. The simplest forms of spears are only sticks with a single sharpened point. As mentioned before, the success of spearing is determined by the right calculation of the light refraction of water. The fish is not exactly at the place where it is to be seen from outside the water, but appears to swim higher and further away (*Fig 37*). An experienced spear fisherman will know this. But when the calculation of the fish's position is out even by a short distance only, the fish may still escape. For this reason, in fisheries as well as sometimes in spearing birds or bats, the single prong of a spear is inadequate. The same is true when spearing blind *eg* in turbid water, in mud, or under ice (*Fig 38*). In such cases a single prong will not give much chance of hitting a fish. Therefore spears are provided with several prongs so the accuracy of aim is increased (*Fig 39*). The number of prongs varies. Their arrangement can be in a row like a comb or in a bunch. It seems that in tropical areas the latter is preferred (*Fig 40*). In this case many prongs are fixed around the head

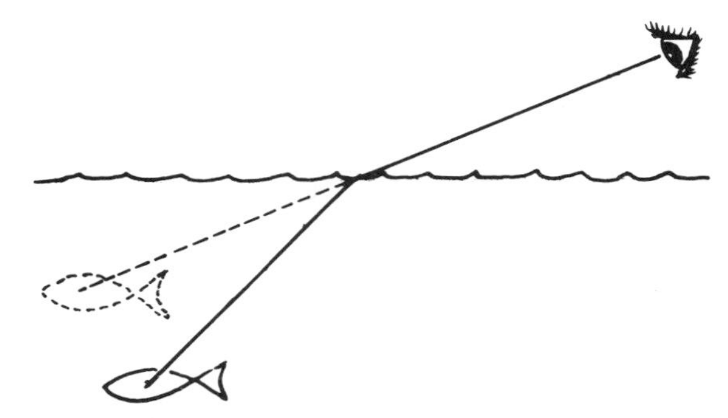

Fig 37 Due to the refraction of light by the water surface the fish seems to swim higher and further away than its true position.

Fig 38 A Danish fisherman spears eels through the ice on a frozen lake in Jutland.

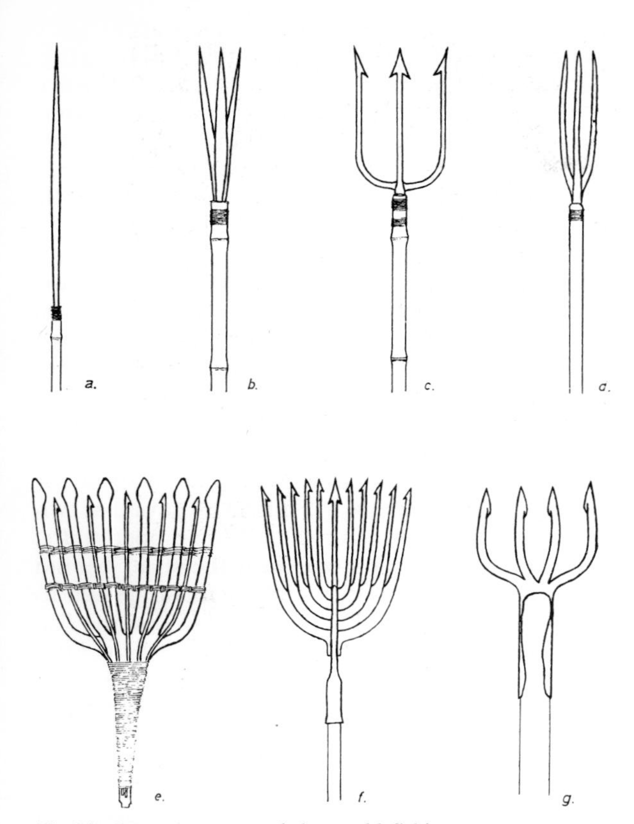

Fig 39 In every corner of the world fishing spears were evolved: (*a*) simple fish-stick of Guinea; (*b*) fish spear with three points arranged as a bundle; (*c*) trident spear with barbs; (*d*) Arabian spear of Syria, without barbs; (*e*) fish spear of Northern Germany; (*f*) Italian spear for cuttlefish; (*g*) spear for sponge fishing off the coast of Libya.

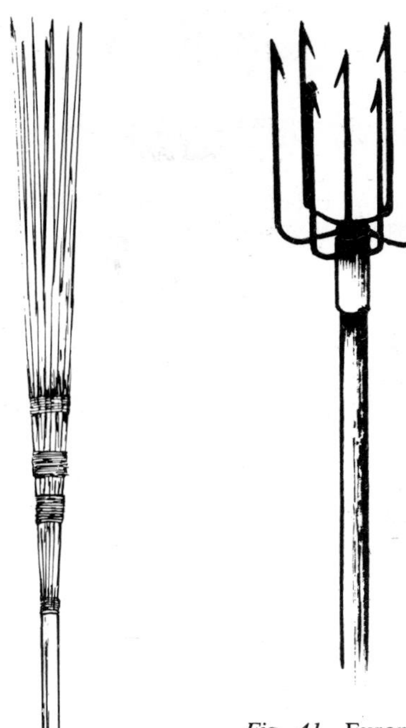

Fig 41 European multi-pointed spear with barbed points.

Fig 40 Multi-pointed fishing spear, without barbs, as used in many tropical countries.

of a stick rather like a yard broom. By this means the effectiveness of the spear will be increased. Many prongs are the same as a bundle of single one-pronged spears. This is done also in some African areas where one man may fish with as many as six spears held in a bundle.[361] In temperate countries as in Europe, spears with prongs arranged in a circle are seldom used (*Fig 41*). The more modern iron spears, so-called 'fish irons', with five, seven or even twelve prongs are frequently found. Very often the trident can be seen, today more for decoration than for practical use. This symbol of Poseidon or Neptune is but the ancient tuna spear of the Mediterranean. There are some who think that the trident is too inaccurate for fishing[317] and therefore that its origin lies not in fishery but as a protective symbol in the form of a spear. Nevertheless, two-pointed spears as well as tridents are used even today in practical fisheries, although there is no doubt that more prongs and points invariably give more success.

When a fish is speared it can escape from a simple point by vigorous wriggles and twistings. That can be prevented by barbs. Such barbs are a feature used not only for fishing spears but also for the construction of various other gear. The barb, however, is not restricted to fisheries alone; it is an equally important element of hunting gear. Without a barb the spear is more generally called a lance. The fishing spear may have a single barb on one side; there may also exist several such barbs arranged in a row along the point of a spear.[515] When the points are arranged in a row all barbs can be directed in the same direction (*Fig 42*) or they may be arranged quite arbitrarily. And the barbs may be bent not only to one side but be in pairs as is usually the case at the point of an arrow. With spears and similar gear a special form of barb may be used which is movable (*Fig 43*). This type of barb penetrates the body of the prey and will stay in when under tension. By this means the spear is anchored very firmly into the body of the prey.

The range in the size of pushed hand spears in fisheries can be considerable. They may have shafts of six, ten, twelve or more metres in length. Very

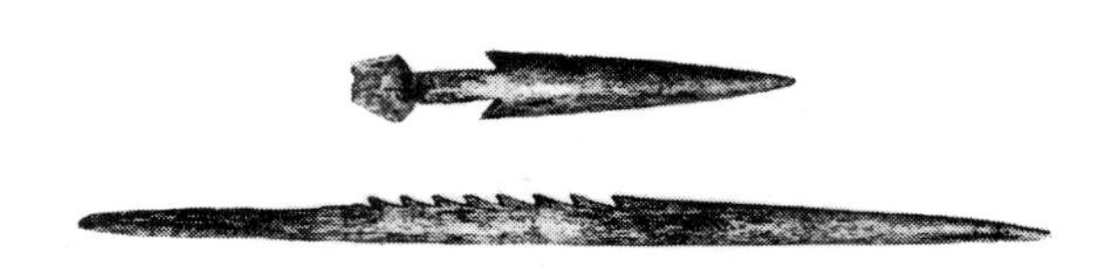

Fig 42 Heads of harpoons made of bone, double and multi-pointed as used in Tierra del Fuego.

Fig 43 Spear with movable barb. The barb will pivot in the fish or whale when the spear is pulled back after piercing.

long spears are especially useful when the fishermen are trying to spear at random under ice or in turbid water or even at great depths (*Fig 38*). The buoyancy of a spear increases with the length of the wooden stick and to overcome this, larger and heavier prongs are used in deeper waters,[66, 302, 657] or some extra weights are added. On the Baltic coast of northern Germany the long spears are tarred very carefully with the result that they are nearly weightless in deep water. Therefore it is helpful when describing spears with long shafts if the weight of the iron prongs is given; also any additional load, if any. It has to be mentioned that the points and the shaft of a hand spear do not always lie in the same line. Because spearing is seldom done in a perpendicular direction but more or less obliquely, not all points of a spear can work simultaneously. For this reason spearheads with a curved neck are

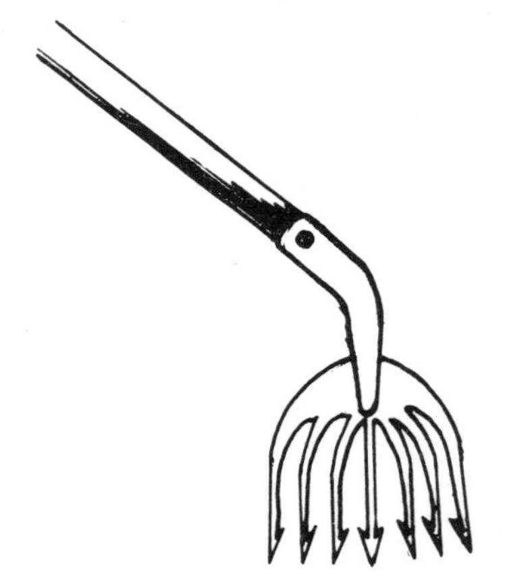

Fig 44 North European spearhead with curved neck.

sometimes used (*Fig 44*). Rarely bait is used to lure the prey into a position favourable for spearing. Sometimes, the spear itself can attract fish when plunged several times and at random into the water. Fishes can be attracted into striking range not only by the splash but also by the flash of the spear.[82] Sometimes, artificial baits are used, as in the fisheries of Hong Kong for catching pomfrets.[353] The lures are made of an oval-shaped thin board of any kind of wood, cut to the approximate shape of a pomfret and painted white. From five to seven are strung in a long line and towed slowly through the water. When fish are seen chasing the lures they are speared or caught by other methods.

It has been already stated that spearing can also be done with artificial light at night (*Fig 36*). A description of night fishing with a hand spear for salmon, done formerly in Finland,[639] says that two men would fish together. One had to operate the boat while the other stood with the spear behind the light. As soon as he could see a fish he had to spear the prey, if possible, in its tail so that the fish could not flap so much when lifted into the boat as when speared behind its head. Originally the attracting light for this fishery with hand spear was torch-light. In the fisheries of many countries torches were made of pine splinters about 70cm long, burning with a small flame. The material for them was collected in wintertime. They could also be of other resinous wood. Splinters of fir or birch were not considered as good because they burnt too quickly.[345] In olden times, fishermen in Europe knew which material was the best for torches or fire baskets. Nowadays gas lamps and electric light have replaced the naked flame (Chapter 11).

Another well-known use of the hand spear in fresh water is in eel fishing. This can also be done with light during the night and, especially in northern Europe, by blind spearing under ice in wintertime. The inactive eels will be found concentrated around entrances to lakes or rivers or streams, or in deep holes near tidal entrances to fresh water or estuaries.[338] For this purpose a hole is made in the ice and spearing is done systematically by pushing the spear into the mud in a circle (*Fig 38*). In this case not only spears but also clamps (Chapter 7) are used to bring the eels out of the mud.

Fishing with pushed hand spears is better known in sea fisheries. In this they are used less for stronger, valuable fish than for smaller and slower ones. In the USA (North Carolina) flounders are speared in shallow coastal waters.[647] This is a night fishery operated with transportable underwater lamps by wading fishermen. Only a short spear of one to two metres is needed. This can be an iron rod sharpened to a point at one end, often fashioned with a barb, but spears with many prongs and barbed points are also in use. When a fish is detected, the spear is brought directly over the prey and with a quick thrust plunged into the fish. Unlike the technique described earlier, this is done in the head region to minimize the damage to the edible portion of the fish.

An example of a fishery for large sea fish with pushed spear is that for the ocean sunfish, *Mola mola.* This nearly circular but very flat fish swims near the surface in small schools where it can be caught very easily. In the Strait of Messina the fishery for this fish is operated from small motor boats with a characteristic low mast (*Fig 67*) which gives a high platform for an observer. As soon as the sunfish are seen near the surface the observer directs the boat towards the fish to be speared. The spear is made of an iron tube of about three metres in length and fitted with seven barbed prongs. The speared fish is hauled, with the help of the spear, on board the boat. To prevent the loss of the spear a line is run along the shaft connecting it to the vessel.

6.2 Fish plummets

As mentioned before, the length of a pushed spear is limited in greater depths of water by the buoyancy of the wooden shaft. Moreover, a spear of some several metres in length is difficult to handle in a small boat. In this case other devices are needed to bring up the prey from the bottom. This can be done with the help of fish plummets or plumb lines (*Figs 45, 46* and *47*). These are gears operated according to the principle of the spearing gear but the stick is replaced by a rope. Now the depth of

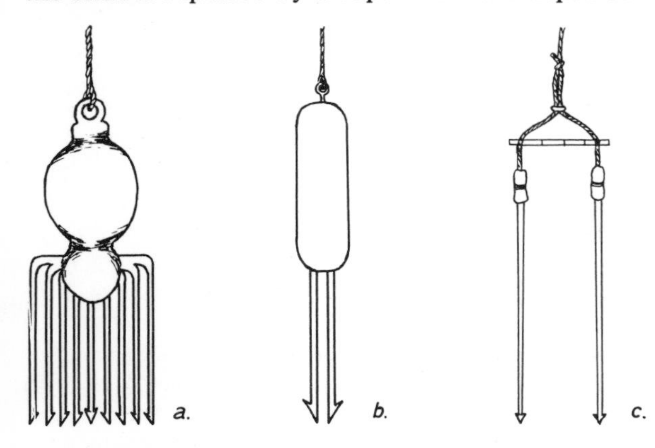

Fig 45 Again the need produced the same answer in different areas of the world. Fish p'ɩmmets: (*a*) Mediterranean plumb-line of Malta (*Burdon, 1956*); (*b*) Norwegian 'pigglodd' (*Brobak, 1952*); (*c*) Japanese 'yasu' (*NN, 1959*).

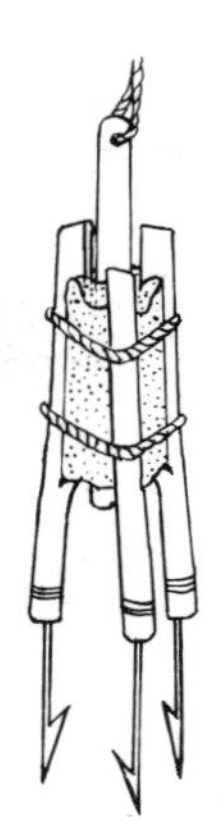

Fig 46 Fish plummet of the Sunda Islands. (*Courtesy of the Museum für Volkerkunde, Berlin-Dahlem.*)

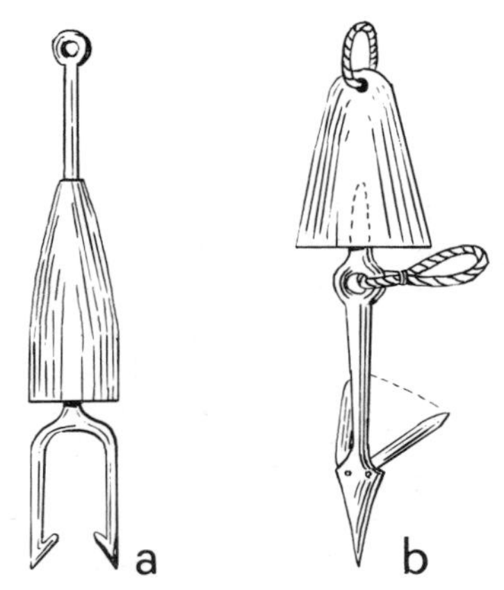

Fig 47 Older European plummets for: (*a*) flounder and (*b*) halibut. (*Duge et al, 1902*).

the fishing water is no longer a problem. A rope can be almost weightless, is easy to store, and can be as long as needed. On the end of such a line, instead of a spearhead, the so-called plummet is tied. Plummets are heavy weights, mostly made of metal but also sometimes weighted with stones, with one or more barbed points, which can be dropped down in deep water in order to pierce flat fish and other creatures lying on the bottom. With such plummets quite remarkable depths can be worked successfully – much better than is possible with any spear, so far as the transparency of the water allows a visual control of the plummet. This special form of fishing gear has been invented and applied in several parts of the world, in east and southeast Asia as well as in northern Europe (*Figs 45, 46* and *47*). From the early European ones some were like short-handled spears or clamps with additional weights added (*Fig 47*) operated over a roller on the gunwale.[142] In general, plummets are operated from a boat, directed by a fisherman controlling the operation with a looking-glass. Therefore clear water is needed to fish with the gear in anything other than shallow depths. An interesting variation of this method is used by the fishermen of the South Pacific where a diver guides the plummet to catch sea cucumbers in deeper waters (*Fig 48*).[591]

Fig 48 Directing of a plummet by a diver to catch sea cucumber in deeper water off the Solomon Islands. (*Courtesy of South Pacific Commission, 1974.*)

6.3 Eel combs

There is a curious group of instruments which are considered as a special form of rake, or horizontal-working, multi-pronged gear, wounding and piercing the prey like a spear.[689] The so-called eel rakes or eel combs which are comb-shaped implements especially useful in eel fishing, are mentioned here together with spears and other wounding gear. In operation they are pressed into the mud and pierce the fish with their prongs when towed sideways.

Two types of this gear are rather widely distributed; the eel combs found in Europe, and the Chinese form found in east and south Asia (*Figs 49* and *50*). The European eel comb is an iron comb with many prongs, often of uneven length and mostly without barbs. In earlier times this instrument (which is now forbidden) was handled from a sailing boat by being pressed vertically into the sea-bed mud with the prongs facing forward while the boat was slowly sailed on. A precondition for the successful use of that instrument was, of course, that the bottom be soft and even. This comb, which was named the 'Hölger' was used off the east Friesian coast and in the waters of the Baltic bays. The fisherman holding the handle immediately felt when an eel was pierced by the comb scraping the ground and hauled up the implement. But often the injured eel was able to escape. This, together with the fact that very young eels were also pierced, caused the implement to be condemned and banned many years ago. Owing to its simple design, however, it has been used again and again,[30] very often by the crews of sailing transport vessels who were not entitled to fish in territorial shallow waters but who sought a private fish meal with their eel combs.

The asiatic eel forks, with only one or two sharp prongs on a handle of up to five metres in length, resemble the European eel combs (*Fig 49*). They are handled in the same manner but without the movement of sailing. The fisherman presses the fork into the soft ground where he suspects an eel to be and moves it through the mud by bending the upper part of his body backwards. Such forks are still in use in Japan and Korea and as far away as Thailand. Such comb-like gear has also been used in open waters by moving the implement like a scythe through dense fish schools, piercing with their sharp pointed teeth any fish which came within their range (*Fig 50*). Such scythes for fishing are known in northern Europe but they may be used much wider. It was reported by Rau (1885)[515] that, according to the notes of James Cook (1728-1779), he met some people in the Pacific Ocean fishing

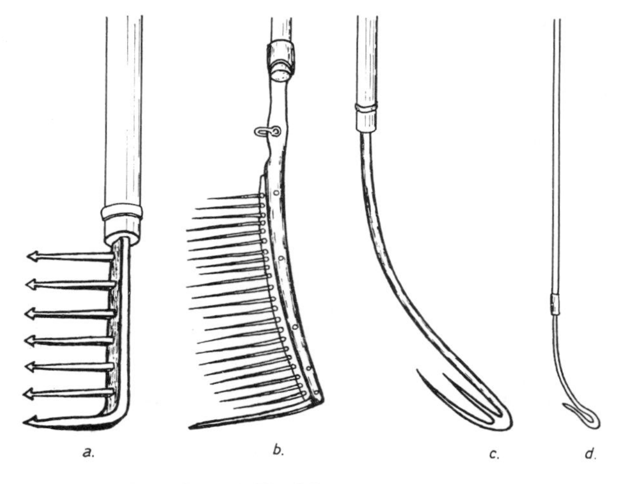

Fig 49 Eel combs: (*a*) Finnish eel comb (*Jankó, 1900*); (*b*) 'Hölger' from the German Baltic coast (*Znamierowska, 1957*); (*c*) Japanese eel fork with two points; (*d*) Thai eel fork with one point (*NN, 1953*).

with an instrument like an oar of six metres in length. About two thirds of its length was set with sharp bone teeth. With this gear smaller fishes were attacked by striking the instrument into the schools so that some fish were caught either upon or between the teeth of this gear.

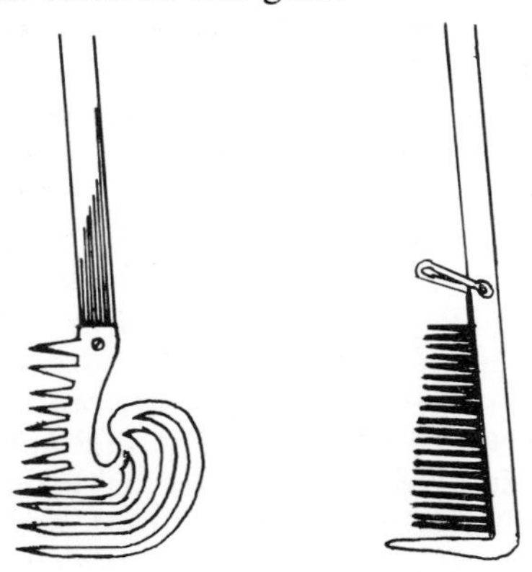

Fig 50 Fish scythe and eel comb of Northern Germany.

6.4 Fishing with thrown spears

The reach of spears pushed by hand can be extended by their being used as casting gear. For casting by hand to be reliable the spear shafts must not exceed a certain length. The relation of spear length and its reach regulates the size of javelins used in sport. In order that the thrown spear may reach further after fish or prey, its range may be considerably increased by the use of a casting mechanism. Such casting mechanisms or catapults again have an influence on the form of the spear. The catapults or throwing sticks of the Eskimo and Australians, for instance, provide the spear with a much longer flight and greater striking power than mere casting by hand. The spear thrower – also called a throwing board, propulseur or atlatl (the Aztec name for this throwing gear) – is about half a metre long and works like a lever, giving more speed to a spear. This implement was invented in the middle or later palaeolithic times and this knowledge was spread all over the world. In tropical areas, throwing boards are made of a bamboo tube at the end of which is cut a hook to engage the shaft.[611] The throwing board increases the efficiency of the spear immensely. However, the propelling power is supplied by the human arm, which means that the velocity of the spear is limited by the speed with which the arm can move. There are better and more powerful instruments for increasing the speed of a spear and its piercing power, but they will be mentioned later, because nowadays they are used mostly with harpoons (see the next section but one).

With the exception of the shorter length, the construction of a spear or dart thrown by hand or with a spear thrower is the same as for a pushed spear. There is one problem only. A pushed spear remains in the hand of the hunter and generally will not be lost. But a thrown spear, especially when thrown into water, can get lost or become unreachable. Therefore the thrown spear is usually fastened to a rope (retrieving line) of suitable length. It can thus be recovered after being shot, especially if the shot fails. This ability is particularly valuable to the fisherman because one cannot traverse water as easily as one can land, but with a retrieving line the spear, with or without the prey, can be recovered even under difficult conditions. A simple form of operation is to fix a line of about ten metres near the head of the spear, to throw the spear with the right hand, to guide the retrieving line with the left, and to hold fast the end of this line with the foot.[345] It may be of interest to know that retrieving lines for thrown spears (and also harpoons) were already known in early Egyptian fisheries and even earlier.

Some African people know how to operate not only a single spear but many at the same time. It has been reported from the fishery in Zululand that small spears used by children are also employed by men who use a handful at a time and throw blindly into the marshes and marginal aquatic growth.[622] In localities where crystal clear shallows often occur next to deep water, men and/or boys walk and run through the water in a line and throw their spears at any fish they may see.

6.5 Fishing with bow and arrow

A spear in the form of a small arrow is shot from a bow. The bow differs from all other weapons in being able to store the energy supplied by human muscles. On release, this pent-up energy is suddenly transferred to the arrow, which can thus be projected at much higher velocity than that at which it can be thrown by hand even with a spear thrower.[236, 366, 518] No special advice for the construction of bows and arrows formerly operated in fisheries has been published. Arrows seem to have been used longer in fisheries than for hunting. When used in fisheries they have no feathers, or only very small ones, on their trailing end. Also the feathers are not arranged in such a manner as to give stability and some twist to the arrow in flight. For the same reasons mentioned for spears, the arrows can have more than one point to increase the chance of impaling a fish.[8, 611] This method – shooting fish with arrow and bow – is widely known in many areas. It is, or has been, known in Oceania, southern India (*Fig 51*) Nepal and Sri Lanka, in

Burma, on the Andamans,[261] in Indonesia and in Formosa.[100] The bow and arrow are also known in the New World as used by the Indian fishermen of North and South America on the Pacific coast,[528] but in particular by the native fishermen of the Amazon basin in Brazil and Guyana. Alexander von Humboldt observed and recorded that he saw Indians on the Orinoco River shooting fish with bow and arrow. Fishermen in the Xingu area are said to be able to strike a fish at a distance of 100 metres – which may be doubtful! In central Asia fish were shot with arrows up until the recent century.[278, 581] Bows have also been used to catch fish in Europe. Pike and carp, also salmon and huchen, were caught in this manner. Generally, slow-swimming fish were prefered for this method and shots were usually made at no greater distance than five to six metres. To shoot a fish from a greater distance was considered too difficult. Like the spearing of fish, shooting with bow and arrow requires clear water and an appropriate allowance for the refraction of light in order to hit the victim as seen in the water. The young men of the Amazon region learn accuracy by first holding the arrow point in the water when they are shooting in order to gain experience in allowing for the refraction of light.[579] To overcome this difficulty the use of multi-pointed arrows has already been mentioned. This problem is also the reason why fishing with bow and arrow is seldom operated during the night.

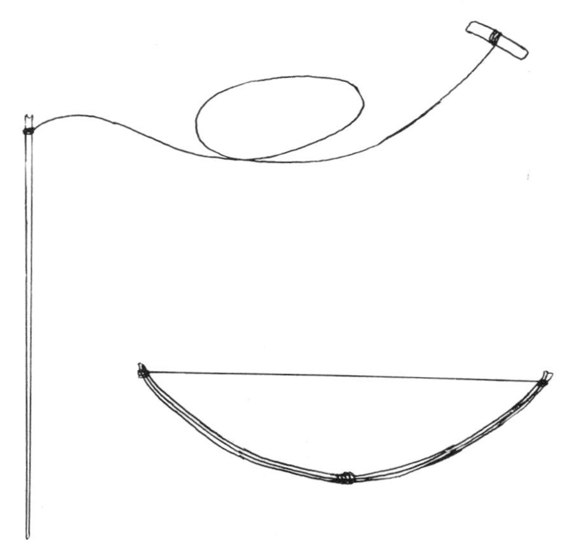

Fig 51 Fish bow and arrow with float and retrieving line. Kerala, S. India (1973).

Not only fish are shot with bow and arrow; sometimes also crabs and other water animals, even sea mammals, are hunted. In Mesopotamia, Tiglatpileser I (1170-1090 BC) claimed to have killed not only wild bulls, elephants and lions with bow and arrow, but also from his ship off Arvad on the Syrian coast[518] a 'nose-blower', which is considered to have been some form of whale.

From the simple bow the crossbow developed which was also used to shoot fish. In Europe, crossbows replaced the simple bows by the twelfth century. Until recently crossbows were known on the Philippines in the Laguana de Bay,[630] in western Africa,[261] and also in Norway for shooting whales with poisoned arrows. In the Fishery Museum of Bergen, Norway, a crossbow can be seen which was used during World War II when guns could not be employed to kill whales. Poisoned arrows were used which did not need much power because the arrows did not have to penetrate to a vital area in order to kill. A mere scratch is sometimes enough.[518] The crossbows used in southern India are especially interesting because they are just the same as those that were used in Europe in the sixteenth century and were then taken to India by the Portuguese (*Fig 52*). An old French publication of 1834 (*Fig 53*) shows a very elegant crossbow (arbalète) with a very long arrow, at least 1·20 metres long with a strong iron point especially used for catching frogs, *Rana esculenta,* in fresh water ponds.[498]

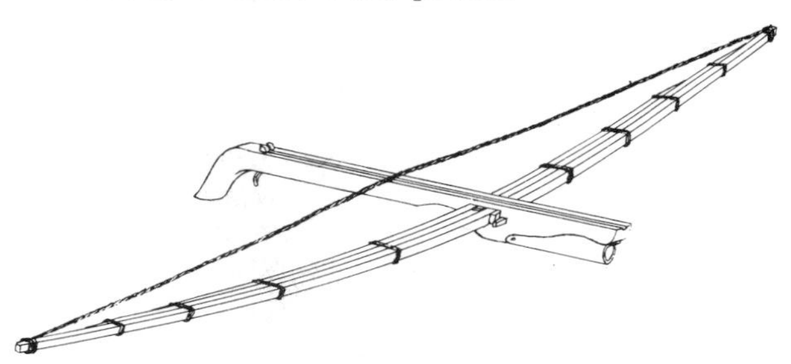

Fig 52 Striking and throwing spears, useful as they were, led to the crossbow being adapted for throwing harpoons at fish. This specimen is from the Malabar coast, S. India. Under the top of the crossbow is a small box of bamboo for the retrieving line.

With arrows, as with thrown spears, when shooting from the shore in swamps or deeper water the problem is to retrieve the missile especially when it hits prey. The problem is resolved in the same manner as with thrown spears. A retrieving line is tied to the end of the arrow and the other end to a float or to the bow. *Figure 54* shows such an arrangement for retrieving the arrow, just like the children's bow still used in southern India (*Fig 51*). It is very interesting that the native fishermen of North America and Alaska[528] also had such retrievable arrows as did some Oceanic

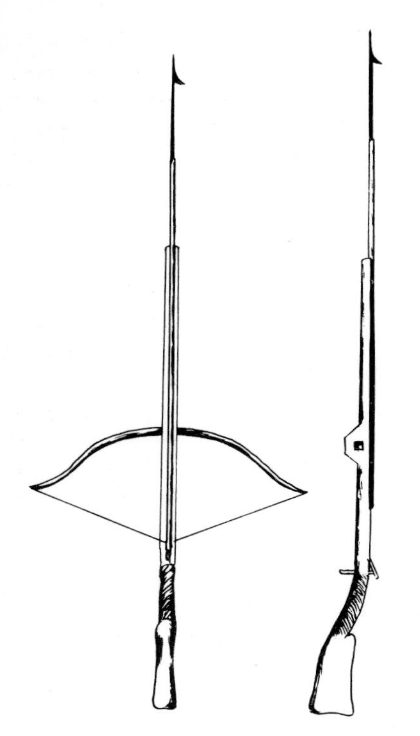

Fig 53 Old French crossbow. (*Pesson-Maissoneuve, 1834*).

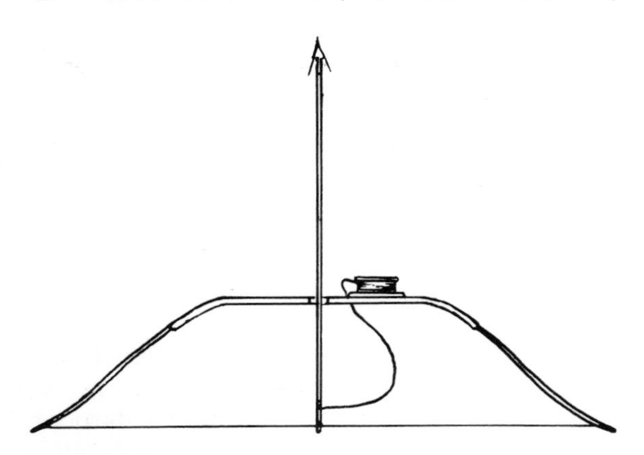

Fig 54 Modern American fish bow with retrieving line.

fishermen.[313] Even the bushmen in southern Africa were originally familiar with these fishing methods before being forced into the desert. They fastened a light line to the shaft of the arrow, which they shot at small surface fish.[104] Small harpoons can even be shot by bow and crossbow. These are considered in the next section.

Today archery is a modern sport influenced by Japanese customs. In the USA hunting and fishing with bows has been revived. Now very modern and expensive bows are used for bow fishing in fresh and salt waters (*Fig 54*).[236] The fibreglass arrows are fitted out with easily removable heads which may be double barbed. The fishing targets are mostly coarse fish according to the different laws in the American states. These may be carp and eels as well as sharks and rays, migrating saltwater fish (when found in inland waters) but also frogs (*eg* bullfrogs) and turtles (*eg* soft-shelled ones).

6.6 Harpooning

Beside barbless one-pointed lances, and spears (with many points mostly with one or more barbs each; with or without retrieving line), harpoons are widely used in fisheries. This gear has replaced the older spears in many instances and is today known not only in small-scale but also large fisheries, and in sport fishing.

Harpoons differ from spears in that the point becomes separated from the shaft when it penetrates the victim, and the shaft floats to the surface – both the point and the shaft remaining connected by a line (*Fig 55*). The shaft floating to the surface tells the fisherman where his victim is and acts as a brake or retarder to impede the fish's flight and tire it.

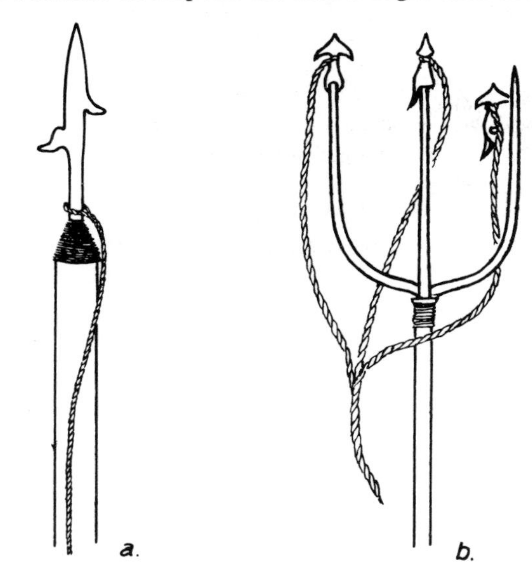

Fig 55 Special points for harpoons: (*a*) for turtles in Madagascar (*v.Brandt, 1964*); (*b*) Japanese trident harpoon with electrified points.

The fisherman then follows to pick up the floating shaft and to haul it in together with the harpoon line connected to the separated harpoon head in the prey. In this case after shooting there is no direct contact between prey and fishermen. It may be better not to lose such contact, as with a thrown spear which remains directly connected to the fisherman by a retrieving line. Therefore harpoons often have two separate lines; the harpoon line tied to the head of the missile, and the retrieving line to the end of the shaft, both connected to the harpooner (*Fig 56*). It is much simpler to use one line connected with the head or heads of the harpoon and running through a ring on the shaft to the hands of the fisherman. Between the harpoon head and this ring on the shaft the line has a stopper, so that when this line is retrieved not only the harpoon head but also its shaft is hauled in (*Fig 57*). Modern harpoons, especially when shot with rifles or guns, are like thrown spearheads because there is no separation between the head and the shaft. Nevertheless, the traditional name harpoon has continued in use, *eg* in whaling (next section).

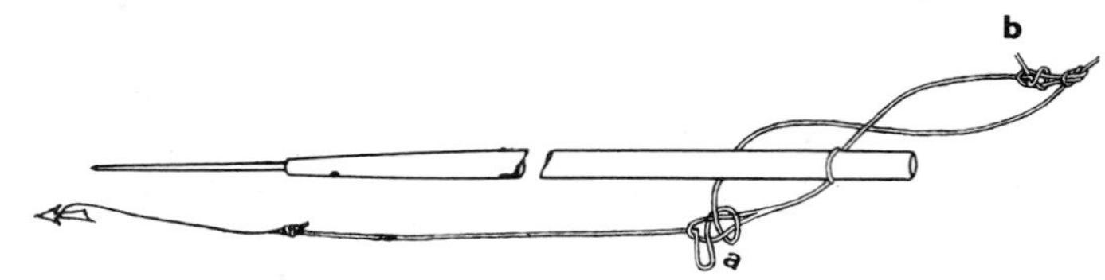

Fig 56 Example of the rigging of a Chinese harpoon. The iron point is held by the harpoon line to the shaft of the harpoon by knot (*a*). When the point is in the prey, knot (*a*) is loosened, separating the point of the harpoon from the shaft, but the shaft is also fixed on the harpoon line by knot (*b*) so as not to be lost. *Courtesy of Capt. L C Hu, Christchurch.*

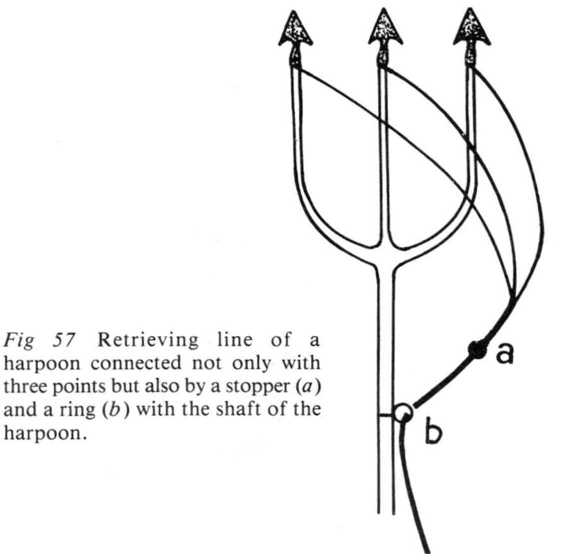

Fig 57 Retrieving line of a harpoon connected not only with three points but also by a stopper (*a*) and a ring (*b*) with the shaft of the harpoon.

The shaft of the harpoon is shorter than that of the spear and the detachable point is necessarily barbed.[302] Often a movable barb like a toggle is used (*Fig 43*), reducing the risk that the harpoon may be pulled out. Generally, harpoons have one point only but there are a few two- and three-pointed types (*Fig 55b*). Nowadays the points are made of iron but points made of bone and the horns of deer and reindeer were known and handed down from ancient prehistoric fisheries.[322] Masters of harpooning are the Eskimos. In olden times their gear was made partly from walrus ivory and the line from walrus rawhide. Archaeologists consider these lines as the strongest known before the invention of the steel cable. It has therefore been suggested that the harpoon line was actually the first line to be used in fisheries.

Like lances and spears, harpoons can be pushed or thrown by hand as well as by various casting mechanisms. In extreme cases, harpoons can become quite small projectiles (*Fig 75*). Harpoons have become a favourite gear for underwater fishing, although they are illegal in many countries. Divers use harpoon guns – commercial fishermen as well as sports divers. There are very simple catapults propelling a projectile towards the fish by the action of stretching a piece of rubber (*Fig 58*).

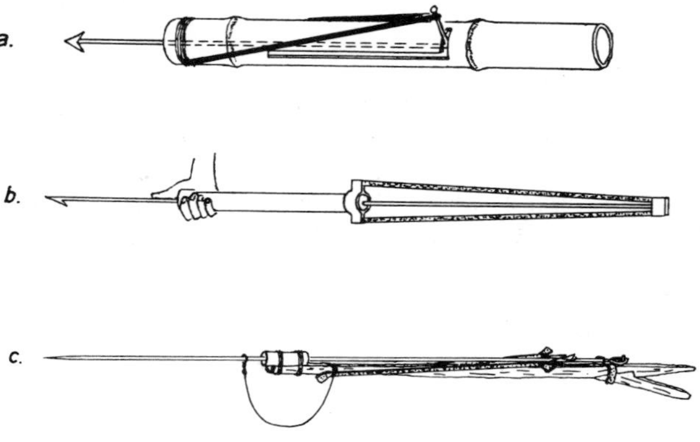

Fig 58 Simple types of catapults with rubber bands: (*a*) Japanese underwater gun with elastic cord (*NN 1959*); (*b*) Hawaiian sling gun (*Ivanovic, 1954*); (*c*) harpoon used by divers of Botel Tobago (Lan Yü).

This projectile can be a spear when released freely (seldom) or a harpoon connected to the gun by a line as is usually the case.[276] The simple harpoons with an elastic pull and a trigger to release the arrow at the right moment, the so-called 'fish guns', have been adopted especially in Southeast Asia from the Ryukyu Islands to the Philippines during this century.[226] Nowadays fish guns are even used by the natives of the most remote fisheries for shooting fish from both above and below the surface of the water.[29] Sport divers use more sophisticated underwater spear guns for propelling the spear by means of a metal spring or powered by compressed air and gas springs or even real shotguns with a propelling charge (*Fig 59*). Over water, harpoon guns with particularly strong missiles are required for killing large fish like tuna, swordfish, shark or sea mammals such as porpoises, whales or seals.

Especially well known in some areas around the North Sea were the Norwegian rifles to shoot harpoons to catch tuna.

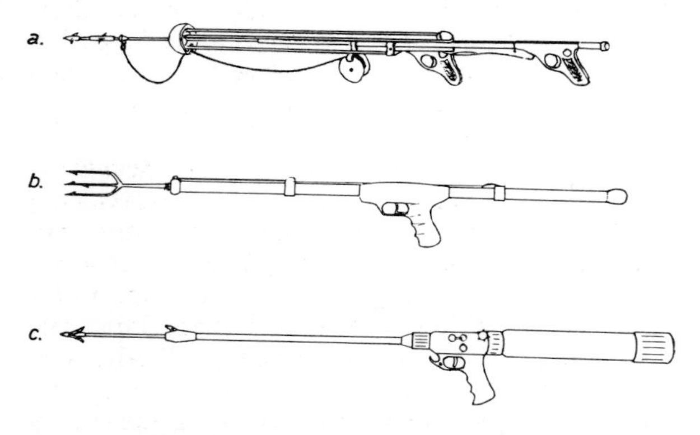

Fig 59 Harpoons used by sport divers: (*a*) French elastic-powered harpoon (*Ivanovic, 1954*); (*b*) spear gun powered by compressed air (USA); (*c*) Italian spear gun with gas propulsion.

6.7 Whaling

In modern commercial fisheries harpooning is no longer used due to the cost of modern gear and fishing vessels, except for large species having high individual value.[536] The most important harpoon in commercial fisheries is the whaling harpoon. In 1660 the Dutch whalers first ceased throwing their whaling harpoons by hand and began firing them from blunderbusses. The fishermen of the Azores and Madeira even today use hand-pushed harpoons to catch sperm whales (*Fig 60*).

The first whalers in the Azores were Basque fishermen who arrived in the 15th century. From the 18th century to the beginning of this one, American whaling fleets with their typical Indian canoes visited the Azores every year for catching sperm whales. Both have influenced the catching method which is operated even today (though on much-reduced scale). The whale is located by one of the observation points (vigias) and the catching canoes are towed by a motor vessel near to the place where the animal may be expected. Each canoe has two or four harpoons. Two form one set, connected with each other by lines stored very carefully in two wooden barrels (*Fig 61*). Only when the canoe can come within a distance of two or three metres of the whale can one or both harpoons be pushed – with both hands. Much power is necessary because only when the head of the harpoon has pierced the blubber can it be anchored in the flesh of the animal without being pulled out again. Here should be mentioned that originally the hand-thrown harpoon with strong barbs did not kill, but

Fig 60 Hunting sperm whale with the hand-thrust harpoon of the Azores. (*Photo: T Housby, Lymington.*)

simply caught the whale on a line to prevent its escape. The line of the harpoon remained attached to the vessel and the whale could tow the boat like a retarder, maybe for hours. The killing of the whale was, and is, done by hand with a long barbless spear or lance, piercing the lungs or heart of the animal.

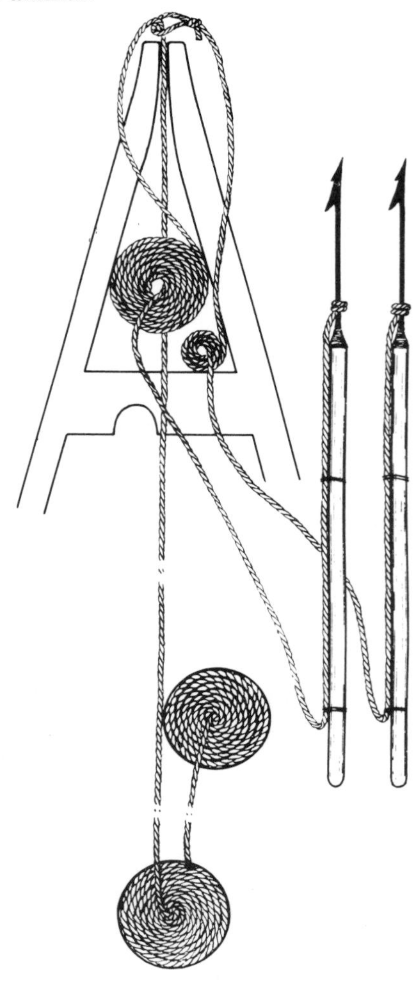

Fig 61 Position of the harpoons and their lines in the bow of a canoe used for catching sperm whales off the Azores in 1962. (*von Brandt, 1973.*)

In 1731 the first whaling cannon was constructed, but it was not until 1772 that it was generally used.[649] In the middle of the last century (1864) the Norwegian Svend Foyn made the first attempt to design a whaling harpoon in the head of which was placed a grenade. The idea was that when the grenade exploded the whale would be killed quickly. The black-powder bomb in an 1870 shoulder gun became the main whale-hunting weapon of the Eskimo. In the beginning of the seventies in the last century Foyn owned a factory for whale processing, operating two small steamers. These catching boats were already fitted out with a gun turntable of 360° for shooting the harpoon (*Figs 62* and *64*). With this newly developed equipment Foyn was successful in the seasons of 1873 and 1874.[369] Harpoons with grenades are also used today, but

Fig 62 Norwegian harpoon gun for catching small types of whales. (*Photo: G Hass, 1942.*)

the form has been changed. The pointed grenades (*Fig 63*) have been replaced by truncated ones. The reason is that pointed grenades sometimes can pierce the tail of the whale without exploding or be bounced off the back of a diving whale.

Fig 63 Whaling gun with pointed grenade. (*Photo: Erste Deutsche Walfang Gesellschaft.*)

Otherwise the construction of the whaling harpoon has not changed much since the times of Foyn. It has an iron head with two movable barbs, spreading in the body of the whale by a pull on the line, and firmly connected to the shaft (*Figs 63* and *65*). Attached to the shaft is the whale line, called a retrieving line, beginning with what is known as a 'forerunner' made of manila or polyamide of best quality, 100 to 120 metres in length. The forerunner is connected with the real whale line running up to an accumulator on the mast (*Fig 66*). This is an arrangement for adjusting differences in the pull on the line, to prevent breaking by sudden shocks. From here the whale line is led round the drum of the whale winch and then down to the hold of the vessel. So the full retrieving line, now with a total length of 1,000 metres, became a decisive – and expensive – part of whaling equipment.

Fig 64 Modern Icelandic whale gun in Reykjavik (1970).

Fig 65 Harpoons on an Icelandic whaler. The harpoon heads are stored separately. (1970).

Much greater success in killing a whale swiftly has been achieved by the use of electrified harpoons. Electrical killing of whales is much more satisfactory than by grenade harpoons by which the interior parts of the animals are torn and may become infected. Electrical harpoons are equipped with a cable which conducts the current into the body of the whale. The particular species of whale, the age of the animal, and its physiological condition all have a bearing on the success of

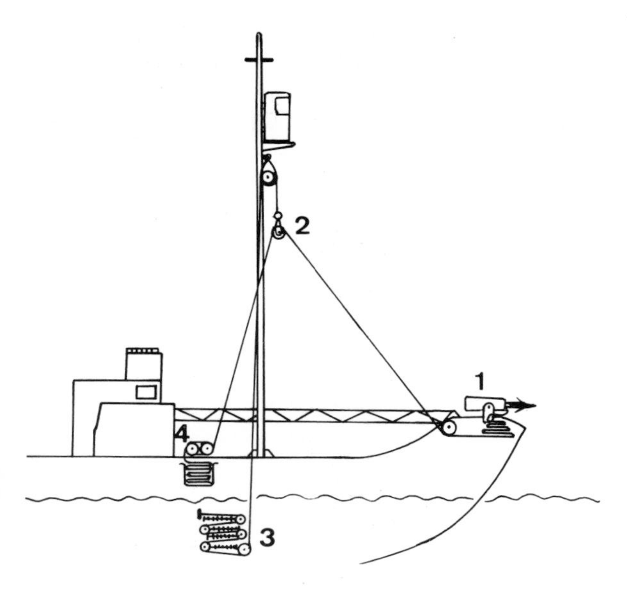

Fig 66 Leading a harpoon line from the gun (1) over a block (2) hanging on the mast and connected to a tension absorber (3). The line is coiled with the whale winch (4) and stored in the hold of the vessel.

catching and killing by electricity. By electrified harpoons the destruction of the intestines and blood vessels occasioned by the explosion of a grenade is avoided.[559] This very modern method of killing whales by electricity dates back to experiments first carried out in the last century.

The whaling harpoon is also an example of the way in which the most primitive fishing gear, like the original fishing spear, can be so developed as to become a fishing instrument of the greatest importance in the modern fishing industry. Commercial whaling as a large-scale business is diminishing due to declining stocks of whales. For this reason the hunting of some species of whales, or in some areas, is forbidden. Even the old coastal whaling is diminishing for the same reason. Nevertheless, some exceptions are made for the Indians of Alaska and inhabitants of the Aleutians, and the Eskimos, who are allowed to continue traditional whaling for their own benefit.[170] Their aboriginal technique of whaling is a combination of tradition and modern equipment. They use harpoons and bombs, which have continued in use almost unchanged since their introduction by commercial whalers in the late 19th century. They hunt from skin-covered boats, the old umiaks, and also from wooden and aluminium boats – all of which are now fitted with outboard motors. When the harpoon is fastened in the whale the line is attached to a float (formerly seal skin, now plastic).

The float replaces the shaft of the harpoon or the retarder. Then a bomb can be shot with a shoulder gun into the whale and if properly placed may kill the whale. Otherwise a further shot with the shoulder gun may be necessary to finish off the whale.

6.8 Harpooning swordfish

Swordfish fishing is known not only in the Mediterranean but also on both sides of the Atlantic; off the coasts of California, Peru and Chile, as well as in Japanese waters.[601] The swordfish are mainly taken by hand-thrown harpoons, a technique which is also used for catching other fish. The following example is based on a present-day fishery for swordfish and tuna in southern Italy between the Calabrian coast and Messina, Sicily. This fishery developed quickly in this century. The original size of the vessels used was not much more than that of rowing boats with small masts – not so different from the boats still used today for sunfish spearing (*Fig 67*). The size of vessel gradually increased up to 20 metres in length. This fishery was influenced by other fishing techniques, as can be seen from older literature.[45, 113, 207, 209, 346, 606] The Italian swordfish industry in the Strait of Messina uses characteristic vessels with a very high mast and a very long bowsprit (*Fig 68*). The mast, the so-called 'antenna', roughly in the centre of the boat with a lookout for one to four observers or 'speculatores', can have a height of up to 30 metres and more. This very much elevated crow's nest permits a greater field of vision for spotting fins. The boats are steered by a simple arrangement of lines from the crow's nest. The motors are also regulated from the same position by a similar arrangement. The boats have two motors (each 100 to 150hp) with one propeller each. With these the boats have not only a high speed, but also the necessary flexibility and manoeuvrability.

As mentioned before the vessels have a remarkably long bowsprit, or 'passeralla', ending with a small 'pulpit' for the harpooner or striker to stand on. The reason for this platform, swinging more than 30 metres in front of the vessel, is to place the harpooner as close to the fish as possible prior to the arrival of the vessel's hull (*Figs 68* and *69*).[179] This principle is also used on vessels for harpooning sharks off California (*Fig 70*). Taiwan Chinese also use this principle for catching marlin during the winter season (*Fig 71*). In this instance two harpooners stand side by side, secured to the platform of the extended bowsprit by sticking their feet into loops and operating a long harpoon with three points, the overall length being over four metres.

In the Italian swordfish fishery a bifurcated harpoon with two detachable harpoon points, each with two or four movable barbs, (*Fig 72*) is used.

Fig 67 Boat with lookout for spearing sunfish in the Strait of Messina (1979).

Fig 68 Italian vessel for spearing swordfish and tunny in the Strait of Messina (1979). Note, the elevated lookout and the spearman on an extended bowsprit.

Fig 69 On an Italian swordfish vessel. In the foreground, storage of different types of spears. The harpooner stays ready for throwing in the 'pulpit' of the long bowsprit (1979).

Fig 70 Californian vessels with long bowsprit and high lookout for spearing sharks (1962).

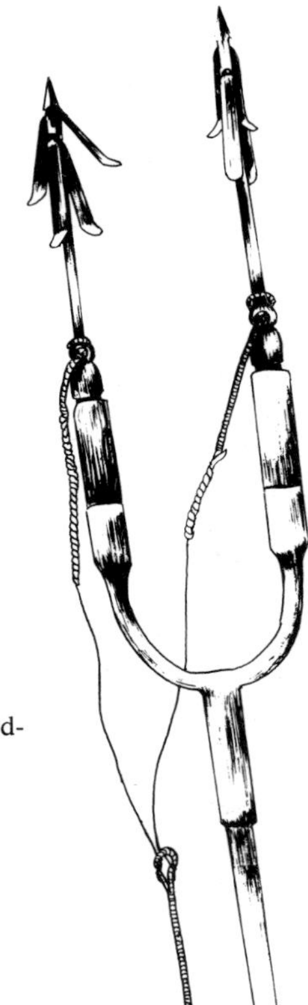

Fig 72 Italian harpoon for sword-fish. (*Ghigi, 1965*).

Fig 71 Chinese vessel with two harpooners for spearing marlin around Taiwan. Courtesy of International Commission on Rural Reconstruction, Taipei.

When catching large tuna with the same vessel a single-pointed harpoon is preferred. The harpoon has a shaft made of an iron tube of up to four metres in length. The two heads of the harpoon are tied to a line with two branches. As soon as a fish is hit, the heads break from the shaft and the hunting line from the harpoon heads runs out. A large plastic buoy marks the way of the line and then one or more iron barrels (formerly wooden kegs) are thrown overboard. By this method the stricken fish quickly tires itself out. The separated shaft is hauled in by the retrieving line. Barrel, buoy and fish are towed by a small rowing boat to the vessel and hauled on deck by a winch. It may be added that a harpooner will only strike fish of reasonable size. That means fishing with spears and harpoons is not carried out in an indiscriminate manner; therefore spearing and harpooning can be considered fishing methods with a good degree of selectivity.

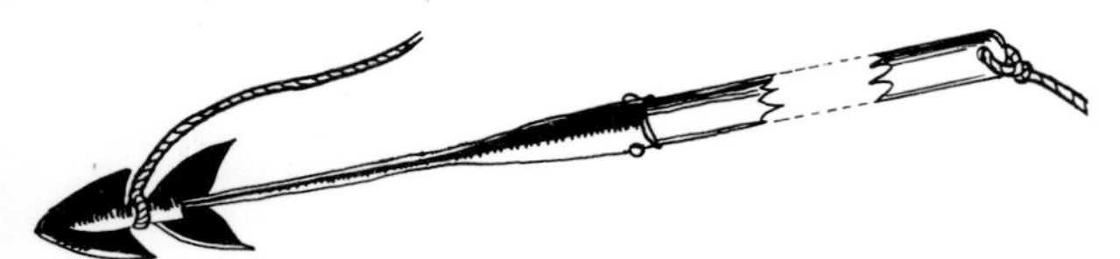

Fig 73 American swordfish harpoon. (*Dumont and Sundstrom, 1961*).

6.9 Fishing with blowguns

Generally speaking the blowgun is known as gear used for hunting birds in the virgin forests of Central and South America and of southern Asia. But this gear is used just as frequently for fishing in Thailand and southern India (*Fig 74*). It seems that blowguns were also known for fishing in the Philippines.[630] The blowgun consists of a tube made from bamboo or similar material and with a mouthpiece sometimes decorated in an artistic manner. The tube has a length of about 1·8m into which a small harpoon is so fitted that it completely

Fig 74 Indian fisherman with blowgun shooting fish on the Malabar coast, S. India.

closes the pipe with a tassel at the end from which one blows (*Figs 75* and *76*). To fill out the space between arrow and tube completely, and in addition to the tassel, a netting yarn is wound very carefully around the shaft of the little harpoon, with the tassel on the one end and the detachable point on the other. Although mostly called an 'arrow', the missile of the blowgun used in the fisheries of southern Asia is a true, but very small, harpoon about 15cm in length.

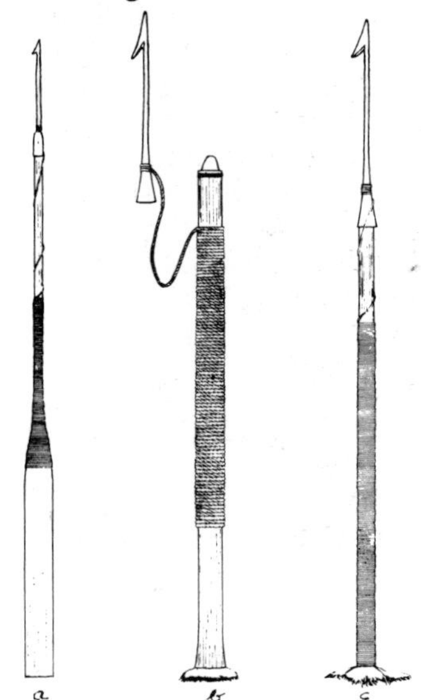

Fig 75 Harpoons for blowguns from: (*a*) Thailand; (*b*) and (*c*) S. India – all with iron points.

The operation of the blowgun in fisheries is the same as in hunting; the arrow is forced out of the tube by a strong blow. When the little arrow (harpoon) has pierced a fish, the point will be separated from the stick which is towed behind the fleeing fish like a retarder. The fisherman will try to pick up this floating stick and sometimes a hook is fixed to one end of the blowgun (*Fig 76*) to assist in this operation. The floating missile shows the position of the prey in the water.

6.10 Shooting fish

Fish shooting includes some of the fishing techniques mentioned before in which spears or harpoons are propelled by rifles or guns. Fish shooting also includes a technique designed not to wound or kill the fish, but to stun it by the shock of the bullet hitting the water near its head (Chapter 5).

In some cases rifles are also used to kill fish caught by another method; to avoid a long struggle and/or the fish's escape by, for example, breaking

Fig 76 Blowgun of the type used on the Malabar coast of southern India. At one end the wooden tip is sometimes wonderfully carved. On the other end is a hook to retrieve the line of the floating harpoon.

the line by which it is hooked. In the Danish fishery, tuna caught by line have sometimes been killed by shooting, and the same method is known in shark fishing. As soon as the fish can be gaffed, it is killed by shooting.[601] Today most people will not agree to porpoises being killed by shooting. Dolphins are mostly protected but Italian 'sports fishermen' have said that every year they kill many dolphins off the Ligurian coast by shooting at random into schools of these animals. Also the fishermen of the eastern part of the Turkish Black Sea coast hunt porpoises with rifles. It is not so easy when perched on a small platform on the bow of the boat, or on the roof of a wheelhouse, to hit such a fast-moving animal as a porpoise. On average, to hit about one in ten is a good success rate. These experienced fishermen also shoot large fish like mullet. But they have to be trained from their boyhood and become very fond of this practice. In many cases the harpoon, formerly used for hunting larger fish and water mammals, has been replaced by rifles. The rifle is now used by the Eskimos when hunting seals. Also crocodiles are no longer speared but shot in the night with the aid of spotlights. (There may be some doubt if this can be included in 'fish shooting'!) The prey will normally remain fixed in one spot as long as the spotlight is held steady, and if when hunting from a boat, the motor does not change pitch and startle the animal.

Chapter seven

Fishing with clamps, tongs, rakes and wrenching gear

It has already been noted that spears with one or more points, without or with barbs, are used for securing fish and crawfish and also for catching such other aquatic animals as sponges and sea cucumbers. This method involves some injury to the animal being captured and it would be unwise to use spears to pick up molluscs, sea urchins or small crabs. To pick up delicate prey without damage a number of grasping instruments have been developed. These enable fishermen to capture aquatic animals like mussels, snails and sea urchins in undamaged condition. The instruments are usually not very complicated: complex instruments are in fact unnecessary as the victims can scarcely escape and there is usually sufficient time to trap them properly. When searching for suitable prey in not so deep water with the help of a boat, so-called 'water-searchers' (*Fig 77*) are commonly used to overcome the refraction of the water surface and find the wanted prey like octopus, sea urchins and shellfish. These water-searchers can be a simple box, tube or bucket made of wood or metal with a bottom of glass. These instruments, also called 'look-boxes' or 'water-glasses' are known in coastal waters but sometimes also in fresh waters, *eg* in Finland where they are used to locate pearl mussels, *Margaritana margaritifera* L. When this equipment is used, however, the water must be clear and the surface should be smooth. Sometimes fishermen spray a few drops of oil, maybe mixed with sand, on the water surface to quell small waves.

Fig 77 Bucket with glass bottom operated by a Greek fisherman of Mithymna, on the island of Mytilini, searching for sea urchins (1958).

The wanted prey found in this manner can be hauled out of the water with the help of one of the grasping instruments mentioned in this chapter. Like pushed spears and harpoons, these instruments are preferably long-handled so as to operate as deep as possible. As in the case of pushed spears the length of the handle is restricted to what is manageable. These non-damaging grasping instruments all have the same aim – to pick up the wanted prey in deeper water – but they are constructed in different ways according to the animals or to the plants which are to be taken.

7.1 Clamps

Clamps are well known in many parts of the world, especially for taking mussels out of the water without injury. The simplest forms are hand-operated sticks with one end split into at least two branches (*Fig 78*). Mussels, snails, sea urchins, or any other prey can be jammed between the branches. To give the grip more security some barbs can help (*Fig 78a*). Other hand-operated gear is used by fishermen in the Mediterranean to collect fan mussels. Their implement looks like a two-pronged fork. Big mussels are clamped between the prongs and pulled up from the bottom. The stick may have a length of as much as nine metres.

Clamps can be used also for catching fish. In this case stronger implements made of iron, looking like multi-pointed spears, are used. To avoid damaging the flesh, so far as possible, the gear does not pierce the fish but presses it between the more or less elastic prongs. To prevent escape, especially in eel fishery, the sides of the prongs are barbed or serrated and look like a saw (*Figs 78* and *79*). The distance between the prongs can be regulated by law. This implement is also known as a spear or fish iron. But for fish, pointed spears combined with elastic clamps can also be used. In this case the

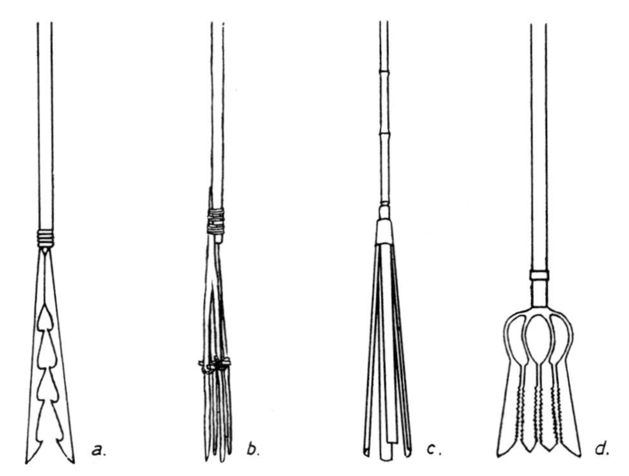

Fig 78 Types of fish clamp: (*a*) clip of Eskimo clamp (*Rau, 1884*); (*b*) fork for shrimps of Tierra del Fuego (*Gusinde, 1946*); (*c*) Japanese shellfish clamp (*NN, 1959*); (*d*) eel clamp of northern Europe.

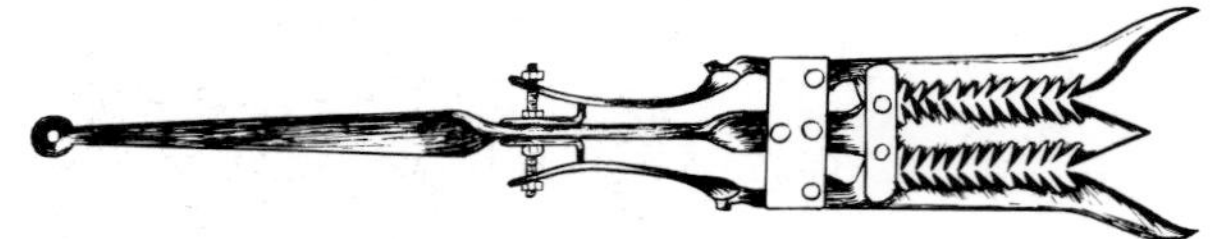

Fig 79 Modern Danish clamp with flexible sprung points for catching eels (1979).

clamps are like arms guiding the fish on to the central point.[689] *Figure 80* shows such grasping or gripping implements with squeezing devices and piercing points, which can be also equipped with barbs and may, in this form, wound the prey considerably. A similar implement for catching fish was shown (*Fig 39e*) in the section on fishing spears. Clamps, like spears, can also touch the bottom not vertically but slanting at a slight angle. To equalize the unequal movement, one of the two elastic prongs of the combined clamp/spear can be shorter than the other, similar to the arrangement shown in (*Fig 44*).

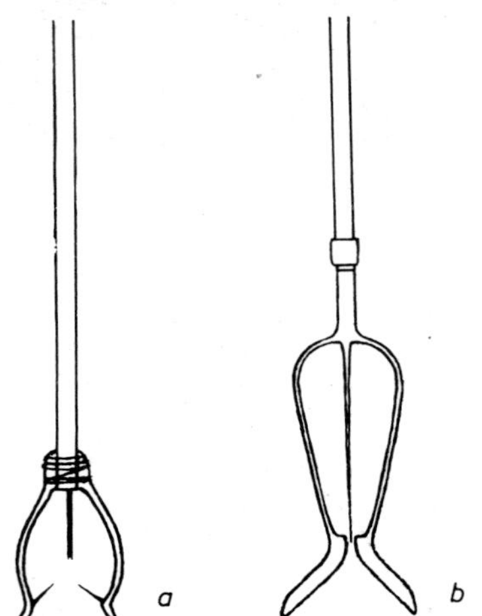

Fig 80 (*a*) Eskimo spear of Arctic Canada; (*b*) eel spear of the Baltic coast.

7.2 Tongs

Objects may be taken from the water in uninjured condition by means of tongs – that is, with instruments provided with two tong-like clasps moving one towards the other. Originally they were in their form and construction real tongs as used in any workshop (*Figs 81* and *82*). Today their construction is more adapted to fishing conditions (*Figs 83* and *84*). Tongs are used especially for mussels. Two hundred years ago small tongs were the main gear of fishermen looking for fresh water pearl mussels, *Margaritana margaritifera,* in some Saxon areas of Middle Europe (*Fig 82*).[533] Today tongs with long handles are used to bring oysters and other types of shellfish to the surface (*Fig 84*). These may be cross-shaped forks with two or even several points, the rigid levers of which – several metres long – are operated from a boat (*Figs 83* and *84*). The deeper the water the more difficult, however, it is to use tongs with two rigid arms. A depth of seven metres is considered to be the limit of practicability.[443] But tongs can be so designed that only one side is rigidly attached to a rod while the other is moved by a line (*Figs 81* and *83*). Such a type is used on the coast of Chile to collect colonies of mussels. Three men have to operate this gear. One operates the stick of the tong, another its line and the third one has to take the mussels

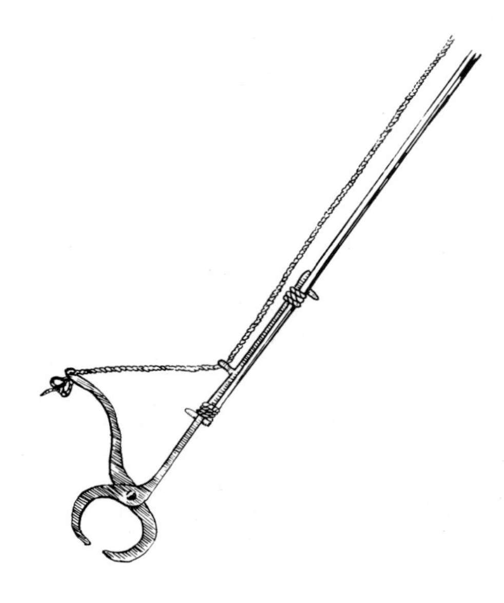

Fig 81 Old Danish fishing tongs. (*Olaus Olavius, 1787*).

Fig 82 Saxon pearl-fisher with mussel tongs. 1726 (*Rudau, 1961*).

out of the cross-shaped forks when the gear is lifted up.[560] In addition, mussel tongs are used which can be operated even by two lines (*Fig 83c*) and, by this means, the depth that is attainable can be increased.[11] In this implement again there occurred the same development which led from the use of spears with a rigid shaft to the adoption of the fish plummet operated by lines, as described in the previous chapter. The line thus replaces the rod and allows the animal to be grasped in greater depths than is possible by the use of rigid gear. This, however, can only be done vertically. Such tongs are widely used in the mussel fisheries of east Asia, Europe (mainly Mediterranean but formerly also on the coast of the North Sea), on the west coast of

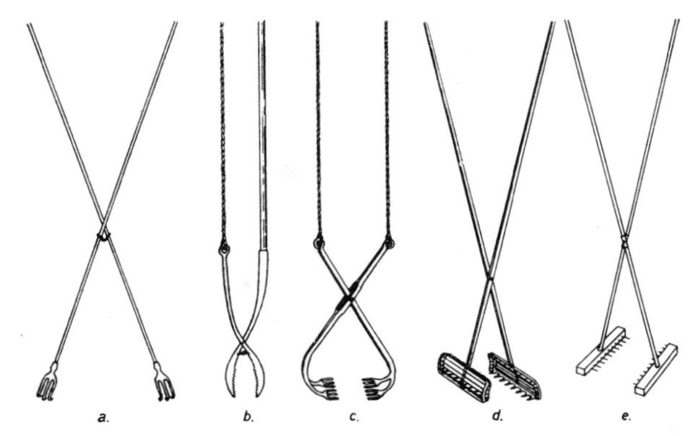

Fig 83 Tongs for gripping: (*a*) long-handled Japanese type for shellfish; (*b*) French tongs with a movable arm for lobsters (*Boudarel, 1948*); (*c*) Maltese tongs with two movable claws (*Burdon, 1956*); (*d*) North American shellfish tongs; (*e*) Mexican tongs made of two rakes (*Sanchez, 1959*).

Fig 84 Rake-end, scissor-like tongs are used to bring mature oysters to the surface by Canadian fishermen. (*Photo: FAO.*)

North America, and in Central America.

The shape of the tongs may differ very widely. They can be made up of two forks, or of two scoop nets. There is even a report of a type formed by two short-pointed rakes (*Fig 83e*)[539] that is used in Mexican fisheries. Essentially it must be appreciated that the shape of the tongs depends on the specific purpose for which they are to be used. A gear like a double tong is known in Indonesia for grasping mussels seen from the water surface. The gear is lowered over the mussel with the clasps pressed open and takes the animal from the bottom when the clasps are closed by a simple mechanism which can be seen in *Figure 85*.[682] It is not surprising that some types of tongs are damaging to the prey. The Danes use mechanical tongs in the eel fishery of Bornholm Island. These tongs close mechanically by a spring or rubber band when an eel is between their claws and the trigger is set free (*Fig 86*).[340] In a few cases rough tongs made of wood, short-handled and with strong metal teeth, have been used to catch eels, conger, and other fish, when they are lethargic in wintertime.[279, 690] Of course, sometimes heavy damage to the fish cannot be avoided in this case.

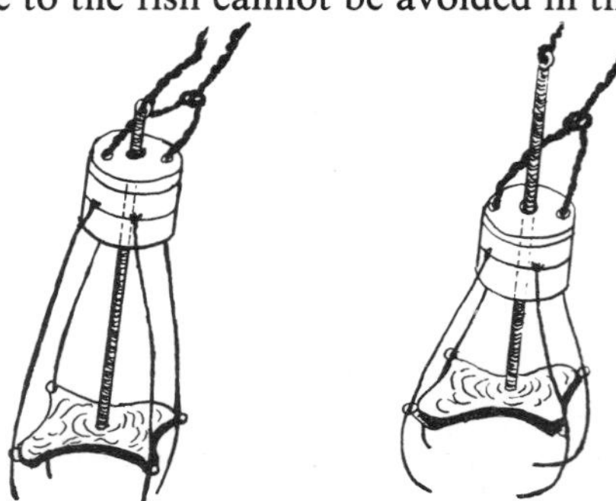

Fig 85 Tonglike clamp from Indonesia. (*left*) stretched; (*right*) closed. (*Yamamoto, 1975*).

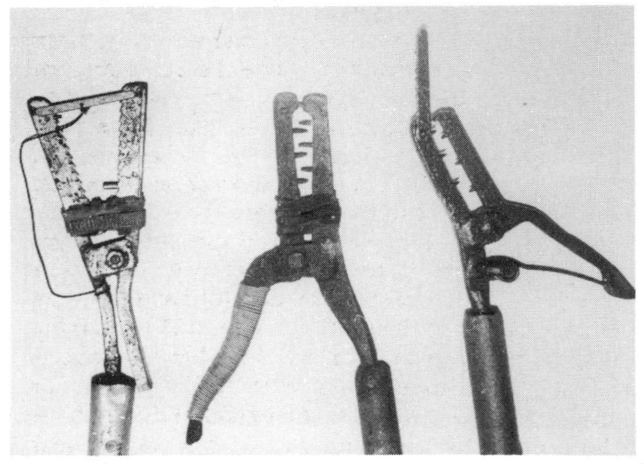

Fig 86 Danish mechanical eel clamps from Bornholm Island. (*Photo: K Larsen, Copenhagen.*)

The same may be true for other wooden tongs with sharp iron teeth (*Fig 87*) which are used, for example, by the fishermen of the Azores to hold and to kill 'murries' (Moray eels) that are lifted out of the water when caught with hook and line. From earliest times these fish have been considered dangerous.

7.3 Rakes

Instead of tongs, simple rakes may also be employed to catch the desired aquatic prey.

Fig 87 Azores tongs with sharp iron teeth to hold moray eels.

Primitive and also modern complicated rakes have already been mentioned in Chapter 2, dealing with the collecting fishery. There they are used for raking and digging animals hidden in the mud at the bottom. Rakes so described are generally used in the seaweed and mussel fisheries in different parts of the world (*Fig 3*). Off the western coast of Malaysia, large-sized edible jellyfish are caught with long-handled rakes of a type formerly used for the harvesting of seaweed (*Fig 88*).[93] For deeper water the handles of rakes can extend to more than ten metres. To make the capture of mussels, sea urchins and so on by rakes easier, the prongs are made somewhat differently in that they are either bent, or the rake is equipped with a collecting bag (*Fig 89d*), but in that case the gear has already assumed the shape of a dredge which will be discussed later (Chapter 20).

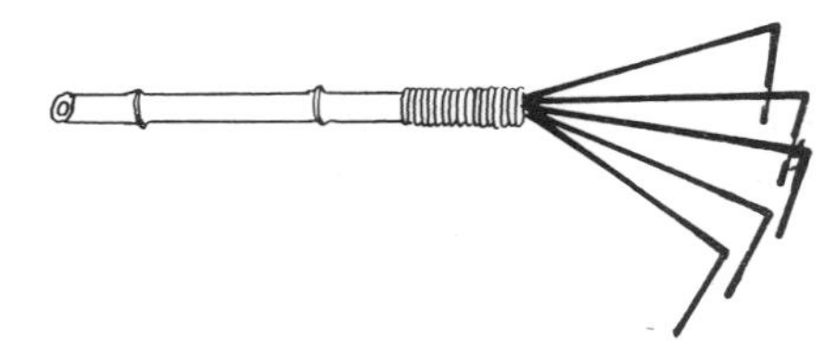

Fig 88 Rake for catching edible jellyfish from the surface waters off the western coast of Malaysia (1978).

7.4 Wrenching gear for harvesting seaweed

Many methods have been used for harvesting seaweed and other water plants. There are different gears such as scythe-like tools for the harvesting of sessile underwater algae by divers, and rakes to scrape the floating seaweed stranded along the beach. There are even dredging machines such as those used off the French coast to collect crustaceous algae like *Lithotamnium calcoreum* which can be harvested like sand. But the harvesting of seaweed is mostly concentrated on large sessile

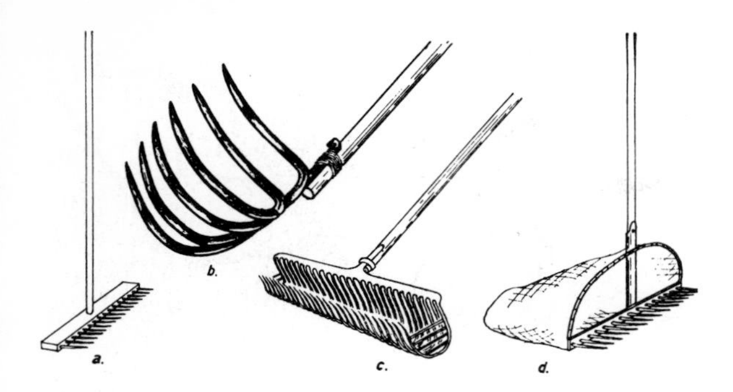

Fig 89 Rakes for fishing: (*a*) simple rake; (*b*) French 'grappin' for sea-urchin (*Naintre et al, 1967*); (*c*) 'Bull rake' of the North American Atlantic coast for shellfish (*Sundstrom, 1957*); (*d*) English mussel rake with bag net.

algae like *Laminaria* sp. For this another method of harvesting is used. With a special implement, operated from a boat, the seaweed is twisted together and removed from the bottom with a sharp jerk. This gear for wrenching the plants can be an agricultural fork which is struck into the bulk of the plants before twisting. In most cases, especially in the Far East, this wrenching gear is a stick up to six or seven metres long. To facilitate twisting, the stick has a handle on one end and some branches or a spiral on the other (*Fig 90*). To overcome the buoyancy of the wooden stick, some weighting may be necessary (*Fig 91*).

A wrenching or twisting method was also known in western Europe in the last century, not for harvesting waterplants but for catching the small fish hidden within them (Chapter 30). Nowadays in France and the USSR the wrenching method for harvesting seaweed has been mechanized by turning the wrenching or twisting spiral, the 'scoubidou' of the French fishermen, with the help of a motor (see Chapter 31, (*Figs 730* and *731*).

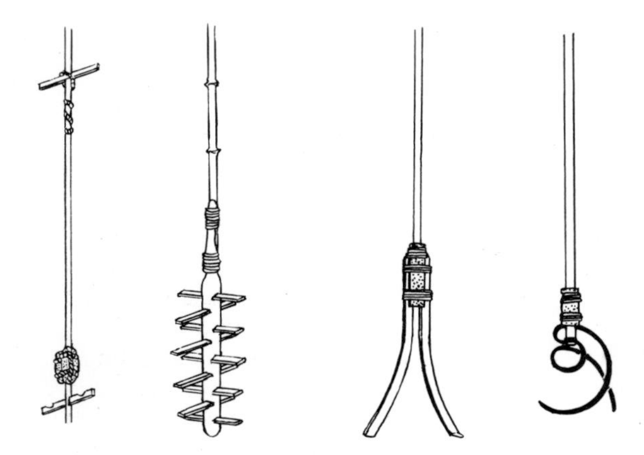

Fig 90 Wrenching gear for gathering seaweed, used in Japan and Korea.

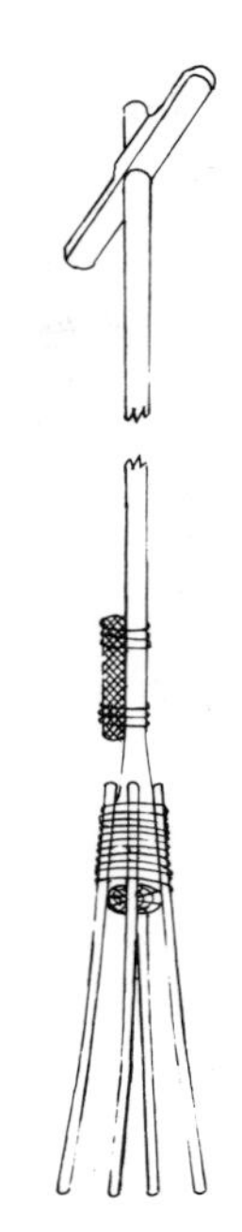

Fig 91 Russian wrenching gear, with weight to overcome buoyancy, for harvesting algae. (*Spakov, 1977*).

7.5 Further developments

Of the gear mentioned in this chapter only those for harvesting mussels and seaweed are of any great importance. Like the spearing and shooting gear described in the previous chapter they have been invented to extend the range of the human arm and to grasp and scrape and secure more than is possible with the bare hand. They are thus improved auxiliary instruments of the collector and are in the early stages of further development. From the primitive rake, however, the development leads on to the creation of the dredge (Chapter 20) and from that to the dragged stow net and the trawl (Chapters 21 and 22). Fishing gears, invented originally for securing small quantities of personal food, have thus gradually been converted into larger gear working on the same principles for mass production to supply wholesale markets. But this does not mean that simple gear used for gathering has made no further progress. Hand-picking and gathering is of some value even today, especially for harvesting shellfish. Here the simple rake became the basis for a Canadian development of new harvesters, replacing manual methods to some extent and reducing the problems created by the lack of manual diggers. The simplest and least costly of this new type of development may be the clam rake.[362] As can be seen (in *Fig 92a*) these rakes have tines which are water jets designed to wash the clams out of the sand. The water to operate the rake is forced from an engine-driven pump (carried in a dinghy) through a hose in the handle of the rake and down through the nozzles. A sturdy type of this apparatus can flush clams out of the sand in shallow water of up to 50cm deep. A mixture of water and sediment is produced and the clams, having slight buoyancy, float to the top of the mixture where they can be collected.

There are more ideas for such types of clam digger (*Fig 92b*). This shows how a simple but useful fishing gear can be the origin of very modern harvesting machines for fisheries. But there is one problem. In some countries such as Malaysia, to protect natural and cultured shellfish beds, the use of mechanical apparatus for clam digging is strictly forbidden. Also the manual hydraulic clam diggers referred to have been forbidden in Canada for the same reason until 1964 by fishery regulations.

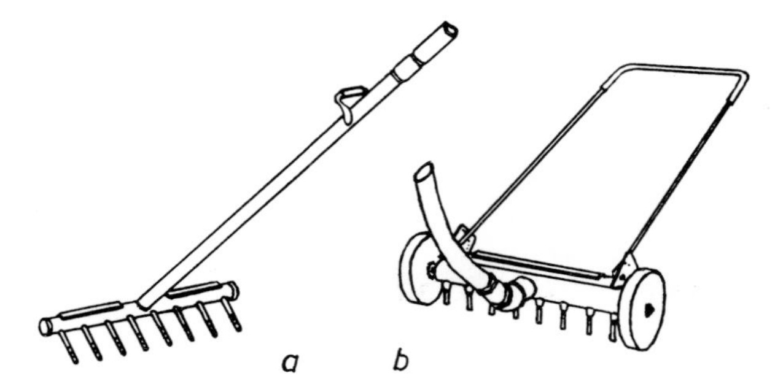

Fig 92 Canadian hydraulic gear for clam fishing: (*a*) hydraulic clam rake; (*b*) hydraulic clam digger (*MacPhail and Medcof, 1963*).

Nevertheless, there is no doubt that mechanized harvesting machines, including those for clam digging, in spite of some temporary and local objections, will become more important in the future (see also Chapter 31).

Chapter eight

Line fishing: basic implements

In his book *Den store Slaederejse* (The great sledge drive), the famous Danish explorer of Greenland, Knut Rasmussen, describes how the Eskimos caught trout by luring them from their hiding places with small fish-shaped lures. The trout were then caught while their attention was fixed on the bait.[512] The fish are taken with a clamp (*Fig 80a*) as is done by the Eskimos of the Canadian Arctic. The bait serves only for attracting the fish; subsequently they are clamped, speared or caught by any other method. It seems that this fishing method has spread all around the northern hemisphere. It is believed that the neolithic hunters of Siberia in the area of Lake Baikal used artificial fish-like baits made of stone or bone in the same manner to attract and to catch fish.[480]

The bait may also be presented so as to serve directly for fishing. This is done by securing it in such a manner that the fish can neither carry it away freely nor escape once they have taken the bait. So presented, we think immediately of the line fishery where these conditions are fulfilled. The principle of line fishing is to offer a partly fixed bait to the fish (or any other aquatic or non-aquatic animal which might be attracted), which accepts it and then finds itself unable to release the bait so that it can be lifted from the water together with the bait. This chapter will deal with the different implements or fishing tackle which may be used to succeed in this method of catching.

8.1 Bobbing

To meet this principle nothing but an attractive bait, fastened to a line of adequate length, is necessary. Many primitive line fisheries operate in this way. It is a method that will suffice provided the victim maintains hold of the bait until it can be pulled from the water onto the shore or into the vessel. This method is practiced not only in commercial fisheries but also in sport fishing. Crustaceans and molluscs, more than fish, are caught in this manner.[605] Crayfish especially can clasp and hold the bait so fast with their claws that they may be caught in this way without any difficulty. In lobster fishing at night, a line with a small sinker and sufficient mussel meat attached to it is released from a catamaran to the bottom of the fishing ground. As soon as the bite of a lobster is felt, the line is hauled up very slowly and the lobster is caught with a scoopnet before reaching the water surface. This method is used in many countries. Finnish fishermen even today use set sticks with bait for catching crayfish (*Fig 93*). The stick extends above the surface of the water and sometimes leaves are attached to show by their movements if a crayfish is gnawing at the bait.[342] How widely this idea is known may be determined from the fact that a similar method for catching crabs is known in Hawaii. There a bait, marked by a float, is put on the sea bottom and hauled carefully with the help of a scoop net.[262] The Finns know how to use single and multiple lines with bait for catching crayfish. Such lines can be replaced by the long intestine of an animal. The crayfish will take the intestine and can be caught. This recalls a strange story told by the Greek poet Oppian (about 149-179AD).[482] For catching eels a long clean intestine was used. The catching principle was explained by Oppian in the

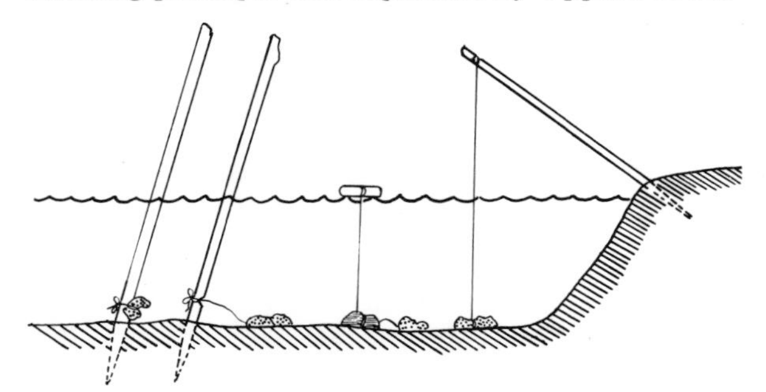

Fig 93 Different types of Finnish set lines for fishing crayfish. On the left side, bait fixed directly on the stick without any line (*Lehtonen, 1975*).

following manner: as soon as an eel begins to swallow one end of the gut, the fishermen blows it up from the other end, so that the eel cannot let go of the intestine! The Finnish description of how this method works for catching crayfish will give a better explanation!

Not only are crustaceans caught by this method, using a line and bait only, but also gastropods. Whelks fasten themselves so firmly onto submerged pieces of crabs by the sucking action of the foot that they can be drawn with them from the water. Octopi hold so fast to a supposed prey such as the boat-like lure named 'specchio per seppie' provided with mirrors and towed by Italian and other Mediterranean fishermen, that to catch them is no trouble at all. A similar gear is the octopus trailing line used in Oceania (*Fig 94*). This gear is made of a large cowrie shell (*Cypraea tigris*) and a polished limestone, fixed together with a wooden stick with the help of fibres of coconuts and hybiscus. This gear imitates a swimming rat which, according to fishermen, will be attacked by the octopus. These animals are alleged to have hated each other since time immemorial. Tradition has it that a long time ago a rat wanted to travel from one island to another but the distance was large and the rat was afraid of the long swim. The rat told the problem to an octopus offering help. The rat was asked to sit on the head of the octopus, who brought the faint-hearted rat safely to the other island. The rat was happy to jump on the shore but then the octopus was asked to touch his head. When he did so he found that the rat had been not clean!

Fig 94 Trailing lure known as the 'swimming rat' for catching octopus in Oceania. (*Photo: G Croom, Museum für Völkerkunde, Abt. Südsee, Berlin-Dahlem.*)

Therefore it is not surprising that the octopus hates the rat even today, and fishermen exploit this for their own benefit with the 'swimming rat' lure. To catch the octopus the gear is moved up and down in a water depth of 20 to 50cm to imitate the swimming movements of a rat. If an octopus takes the gear, it will be killed immediately under water by the fisherman pressing his fingers into its head.[316] Nowadays, this gear is also used in Hawaii, combined with a fishing hook in contrast to the other gears discussed in this section which are hookless.

Much simpler is the method used by French fishermen for catching cuttlefish with a hookless line. A small fish is split and attached to a fine nylon netting yarn. The cuttlefish will attack the bait and begin to feed even as it is hauled.[577] The method for catching squid is not so different. In the coastal fishery of Dar-es-Salaam a red mullet is tied to a line and thrown out to attract squid.[655] When the animal has attached itself to the bait, the line is gently drawn in. In all these cases the animal to be caught is endeavouring to keep the bait and retain it, even if it is removed from the water together with the bait. In this way it is easy to catch some species of crab, snails or octopi by bait alone.

Attempts to catch fish in this manner will be more difficult. They let the bait go when they are lifted from the water or, feeling some resistance, they spit it out before they are lifted, and so escape. To prevent that, the bait can be presented in such a way that the fish hangs on to the bait involuntarily with its backward-pointing teeth and is thus unable to let it go or to spit it out. A clear description of this method was given more than 200 years ago by D G Schreber (1772) in a German book[557] based on a publication of the famous Frenchmen, Duhamel du Monceau and La Marre.[143, 144] According to them a bunch of the moss used for caulking vessels is fastened at the end of a long line and towed through the water behind a vessel. Fish taking this 'bait' become entangled by their teeth and are quickly taken by the fisherman. A similar device is well-known today as an 'eel bob', used for eel fishing on dark stormy nights in northwest Europe[338, 411] (*Fig 95*). Accordingly this method is known as 'bobbing' or 'blobbing'. It has been suggested that lines without hooks, but with bait only, should be called 'bait-lines'.[358] Even if this designation may be the right one, it could be mixed with 'lure-lines' and 'luring', therefore the name 'bobbing' for this method of fishing has been retained. Bobbing as a method for catching fish seems to be practised all over the world. Different materials are used to make the bob: wool, hemp, hair and many others. Bobbing is practised in Turkey, by the Australian aborigines[529] and also in the aboriginal fishery of southern Africa.[361, 666] The

Fig 95 An eel taken by eel bobbing is hauled into a wooden box (*Quedens, 1963*).

Indians of California attached a bundle of vegetable fibres or human hair to the line, sometimes with a live worm fastened to the bundle.[271] Turkish fishermen practise a more modern form of bobbing by ingeniously laying together small bunches of silk which they use when fishing for garfish in the Bosphorus (*Fig 96*).

In eel bobbing the bait is either made from a piece of meat or more often from lobworms or sand worms, 30 to 40 being threaded lengthwise on a length of twine. This twine can be either single, as is often made of rough hemp twine, or double. In the latter case a stronger twine is combined with a rougher one such as a woollen thread. Some people think that it is essential to use woollen twine. The 'eel bob' is ravelled up into a bunch, weighted with a lead of 100 to 500g, and fastened to a strong line at least as long as the pole being used or much longer usually about nine to fourteen metres.[656] By means of a short, strong angling rod of about one to three metres, the bob is lowered into the water until it rests on the bottom and then is slowly moved up and down a handbreadth over the bottom. If an eel bites it, its incurved teeth become entangled in the rough threads of the bob long enough for it to be drawn from the water and thrown onto the bank. This must, of course, be done very quickly before the eel gets loose. Sometimes an old open umbrella is held upside down under the eel so that it falls into it, as into a funnel, even if it does get loose from the bait. Nowadays, fishermen make little eel bobbing bags out of pieces of nylon hose with bait and weights.[344]

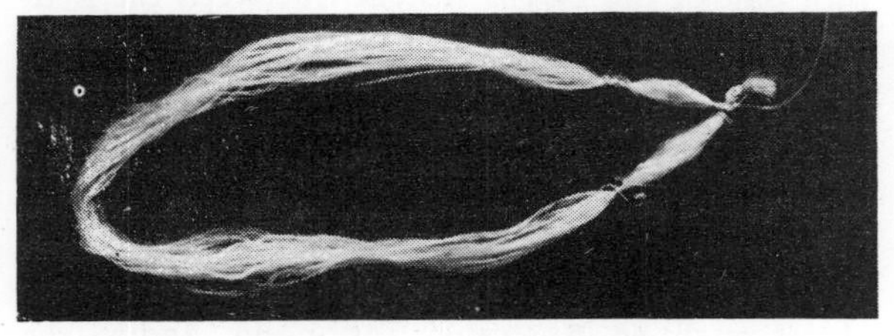

Fig 96 Yarn of silk for fishing ***Belonidae*** when towed by Turkish fishermen in the Bosphorus. The yarn is ingeniously wound around the hand and tied together for this purpose.

Another fishery which uses bait into which the fish pierces its small pointed teeth is perhaps better known. This is the garfish fishery by aborigines in the north of Australia.[529] The bait here is made of a ball of thick spider-web threads (*Fig 97*)and has the same function as the rough twine of the eel bob. The garfish remain hanging with their small teeth entangled in the spider-web. Fishing with spider-web is known in New Guinea, the Solomon Islands and Santa Cruz Islands. The use of spider web bait on the last-mentioned island was described recently. Two boats work together with three fishermen in each. Two, on the stern and the bow, are rowing. The third man in the middle of each of the two boats is responsible for a line by which the two boats are connected. Usually, five baits of spider web are fixed on this connecting line. The bait jumps over the water surface as the boats are rowed forward, thereby attracting the garfish. The fish try to take the bait and hang themselves on the line. When the fish is removed the bait can be used again.

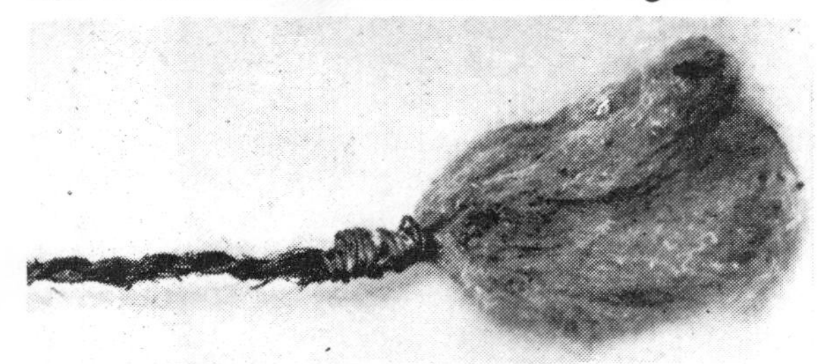

Fig 97 Spider-web bait designed to entangle the teeth of fish. This is used on some islands of Oceania. (*Photo: Übersee-Museum, Bremen.*)

8.2 Gorges

The danger that the fish may let the bait go and escape is, of course, very great even with the methods just described. Effort has therefore been made to find safety devices which will completely prevent the bait from being released by the prey. The oldest device of that kind is apparently the gorge (*Fig 98*). This is a small straight or slightly bent stick, pointed at either end, tied at the middle, and inserted lengthwise into a bait held more or less parallel to the line. Thus the gorge goes easily into the fish when it swallows the bait. But when the fish swims away or the line is pulled, the gorge takes up a transverse position in the victim's throat or belly so that it cannot spit it out. Gorges have been used in all five continents, not only in fishing but also in hunting, especially for taking birds and sometimes also for catching larger beasts of prey.

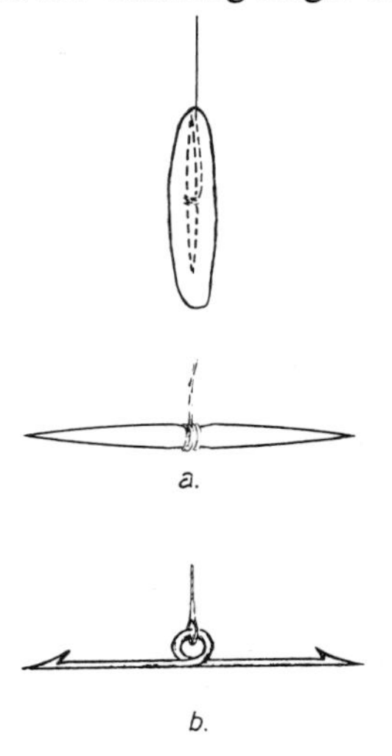

Fig 98 Gorges were used before hooks: (*a*) wooden gorge hidden in a bait which when swallowed, is pulled across the gullet of the fish: (*b*) Modern French gorge for eel, made of steel.

Very often gorges and gorge-like devices are used for catching crocodiles (*Fig 99*). Gorges used in line fisheries are especially common from Oceania and neighbouring countries (*Fig 100*) as well as from the northern areas of Asia, Europe, America, Africa[361] and the Arctic.[9] In Europe, gorges have been used since the palaeolithic period. They were made of wood, stiff grass, bone, horn, flint, and later, right up to the present time, of metal. Gorge fishing is certainly one of the oldest fishing methods of all. Besides the wooden gorge pointed at either end with a line fastened in the centre, there are also gorges with only one pointed end and a line fastened at the other end. And finally there are cross-shaped gorges which spread open when the line is pulled, and others in the form of arrowheads which have the same effect. In books on angling, especially in those written in the last century, there are usually descriptions of how to use darning needles for

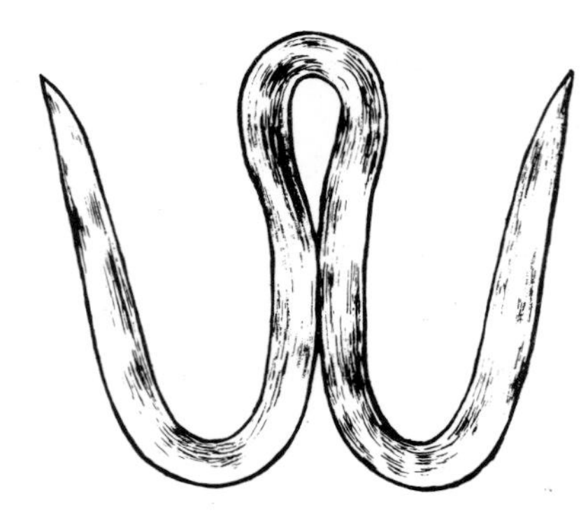

Fig 99 Mustad double hook for catching crocodiles.

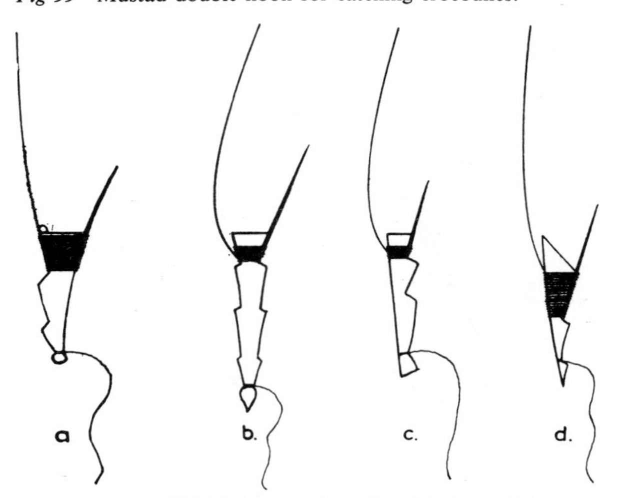

Fig 100 Gorge-like implements from Botel Tobago (Lan Yü) for catching flying fishes (1970). The small yarn on one end is for fastening the bait.

'sniggling' – primarily for eels.[56, 150] In the French fishery, metal gorges with central fastenings are recommended even today for catching eels (*Fig 98b*).[193, 520]

A special form of this gorge method of fishing is the 'spring angle' such as was known, and is also still used today, in China.[289] The catching or, better still, the holding device of the spring angle consists of a small bent wooden stick pointed at both ends and bound in the bent position. It is either covered with bait or the bait is fastened between the tied-up sides of the spring gorge (*Fig 101*). As soon as the bait is swallowed the fastening becomes loose and the small piece of wood springs open in the throat of the fish. This, too, is a gorge, since the elastic material such as bamboo which is used takes up that special form. Spring gorges are also known for hunting and fishing from many widely separated places such as Australia, Indonesia, India, the Congo, southern France, Alaska and northern Canada and southeastern North America.

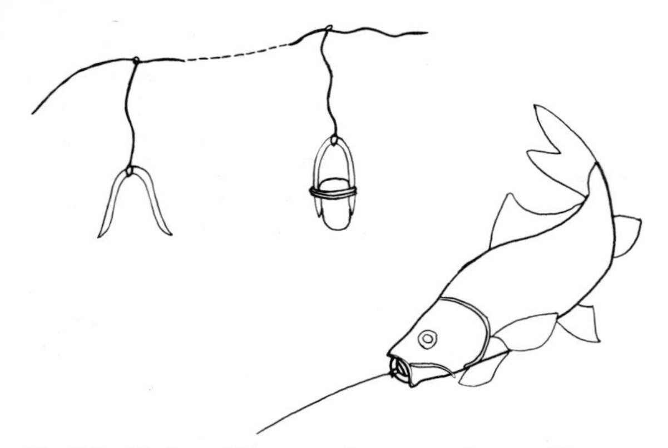

Fig 101 Modern Chinese spring gorge for catching carp. (*Kasuga, 1975*).

8.3 Forerunners of modern hooks

The bent hook is another and even better-known device for holding a fish captive once it has taken the bait. The gorge is certainly older than the curved hook. Some people think there could be some relation between a W-shaped gorge (*Fig 99*) and a curved double hook (*Fig 106e*). The modern angling hook has probably not developed from the gorge, but is a different solution to the same problem. Also the curved hook is not a specific fishing implement. Like the gorge it is also used in hunting, especially for catching birds. There have been many theories on how the bent fishing hook, as the basis of modern hooks, came to be invented. There is some evidence that implements like a bent fishing hook may originally have been made of various perishable materials of plant and animal origin. Hooks of thorn were used. They were made of small parts of plants with thorns such as hawthorn (*Fig 102*). These thorn hooks were still used in Europe up to the last century. They were even described as being used around the Thames estuary up to 1895.[42] On the coast of Wales, wooden hooks made of blackthorn, *Prunus spinosa,* were still used in 1929.[372] The thorns were hardened by baking and were considered 'fairly effective' for longlining. Such a wooden hook, grown naturally as a part of a twig with a thorn, can be considered like a stick with a point or even barb. Maybe man has learned by chance how useful this pointed or barbed stick may be in fishing, but larger ones are not found. Man had to make them himself by joining two pieces of wood together to form a compound hook (*Fig 103*). The result is not exactly a 'bent hook' because the point is attached to the stick at a narrow angle.

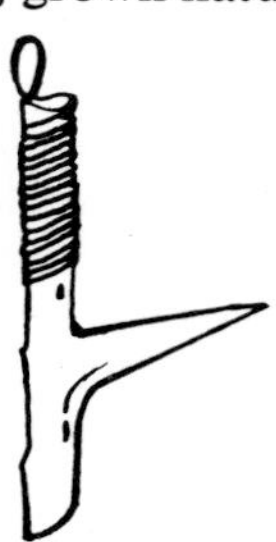

Fig 102 Natural thorn hook of a type used in the Towy estuary, Wales. (*Matheson, 1929*).

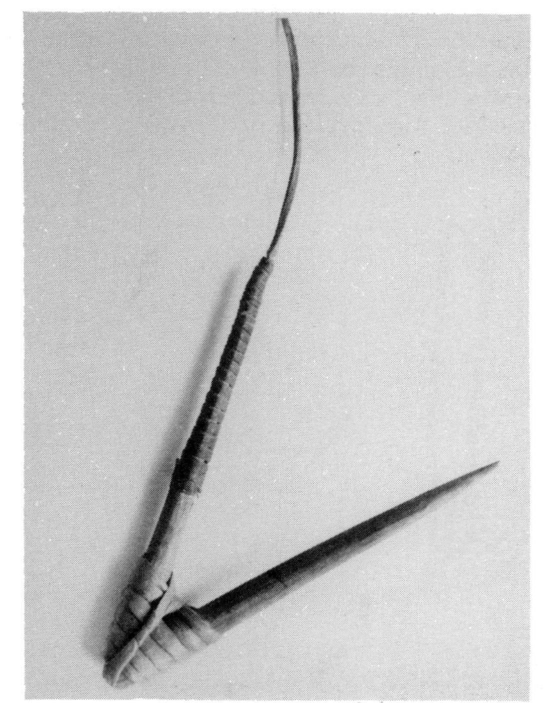

Fig 103 Compound steam-bent halibut hook made of cedar wood by the Bella Coola Indians in Western Vancouver.

Wooden hooks have been known not only in small-scale fisheries *eg* in Scandinavian countries from the end of the last century,[271] but also in developed fisheries such as those for sturgeon, halibut and oilfish (*Ruvettus pretiosus*). But there is one problem: wooden hooks, in contrast to hooks of metal, may float and this had an influence on the construction of the fishing gear as will be shown with the sturgeon hooks in Chapter 12. Man learned to make hooks from more durable materials than wood. The hooks, of compound structure or in one piece, were made from shells, bones and other animal products. Even bent hooks of stone have been found. In general, compound (or composite) hooks are considered to be cultural elements of nothern Eurasia.[9] Their use was widely spread and they probably reached their maximum development in the bonito fishery of Oceania.[335] The compound hook spread as far as Madagascar. The Oceanian bonito hooks are of great interest (*Fig 104*). They combine an attracting lure with a point. The shank of the hook is a glittering lure made of shell and/or bone; the point is made sometimes of stronger material, also shell, turtle shell or other material. To increase the luring effect some feathers, hackle and also pearls are fixed to the end of the hook. The most popular Polynesian type of hook has the line attached to the head of the shank with a lashing of fine cord.[476] The knowledge however, of how to make such compound hooks had almost vanished from Oceania by the second half of the last century because of the intrusion of European influence.

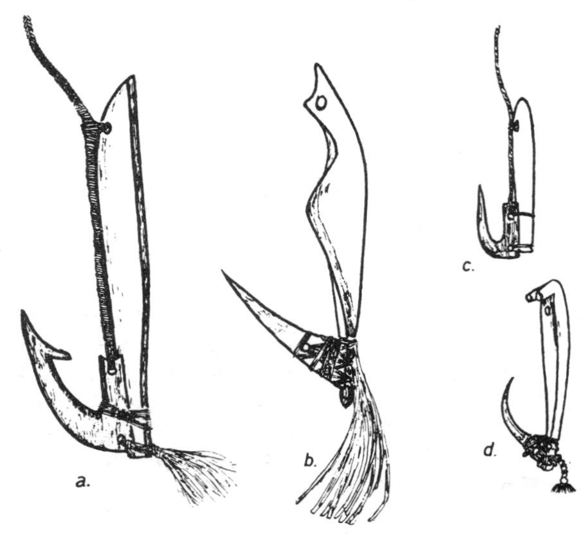

Fig 104 Compound hooks used in the spinning fishery for bonito in Oceania: (*a*) Big hook – the shank is made of whalebone and mother-of-pearl, the barb of tortoise-shell; (*b*) hook made of mother-of-pearl; (*c*) small hook made of bone and mother-of-pearl; (*d*) small hook of mother-of-pearl and tortoise-shell.

Thus today the beautiful hooks composed of mother-of-pearl, tortoiseshell, whalebone and especially human bones, as made by the old-time craftsmen of Oceania, are to be found only among the carefully protected treasures of fishery collections. But some people think that these hooks, especially the compound hooks of Polynesia used for trolling bonito, are among the most highly specialised fishing hooks in Oceania.[476] Therefore it is not surprising that some knowledge of their construction has survived. After the end of World War II, compound hooks for poling skipjack and small yellowfin were found in use on the Gilbert Islands with a shank roughly made of mother-of-pearl and an unbarbed point made of plastic material. The hook ended as usual with some feathers. In another case the same trolling lure for tuna had a hook made of aluminium from a downed World War II aircraft and the twine needed for lashing, as well as the decorative 'feathers', had been replaced by material of plastic.[105] In 1975, FAO in Rome published a gear catalogue to help small-scale fishermen.[417] This catalogue includes a modern compound hook from Tahiti for pole and line fishing for skipjack (*Fig 105*). The shank is made of shell, but the earlier form of point is replaced by a long hook of metal fixed to the shank by a synthetic line. Instead of feathers a bunch of monofilaments forms the lure.

Fig 105 Modern compound hook used for skipjack in Tahiti. (*Photo: FAO.*)

8.4 Modern fishing hooks

Important progress in line fishing came with the invention of bronze. Now hooks in many forms could be made in one piece; compound ones, labour-intensive in their construction, were no longer necessary. Metal replaced the former materials. Iron hooks were used for fishing as were hooks made of copper or brass. Even hooks made of gold, originating from prehistoric times in Europe or from pre-European times in other continents, have been found. The modern curved hooks used nowadays in commercial fisheries are always well-tempered metal hooks. They should be neither too soft, to avoid their straightening out by pulling, nor too hard to prevent their breaking under strain. Iron hooks, however, when not made of stainless steel or nickel alloy will become rusty, especially in sea waters. They must be protected, which is done by several different methods including galvanizing, tinning, gilding, bronzing, enamelling, plating with gold, silver, nickel, cadmium or copper, lacquering (japanning) or by simple 'blueing'. Generally, tinned hooks are preferred. Some manufacturers have acquired great skill and experience in this field and supply commercial and sports fishermen all over the world with their hooks.

Before describing the modern bent form of hooks, the circular ones made of metal may be mentioned (*Fig 106a* to *d*). These more or less completely round hooks are found in different places and are considered very effective as the fish, when caught, slide towards the centre of the hook and cannot escape.[82] This is why circular hooks are also used today in tuna fishery. Moreover, Norwegian investigations showed that hooks with the point in the line of the pull, or with the point in the direction of the hook eye, have a higher hooking frequency than conventional ones. Nevertheless, modern hooks are more v- or u-shaped. Different parts are distinguishable and are named for comparison: head or eye, shank, bend, crook and point (*Fig 107*). The head of the hook serves for fastening the line and is shaped as an eye, loop, plate, or is simply notched on the front of the shank so that the line can be fastened on properly. The shank can be of varying length and form. Its cross section can be round (regular) or flattened (forged). Specially long shanks are designed to prevent a fish, after swallowing the hook, from biting the line and escaping. The bend and crook of the hook varies in shape; round or angular with all possible variations. The point of the hook may be either straight or even reversed and curved.

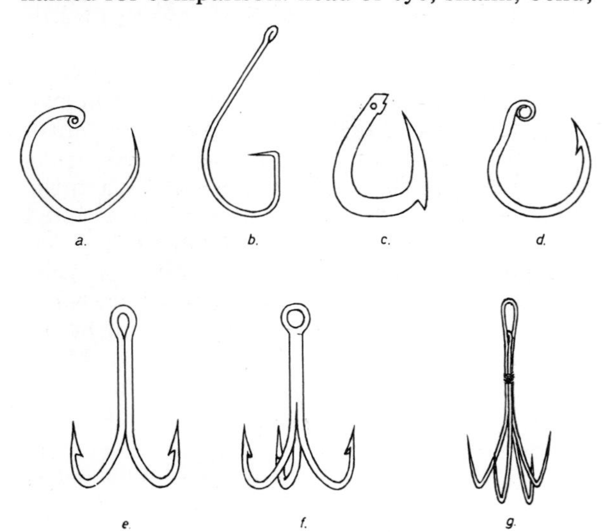

Fig 106 More variations of the simple hook: (*a*) hand-made iron hook without barb from Lake Tanganyika; (*b*) hook made in Norway for the Japanese tuna fishery with a point like a barb; (*c*) shellfish hook of Oceania with the barb outside, from the Island of Yap; (*d*) hand-made Japanese iron tuna-hook with the barb inside; (*e*) double hook; (*f*) triple hook; (*g*) Chinese quadruple hook.

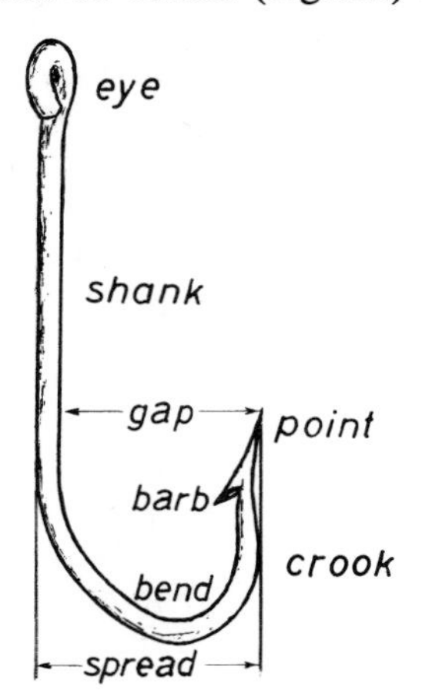

Fig 107 The parts of the modern bent fishing hook.

There are well known hook types in many different sizes but unfortunately, different systems of numbers are used for hook designation. Very often no detail is given about the form, size or real length of the hook, nor (which is much more important) its gap and especially its spread (*Fig 107*). Sometimes the throat is mentioned – that is, the depth between the gap and the inside of the bend. There is no way of knowing something about a hook by the number alone, unless the name of the manufacturer and the type of the hook (quality number) is also given and a catalogue is available. The number alone indicates only if a hook of the same type is smaller or larger. In general the higher number indicates a smaller hook and vice versa, but this is not always so! Usually No. 20 is the smallest size and hooks increase in size from No. 20 to No. 1, beyond which larger hooks are designated 1/0, 2/0 and so on, sometimes running up to 12/0.

The purpose of the fishing hook is to ensure that the fish shall be unable to spit it out with the bait after biting or swallowing it. It penetrates into the mouth of the fish when the bait is taken or the line is pulled, so that the fish becomes fast. For this reason a good hook needs to have a needle-sharp point for effective penetration, correct shape for holding the catch, perfect hardening to avoid breaking, and high rust resistance. One of the weak points can be the point. In many fisheries sharpening the point is done regularly and needs much working time, particularly in the sturgeon fishery. A sharp point depends also on the material of which the hook is made. Those made of nickel alloy do not rust, but their points cannot be as needle sharp as required.

Even though the history of fishing hooks goes back thousands of years, it is well known that the first bent hooks were barbless. Older Egyptian and Roman hooks made of metal were without barbs. These were introduced later. In southern and central Africa, no barbed hooks were known until imported hooks from Europe became available to be copied.[361] There are different reasons for attaching barbs on fishing hooks. The most important is to prevent the fish slipping off the hook. In the chapter on spears and harpoons, mention was made of the barb as being a method of preventing the victim from escaping. But as long as the fishing line can be kept under tension, no barb is required on the hook. Accordingly, in some modern line-fishing methods where it is desired that the fish be removed quickly from the hook – such as with the commercial tuna pole-and-line fishery – the barbed hook is abandoned and only a plain hook is used. This is done because a barb would only hinder the operation of freeing the fish and releasing the line for further catches. In this case tension must be kept on the pole-and-line so that the fish does not slip off the hook before being landed on deck. Some sports fishermen also use barbless hooks or those with wavy points, especially when they wish to return small, undersized fish to the water without injury. Nevertheless, most modern hooks made of metal are, with few exceptions, barbed. Even older types of fishing hooks like the compound ones, which were originally barbless, can now have a barb for this reason (*Fig 104a*).

But there are other reasons why a fishing hook can be barbed. The hook also has to serve the function of holding the bait. For that purpose, too, the barbed hook is useful, but in this case it is not necessary that the barb be fitted directly to the point of the hook. This explains why in some hooks of ancient fisheries the barb is further away from the point than with the others. Its purpose then is mainly to secure the bait and less to effect the catch; the hook, but not the barb, does that. Usually the barb for holding the fish points to the inner side of the hook, that is, it is fitted into the bow of the hook in Europe, Asia and Africa. It can, however, when made to secure the bait, also be pointed to the outside, as is done in large areas of South America, Oceania (*Fig 106c*) and in the ancient Japanese fishery prior to the Buddhist era. There is always one barb only pointing to the inner side, but there can be as many as three on the outer side.[302] Modern hooks with additional barbs are nowadays called 'sliced' hooks (*Fig 108*). There can be up to four 'slices', two inside and two outside. The slices were, it is said, originally made for a very special bait, namely salmon roe. But now sliced hooks are also made to secure other types of bait like worms, flesh of mussels, and so on (*Fig 108* and *216*).

Fig 108 'Sliced hook' for fixing special bait.

Bait can be fixed on a hook also in quite another manner. A special form is the rubber covered hook used in cod fishing. In this case the shank of the hook is curved in a special manner to keep the rubber 'worm' in its place (*Fig 109*). Mostly the bait has no influence on the form of the hook. Another method is to provide the hook with a little piece of yarn to fix the bait. Such 'bait cords' are known in Oceania up to Taiwan and Hawaii in the north (*Figs 100* and *111*). Two other reasons why hooks have a barb beside securing the hooked fish or the bait, have to be mentioned. A barb can be required to prevent the point of a hook penetrating too deeply into the fish.[476] This seems to be in contrast to the idea that the barb has to anchor the hook into the fish. Another reason is with ripping hooks (Chapter 12) for sturgeon lines (*Fig 203*). These hooks have a barb designed to prevent the line of a little float, fixed on the bend of the hook, from slipping away.

In general, fishing hooks are used singly, but several bent hooks of the same type can also be combined in a bunch. Double and triple hooks, and in some places also quadruple hooks (*Fig 106*) are

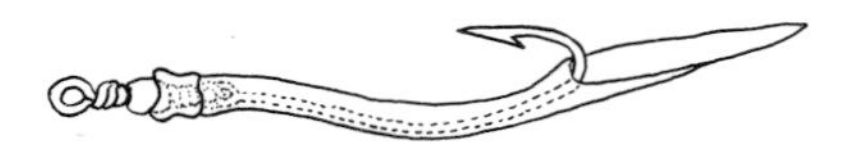

Fig 109 Rubber-covered hook.

used. Hooks of the same type and size can also be combined one after the other. The Turkish fishermen use such 'tandem hooks' (*Fig 111*). In this case three hooks are soldered to two or three pieces of connecting wire.[384] This tandem can be considered as one multiple hook, because all hooks

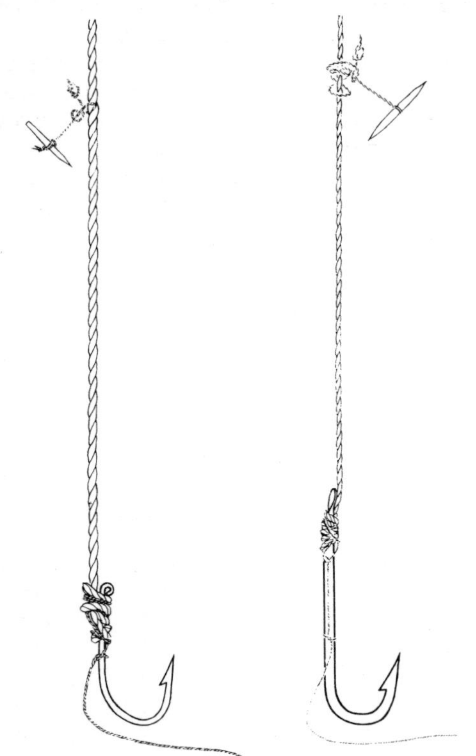

Fig 110 Fish hook from Botel Tobago with a piece of yarn to fix the bait, in this case a flying fish, which is also secured to the line by a gorge. The line is used to catch dolphin.

are hidden in one fish used as bait. Moreover, there is a little barb above the hooks to attach them to the bait. Tandem hooks are also used in other places for catching trout with worms.

There are many complicated hooks with and without barbs both on the outer as well as on the inner side. But it must not be forgotten that often hooks are made for ceremonial and other purposes only. There are even hooks which take the place of money (south India 1600-1900). Therefore, it will become understandable that such hooks as are never used for fishing have not only strange forms but are also made of unusual and often precious materials.

8.5 Lines and casts

Fishing with bait, with or without a hook, or with a hook, with or without special bait (sometimes the

Fig 111 Turkish tandem hook (1971).

hook itself can be an attractive bait) is known as 'line fishing' or 'hook-and-line fishing', but the gear is called only 'line'. This method of fishing is considered very inexpensive because very little capital is required for the simple but effective gear and a vessel, if one is needed. Therefore line fishing is used all over the world with the exception of that fishery which is practised in virgin woods. For obvious reasons, a line that would be easily entangled in trees and bushes is unsuited for such areas.

Since olden times lines have been made from many different natural plant fibres like cotton, linen, hemp and even manila, or from fibres produced by animals, like silk and hair. Nowadays, fishing lines are of synthetic material, especially transparent monofilaments of PA (polyamide) but also of twisted PE (polyethylene). The breaking strength of lines in commercial fisheries must be high enough to cope with the weight of the fish to be caught to avoid losses by breaking. On the other hand the lines should not be excessively thick because this can decrease their efficiency in fishing. Neither should they be too fine for ease of handling. Nevertheless, some fish can bite a line in two, especially after swallowing the hook, which may have a short shank. To avoid this, hooks with longer shanks can be used or a special strong section of line, known as the 'cast' or 'leader', is fixed between the hook and line. This cast can be made of wire or even chain and be of more or less rough structure, depending on the size of the hook and the biting power of the fish aimed to be caught. Horse-hair, whalebone, leather strips, rubber cord, silk or, as is usual today, synthetic monofilaments, are also used as casts. For sharks, piano wire is used because these animals can not only destroy the line with their teeth but also with their hard, rough skin.[601] In general it can be said that a long line will let the hook sink in deeper water but also allows the hook to be thrown further away from the fisherman on shore or in a boat. This is also why lines are fixed on long rods as is done in the so-called pole-and-line fishery. It is also possible to fish without any line, when the hook is fixed directly on the end of the pole. The Japanese use poles of about four metres in length, on the end of which are very short lines with weighted quadruple hooks, to catch bullfrogs at night using lights. They also use a hook on the point of the stick, baited by a frog, to catch catfish. This method of a 'lineless line fishing' was known in ancient times. There has even been found a pre-Columbian vase with a relief showing a Peruvian fisherman with a stick in his hand. This pole ends in the mouth of a fish which may have been caught in the same manner.[413] It seems that lineless line fishing was spread over wide areas. In a report about endemic fishing in central and southern Africa, such a method is mentioned, in addition to hookless angling. In this case men of the BaVenda tribe cut from a branch all thorns except the last one. This lineless gear was then used for angling.[361] Finally, there exists an old German report, printed in 1772,[557] in which catching eels is described by using a pointed stick on which a fat worm has been pierced. The eels are so eager to take this bait that they can be lifted with the stick out of the water, similar to bobbing. Such gear without lines are exceptional; however they are a form of line fishing in spite of the misleading name.

8.6 Otter boards

Some may wonder why otter boards and other types of shearing device are mentioned as accessories of line fishing. There is evidence that such implements were used in line fishing *before* they were used with other types of fishing gear like trawls (Chapter 21; *Figs 480* and *481*), stow nets (Chapter 19; *Fig 447*) and seine nets (Chapter 24; *Figs 551* and *552*). This does not mean that the other fishing methods have acquired the use of otter boards from line fishing. It may be that there have been at least two independent developments, for lines first and later for other fishing gear.

It is on record that the old English or Irish sport fishermen used small boards shearing sideways (now forbidden in Britain) to carry their lines out from the bank into the current of a river for catching trout and pike.[127] If there is some current to tow a line away from the bank it is only necessary to fix a small board, fastened to a so-called 'crow's-foot', at an oblique angle to the current. The more oblique its position, the more will it be pressed to one side. But it should not be put into the water too obliquely (the so-called 'angle of attack'). The aim is to maintain the sideways pressing power of the current as much as possible but to suffer from the backward pressing power as little as possible. A board held directly across the current is pressed backwards only and no longer has any shearing power. A board held in line with the current also has no shearing power. So a mean or compromise position has to be found. Otter boards operate on the principle of the kite, but it is the water and not the wind which creates the shearing effect. Water currents permit otter boards to shear both vertically and horizontally. The purpose of the otter board in line fishing, here described first, is to shear in the horizontal direction. The same effect can also be achieved by towing a line with a shearing board through the water, *eg* by a man moving along the shore, or in a boat. In either case the line will be moved away from the fisherman by the board as far as the length of the line will allow. On the line connecting the board with the boat or the fisherman are tied short branch lines with hooks at intervals. In this manner four or more artificial flies, spinners or other lures can be operated. In some cases the flies are attached directly to the otterboard. The wooden board has a strip of lead on the lower side, so that it floats upright. It may also have a strip of cork on its upper side for the same reason. As far as is known, the oldest publication describing the use of otter boards in this manner by sports fishermen appeared in 1855[551], that means at least twenty years before the otter board was first mentioned for use with trawls.[250] It has also been stated that the weighting of the board and the movement of the water would be sufficient to allow the board to drift completely free like a floatline, and that safe return to the bank was assured.[279] In commercial fisheries such boards have been, and still are, used for a slightly different purpose. When trolling many lines behind a boat, it is necessary to keep the lines clear of each other to avoid entangling. That was the reason why shearing boards were used off the coast of south Devon. The implements were operated with the concave side facing toward the direction of the towing vessel.[496]

Until recently the German mackerel fishery in the western Baltic used small wooden boards towed behind a boat (*Fig 112*). In this case the branch-lines were not hung on the connecting line but on the board itself.[59] That is an advantage in so far as the board, when the fish bites, is tilted and rises flatly to the surface. Thus it signals that a fish has been caught by that line. The same method is also known in the lake and river fisheries of Norway, Sweden and Finland, and also in other parts of the world such as California. In the Gulf of Bothnia the Finns catch mullet with troll lines equipped with simple shearing boards and artificial flies.

The shearing equipment may be a simple board only, but there are also more complicated ones such as the Swedish otterboard used for catching char in Lake Vättern or for salmon and trout on the Swedish sea coast (*Fig 113*). Compared with these boards, some of the so called 'Seehunde' (this word means seals) of the Swiss lake fishermen, which are used for catching single lake trout, must be regarded as perfect. As can be seen from *Figure 112d* the connecting line between vessel and board is connected to the top of the mast. The reason is to prevent the resistance of the line towed through the water from decreasing the shearing effect of the board. In some cases the special design of some of these boards, which is favourable for steering, makes them, of course, far more expensive than the simple little boards used by the mackerel fishermen. They are therefore much more suited to the sports fisherman than to the commercial fisherman, who prefers simpler boards.

Besides lateral shearing boards there are boards used in line fishing which shear downwards in order to take the line down to certain predetermined depths. The mackerel paravane developed in Sweden is an example of such a device (*Fig 115c*).

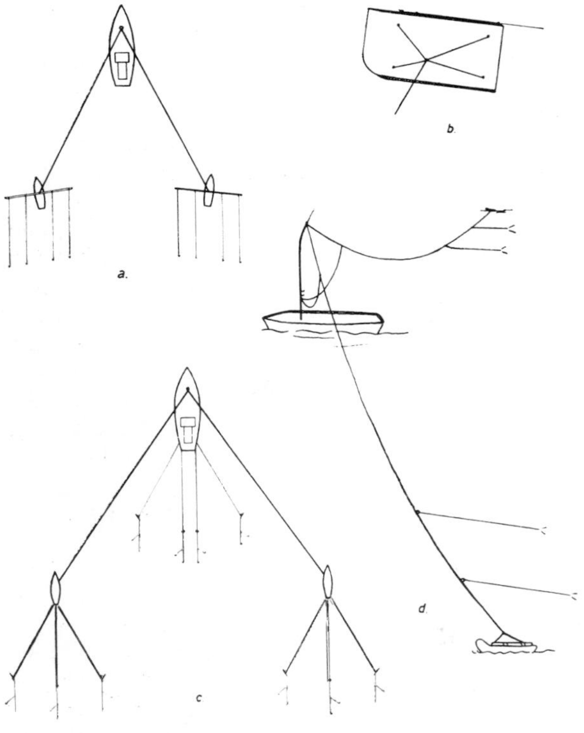

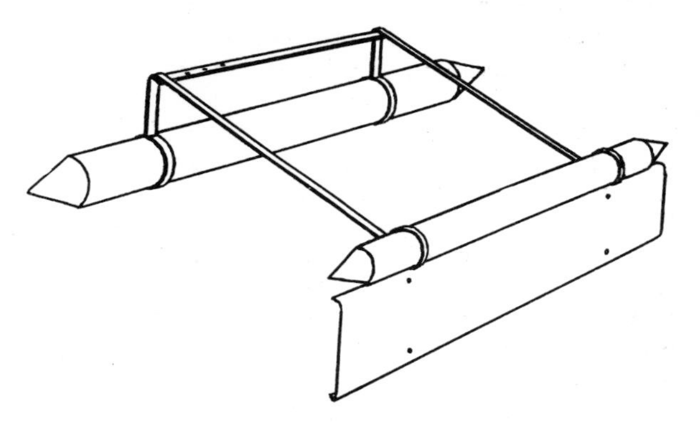

Fig 113 Swedish otter board for fishing char in Lake Vättern or for salmon and trout on the Swedish sea coast.

Fig 112 Equipment for directing horizontal shearing; (*a*) shearing boats with troll lines for mackerel in the Bay of Kiel, Germany; (*b*) otter board for mackerel lines; (*c*) mackerel fishery with otter boards; (*d*) Swiss 'Seehund' (seal) for troll lines for catching sea trout (*Hunziker, 1950*).

When the fish strikes, the paravane returns to the surface when the line is hauled in. Better known in commercial fisheries by way of downward shearing devices are the shallow-depth shearing boards used by Japanese professional line fishermen (*Fig 115a*). They are narrow little boards either flat or slightly bent, and weighted with lead at the lower side of the front edge. At the rear end the boards have two wings. These little boards are towed by a connecting line which begins quite near the anterior edge of the board. The line with the hook is fastened to one of the two rear wings or else in the centre between the two wings. This little board has three functions, and they are; first, to take the fishing line to the desired depth; second, by wobbling, to move the hook so as to simulate the actions of a tumbling, sick fish; and third, to announce the catch. When a fish takes the hook, that fact is revealed by the board tilting and rising to the surface. Several hooks

Fig 114 Double otter board for fishing with troll lines on Lake Constance. (*Langenargen, 1981*).

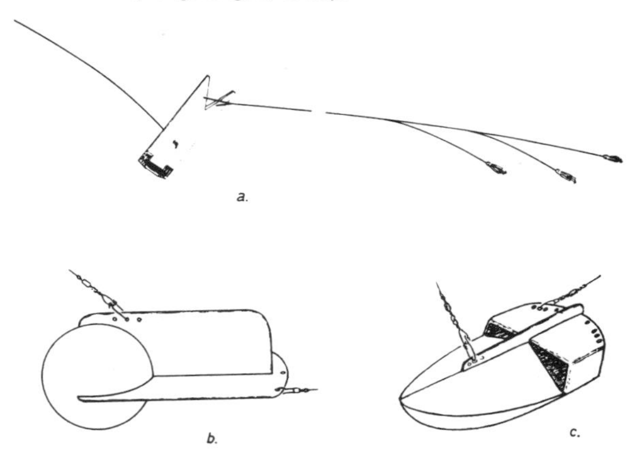

Fig 115 Equipment for causing vertical shearing in deep water; (*a*)Japanese type; (*b*) surfing paravane for sport fishermen; (*c*) Swedish paravane for mackerel.

can be towed with this line. It is interesting to note that dummy baits (but without hooks) are also attached to the towing line in front of the board. The Japanese use these shallow depth shearing boards, also called divers, for catching small tuna and dolphin, but also for catching large mackerel.

As the shearing boards are made of wood, fishermen can make them themselves. But wood may not be available. Recently, a new idea was conceived on how such a diving implement for a troll line can be made in a very simple manner (*Fig 116*).[264] In this case a tin can, with top and bottom removed, operates as shearing device, held with a line system by a clip. To keep the can at the right angle some lead is fixed to the bottom side. When a fish takes the hook, the shock releases the can from the clip and the shearing device will come to the surface announcing the catch!

8.7 The kite

The description of shearing devices used in fisheries with troll lines would be incomplete without mentioning an instrument which may be called the mother of all shearing devices; namely, the kite. China is thought to be the homeland of the kite and from here the knowledge of how to make and use it has gradually spread throughout Asia and beyond. Originally the kite may have been used for religious and ceremonial purposes only. Kites were also used for prize-fighting in Japan, and for toys all over the world. Kites have been used for physical experiments and for meteorological observations. Since old times kites have also been used for

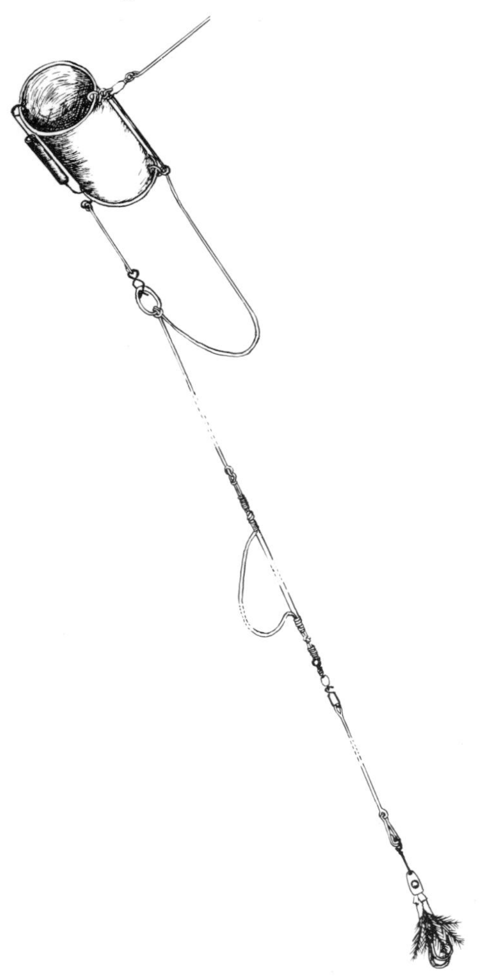

Fig 116 Troll line for tunny with diving can, according to Capt. L C Hu, Christchurch, New Zealand.

operating lines in the fisheries of southwest Asia, especially to catch garfish, sometimes bonito and others in Micronesia, Polynesia and the Philippines.[9, 174] Formerly kite fisheries may have been widespread, even though it may be presumed to have been hampered for religious reasons.[358] According to tradition, kite fishery was introduced into Indonesia from the Philippines, from the Larantuka Islands, or from the Banda group. Like the kites of our children, the Indonesian kite is made of paper or dried pandanus leaves, sewn together and set in a bamboo frame. Such a kite can be quite large, about one metre in length and 50cm in width. The line for taking the kite into the air is about 100 metres long. The tail line runs to 75 metres and carries at its end the spider-web lure or a ball of cotton waste. Fishing is operated from little boats or canoes with a crew or two. One man keeps the boat up against the wind, or if the wind is too strong, then athwart it. The other man handles the kite. He must continuously pull the line to keep the bait moving on the water. Once the fish (garfish) has been caught, both kite and line are hauled on board for the fish to be removed and the kite prepared for another flight. This fishing takes place from about May until October when the easterly and southeasterly winds are in strength. The fishermen operate at a distance of about 200 metres from the land. In general the different reports and observations repeat this description, but the technique of kite fishing may have been different in some areas. It has been said that the kite is generally made of leaves strengthened with palm veins. The kite is flown at the end of a line of sufficient length, when the boat is rowed against the wind. In some areas of Indonesia the first part of the line was led through a ring at the top of a bamboo stick,[140] looking like a fishing pole held by one man in the anchored boat. From the tail of the kite hung a second line with the bait at the end. This bait could be, as mentioned, a bunch of spider webs (*Fig 97*) to catch garfish, or a hook with a piece of sharkskin to catch bonito. The bait can be also a small fish with a snare to catch garfish, *Belone belone*. Reports agree on the fact that the kite has to fly in such a way that the bait more or less dances on the surface of the water and thus induces fish to snap at it. When the fish is taken, the kite has to be hauled in to get the prey.

This old method includes much observation of fish behaviour and has not disappeared completely in commercial fisheries. On the contrary, the method has been improved as can be seen from the following report published some years ago from the Santa Cruz Islands.[315] Here also two persons, a man and his wife, are needed for the operation of the gear. One person sits in front to row the boat against the wind while the other operates the kite flying ten to twenty metres high. As usual the jumping of the spider-web bait over the water surface is considered the ideal technique. If the bait is taken, the line of the kite is hauled in by rowing backwards but only so far as is necessary to reach the line with the fish, leaving the kite flying so that fishing can be resumed immediately after the catch is removed. This can be considered as a modern improvement of a very old fishing method. As will be shown later (Chapter 10) kite fishing has survived not only in some commercial fisheries but has also been adopted in modern sport fishing.

8.8 Stabilizers

These are not shearing boards and they do not work directly with the fishing gear, but they are often mentioned with troll lining, especially for salmon trolling. They consist of two boards hanging from the main poles of the troller, one on each side of the vessel. Originally made of wood, they are now made of galvanized metal and are available in different sizes according to the size of the trolling vessel.

The purpose of the stabilizers is to eliminate jerking and to minimize the roll of the vessel when cruising or trolling during poor weather conditions. Mostly the boards are triangular, with a vertical vane on the upper side which serves to keep the board on course. The stabilizers make it possible to work more safely on the deck of the vessel in rough waters, and so probably increase the time that can be spent at sea.

Chapter nine

Line fishing: gear and methods

Various methods have been developed for line fishing. There are simple ones for the needs of small-scale fishermen and for 'mini-fishermen', fishing for subsistence only, with little capital and no specialized boats. There also exist complicated and expensive tackles for sports fishermen fishing for fun and recreation (Chapter 10). And finally, there are methods of line fishing for large-scale commercial fisheries operating some thousands of hooks on lines several kilometres in length. Whether in large- or small-scale fisheries using lines, each fish is caught individually and the catch is considered of a better quality than when caught by other methods in which large quantities of fish may be pressed together. With line fishing it is possible to catch fish on rough ground, even in their hiding places between rocks. On the other hand line fishing is a labour-intensive fishery. Therefore, simple mechanical methods were soon devised. Today, in large-scale fisheries, there is more or less completely automatic line fishing equipment in use. Whatever method is used, natural or artificial bait is needed. The lack of natural bait can sometimes hamper this fishery – a problem which has not yet been resolved satisfactorily.

9.1 Handlines

The simplest form of fishing line is the handline. It is composed of a line of certain length, a sinker (lead, chain or any other weight), a cast snood (usually) and at least one hook (*Fig 117*). There may be added swivels, special lures, and possibly floats – especially for some handlines used by sports fishermen (Chapter 10). There may also be other devices to equalize the sudden jerks caused by the prey. Furthermore, equipment for landing the prey such as gaffs (Chapter 12), scoop nets (Chapter 19), and even lift nets (Chapter 27) may be needed.

Handlines may have a single hook but usually have several. The additional hooks can be fixed on the weighted main line at small intervals with short branch lines (*Figs 117g* and *h*). Another form is to arrange more than one hook on the so called 'balance lines', where the hooks are mostly attached in pairs and consist of several balanced parts. In this case a slightly bent metal or wooden spreader, provided with casts and hooks, is put through a weight (*Fig 117e*). The bent spreader instantly

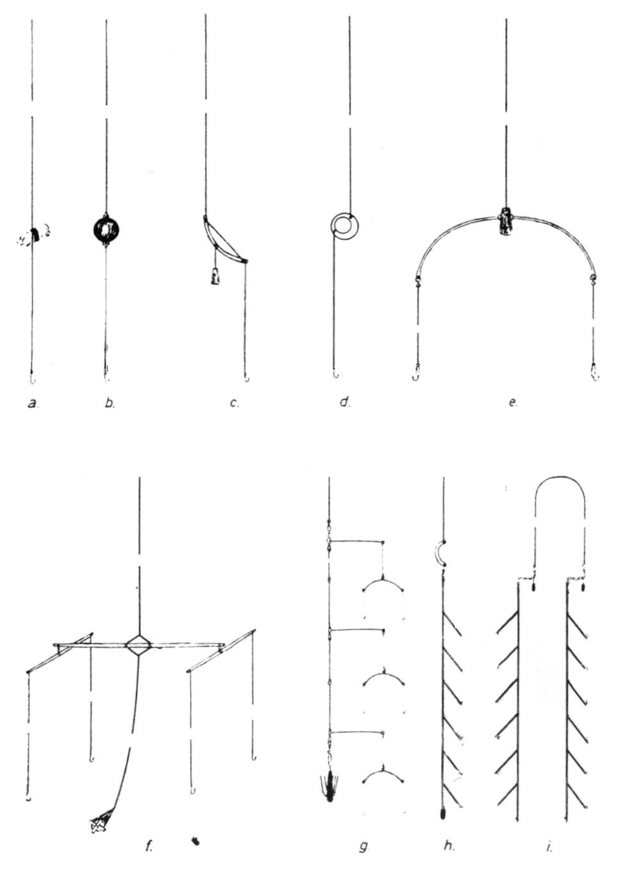

Fig 117 Handlines: (*a*) simple handline of Ireland; (*b*) handline for mackerel of Heligoland; (*c*) handline of Guinea (*Sahrhage, 1961*); (*d*) Japanese handline with ring; (*e*) balance line of Faeroe Islands; (*f*) Icelandic handline for sharks with main and secondary balances (*Peters, 1935*); (*g*) English paternoster; (*h*) vertical longline; (*i*) Chinese double handline of Formosa.

adjusts any sudden loads. 'Balance' fishing lines are found especially in the northern fisheries. To the main balance device a secondary balance can be attached, so that this method of fishing with more than one hook may lead to the development of a whole system of fishing hooks (*Fig 117f*). Balance lines have the advantage that a sudden jerk caused by a biting fish can be compensated for.

In eastern and southern Asia, and also in African and European fisheries, another method is known to achieve the same purpose. Here a bow-shaped or moon-shaped implement – sometimes a strong wire bent in this shape – can be tied between the line and the cast so that a sudden strain or load can be adjusted (*Figs 117c, h* and *i*). This material also has to serve as a weight. Nowadays it is therefore often made of lead. When it is made of wood or wire an additional weight is fastened to it (*Fig 117c*). This is also done with the modern Malaysian 'ranggong' made of buffalo horn combined with synthetic material (*Fig 118*). This implement gives the line not only the necessary elasticity, but also keeps the snood and the hook free from the lead.[271] It also serves to prevent the line twisting. There may be another reason why a curved wire is used in this manner *eg* in cod fishing – and that is so that it may give the hook an attractive movement.[95] The same objective is achieved by the use of a lead ring with an eccentric weight to which the fishing line is attached on one side and the cast with the hook on the other (*Fig 117d*). Handlines with more than one, or only a few, hooks are not so often used. In this case a main line with an end-lead can have many hooks on smaller branch lines as a so-called 'vertical longline' (*Fig 117h*). The Chinese use vertical longlines carrying hooks at either end of the line (*Fig 117i*), especially to catch sea bream, *Restrelliger* sp., and mackerel.

The operation of a handline is very easy. In general the fisherman holds one end of the line (maybe wound on a reel) in his hand, feeling with the finger for the bite of the fish. He then tries to 'set' the hook at the right moment to prevent the fish from escaping. As can be seen in the next section, the handline can also be used with a pole or stick.

Speaking of handlines it has to be mentioned that they are not always held by hand during fishing. Canoe fishermen of Madagascar, working alone in outrigger canoes, wind the end of the line around their naked bodies to feel the bite of the fish – a method which leaves the hands free for manoeuvering the boat with the paddle. A special 'handline' used in Formosa is actually manipulated by the toes, and a practised fisherman can work several lines with each foot. This method is especially used for eel fishing and it is remarkable that three hooks, hanging one upon another, are hidden in the bait (*Figs 119* and *120*). Multiple hooks like 'tandem hooks' (*Fig 111*) are also known in other parts of the world.[529] The bait is sometimes attached to the top hook only and it is the bottom hook which usually secures the fish. Fishing with

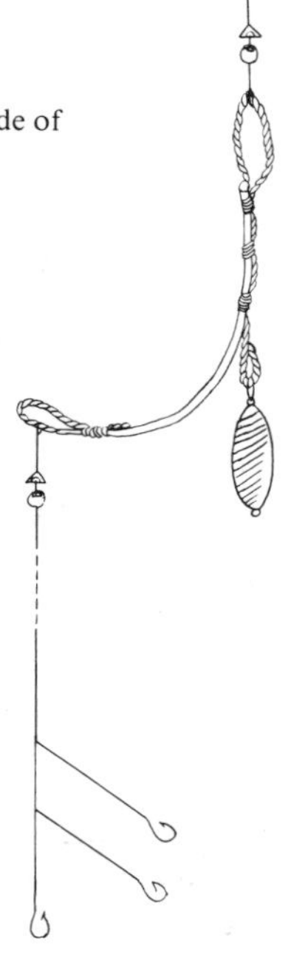

Fig 118 Handlines with 'Ranggong' made of horn and plastic. Malaysia (1978).

Fig 119 Chinese handline of Formosa held with the toes. Three hooks are joined to each other.

the foot was also known in European fisheries. Persons swimming had lines attached to their big toes, especially when fishing was not allowed![650] Another strange method of using a 'handline' was known in Rumania. The fisherman rowed his boat with his two hands and held the end of the line in his mouth. From there the line ran over one of his ears and when a fish took the hook he could feel it.[13]

Fig 120 Chinese fisherman using his toes for holding the line.

To 'shoot' the line, the weight is dropped into the water at places where fish are expected, although when fishing in deeper water it may be better to get the hook down to the required depth as fast as possible. This may prevent other fishes or crabs gnawing away at a slowly sinking baited hook. Even the fishermen of ancient times knew how to increase the sinking speed of the line with the hook by winding it around a stone. When thrown into the water the line unwinds as the stone falls to the bottom and the hook rises by means of a fixed float to the surface. This is a technique also much used in Oceania,[313, 410, 476] but is also known in other parts of the world. The people of Heligoland employed a similar method – they cast a stone with a very long line wound around it from the beach into the water. The line rolled off the stone and released the hook a long way out. That form of line fishing was called 'Hogeln'.[556] In the Amur area, sturgeon hooks were used from which the weight separated only after a fish had taken the hook, and a float rose to the surface as a signal for the line to be hauled.[9]

Theoretically, with handlines, the hook can be lowered to any depth provided the line is long enough. However, due to the effect of currents and the drift of a vessel a line needs to be much longer than the depth of the water. It has been suggested that in line fishing the maximum length of a line should be about six times the expected maximum depth of water.[95] A line 120 metres in length may therefore fish in a water depth of only 20 metres or less. There are handlines of astonishing length operated in commercial fisheries. In the wintertime of 1973/74 some fish were caught in a depth of up to 180 metres in Lake Constance, and fishermen of Senegal catch fish with handlines near Dahomey at a depth of 200 metres. The famous coelacanth, *Latimeria,* has been caught near Comores with handlines as long as 390 metres,[394] and men of the Caroline Islands in Micronesia have fished for the escolar, or oilfish, in depths of one hundred to four hundred fathoms (180-720m).[393] In Japan the handlines for bottom fish are operated at depths of up to 990 metres, while the fishermen of Madeira catch *Aphanopus carbo,* living at depths of 700 to 1,000 metres with lines of up to 1,000 fathoms in length or about 1,600 metres. How did the fishermen ever become aware that there were fish to be caught at such depths, so far away from their own coasts? The Indians of the northwest coast of America made a handline for halibut with a curved wooden hook which had a barb of ivory or bone. The hooks were baited with squid and weighted with a stone sinker so as to float a few feet off the bottom. How did they know that they should float a few feet off the bottom? How did they know, in the first place, that the halibut were there, living on the bottom of a rough and stormy sea? These are questions that will never be answered unless we believe that old-time fishermen, like former hunters, had presentiments and instincts.[41, 235]

When fishing offshore, hauling some hundred metres of line by hand and winding it up on a square wooden frame is tiring work. Therefore commercial fishermen quickly introduced mechanization for hauling the line. This was achieved by small hand-driven reels mounted to the gunwhales of the boat. *Figure 121* shows such a manually operated hauling device for handlines used, in this case, by snapper fishermen setting their lines in the Gulf of Mexico. A small pulley is incorporated, hanging on an elastic spring outrigger to give the hook an attractive vibration and also to absorb the shock when it is taken. This may be the basis of further mechanization in line fisheries which will be discussed in the last section of this chapter.

9.2 Pole-and-line fishing

It has already been stated that the line itself is not always held in the hand of the fisherman, but may be fixed to a pole or rod instead. By this means the

Fig 121 Hand-operated reel of Mexican vessel for line fishing of snapper and grouper in the Gulf of Mexico (1976).

line with the hook is taken further away from the fisherman, whose figure or movements may frighten the fish away. This method is common to sport fisheries (Chapter 10) but it is also used in commercial fisheries. It is a technique known for four or more thousand years.

Originally, only simple wooden sticks were used but soon it was discovered that for successful operation of a fishing line, a pole with a good balance, lightness, pliancy and strength was required.[262] However, in primitive times fishermen had to use what they could get, even though that may only be ribs of the leaves of palm trees. To overcome loss by rods breaking, special techniques are used. In the Cape Verde Islands, even large tuna have been caught with weak rods by avoiding lifting the fish out of the water with the rod, and by leading it instead to the vessel and then taking the heavy fish out with the help of a gaff (Chapter 12). Another method of avoiding losses from weak fishing rods is to strengthen them with wire. In general, strong material is chosen for fishing rods such as special types of bamboo or good wood or other natural materials like whalebone.[412] In commercial fisheries, fishing rods are made not only of simple naturally grown poles of wood or bamboo but are also constructed of split cane and increasingly of fibreglass. In commercial fisheries, many different sizes of rods are required: very short ones for fishing in iceholes (*Figs 122* and *169*), or very long ones (seven metres and more) for surf fishing. In the commercial pole-and-line fisheries the line is fixed to the end of the pole and its length is nearly the same as that of the rod. No reel or

Fig 122 Korean fisherman fishing on the Han river during winter. The special form of the rod permits winding up the line for storing and drying. (*Photo: Chun Nam Cho.*)

other mechanism to wind up and store the line is used; neither are floats used as they are in sport fisheries.

Usually one pole has only one line of equal length and one hook (*Fig 123*), but there are also bifurcated sticks with two lines operated by commercial fishermen. On Lake Tanganyika the fishermen sometimes use rods made of bifurcated or even trifurcated branches, so that two or three lines with their hooks can be used for fishing simultaneously.[503] Two-armed fishing rods are also known in the east Asian squid line fishery (*Fig 211*). On the other hand there are also single poles to which more than one line is attached.[82] Such fishing rods with more than one line are known from paintings found in Egyptian tombs of *ca* 1400BC (*Fig 124*); whether for sport only or also for commercial fishery is not known. Moreover, there are also paintings of fishing rods with one line ending in two branches with one hook each (*Fig 125*). The use of a pole with more than one line is also reported from another African location where the Batra of Lake Bangweulu fish with a tough reed to which are tied three lines, one carrying two recurved barbless hooks, and two with one hook each.[361] In Polynesia also, bonito is fished with rods with more than one line. Three, four, and sometimes even five hooks are attached, with their lines, to each bonito rod. But these lines with hooks are not used at the same time, only one is used, with

Fig 123 Fishing for small surface fishes concentrated near a large vessel off the coast of Praia, Cape Verde Islands.

Fig 124 Egyptian drawing of pole-and-line fishing (*ca* 1400 BC). It may be that the pole has more than one line.

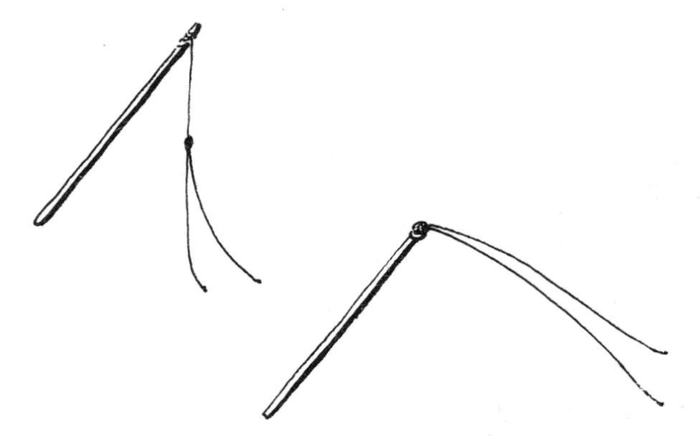

Fig 125 Old Egyptian drawings of pole-and-line fishing with two lines. (*Drawing: G Pullem*).

the others held as reserve. On the butt end of the rod, old netting or some other material is fixed on which the lines are turned around and the spare hooks fixed.[634]

Not only can one rod have more than one line and hook, but one hook can be connected to more than one pole. Handlines, operated with a pole, are important in small traditional fisheries and also in large-scale fisheries such as that for bonito or skipjack, albacore, frigate mackerel, and the juvenile stages of large tunas living near the water surface. This is what is usually understood as live bait pole-and-line fishing or 'poling'.[34] In this fishery the bamboo poles may be two to three and more metres long with a line of nearly the same length. Barbless hooks are used, so as to disengage from the landed fish very quickly without losing time. The hooks are baited either with live bait or with artificial lures. 'Chumming', that means scattering of live bait fish, and water spraying, are used to keep the tuna near the fishing boat in reach of the poles. Different reasons are given why water spraying is effective in this fishery. One is that the water sprayed on the surface of the sea prevents the fish seeing movements of the fishermen and boats and being frightened away. Another explanation is that the sound of sprayed water is similar to that of fleeing small fish jumping over the water. Special arrangements are made for the fishing crew to stand on outboard platforms (racks) rigged along the bulwarks below deck level, a few feet above the water-line (*Fig 126*). The hook is operated near the water level when bait fish are scattered over the sea. The hooked fish are swung on board, and release

Fig 126 Pole-and-line fishing for tuna in the Caribbean. Fishermen stand on racks lowered outboard the vessel. These racks are provided with sprinklers which, as they spray on to the sea, tend to excite the fish. (*Photo:* (*H Menjaud/FAO*).

themselves from the barbless hook when they touch the deck of the vessel. In traditional fisheries for smaller fish the prey is swung under the left arm and liberated from the hook by hand (*Fig 127*). Different techniques have been developed to catch larger pelagic fish without breaking the pole. In contrast to sport fishing, commercial fisheries do not give the fish a chance to escape by using a longer and finer rod – which means a more easily breakable one – or by using finer lines according to the weight of the fish sought. The American method for catching larger fish by poling is to connect one

Fig 127 Pole-and-line fishing for bonito off the Azores. The fish are 'chummed' with bait fish by a boy on the right side of the picture. The caught fish are swung under the left arm and detached from the hooks.

single hook with two or more lines to two or even three or four fishing rods according to the expected weight of the fish to be caught. From each rod a line is tied to a common ring from which is connected the hook with a short line. With this equipment and precise co-operation four men can swing a fish of more than 45 kilograms on to the deck.

The French use a different method for catching tuna by poling, which also allows them to take heavier fish without breaking the pole. In this case from the top of the rod a second line runs over a block hanging in the rigging of the vessel (*Fig 128*) to end in the hand of à man called the 'maroquin' placed behind the fisherman with the pole and the 'ligne à thon'. When the fish is hooked by the man with the pole it is the job of the second man to haul the large fish on board without putting a load on the rod. The French tuna boats have three to eight such blocks, which needs a crew of six to sixteen men. These blocks are typical in French vessels (*Fig 128*) as also are the small power-blocks for operating a small purse seine for catching the bait, and the white-painted openings of the interior illuminated tanks used to keep the bait fish alive. Unfortunately, this live bait method of fishing has the problem of getting enough bait for chumming. To catch one metric ton of tuna, roughly 100 kilograms of live bait fish are needed.[475] Nevertheless, pole-and-line fishing is one of the most interesting methods of catching oceanic surface fish.[358]

9.3 Set lines

Simple handlines have one or a few hooks only. This means that the catch is restricted. Moreover handlines must be watched during fishing in order to set the hook in the fish at the right moment in so far as the fish does not hook itself. But commercial fishermen need large catches to earn money. Therefore the commercial fisherman tries to replace handlines which have to be constantly watched, by 'semi-watched' lines, which do not have to be held but simply need someone to be on hand to secure the fish when taken by the hook. It is better to work with unwatched lines which may be set in the evening and hauled with the catch the next morning or later. By this means many lines, with maybe hundreds of hooks, can be operated at the same time. The construction of such a set line, in the simplest form, can be like a handline, usually with one hook only but fixed on a rod placed on the shore. Fishing rods, set in great numbers by commercial fishermen, can often be seen in Asiatic countries as well as in the Old and New Worlds. These rods carry fishing lines with one or even several hooks. It is common practice, too, for some of these to be set at suitable places during the night. This can be done very easily because a fishing rod can be thrust firmly into the ground on the beach or in shallow water so that the baited hook floats freely in the water (*Fig 129*).

Another set line well-known in the north European fishery is the so called 'roll line'. This is a wooden prong on which the twine is rolled, lightly fastened so that it unrolls easily and quickly when the fish bites, and so follows the pull of the fish (*Figs 130* and *168*). Such roll lines are attached to

Fig 128 French pole-and-line fishing vessel in the harbour of Dakar, Senegal (1971). The picture shows typical French rigging of the lines with poles.

Fig 129 Wandering fishermen of Thailand with sticks for setting hooks in shallow water.

trees on the beach or to rods that can be set even over ice. A line with a single hook can also be set on ice with the line and hook duly baited hanging through a hole into the water (*Figs 130* and *131*). Fishing with set lines as ice lines is practised in the northern area, *eg* in Scandinavia.[483] This type of set line has to be semi-watched all the time. In order to supervise a greater number of these lines set on the ice, signal devices have been invented which enable fishermen to see from afar when a fish has taken the bait (*Fig 130c*). Such a device can be a pliable stick (*eg* of horn) which is set free, showing a vibrating red-coloured piece of cork on its top as soon as a fish has taken the hook (*Fig 130b*). These alarm devices, often also in the form of little bells, were known many years ago and used in China with various fishing gear. They are employed by many sport fishermen as well as by commercial fishermen for their widespread set lines (*Fig 132*). Set lines with a single hook or a few hooks only are operated in fresh waters as well as in coastal waters. In the simplest form, the hook is held by a line stretched between a sinker on the bottom and a float on the surface. Such lines are used to catch better-paying fishes such as salmon, but also some sharks. Such fishing lines can remain unwatched for a certain time, but in some fishing areas it is impossible to set lines, nets or traps to last for any length of time because predatory fish and crabs would be apt to eat any fish caught. This is particularly so in the warm waters of tropical and sub-tropical areas as in the Mediterranean. Hemingway's famous story *The Old Man and the Sea* describes most graphically how his character, a veteran fisherman, lost a prize game fish through attack by sharks. Even in northern countries fish suspended on a line can easily be snatched by sharks or seals.

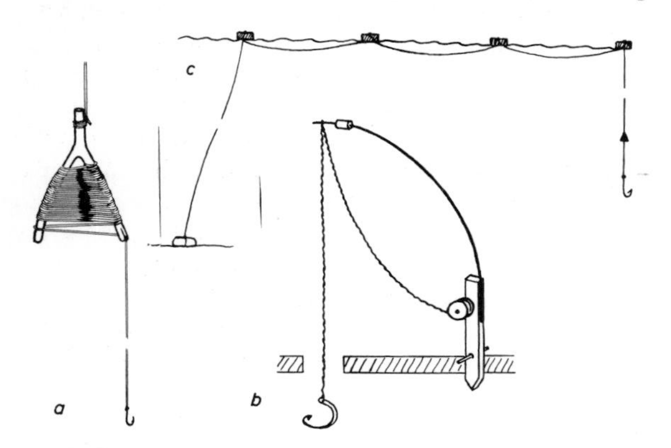

Fig 130 Simple set lines: (*a*) roll-line; (*b*) Swedish ice-line; (*c*) setline for salmon formerly used in the eastern part of the Baltic.

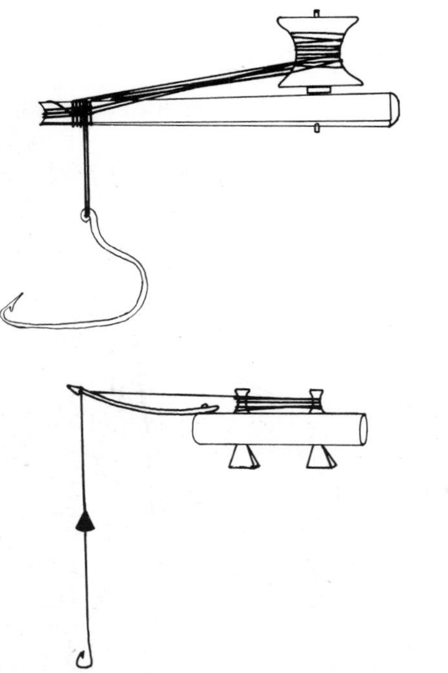

Fig 131 Ice fishing lines: (*above*) handline; (*below*) Finnish line with the hook hanging on a flexible strip of horn placed on the surface of the ice.

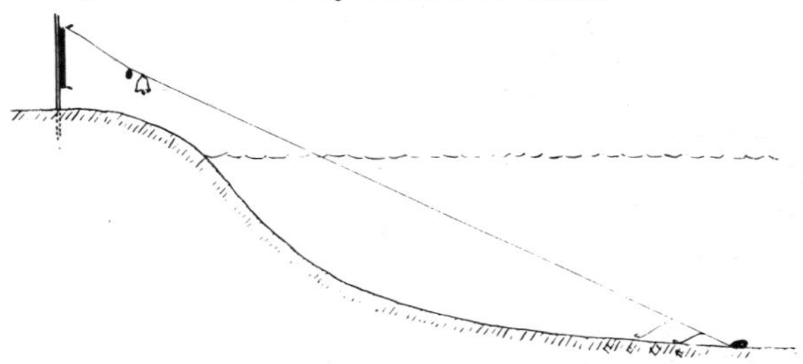

Fig 132 Setline with alarm bell near Moscow in the Moskva River.

9.4 Bottom longlines

As explained before, lines with a single hook or a few hooks only may be sufficient for small-scale fisheries or for the catch of a small number of high-priced fish. But in commercial fisheries there will always be a tendency to increase the number of hooks as far as possible. This has been done with handlines in the form of the so-called 'vertical longlines' (*Fig 117i*), but in this case the number of hooks cannot amount to more than 100 for technical reasons. By contrast an almost unlimited number of hooks can be operated with a form of set line called the longline, operated in a more or less horizontal configuration. There can be hundreds or even thousands of hooks, each fixed to the main line with a short line called a branch line (snood, leader, dropper-line, dropline or dropper, gangion or gangin) (*Fig 133*). This 'longline system' is one of the basic types of gear construction and is known in other forms of fishing as explained later.

Bottom longlines with many hooks have been known in northern Europe and in the Mediterranean area as well as in the Far East since early times. In Norway, longlines were known at least since the middle of the 16th century. However, the belief that longlines may be 'one of the original African fishing methods' operated in the great lakes of Eastern Africa[244] is doubtful. For bottom longlines the ground should be fairly regular since

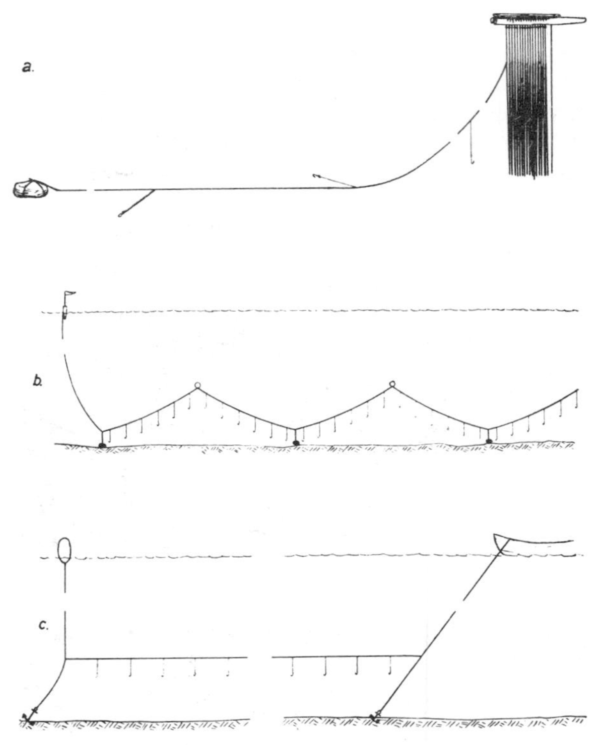

Fig 133 Bottom longlines: (*a*) European longline for eels, with clamp for storing the hooks; (*b*) bottom longline with alternate sinkers and floats (*Peters, 1935*); (*c*) Portuguese longline for cod fishing by dory – men. The semi-pelagic line hangs at some distance above the seabed.

projecting rocks or coral heads may chafe and break the lines, or entangle them in such a way that they cannot be retrieved. Where muddy bottoms are found, the longlines are not set to rest on the bottom but are held off the seabed by floats as demonstrated in *Figures 133b* and *c*. These can be arranged so that they suspend the bait at any desired distance from the bottom.

As has been found out by many investigations[43] the efficiency of the longlines (and also of the pelagic longlines mentioned in the next section) is influenced not only by the design of the hook and the type, size and shape of the bait, but also by the material, length and spacing of the snoods. Their distance from each other should be at least twice that of their length to avoid entangling. Moreover, bottom longlines with snoods set at larger spacings fish better than those with the branch lines set more closely together.[341] The snoods should also not be too short; short ones are considered to be less effective than long ones. With longlines operated from boats, the length of the branch lines should relate to the freeboard of the vessel which is used. When the main line is held, the branch line must be long enough to reach at least to the surface of the water, so that the fish can be gaffed and pulled aboard the vessel without its full weight bearing on the branch line or on the hook,[446] and without the next fish being lifted clear of the water.[96] The snoods can be more or less permanent – knotted directly onto the main line. They can also be fixed with removable stainless steel spring clips (*Fig 134*). This has the advantage that the snoods can be exchanged easily and can be stored separately, and their spacing on the main line can be altered when necessary *eg* for increasing hook spacing with decreasing fish density and vice versa.

Nowadays in many cases main line and snoods are made of monofilaments. In this case the snoods can be connected with swivels, which have the benefit of eliminating entanglements of the snoods and so reduce the labour of gear handling.[43] The efficiency of the longlines made of monofilaments is also improved by their lower visibility.

In most parts of the world the branch lines are usually of equal length, but the Chinese, on their longlines for catching sea bream, employ a different concept: they place longer by-lines at certain distances on the main line. These longer subsidiary lines act like main lines and carry a number of small branch lines with hooks.[108] Apparently such a build up of by-lines is to be found exclusively in Chinese

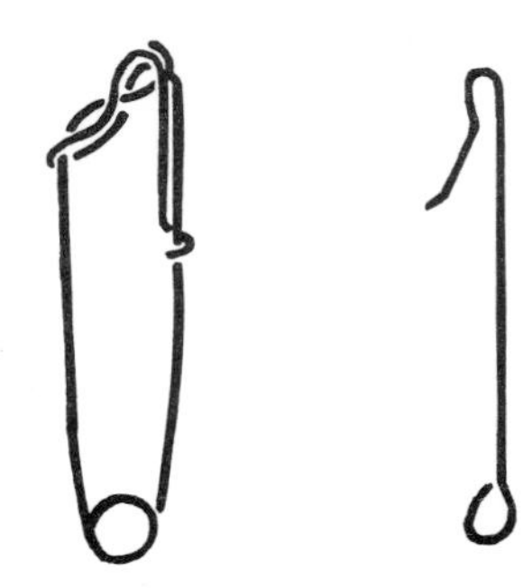

Fig. 134 Clips for fixing branch lines (snoods) onto the longlines.

fisheries (*Figs 135* and *136a*). The Chinese also know about near-bottom longlines for sharks, on which are fixed short branch lines and longer ones with stronger hooks (*Fig 136b*). Bottom set longlines, sometimes with as many as several thousand hooks, are well known in many parts of the world and are used in both sea and fresh water fisheries. Large longlines are usually divided into sections to facilitate handling and operation. During shooting, the sections are tied together and the longlines are set in 'strings' or 'fleets'.

Different methods are used for storing longlines, such as hanging the hooks on wooden clamps, as is done sometimes with freshwater lines where the number of hooks is not so great (*Fig 133a*). Also ladder-like implements are used for the same purpose (*Fig 137*). In sea fisheries, baskets (mostly), tubes and wooden or plastic boxes are used for storing the whole line including the snoods with hooks. In many cases each single unbaited hook is fixed on a ledge of cork or rush or the hooks are stuck into the straw-covered rim of the basket or let hang over the rim of the basket. Sometimes the baskets have special lipped edges to store the baited hooks (*Fig 138*).

In most cases longlines are set from a vessel sailing with different speed according to the longline to be shot. The line, or a section, starts and finishes with an anchor and is marked by buoys, flags, radar reflectors or lights to show at night. In some traditional fisheries, methods are known of how to set a longline from a beach without a boat. In this

Fig 135 Longline with by-lines in Tanshui, Taiwan.

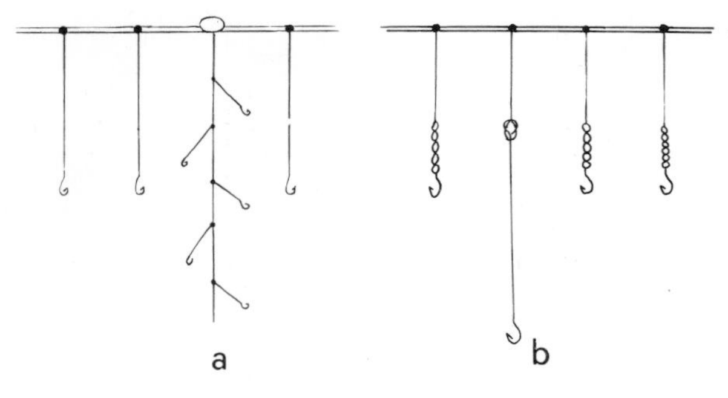

Fig 136 Chinese longlines: (*a*) Sea bream bottom line with by-lines with many branches for hooks; (*b*) shark bottom line with branch lines of different lengths. (*Liu, 1957*).

Fig 137 Freshwater longline for eel fishing stored on a ladder-like implement in a lake fishery of Northern Germany.

Fig 138 Italian fisherman of Lipari Island preparing a basket for longlining (1979).

case the line can be cast out by means of a weight similar to that used on the handlines described earlier. To achieve this satisfactorily the main line (with the branch-lines carrying the hooks), is laid out in an S-curve on the beach. A light twine with a button is tied to the weight. This button fits into the prong-shaped end of a stick. By means of that stick the longline is then swung out, as in fly fishing, and so the longline is cast far out into the sea.[42] This method is not only known in Great Britain but also in Australia and New Zealand.[139]

Another method of using longlines from the beach is to fasten one end of the line on the beach while the other is towed away from the land by a raft sailing before the wind. This idea has been developed in various parts of the world. The fishermen of Heligoland had the 'Pieptauschiff' (*Fig 139a*) for setting longlines for catching skate; the Italians have the 'Palamito a vela' (*Fig 139b*) for line fishing for garfish; and the Japanese also use sailing rafts to carry longlines from their boats to catch sea perch and mullet (*Fig 139c*). Of course there are not only bottom longlines but also driftlines which are set in this way. This is outlined in a French proposal, made recently (*Fig 140*), for a small 'unmanned' sailing boat, made from cork, which can set a (drifting) longline not only from the shore but also from an anchored buoy.[368] In the latter case the line can follow the current.

The most technically advanced sailing craft for towing out fishing lines from the beach is the so-called 'Kon Tiki' sailing raft of New Zealand. It is considered to be a development of the Italian 'Palamito a vela' mentioned before. *Figure 141a* gives a simple wooden form of this raft, together with a longline stored in a wooden box. There are also other constructions, not only larger but also more complicated (*Fig 141b*), which are said to be some of the most efficient in use.[139] In the latter the floats are made of galvanized iron, one and a half metres in length. As soon as the land-line, according to its length, has been towed by the raft to the desired position off the shore, the line keeping the mast upright is set free by a simple mechanism; the mast falls forward, drops the sail and releases the sinker of a vertical longline stored with paper-wrapped baited hooks on a small winch.

On the Spanish coast they have even made use of children's kites for setting longlines from the beach. One end of the longline is made fast on the

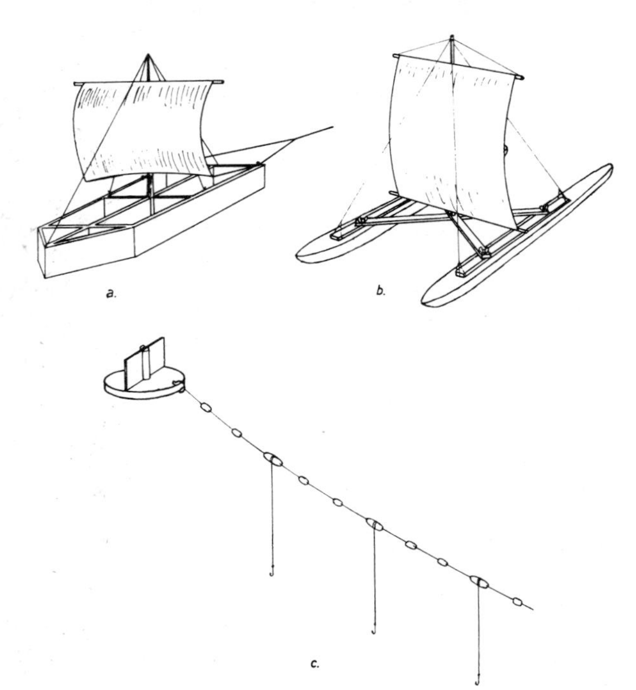

Fig 139 Sailing rafts for longlines: (*a*) reconstruction of a so-called 'Pieptauschiff' used in olden times by fishermen of Heligoland for the ray fishery; (*b*) Italian 'Palamito a vela'; (*c*) Japanese sailing raft. (*NN, 1959*).

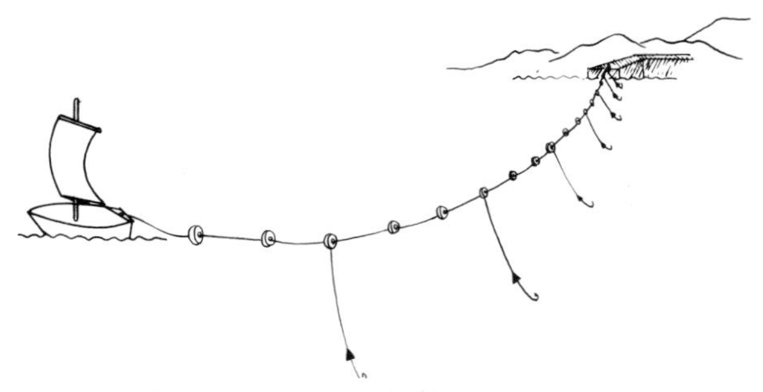

Fig 140 Plan for setting a driftline from the shore (or an anchored buoy) with the help of a small sailing float made of cork. (*Marin & Gilles, 1978*).

Fig 141 'Kon-Tiki' sailing rafts for setting shark-lines from the shore in New Zealand: (*a*) simple construction for towing a longline from the shore;

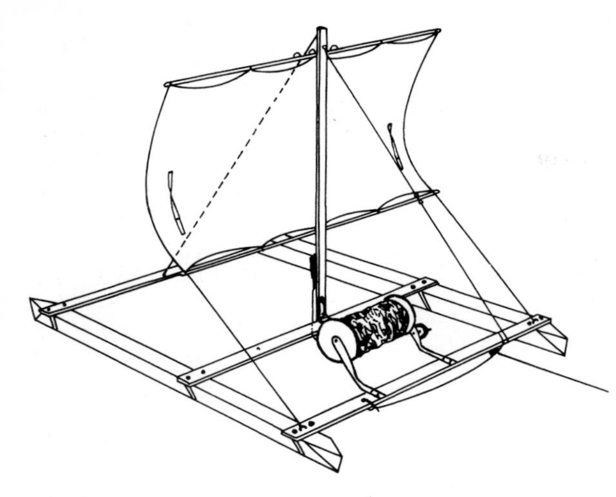

Fig 141(b) complicated construction of galvanized iron for setting a vertical longline in the desired position offshore. (*Doogue, 1977*).

beach and the other, tied to a kite's tail, is then towed off by the wind.[356]

Bottom longlines are operated in fresh waters as well as in sea waters, not only in shallow waters but also in deeper ones. Only a few examples can be given. Icelandic longliners, fishing for cod, operate a bottom longline with sections of different lengths carrying from 100 to 400 hooks each. The total line can be more than 30 kilometres in length with 20,000 to 30,000 hooks. The hooks are baited and this takes a long time: 20,000 hooks will take six men ten hours!

An important longline in sea fishery is that used for halibut in the Pacific. This is a bottom-set line with baited hooks, divided into a great number of single units. Each unit was originally the amount of set line which one man could conveniently handle. Each vessel carries 50 or more units of longline, each of 250 to 300 fathoms. The gear is set while the vessel is proceeding at full speed. Various numbers of the units are tied end to end in a 'string' and the two ends of that string are anchored and marked by buoys with flags or lights to show at night.[562]

In eel fisheries two fishermen can bait and shoot 1,000 hooks in two hours; more experienced men may manage 2,000 hooks in the same time, but in lake fishing only 150-300 hooks are needed for one line, and in rivers it may be much less – perhaps 30 to 50 hooks. There are many types of bottom longlines varying both in length and numbers of hooks. The short longlines set for cod by Portuguese dory-fishermen have to be mentioned as well as the long lines used for 'Golden-thread' *Nemipterus virgatus* off the Hong Kong coast,[17] or for groupers, sea bream or shark in many parts of the world. They are also used for haddock, hake, pollock and all forms of flatfish. In Thailand, crabs are caught with baited longlines during the night. Of course the hooks have only to hold the bait which will be taken by the crabs. As stated earlier at the beginning of the last chapter, with hookless lines crabs continue to hold the bait when taken out of the water.

In contrast to handlines and also some smaller types of set lines, fishing with longlines is considered a labour-intensive and time-consuming method. Not only does the setting and hauling of some kilometres of line need time and considerable manpower, but also the baiting of the hooks must be done by helping hands at home, on the shore, or on the way to the fishing grounds. Furthermore, when the line is hauled the catch must be removed, the hooks must be cleaned, and the lines and snoods untangled and, if broken, repaired or replaced. Some winches have been introduced for hauling, and efforts have been made to solve the problem of storing longlines with many hooks and keeping them clear for setting. Also of interest may be hydraulic longline reels which are offered in the USA, especially for swordfish, shark, tuna, snapper and other large fish caught by longlining. These efforts have so far not been sufficient and as will be shown in the last section of this chapter there are now some new attempts being made to convert hand-operated longlining to a modern mechanized system of fishing.

9.5 Drift lines

Bottom-set lines with few or many hooks are anchored at a certain place and have to be found by the fish on its daily migration for food. Therefore it is necessary to know the right place for setting to be successful. In contrast to bottom lines, drift lines are kept on the surface or in midwaters by floats, and the depth to which they fish is regulated by the length of the line hanging from the float. They are not limited to any specific place, but can operate over large areas. 'The drift line searches for the fish' is a fishing slogan. Like bottom-set lines, drift lines can have a single hook or several or they can be vertical or horizontal long lines with many hooks.

In principle the construction of drift lines does not differ from the sedentary fishing lines previously described (*Fig 142*). Small drift lines with a single hook only are used in freshwater and inshore fisheries. The heavy drifting longlines with some thousands of hooks are typical in high seas fisheries. On enclosed waters like lakes, the fishing lines can be allowed to drift freely, attached to a float. Experienced men know in which direction such lines may drift (*eg* throughout the night) and where to find them again. If a fish does take the hook the float acts as a brake to tire the fish and prevent its possible escape. Drifting longlines as used in sea fisheries are mostly not unattended but are fastened to a fishing vessel which recovers the drift lines in due course. Many small drift lines with a single hook (*Figs 142a* to *c*) operated in inland and coastal waters, can be set at the same time. Malaysian fishermen watch 20 to 30 such single lines with vertically floating cylindrical floats. When the hook is taken this can be seen by movement of the float. This can be shown much more impressively by using floats which change their swimming position when the hook is taken. Formerly, in the area of the Zaire River, fishermen used shaped floats which acted as 'tell-tales' by turning over when the bait was taken.[361] *Figure 142a* shows a French drift line for pike with a wooden float or 'trimmer' which will turn upside down when the hook is taken. Because each side of the float has a different colour the catch can be seen very easily. Among the smaller types of attended drift lines is a special Malaysian type.[93] The gear looks like a balance line (*Fig 143*) but the weight is replaced by a piece of floating wood. This gear is secured by a retrieving line held by a fisherman on the shore. As soon as a fish takes one of the two floating hooks, the line is drawn ashore. A similar method is known as 'whipping' in Hawaii. Here the line is directed by a pole of six to eight metres in length.[262] Single drift lines are also used to catch large fish like sharks. Here also the fish tires itself by towing the float to and fro, as when working with retarders. The use of a retarding effect is one of the basic ideas in gear construction. In some cases the resistance of a float is considered insufficient to tire the prey and therefore special retarders have been introduced. For this reason even small parachutes have been used for catching tuna with drift lines in the Mediterranean (*Fig 144a*),[159] while propeller-like devices are used for retarding sharks when fishing with snares (Chapter 14) in Oceania.

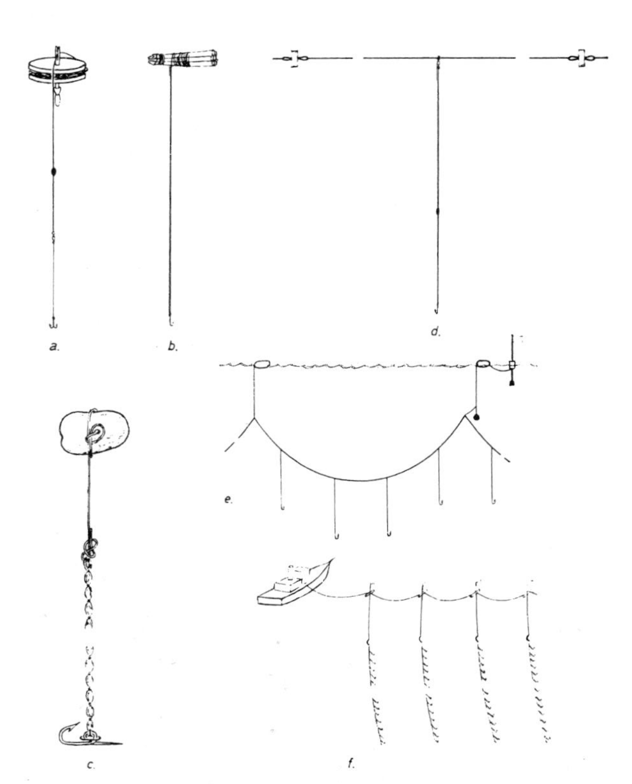

Fig 142 Driftlines: (*a*) French driftline for pike; (*b*) driftline for eel in western and eastern Europe; (*c*) Javanese driftline for crocodiles; (*d*) part of driftline for salmon in the Baltic; (*e*) drifting longline, tuna type, used in Malta for swordfish; (*f*) vertical longlines of Formosa. (*Liu, 1956*).

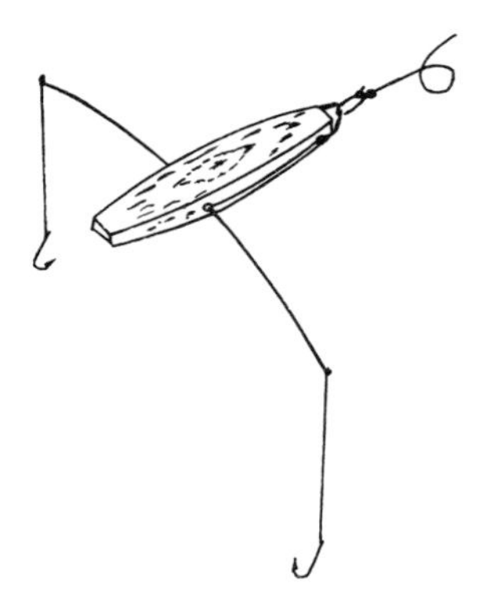

Fig 143 Drifting double line from Singapore. (*Burdon, 1954*).

Today the most important drifting longline in commercial use might well be the tuna line (*Fig 145*). According to tradition, the longline for tuna is said to have been invented by the Japanese of the Wazayama Prefecture on the Kii Peninsula southeast of Honshu more than 250 years ago. Originally it was a short floating longline with only a few hooks, used by inshore fishermen. Such short lines are still used in Japan for tuna fishing from small fishing boats. When this fishery was extended to cover tropical seas where tuna may be caught, this line was enlarged and is considered today as a very effective gear for tuna which swim dispersed in the deeper layers of the sea. This is why some lines are reputed to be up to twenty miles in length. Tuna longlines, like most of the longlines in sea

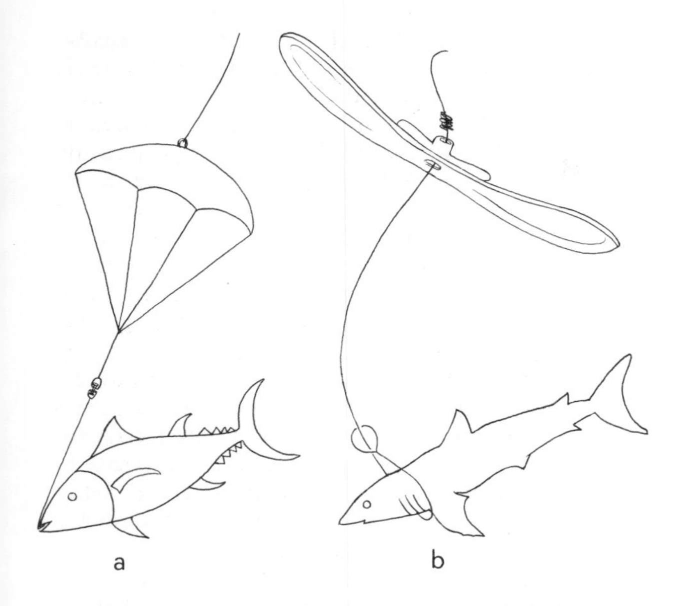

Fig 144 Retarder in line fishing: (*a*) parachute used as 'freineur' (brake) in the tunny fishery of the Mediterranean; (*b*) retarder used in Oceania for shark snaring. (*Parkinson, 1907; Anell, 1955*).

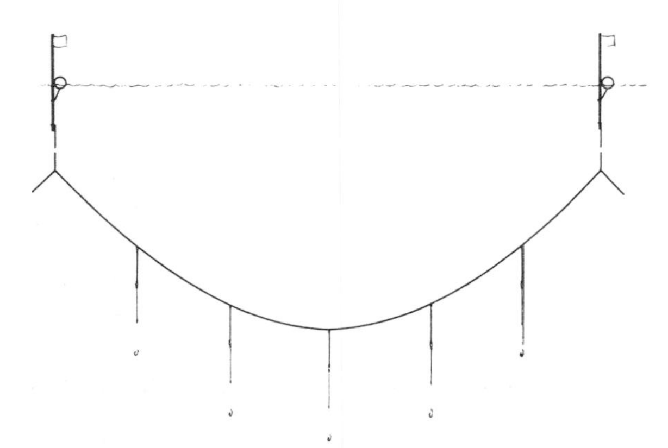

Fig 145 Section of a Japanese drifting tuna longline.

fisheries, are composed of many sections or 'sets'. Each set measures 150 to 400 metres in length, with one to twelve branch lines each bearing one hook. Typical branch lines for tuna longlines consist of three sections and each branch line is attached with a special snap-on metal clip to the main line (*Fig 145*). Each set is stored in a basket, or two sets in one bag of netting. Japanese fishing boats, ranging from 200 to 800 gross tons in size, usually carry 350 to 400 baskets of longline; that means as much as 160 kilometres! When each set has three to five branch lines, with the same number of hooks, up to 2,000 hooks have to be operated. In the Caribbean 250 to 400 baskets of six each are used, carrying 1,500 to 2,400 hooks; but the Korean longliners for tuna are said to shoot and haul up to 3,200 hooks a day! The Japanese tuna longline is set early in the morning from the stern of a vessel. At the end of each unit (basket) a buoy with a flag or lamp is set. With the help of the length of the buoy line the fishing depth can be regulated. The same can be done by the speed of the vessel; at low speeds the buoys are set closer together and the lines hang deeper. Setting 2,000 hooks will take more than four hours. The hooks are baited and the branch lines are fixed on the main line during the setting. When the whole line is set the gear is left to drift alone and the vessel returns to the beginning of the drift line for hauling. The line is hauled from the bow with the help of a line-hauling machine (*Fig 146*). Nevertheless, hauling can last up to ten hours and more. With a high catching ratio, that is the number of tuna caught by 100 hooks, more time is needed. The Koreans calculate that the setting of 400 baskets, each with eight hooks, takes four hours; but hauling the 3,200 hooks takes up to 15 hours! There is little spare time to rest. Working in this fashion, from before sunrise to midnight, under tropical conditions and for weeks and months, is very exhausting. Tuna longlining is not only an effective fishing method but also a very labour-intensive one. This is why the number of countries undertaking this lucrative method of fishing is limited to Japan, Taiwan, Korea and to some extent South Africa, Cuba and French Oceania. The lines are considered particularly successful in the tropical Pacific for big fish in depths from 60 to 250 and even 300 metres. This explains too why, not only for bottom longlines but also for drifting longlines, attempts have been made

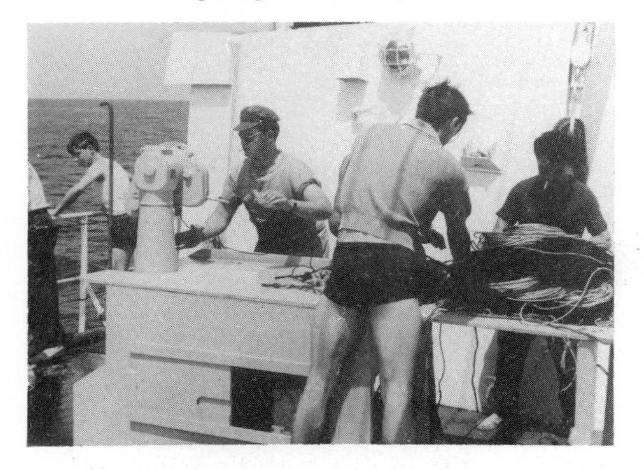

Fig 146 Hauling and packing of tuna driftline in bags of netting on the French research vessel *Coriolis* (1964).

to mechanize this fishing method and if possible to set the lines by a computerized system (see later).

In contrast to tuna drift lines, other types are not so popular. In the Baltic, drift lines for salmon are used even today (*Fig 142d*) when bad weather prevents the use of driftnets because of the waves rolling the nets together (Chapter 30). The salmon drift line in the Baltic can have from 1,500 to 3,000 hooks. Each hook must have, by law, a minimum spread according to an agreement between interested countries. The construction of the salmon drift line has changed very often in line with the increasing or decreasing importance of the fishery, especially since World War II. In the fisheries of the Far East some other types of drifting longlines are used for catching mackerel or hairtails. Longlines similar to those for tuna are also used to catch sharks and swordfish (*Fig 147*). Around Malta, stocks of swordfish have been found by experimental fishing for tuna with drifting longlines (*Fig 145*).

In general, the problems mentioned for bottom longlines at the end of the last chapter are the same as for drifting longlines. Here also it can be repeated that the amount of work and the increasing costs

Fig 147 Setting of a longline for swordfish, Malta. (1966).

of manpower on the one side, and the advantages of longlining on the other side, whether in the form of bottom lines or of drift lines, have led to many investigations into how this method can be made more economic. As will be shown in the last section of this chapter, these investigations have had some success.

9.6 Troll lines

The desire to operate over a larger area and therefore to make use of a movable fishing line instead of a stationary one, lies behind the development and use of troll lines. The troll fishing line is trailed through a certain area and this can better be done from a moving vessel than from the beach. In the United States, troll lines are also called 'trawl lines', which should not be confused with lines used when operating a bottom trawl (Chapter 21).

Trolling is a simple, old, fishing method, and a strange manner of trolling is described by the mysterious 'Dame Juliana Barnes' in the famous *Boke of St Albans* (1496). This was done by tying a short line with a hook to the foot of a goose and letting the poor bird swim! A similar method was described by the admired Izaak Walton (1653) in his well-known book *The Compleat Angler.* This was to tie a line with a live bait 'about the body or wings of a goose or duck and chase it over the pond'! I doubt whether these suggestions will be accepted by either commercial or sport fishermen!

In general, trolling means towing one or more lines with an attractive bait or lure behind a moving boat (*Fig 148*). To attract the fish and induce them to accept the bait, special lures have been designed which either fascinate by their bright colour or so imitate a sick fish by tumbling and whirling movements as to make the predator think it an easy prey. Troll lining is thus primarily a method of attracting and catching predatory fish, and is carried out by commercial and sports fishermen in the sea as well as in fresh water areas. In sea fishing many species of fish are caught by trolling, including large ones like tuna and salmon, and other game fish such as barracuda, Spanish mackerel and marlin. In fresh waters, pike and trout are the special targets of trolling.

In commercial fishing, enticing baits for troll lines can be artificial lures like bone and feathered jigs (*Fig 149*); wooden and plastic plugs or baits in the shape of octopus, cuttlefish, squid or sardines; metal spoons and spinners (*Fig 148b*), and plastic worms, as well as special arrangements with natural bait. It may be that the spoons (*Figs 151* and *173a*) as used by the Californian salmon fishermen and

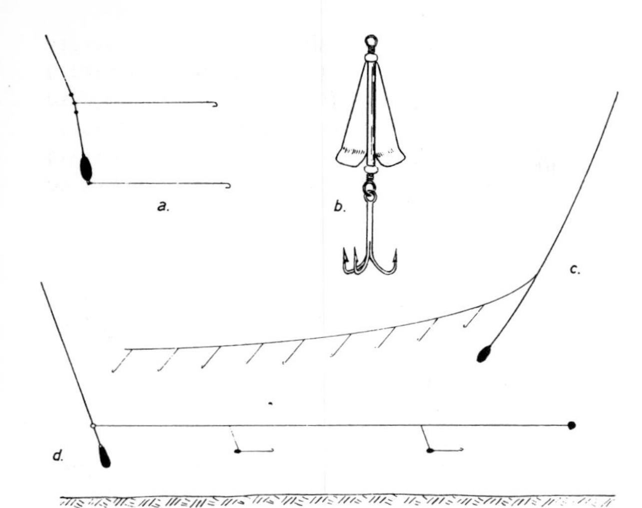

Fig 148 Troll lines: (*a*) Norwegian 'Dorg' (*Brobak, 1952*); (*b*) spinning hook for mackerel; (*c*) English Dartmouth dab line (*Davis, 1958*); (*d*) Norwegian 'Dypvannsdorg' (*Brobak, 1952*).

Fig 149 French double hook for tuna fishing with troll line. The lure is made of plastic fibres, formerly of rice straw (Brittany, 1977).

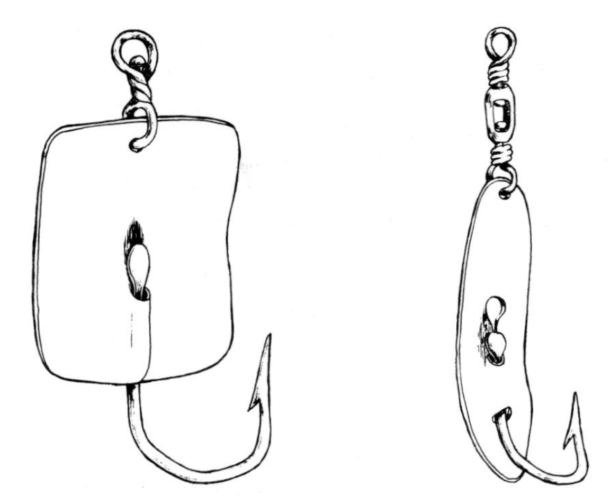

Fig 150 Old French spoons for trolling tuna lines. (*Centre d'Etudes et de Recherches Scientifique, Biarritz*).

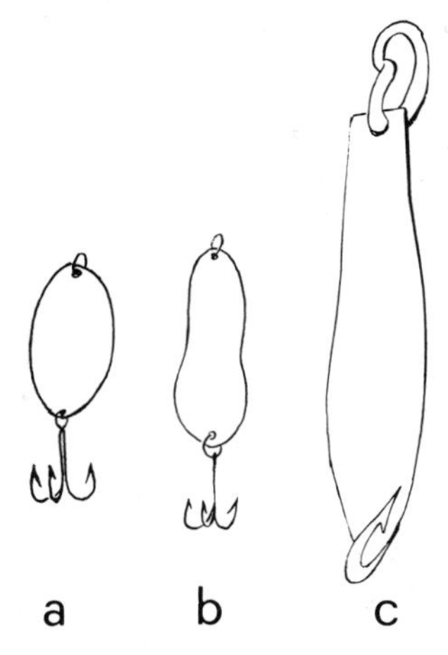

Fig 151 Old types of spoons: (*a*) and (*b*) mediaeval spoons; (*c*) prehistoric hook with broad shank found in middle Finland (*Vilkuna, 1975*).

by the French 'thouniers' until recently (*Fig 150*), are the oldest form of fishing tackle. There have been Bronze-Age hooks found in northern Germany that look like a combination between spoon and hook,[515] and these are similar to those mediaeval hooks found in the central part of Finland (*Figs 151a* and *b*). The troll lines, with spoons or wooden plugs, or with live bait, are considered a part of the old traditional fishery, at least in Europe.[639] According to Heintz, 1903[233], who is considered to have introduced flashing spoons into sport fisheries, the old commercial fishery for salmon in Norway used spoons, as did the fishermen of the upper Italian lakes. The latter sometimes used specific forms in the different lakes (Garda, Como *etc*), always combined with a swivel at the one end and a triple hook on the other. In Lake Constance old spoons used were in the form of a fish or of 'a spoon without a handle'. They were made of copper or nickel or were silver-plated.[305] In non-European areas, like Africa, spoons seem to have been introduced and copied since ancient times.[82]

Sometimes unbaited glittering hooks, *eg* spinners (*Fig 148b*), are sufficient for trolling. Or if baited, the bait is often nothing more than a striking piece of cloth, a coloured ribbon, a bright piece of the belly flap of a bait fish, straw, or similar material which is cheaply available in large quantities. Moreover, live bait, or more often dead bait, fixed on a single hook can be used for trolling in commercial fisheries. To prevent the bait slipping from the hook when trolling, a length of twine is connected near or with the hook and the fish bait is tied on with this (*Figs 100* and *110*). The bait can also be fixed on several hooks in the so-called tandem system (*Fig 111*), or fixed to a special spinning tackle. *Figure 152* shows highly developed dead-bait lures for bigger pelagic fish like marlin or Spanish mackerel, as operated out of Taiwan. In this case the bait fish is not only held by a hook but is also fixed to a torpedo-like piece of lead for trolling at the desired depth.

If only one or two lines are towed by a boat, few difficulties are encountered. But as the commercial fisherman must endeavour to catch larger quantities he will have to tow many lines simultaneously. The problem then is to keep the fishing lines from fouling each other. This can be done by using beams – two or four outriggers, extending out from the sides of the vessel. *Figure 153a* shows an example of simple trolling with the help of two beams in Malaysia. The beams are secured by special lines. In this case each beam has one line (monofilament 0·70) of about 10 metres in length, and each is fitted with a swivel and a large spoon. When a hook is taken, the line can be hauled in very easily by special hauling lines. This is the general principle of many troll lines. The beams keep the lines away from wake of the ship which may frighten the fish (*Fig 153b*). Another way to keep the lines from entangling with each other is to let them fish at different depths. In this case the depth at which the hooks fish is regulated by the use of suitable weights (*Fig 154*) or deep shearing boards (planers). Besides extending the fishery to different depths, this arrangement also helps in keeping the many lines apart during fishing. Another method of keeping the lines clear is to use otter boards (Chapter 8) which spread the trolling lines over a wide area (*Figs 112* and *155*). There are also combinations of weights and deep shearing boards for this purpose (*Fig 155*).

Trolling is an important method in the salmon fisheries of North America, particularly on the Pacific coast. In this case four beams are used, two set amidship with two lines each, and two shorter beams with one line each set at the bow (*Fig 154b*). The stainless steel lines carry lead weights of different sizes so as to troll the hooks at different depths. The troll lines for salmon fishing end with a spoon, a plug, or a baited hook. Each troll line is supported from the pole by a tag line and is reeled in or out by separate gurdy spools driven by the main engine. In salmon fishing, small boat stabilizers are used and between the line and

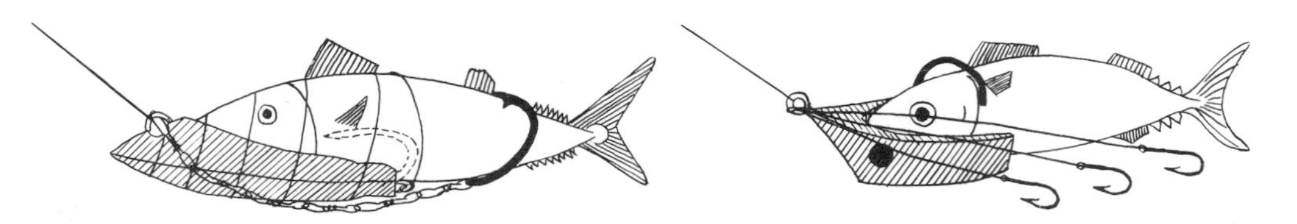

Fig 152 Bait for troll lines; (*left*) mackerel for catching Spanish mackerel; (*right*) skipjack for catching marlin (Taiwan, 1978).

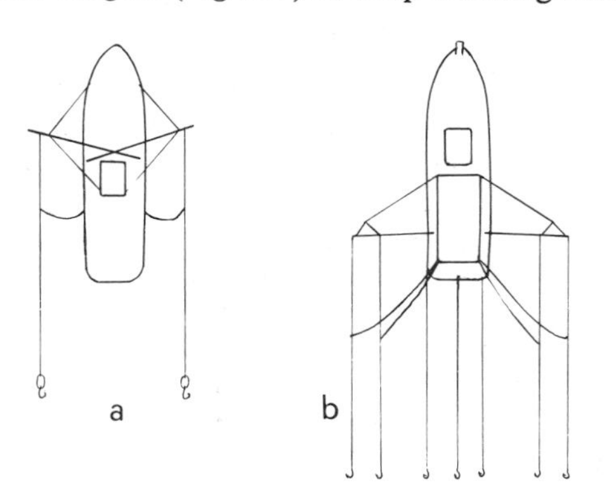

Fig 153 Examples of the rigging of troll lines: (*a*) Malaysia and (*b*) Indonesia (*Yamamoto, 1975*).

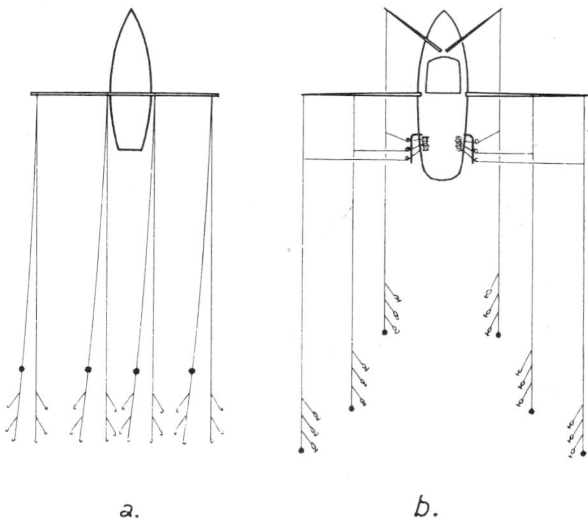

Fig 154 Rigging of troll lines: (*a*) for mackerel in Germany; (*b*) for salmon in British Columbia. The addition of weights allows hooks to be trolled at different depths.

outrigger a shock absorber, in the form of a rubber tube, may be fitted. The purpose of the stabilizers is not only to eliminate jerking on the line, but also to minimize the effect of rolling of the vessel in rough water during trolling.

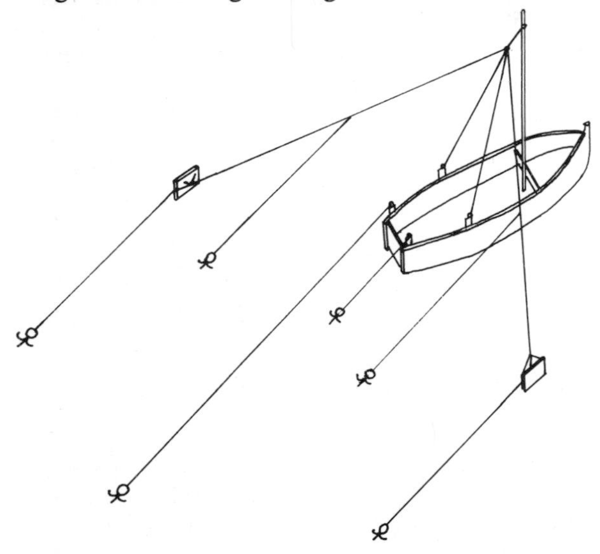

Fig 155 Rigging for trolling for sea trout with weights and otter boards in Switzerland.

Fig 156 French 'thouniers' in the fishing port of Concarneau, with long rods for setting troll lines.

Troll lines are also used to catch different types of tunas. One of the earliest examples may be that of the French method of catching small tuna (especially albacore; in French 'germon') off the Atlantic coast of Brittany (*Fig 156*) and around the Azores. The method is also found on the west coast of New Zealand (*Fig 157*). Typical of this fishery are vessels with two long beams, in French named 'tangons'. The length of the beams can be up to 22 metres, but they may be much shorter, five metres or so, depending on the size of the vessel. The beams can be made of wood or steel. The wooden 'tangons' of the French are composed of two pieces: a long, strong beam with a short very elastic rod at the top. All beams are connected with the mast of the vessel (*Figs 156, 157* and *158*). The two beams are held upright when travelling or in the harbour. They are lowered to an angle of about 45° to the water surface when fishing (*Fig 158*). By spacing the lines with such beams they can be kept at a distance from each other. Each of the beams tows four to seven troll lines (smaller boats have only one line per beam) ending with a strong unbarbed or barbed double hook. Each hook has an artificial bait, formerly made of corn straw but now in Brittany, often a bunch of plastic fibres. In New Zealand they use soft squid-like plastic lures, with and without eyes and in different colours, mostly blue, green and silver. In each line a piece of rubber is included as a shock absorber. The French have this between line and snood, the fishermen of New Zealand place it directly on the mast. Also in this case the lines can have weights added to prevent entangling with each other. Two or four smaller lines can be towed from the stern of the vessel so that each boat can fish with up to 18 lines, (sometimes more than 20).[61] This trolling method was developed in France about 1900 for sailing vessels, but much later, around 1934, motors were introduced. Some years ago it seemed that the old French 'thouniers' in Brittany could not survive the competition of the pole-and-line boat fishery and that of the purse seiners (Chapter 25). However in recent years new fishing grounds were found near the Azores for trolling tuna, enabling the French fishery to recover. The old 'thouniers' have since been replaced by multipurpose vessels like the 'thounier/senneur' (trolling and purse seining) and by the 'thounier/chalutier' (trolling and trawling).

Small boats can troll for mackerel. Single lines are towed or a number of them are held and spread by a beam. In the Baltic a method was devised to increase the number of lines towed by one motor boat by towing two rowing boats with extended rods keeping the lines apart. By this arrangement a

Fig 157 Troll liners for tuna in the harbour of Greymouth, New Zealand (1981).

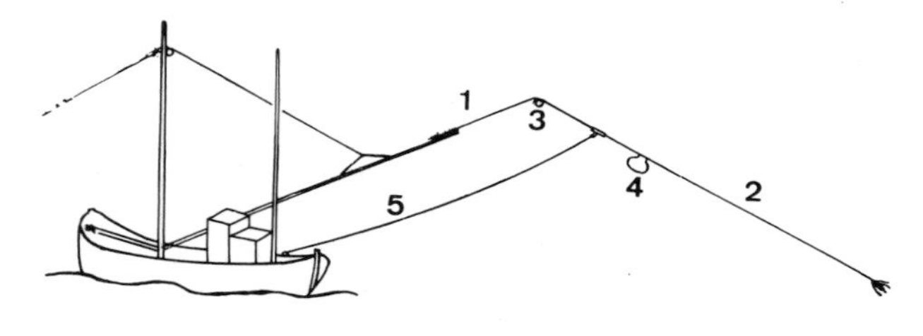

Fig 158 Rigging of a French 'thounier' during trolling. The beam (tangon) has a flexible extension-rod at the end (1). Up to seven troll lines (2) run from each beam, over rollers (3), and are protected by a shock-absorber (4) from the shock of a fish taking a hook. Each troll line can be hauled separately by a special line (5), in order to take in the catch.

relatively large area can be covered (*Figs 112a* and *c*). The lures used in trolling for mackerel are hooks with feathers attached, as are used with handlines. In some places the feathers are now replaced by split fibre bands which seem to have the same effect. It has already been mentioned that trolling with shearing boards is also known in fresh water fisheries, especially in the Scandinavian countries, Switzerland and southern Germany (*Figs 112d, 113, 114* and *155*). The horizontal shearing boards used, originally of simple construction, are known by different names meaning seal, dog or duck.[246] Their purpose is the same as in sea fisheries – to fish an area as wide as 60 metres, especially for fish of the genus *Coregonus.* The gear used on Lake Constance (*Fig 112d*) may be of special interest, because not only do they operate otterboards with a line tied on, but also sometimes more than one fishing line is fixed to the connecting line between the otterboard and vessel.

9.7 Fishing with roundhaulers

Before discussing modern attempts to mechanize line fishing, especially in large-scale fisheries, an interesting form of mechanization which has been developed by small-scale fisheries in northern Europe needs to be mentioned. This is fishing with the 'roundhauler'; that means with a long line, both ends of which have been connected together so that it becomes an 'endless trolling line' (*Figs 159* and *160*). This loop of line fitted with weights and snoods, is moved slowly like a mill wheel. The hooks, mostly baited, enter the water down to a specific depth (according to the situation down to about 100 metres or so) and return to the surface and are led over the vessel so that the catch can be gaffed and the hooks rebaited. Hooks with artificial rubber worms (*Fig 109*) are sometimes fastened without any snood directly on to the line.[388] This method is something between handlining, longlining and trolling. In northern Europe the roundhauler is used for fishing cod, saithe or haddock; in Norway especially for mackerel and coalfish. The idea is not so surprising because when fishing for mackerel with feather hooks off the Irish coast the handlines, with maybe 15 branch lines and hooks with feathers for luring, are plunged into the water and taken out immediately each hook is taken by a fish. With the roundhauler the idea is to work the line continuously, taking out one hook after the other and returning it to the water immediately after releasing the fish. As far as is known it was a Danish fisherman who first used an endless line led down a stove-pipe for continuous fishing. Later on, more specialized pipes were used for this purpose (*Fig 159a*) and it was named 'rolling line trolling'. A more simple device is to lead the free line along a beam and over a roller on each end of the vessel as in Norway (*Fig 159c*). *Figure 160* shows a modern form, in which the line is carried out with the help of a V-shaped hydraulic line sheave led over an outrigger block into the sea, travelling down to the required depth and returning to the vessel on the other side. Although this method is not new, it seems to be becoming more popular in small-scale fisheries, especially in Norway.

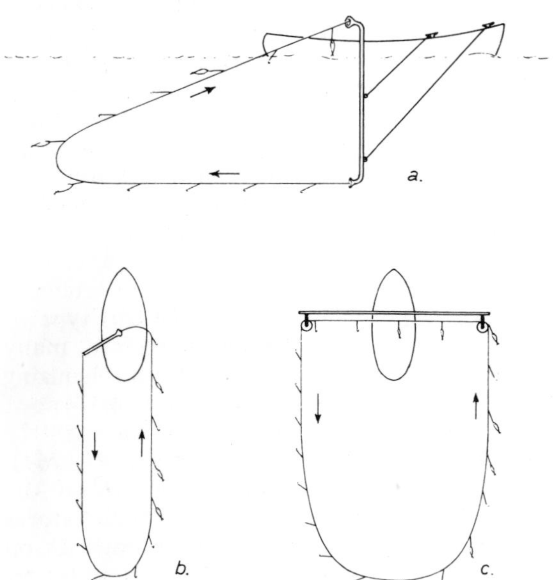

Fig 159 Mechanization of handlines: (*a*) Danish running line trolling; (*b*) Norwegian 'Atom-line-trailing'; (*c*) Norwegian method of handling an endless line.

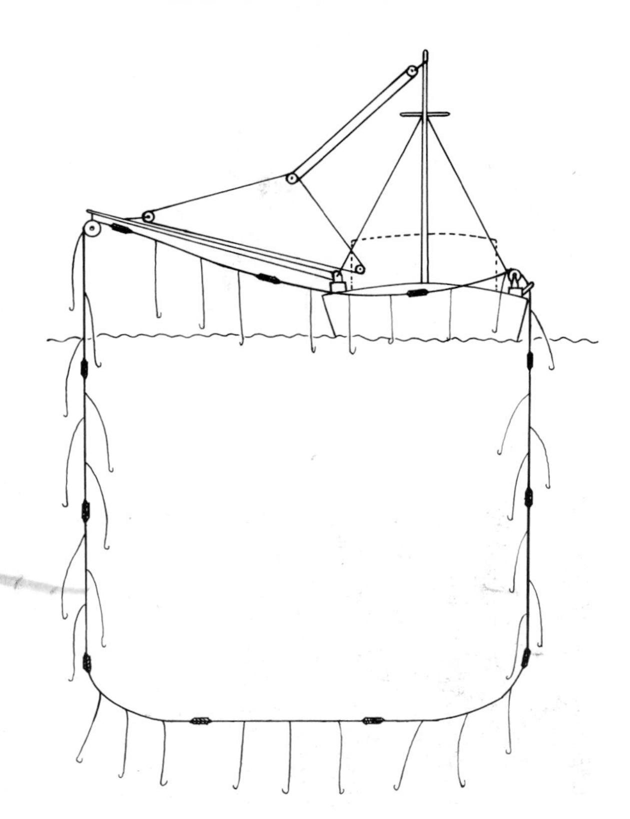

Fig 160 Modern mounting of a 'roundhauler'.

9.8 Modern progress in line fishing

Fisheries, especially the commercial ones, have always tried to improve their methods – particularly when these changes are in agreement with modern trends in working methods. In developing fisheries, sometimes only the fact that materials made of synthetic fibres (more expensive than the traditional ones) are introduced into an old known fishing method can be considered evidence that the fishermen believe the method has a future. Another hint suggesting the favourable judgment of a fishing method is the introduction of mechanization, initially man-powered, later powered by motor-driven machines, to adapt a fishing method to modern needs. Line fishing is an example of this development as will be seen in the following section and also in trawling (Chapters 21 and 22), purse seining (Chapter 25), and maybe also recently in gillnetting (Chapter 29).

The gear for line fishing is simple, usually needs no special arrangement for handling, and can be operated from any vessel or even a raft. In other words line fishing may, in some circumstances be considered a fishing method requiring little investment. This may be true today for some small-scale fisheries, but not any longer in modern commercial fisheries, which need large catches to be economic. Larger catches require not only more effective gear but also increased fishing effort by using more lines, more hooks and making more sets. This becomes necessary as the catch per hundred or thousand hooks decrease more and more. To compensate for this, more lines are set. More lines and more hooks means also more manual labour, which then becomes limited by increasing costs, as can be seen from the earlier example of tuna longlining.

Different types of winding devices like spools and reels have been introduced for hauling and storing handlines. When fishing, the reels are placed in sockets along the gunwhale and are powered by a manually-operated hand crank as shown in *Figure 121*. The next stage of development was to replace hand operation of the reel by a small electric motor fixed between reel and outrigger. The introduction of motors for hauling, together with the use of synthetic fibres, has opened up opportunities for fishing in deeper water.[298] This idea has been adopted especially for cod fishing with automatic deep sea fishing reels, and has become an example of mechanization in fishing methods. Different models were introduced in commercial fisheries according to local needs. Working more or less fully automatically, the apparatus plays out the line to a predetermined depth or until it reaches the bottom. The line stays there or is jigged at a given rate and distance. When the fish take the hook, the weight or pull causes the reel to begin to haul in the line. There are machines which let out more line with increasing pull-force of the fish, and haul the line in again with lower pull, as is usual with handlines playing a big fish like a salmon. After hauling the fish to the surface, the motor stops automatically and remains stationary until the fish is removed by the fisherman. Some machines give an acoustic signal when a fish is hooked. The advantage of such automatic machines in comparison with hand-operated methods can be seen by the fact that one man can operate up to six lines.

Another form of handlining which adopted automatic fishing methods is the pole-and-line fishery for skipjack, albacore, yellowfin and bluefin tuna. Very simple constructions were devised for working with an endless line, with many short branch lines, replacing hand lines tied to poles. This endless line ran from a rectangular frame fixed to the rail of the vessel, into the sea and returned to bring in the catch.[277] But this early idea was not so successful. More successful was an automated pole-and-line method which simulated the well-tried manual method. The fishing rods are now moved by machines fixed on or near the rail (*Fig 161*). This method imitates all types of catching by hand. It operates by dropping the line; luring the fish by small up and down movements of the fishing rod; quickly hooking the fish and swinging it on to the deck; automatically removing the fish by shaking it off; re-dropping the cleared hook outboard into the water and resuming fishing. According to the different models for mechanical 'poling', the pole can be inside, on, or outside the rail. In the last form landing near the rail is possible. A modern rod can be of glass fibre from three to nearly five metres in length and suitable for fish up to 30kg in weight and more. A single man can control four to eight units.

In longlining also, for bottom lines as well as for drift lines, hand-driven reels have been introduced in a few cases as mentioned at the end of the fourth section of this Chapter. In this case the trend to mechanize the whole operation, or at least a part of it, was due to the fact that some people held the opinion that the methods so far used for longlining made it, like handlining, a comparatively uneconomic form of fishing.[529] Special types of powered winches were developed for hauling longlines[295] in order to reduce labour requirements and increase productivity. Most of these small hydraulic winches are also usable for the hauling of gillnets (*Fig 162*).

Tuna longlining operators were especially interested in a system for mechanizing the handling of their drift lines (*Fig 145*) with up to 2,000 and more hooks. Until now these lines have been hauled and coiled by special winches (*Figs 146* and *163*) but every other operation, such as connecting, disconnecting and storing the branch lines and buoy lines; the re-baiting of the hooks and removal of fish; and the casting of the line, has had to be done by hand. Overcoming these labour requirements and making longline fishing less labour-intensive may decide what chance of survival this type of fishing will have in the future. Therefore, many experiments have been undertaken for mechanizing longlining in the Japanese tuna fishery. Up till now, two systems have had some chance of success – the reel system and the line winder system (*Fig 164*).

In the 'reel system longline fishing method' the line is set and hauled by a drum, which also stores the whole line as one unit. Storing longlines on drums is not a new idea (*Fig 165*). It is no longer necessary to connect or disconnect the line units and store them in single baskets or bags. A single undivided line is cast out and hauled when

Fig 161 Automatic pole-and-line fishery on a Japanese skipjack vessel. (*Photo: Iwatan and Co, Tokyo.*)

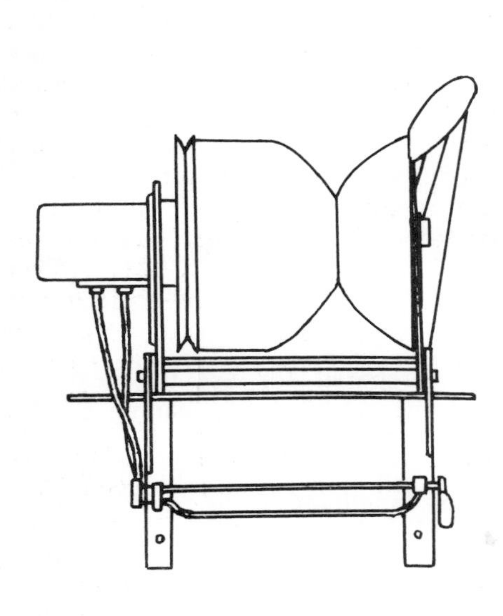

Fig 162 Hydraulic winch for hauling lines or gillnets by small vessels. (*Kaulin, 1969*).

Fig 163 Japanese machine for hauling and coiling tuna longline on the French research vessel *Coriolis*.

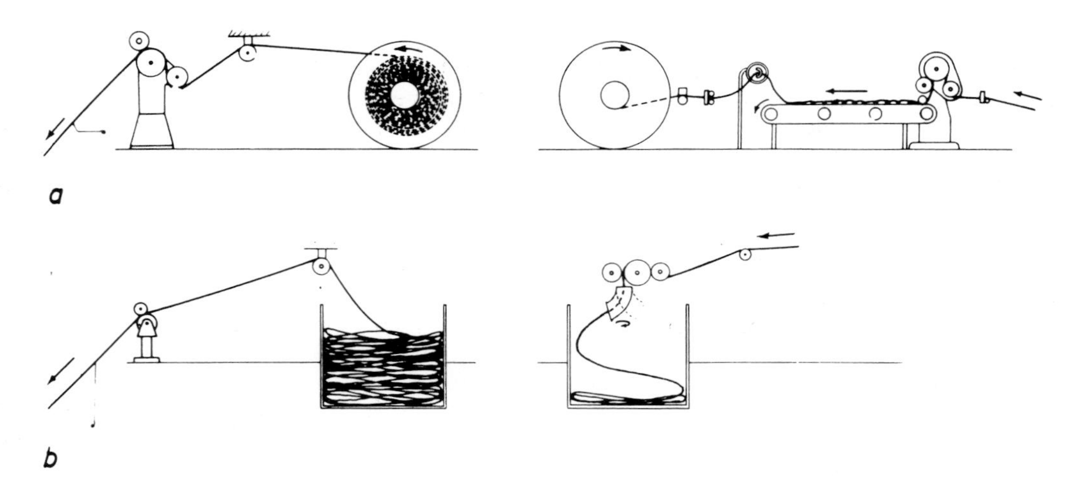

Fig 164 Systems for hauling (*right*) and casting (*left*) Japanese tuna longlines: (*a*) reel system for larger vessels; (*b*) line winder for small vessels.

employing a drum (*Fig 164a*). The branch lines and float lines are fixed to the main line by a special 'coupling apparatus'. Depending on the weight of the drum, the vessel should not be too small and should have an engine of at least 200hp. Since 1966 many Japanese vessels have used drums or reels for longlining even when the snoods have had to be handled by hand. The line winder system (*Fig 164b*) is a practical method for small boats needing an operating power as low as about 5hp. With this system also one line is used, and this is coiled into special storage hatches during hauling with the help of a line winder. The branch lines have to be removed by hand. When casting, the line, after passing the line caster, has to be attached to branch lines and floats.

Mechanized longlining is of interest not only for big game fish like tuna, shark and swordfish but also for many other types of fish caught in large quantities by smaller vessels. Such a catch is of superior quality because less damage is done to the fish by the hooks than by other gear. Some of the northern fish caught by longlining are dogfish (*Squalus acanthias*), ling (*Molva molva*) and cusk (*Brosme brosme*), silver hake (*Merluccius merluccius*) and cod (*Gadus morhua*), Pacific cod (*Gadus macrocephalus*) and black cod (*Pollachius virens*).

In northern Europe longlining for cod is important, but sometimes uneconomic in its traditional form because it is labour-intensive. Some thousands of hooks have to be paid out every day. The hooks have to be baited normally in advance, or when shooting the line ('bait-as-you-shoot' method). Hauling of the lines, with so many hooks, can take more than ten hours. Moreover, the line has to be prepared for use the next day by untangling the snoods and cleaning the hooks. Finally the catch has to be gutted and stored in ice. Here we have the same problem of labour-intensity as with tuna longlining in the tropics, but it may have been the northern fisheries making the first steps towards mechanized longlining systems when, at the end of the 1960s, new ideas arose for a fully mechanized longline handling system including automatic baiting. Automatic baiting machines, even when used alone, brought the first real progress. 'Baiter' machines cut the whole bait fish

Fig 165 Longline stored on a drum in Seattle. (*Photo: J Schärfe, 1968.*)

into the right size pieces and enabled hooks to pick up the bait as the line was being shot. This was considered great progress, especially as baiting often had to be done under bad weather conditions on the unsheltered deck. But baiting machines alone are not enough. The Japanese are using powered drums to store the main line, and the permanently attached snoods have been replaced by detachable snoods fastened by clips (*Fig 134*), which permit a quicker automatic replacement of snoods and hooks. Then came special machines to free twisted branch lines from the main line. The new 'disentangler' also cleaned the hook of bait and coiled up the main line.

At the beginning of the 1970s the first fully mechanized handling system for bottom longlines was introduced in Norway – the so-called 'autoline system'. Such a system had to cover all operations, including cleaning and baiting the hooks and hauling, storing and setting the lines.[453] Some of the key developments were: the hauling mechanism; the hauler and coiler which pulled the line through the gunwhale rollers where the caught fish was removed and the hook cleaned (whether or not it had taken a fish); the guide tubes which carried the line and hooks, preventing snags and protecting the crew from hook injuries; the mechanisms for unravelling and disentangling snoods from the main line; and the separator mechanism for removing the hooks from the main line and storing them on racks below decks while the main line was coiled onto a drum (*Fig 166*). At this point there is a chance for personal inspection of the line and possibly replacement of some parts, if necessary, before the longline is set again after passing a cutting and baiting machine operating at the speed at which the line is pulled out. Any vessel larger than 12 metres can operate this system as long as there is adequate space available. The large Norwegian longliners operate up to 40,000 hooks.

The system described above may be considered a fully automatic one. The fisherman does not have too much work; he has only to see that the whole process is operating. Such a system is expensive. Less investment is necessary when some work is done by fishermen, *eg* when the snoods are detached and stored by hand; when baiting is done manually, or when the lines are stored in sections on drums which have to be handled by men. Such semi-mechanization is useful on smaller vessels (less than 12 metres) operating in small-scale fisheries. Less money and space is needed but the basic work remains always the same: hauling the line; unloading the fish; removing twists on the snoods; cleaning the hooks; storing the snoods, detached or un-detached; storing the line, with or without snoods, complete or in sections; and, at the beginning of each new set cutting the bait; baiting the hooks, manually or mechanically; fastening the snoods when detached by hauling, and resetting the gear.

Another integrated longline fishing system to reduce manpower in line fishing has been developed in the USA. It is known as the Marco Tiliner (Tison

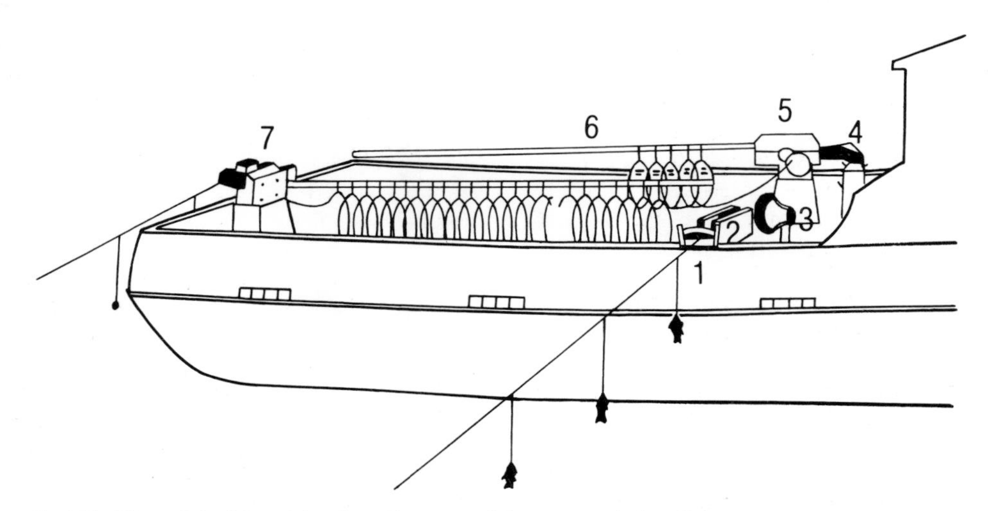

Fig 166 Plan of the Norwegian 'autoline system' for automatic longlining. (*Courtesy of Mustad and Son, Oslo.*) Hauling the line: (1) fish is gaffed before rail roll; (2) hook cleaner; (3) line hauler – line with hooks is guided through tubes to (4) twist remover; (5) hook separator separates hooks from groundline and hangs them in (6) magazines. Setting the line: (7) baiting machine.

longline fishing system) and is designed especially for small and medium-sized vessels (*Fig 167*). The problems to be resolved are the same as referred to earlier but the solution is different. When hauling, the line is towed over an adjustable gunwhale roller (*Fig 167:1*), which is an unwinder roller preventing the snoods winding about the main line. Here the hooked fish are taken by a crew member by gaffing; the same man can also control the boat during hauling by remote engine and steering controls. The line is hauled by a powered line hauler with idler arm and idler sheave (*Fig 167:2*). From here the line is guided to a take-up powerhead (*Fig 167:3*), on which spools are mounted to store the main line together with the snoods and the hooks. Between the line hauler and the powerhead a second crew member is placed to control the hauling operation. This is done by operating a deadman control pedal. This means the hauling gear functions only so long as a pedal is pressed down by the foot of the second man. Moreover, the second crew member has to remove any remaining bait and place each hook carefully on a spoke of the storage reel. Each reel can take a line of 600 fathoms or about 1,200 metres with about 600 hooks spaced approximately two metres apart. When the reel is full, hauling is stopped and the full reel is replaced by an empty one. The stored reels have a fixed place on deck near the setting place (*Fig 167:4*). The spools nest with each other, allowing compact storage. When setting, a full reel is fixed on the powerhead on the setting stand (*Fig 167:5*). Meantime, the bait is prepared to the required size in the hydraulic-powered bait cutter (*Fig 167:6*) for the baiting machine (*Fig 167:7*). The first anchor and buoy are released overboard and the line is run out as the vessel moves forward. The line with the snoods and hooks is then pulled through the baiting machine

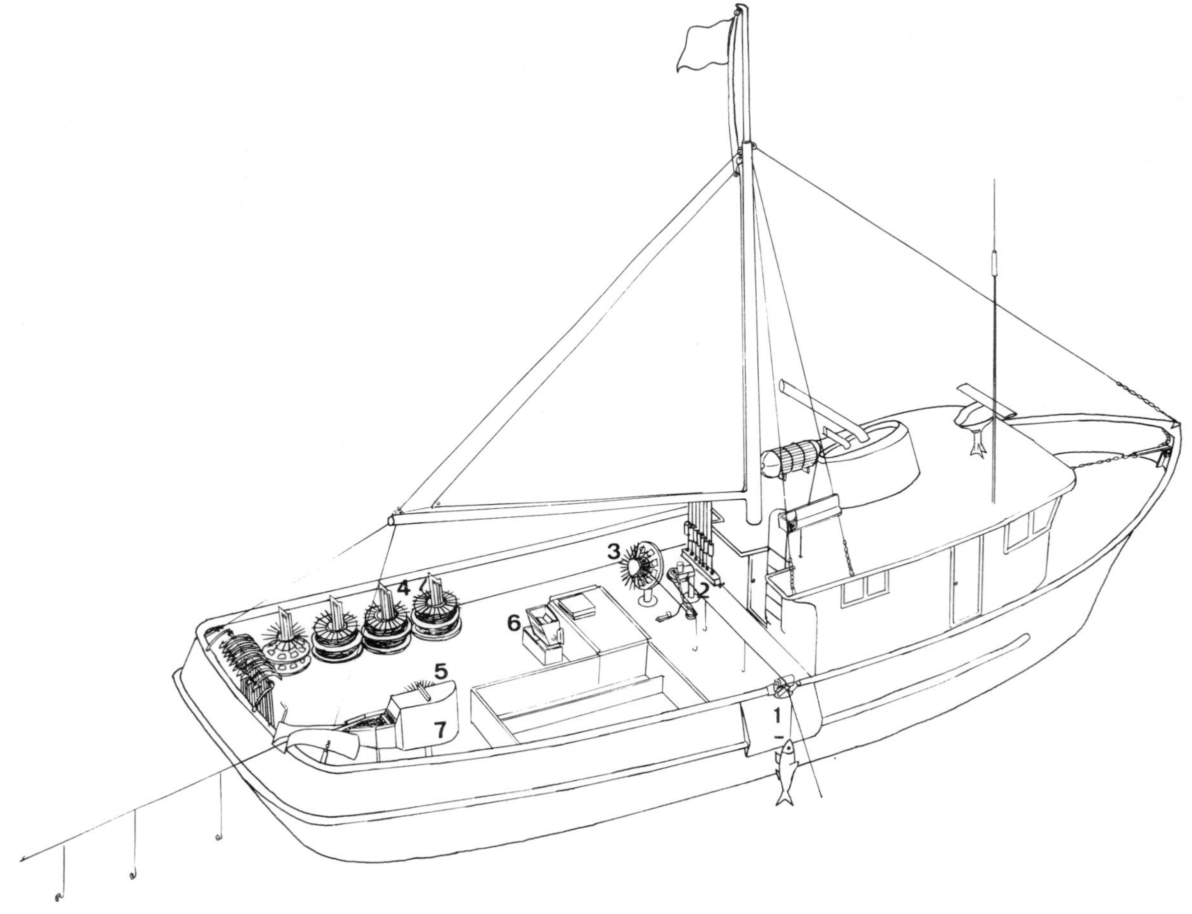

Fig 167 Plan of the deck arrangement for the American Tiliner system. (*Courtesy of Marco, Seattle, 1978*) Hauling the line: (1) adjustable gunwhale roller; (2) line hauler; (3) take-up power head; (4) line storage spools. Setting the line: (5) spool on setting stand; (6) bait-cutting machine; (7) automatic baiter.

where the hooks are automatically baited. The speed of the setting is controlled by a crewman applying pressure with his leg to the hydraulic brake lever, leaving his hands free for clipping floats and weights onto the line. When the required number of spools is set, the last anchor and buoy line are connected and released to complete the set. In case inspection of some parts of the line is necessary, it can be done easily by winding the line from its spool on the setting stand onto an empty spool on the power head. Minor repairs, including removing unwanted bait, can be performed during hauling by removing the foot from the deadman control pedal and briefly stopping hauling. Cleaning the hooks of remains of bait can be done with a wire brush or high-powered hose. This is not difficult because all the hook points are exposed with the bait on them on the outside of the spokes of the reel. When necessary, a hook-cleaning device can be set between the hauling gear and the rail through which the main line with the snoods and hooks is passing.

Another system, the so-called 'Autoclip automatic longlining system', has been developed in Great Britain with the help of the Sea Fish Industry Authority.[464, 467] The aim of this system is to offer smaller boats, ranging from 6 to 24 metres, a less expensive arrangement which can be expanded when needed. In this case the snoods are not fixed permanently on the mainline but are clipped on and off as required. The system includes automatic baiting as well as automatic attachment and removal of the clipped-on snoods. For clipping, a special plastic clip has been developed. The advantage is that the entire main line is stored on a hydraulically-driven drum, or is hand wound. The snoods, carrying 200 to 2,000 (or even up to 10,000) hooks, are removed and stored on special racks, the so-called 'carousels', which gave the system its original name. When setting, the snoods are clipped on again after baiting. According to the original design this had to be done, as formerly, by hand, but additional baiting machines are now available. The advantages of this system are low costs and also greater resistance to bad weather and heavy seas.

An Irish scheme for automatic longlining, called the 'Speedoline system', is based on two units: the automatic baiter, and the hauling unit with the so-called 'fish stripper'. When hauling, this stripper removes the fish from the hook, if required outside the vessel-over the water – when the fish fall into a net bag towed by the boat. This can also be done inboard so that the fish slide into boxes. The hooks are cleaned and guided through tubes, and undamaged and damaged hooks are separated. The magazine has a basket below for storing main line and snoods together. Re-shooting can be started when hauling. Then the hooks are guided through a baiter before setting.

In the meantime, more schemes for automatic longlining are offered. A few are in operation; others are under development. The final version may not yet have been found and it may be that more than one system may be useful for longlining.[43] Their value depends on individual situations in which one system may be more economic than another. One problem should not be overlooked and this is the safety of the crew when so many hooks are guided over the deck. Guiding tubes should, therefore, be used whenever possible.

Chapter ten

Fishing for sport and recreation

All fishing methods have the prime object of obtaining food, either for the catcher's own consumption or for the market or the fish processing industry. Nevertheless, there has been, since time immemorial, some form of fishing for recreation – and this became the basis of modern sport fishing. The definition of this term varies[531] and sometimes it is difficult to make a clear division between commercial fishing and that for sport and recreation. With some fishing methods there is hardly any difference; in others there is a large one. For example, in the casting competitions of sport fishermen, no more fish are caught, only the skill of handling the gear is decisive. (Ever since 1936 there have been attempts to bring such casting competitions into the Olympic games as a special discipline.)

It has been said that the main difference between recreational and commercial fishery is the fact that sport fishermen, in contrast with commercial fishermen, catch single fish, and often also individual fishes known and studied a long time beforehand. Therefore sport fishermen should have a better knowledge of fish behaviour than commercial fishermen. This may be true in some cases for large-scale fisheries, but not for most artisanal and traditional small-scale fisheries. On the other hand, sport fishermen seek to catch specimen fish which are considerably larger than the average size for the water in which they are caught[646].

With increasing urbanization of man, his wish to live in closer contact with nature becomes stronger and stronger, and sport fishing gives some chance for the realization of this desire when hunting becomes no longer accessible for many people. In industrial countries like Western Europe, North America and Japan, non-commercial fishing is certainly the most popular sport and its importance is increasing every year. With the increasing interest in sport fishing, endemic methods have been developed, like fishing in special freshwater ponds or off the sea shore with 'party boats' and around artificial reefs in the open sea.

Sport fishing is equated with angling, and Britain is considered its homeland. However, fishing for recreation with rod and line may have been known for much longer in the Far East, in China, and in Japan. In a Japanese manuscript of the first millennium AD it has been reported that, 'the Empress Zingu (170-269 AD) bent a needle and made it into a hook. She took grains of rice and used them as bait. Pulling out the threads of her garment, she made them into a line which was fixed on a rod. Then she stood on a stone in the middle of the river and cast the hook, and was lucky enough to catch a trout when pulling up the rod'[375]. Some Chinese reports about fishing are much older, reaching back to the mysterious time of the first Emperors.

The fishing rod, even when used in commercial pole-and-line fishing, is still the special fishing tackle of the sport fisherman. Its ancient usage and the link it suggests with the fisherman's need of luck is revealed by *Figure 518* (Chapter 23) in which is described the Japanese patron of fishing – Ebisu, one of the gods of luck – who is holding a fishing rod with which a fine big fish has been caught. Modern sport fishermen tend to use the rod exclusively for catching fish, but in the Far East, cuttlefish and octopus are also caught in this manner. This was not always so. In old books about sport fishing, not only are lines mentioned but also different types of traps, spears, harpoons and lift nets are listed as gear for sport fishing. Moreover, gear needed for catching crayfish[150] was also accepted for sport fishing. In Izaak Walton's book *The Compleat Angler* (1653) the disciple was told how to tame an otter for fishing. Dredging was also considered an amusement of the seashore[227] and some years ago beam trawls were offered for sport fishing by yachtsmen. Nowadays trammel nets are also offered for 'pleasure boats', as are seine nets with and without pockets (Chapter 24).

In Wisconsin lakes sport fishermen learned from the Indians how to handle harpoons to catch sturgeon under ice in the wintertime. Spearing flounder in shallow coastal waters during the night from a boat, or while wading in the ocean surf,[647] may also be considered more recreational than commercial fishing. The same can be said of harpooning sunfish (*Mola mola*) (*Fig 67*) in the Strait of Messina or elsewhere. However nowadays, rod and line is the recognized fishing tackle for sport fishing. Even for such a small gear as a single-hooked drifting eel line (*Fig 142b*) a modern book on eel fishing[354] says that even this gear is 'on the border' between sport and commercial fishing. Longlines will never be accepted as gear for sport fishing: the rod will remain the only acceptable gear. But some forms of commercial fishing gear are required for sport fisheries – at least in fresh water. The knowledge of other fishing methods will be necessary in order to manage fishing waters like large lakes and other natural or artificial waters that cannot be managed by angling only. In this case many different catching methods are needed beside hook and line, including methods for bulk fishing to keep the fish stocks under control. Moreover, some sport fishermen collect bait with different types of gear. Where this is not possible, specialized bait fishermen using many different fishing methods catch live bait for sale to sport fishermen. Recreational fishing with rod and line is one of the many forms of fishing techniques and is linked with other fishing methods. This connection with other catching methods is explained in Chapters 8 and 9 which discuss hook and line fishing in general.

In sport fishing there are at least four different methods of using rods: for float fishing, bottom fishing (legering), spin fishing and fly fishing. Moreover, trolling and jigging are also accepted in recreational fisheries. The principles of these methods are known in commercial fishing, as discussed in Chapters 8, 9 and 12. But as with most recreational activities, their development has become ever more luxurious, and uneconomical from the commercial point of view. There are costly rods and sophisticated reels, specially made lines and casts, a great number of floats and sinkers, and an innumerable variety of hooks, flies, and lures; not to mention ancillary devices for operating the rod and line, and for landing the prey. Therefore, this chapter can provide only a general description, not a comprehensive report, on recreational fishing.

10.1 Rods and reels

The original reason for using a rod may have been the desire to move the hook as far away from the fisherman as possible, so that his figure, his movements, or his shadow may not frighten the prey. This is necessary not only when fishing from the shore but also from the boat, because some fish are considered 'boat shy'. For this a simple stick from the nearest tree was sufficient, and it is not so long ago that recommendations were given on how and when to cut, and how to prepare, a good rod for angling. In Europe springy wood was preferred, like hazel. Ash and fir were used until the beginning of this century. This material was then replaced by some tropical woods like hickory, greenheart, ironwood and bamboo. But the fishing rod has to do more than move the hook away from the angler. It also has to help in casting the hook as far as possible, especially when the line became longer. The rod also controls the movement of the bait and assists in hooking, fighting and playing the fish. All this needs a degree of elasticity in the rod, especially in the top section. As long ago as the 15th century it was recommended to fix a piece of material like whalebone to the tip of the rod to get the necessary elasticity to 'play' the fish. Early rods made of raw bamboo cane – known as 'Tonkin' – were considered the best. It was found that the outer surface of the cane was ideal for rod-making, but the inner section was not reliable. Therefore, split cane rods were developed which are constructed of hexagonal cross-sections of the outer material. These have the best properties for sport fishing, especially for fly fishing.

Since the last war, synthetic materials like fibreglass have been preferred for rod material. Due to its high tensile strength and flexibility, solid and hollow fibreglass rods are now replacing split bamboo rods and even the simple sticks used for fishing by children. Moreover, the hollow fibreglass rods are much cheaper and stronger than the rods made from split cane. The latest development in rod construction material is carbon fibre. Rods made of this have higher strength and can therefore be made smaller and lighter. At the present time the price of carbon rods is very high. Moreover, this lightweight and very flexible rod, very suitable for fly fishing, has the disadvantage of having good electrical conductivity. One person was killed by touching overhead power cables with a long carbon fibre rod, and others have suffered shocks from atmospheric electricity. Therefore, it has been proposed that carbon rods should have a fibreglass butt section to reduce the risk of electrical shocks. There are very short rods with small handles for angling in ice holes and very long ones, four metres or more, for surf fishing. Some people think that the rod should be just over twice their own height.[646]

Rods are mostly made in three sections: the butt section, the middle section and the top section; or sometimes in only two. Originally there were objections to divided rods; perhaps because the joints or ferrules were not good enough. Divided rods have been considered an English whim and some unkind people think of divided rods as the tackle of fish thieves – rather like the folded gun of a poacher!

Originally the line was simply fixed to the top of the rod, as is done today with the rods operated in commercial pole-and-line fisheries (Chapter 9). In this case the line is about the same length as the rod. Often there is a need to have a line longer than the rod. The Eskimos found a solution to this problem (*Fig 168a*) by using a rod with notches cut in each end, enabling the line to be wound lengthwise. A method devised in France (*Fig 168b*) was to wind the line around a separate reel. It may be that the use of separate sticks and boards to wind up lines was the oldest method. The Egyptians wound up the retrieving lines for their fishing spears on separate rolls about 4,000 years ago, and the fishermen of Nepal do this with a board for their angling lines today.[575]

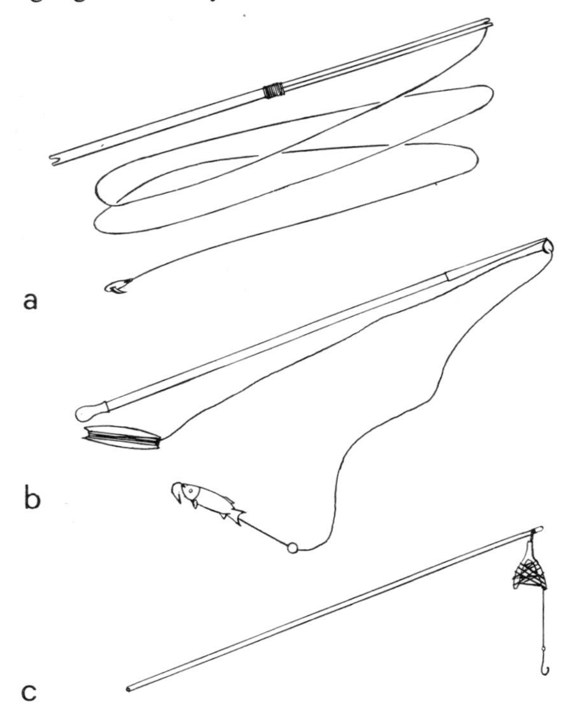

Fig 168 Angling rod and line-storing devices: (*a*) Eskimo angling. The line can be wound around the length of the rod; (*b*) French rod of the 18th century with the line wound around a separate bobbin; (*c*) Swedish angling rod with triangle to store the line as with a roll-line (*Fig 130a*).

Another idea was developed in Sweden. This was to fix a triangular line-holder at the top of the stick (*Fig 168c*) similar to the roll-line used when fishing with set lines (*Fig 130a*). Yet another solution for combining a longer line with a short fishing rod was developed in Korea many years ago and is still used today (*Figs 122* and *169*). In this method the line holder, a broad revolving frame on which the line is wound up, is fixed on the top of a short stick.

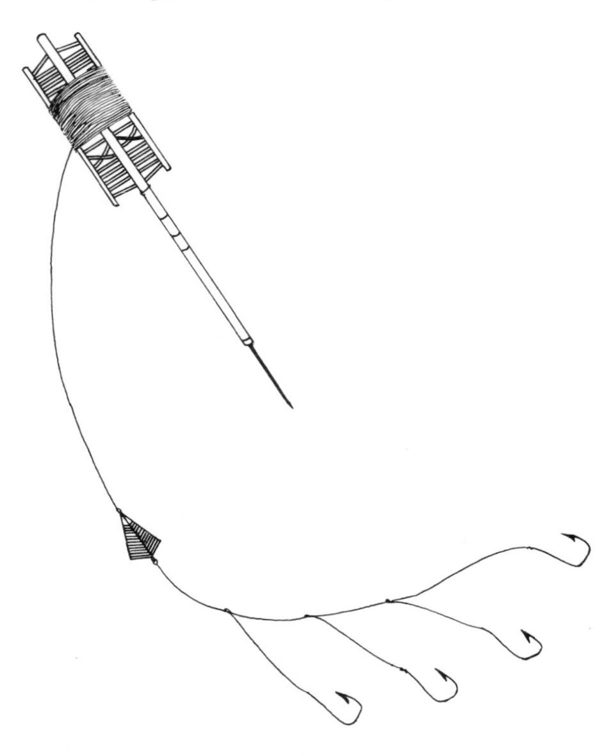

Fig 169 Korean angling rod with a revolvable spool for the line.

Operating a line longer than the rod can also be achieved by fixing a reel on the side of the rod to store the line, as is done for ice fishing (*Fig 130b*). Such reels, also with stopping devices, were already known for handlines.[305] The Chinese were the first to combine such a reel with a rod some hundreds of years ago, as can be seen from the thirteenth century painting in *Figure 170*. There is also a twelfth century woodprint showing a similar arrangement.[626] It is thought that this reel and rod

Fig 170 Chinese fisherman with rod and reel according to a painting of Ma Jüan, 13th century.

arrangement was known in China at least since the eleventh century.[344] The same reel is shown in a drawing of the last century (*Fig 171*). These reels are used today in Taiwan but are now made of plastic. The Chinese have made many basic

Fig 171 Old Chinese rod with reel for catching turtles (*de Thiersant, 1872*).

contributions to developments in fisheries, among which the fishing reel in rod and line fishing may be the most significant. With the use of a reel it became possible to work with a line much longer than the rod. The 'stationary line' – that means a relatively short line no longer than the stick and tied to a loop attached to the top of the rod – was now replaced by a 'running line', not tied to the top of the rod but passing through a top ring to the butt and wound around the reel. A running line may be some hundreds of metres in length. In sea fisheries, running lines of more than a thousand metres are used.

The reels are not only used to store a long fishing line; they are also used in spinning and playing the fish. Modern reels are no longer as simple as the early reels used with handlines, without a stick. Today there are highly sophisticated and expensive reels, carefully designed for the different methods of fishing with rods. It is not quite clear when the first reels were used in Europe. It may have been somewhere between 1651 and 1655[626] – if the interpretation of some old books is right – but, as mentioned before, reels were used much earlier in other countries. The first European reels for rod fishing were heavy large reels made of wood.[140] However, these were inclined to warp due to contact with water. This may be the reason why in the eighteenth century some reels were made of brass. At the end of the last century fishing reels were also made of Ebonite, a vulcanized rubber, and after the First World War reels were made of bakelite, one of the first synthetic materials used in fisheries. Modern fishing reels are made of metal, some with turning spools like small forms of the old reels used for lines ('free-spool' reels); others with non-rotating fixed spools ('fixed-spool' reels). With the original reel, the turning of the handle gave the same number of turns to the spool. This type of centre pin reel is also used today in some cases. But often this old-fashioned reel has been replaced by 'multiplying reels' or 'multipliers', which, with the help of gearing, turn the reel up to four times faster than the handle. Multipliers are very widely used in sea fishing. In troll line fishing some monster reels are used weighing several kilograms and holding more than a thousand metres of line with a breaking strength of more than 30 kilograms. Even motorized or electro-powered reels made of brass or stainless steel have been developed for sea fishing. They are designed to handle heavy fish, from a depth of 1,000 and more metres. With fixed-spool reels the drum or spool has its axis parallel to the rod. The spool remains stationary while the pick-up arm, or bale arm, rotates about it to guide the line when running out over the head of the fixed spool, or to gather the line in when the bale arm turns in the other direction. The fixed spool does not turn but moves forwards and backwards to ensure that the line is wound in evenly. The fixed spool reel can be made in an open form or in a closed one. A closed face reel has the spool with the pick-up mechanism in a domed container with a hole in the centre of the dome for the line to run out or be wound in. From these basic types of reels there are many variations with different names, all of which may have advantages and disadvantages, according to the skill and experience of the user.

10.2 Float fishing

Float fishing is the simplest form of sport fishing in still or very slow moving waters. For tackle, in addition to line and hook, sometimes only some small shots for weight and a float are needed (*Fig 172a*). A rod, however, is not wholly necessary for this method. The distance of the hook from the float is regulated in such a way that it is either fishing near the surface, in mid-water, or lower still, only a little off the bottom. The function of the float is to support the tackle in the water, and also to enable the angler to keep his bait clear, and to reveal by its movement when a fish bites.

Cork has been used for making egg-shaped

floats – also any light wood, but particularly balsa wood. Generally the smaller and slimmer the float, the more sensitive it is. Below water the float should be as dark and inconspicuous as possible, while above water, the tip must be bright for maximum visibility. Sensible floats in a slim form are also made of the shafts of birds' feathers such as those from swan, pelican, goose, turkey and crow. Quills from porcupine have also been very popular. Plastic floats have been made, and fluorescent antennae floats are available for fishing in the dusk. A special type are the bubble floats – transparent balls filled with water to give the necessary weight for casting, but they are nearly invisible in the water and therefore difficult to see. For float fishing, and sometimes legering (see next section), regular ground baiting is considered necessary to encourage fish to the required place. Suitable bait will be spread by hand, and can also be shot further away with a catapult.[626] When the wind is in the right direction the bait can be carried out with the help of a small raft fitted with a sail[646]. A connecting line is fixed to the top of the mast of this little craft to careen the raft and so release the bait at the desired place. Such craft have already been mentioned for longlining (Chapter 9, *Figs 139, 140* and *141*). In sea fisheries float tackle is used because this method allows bait to be presented at the depth considered best. As mentioned before, the float regulates not only the depth of the hook but works also as a bite indicator. Floats used in sea fishing are much more rough in shape and larger, made of wood, cork or plastic. Different waters and different fish call for different floats. This may be the reason why some anglers are said to collect floats as a hobby.

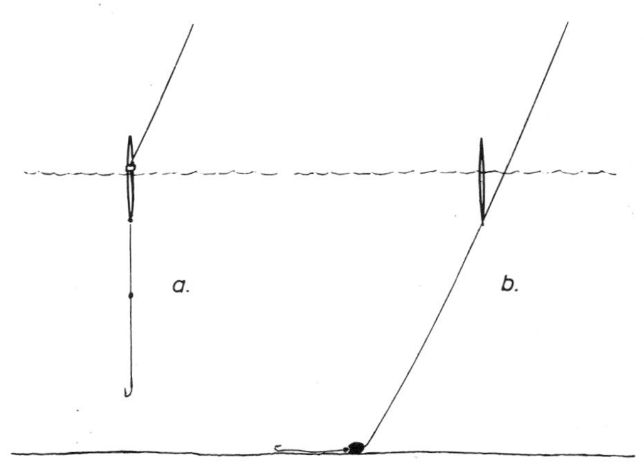

Fig 172 Types of sport fishing: (*a*) float fishing; (*b*) ground fishing.

10.3 Ground fishing and legering

For ground fishing in fast-running waters, almost the same tackle can be used as for float fishing (*Fig 172b*). The depth can be regulated with the float. A heavy lead leger sliding freely up and down, is attached to ensure that the cast with the hook rests on the bottom to catch bottom feeders. The faster the current, the larger the lead will need to be. A fishing rod can be used to place the hook in the right position and to land the fish after striking, maybe with the help of a reel for winding in the line. The rods for ground fishing vary in thickness and consist of two or three parts; they may even need to be operated with two hands according to the design. They are of varying length. They can be four or more metres long but they are also made shorter and heavier for fishing in the sea from a boat. A well-known tackle for ground fishing is the paternoster line (*Fig 117g*) with a heavy lead with side arms like an anchor. Paternostering is generally found to be successful in places where there is a good depth and a strong current.

Another form of ground fishing is legering. This is simply fishing without float. The line with the baited hook is held by a free running weight. Many forms of leger leads are known: round, pyramid-shaped and others, with a hole or loop through which the line passes. A piece of shot is fixed on the line to act as a stop. The free part of the line is allowed to move attractively in the current. The only problem is how to sense a bite, because the system cannot be very sensitive. A bite is difficult to feel with the finger on the line when it is moving in the current, or to distinguish by the movement of the rod tip which may be moved by the wind. Sometimes, when the rod is placed on a rod rest, some glittering material hung on the line can act as bite indicator by revealing unusual irregular movements. An alarm bell can be fixed on the line (*Fig 132*), or the reel may be fitted with a clicker to give an audible warning. Nowadays, specially-made battery-operated electric detectors are available, indicating not only the running of the line but also slack line bites, when the fish swims against the line. Some detectors can be connected to more than one rod and give different forms of alarm. Unfortunately, such devices are expensive and may not be considered sportsmanlike.

10.4 Spin fishing

The spinning method of fishing is appreciated by many. For spinning, a line with lead, hook, and bait or lure is cast by means of a rod and wound in again over a reel. Strictly speaking, spin fishing is something like trolling from a fixed place, and is usually employed to catch predatory fish. Of the different types of rod available, the hollow fibre glass ones are preferred, as well as fixed spools instead of the centre pins and multipliers. Different types of artificial lures with incoherent names are used for spin fishing[4]. In principle, there is not much difference between the tackle used for spinning by sport fishermen and commercial fishermen (Chapter 9). In each case an object designed to make some movement, often spinning, when drawn through the water and armed with hooks, is used.[636] The oldest type of artificial lure used in spin fishing and trolling may be the so-called spoon made of polished metal and already known in prehistoric times (*Figs 150* and *151*). Originally this lure had the form of a spoon, as used for eating (*Fig 173a*). When towed, the spoon moves up and down and also spins, being fitted with a swivel before each lure. Modern spoons used by sport fishermen are generally smaller and can be curved.

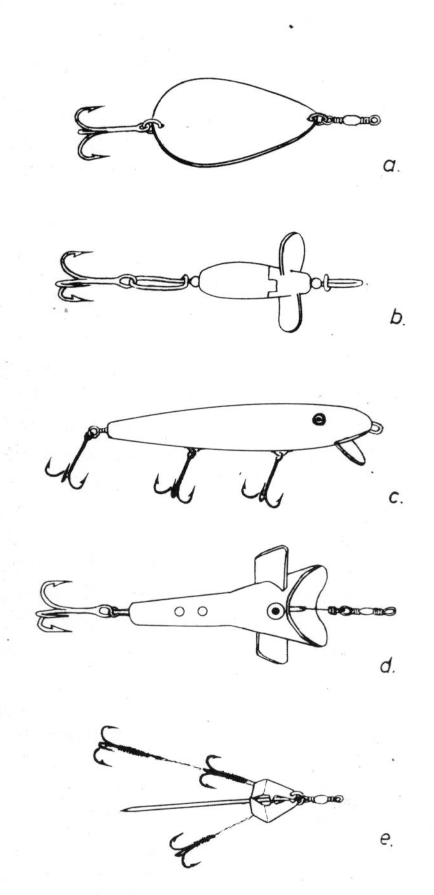

Fig 173 Lures for spinfishing: (*a*) spoon; (*b*) spinner, (*c*) plug, (*d*) 'turbler' — a German form of plug; and (*e*) dead-bait spinning tackle.

Such spoons have no axis, but there are others with a middle part around which the spoon spins and these are, therefore, called 'versatile blade spinners'.

More complicated are lures which have not only an axis, but also something like a propeller which causes a quick turning of the whole lure (*Figs 173b* and *173d*). These are typical spinners known as Devon minnows, turbine spinners, or (in German) 'Turbler'.

Quite another group of artificial lures are the non-spinning 'plugs', first used in America. They are made of wood or plastic in one (*Fig 173c*), two and even three sections. They are fitted with one, two or three triple hooks and are painted with striking colours. These plugs, or 'wobblers', attract the fish by wobbling, wriggling or undulating when towed through the water. Most of them have at the forepart a small shearing board, which is one of the elements of fishing gear (Chapter 8). By this board the lure is pressed downwards or the whole lure is formed banana-like, so that the whole body is shearing when the line is retrieved. There are some types specially made for diving in shallow waters; others which dive deeply; and others which float on the surface and are fitted with a vane which causes them to splash along the surface of the water. Another lure consists of several hooks surrounded with strikingly coloured feathers. These are used in 'feathering; – which is considered very effective because 'a string of six or seven feathers imitates a school of bait fish'.[249] Hooks with feathers can be so effective that some people consider spinning with feathers in the sea no more as sport but, at the most, as a 'bait collection technique'. The feathers can be replaced by natural hairs or strips of plastic, especially by using split fibres (*Fig 149*).

Well known in spin fishing are 'dead bait' tackles (*Fig 173e*) which operate by spinning a dead natural fish. Although in spin fishing the artificial lures are made attractive by striking colours, the movements of the lure and its vibrations are considered the essential factors in attracting the fish to take the hook.

10.5 Fly fishing

The most artistic form of sport fishing is beyond doubt that of fly fishing. In this, the line is cast with an almost weightless bait in the form of an artificial fly, made of carefully tied feathers. Fly fishing as it is known today may be the method of fishing for sport and recreation created by the many improvements of hook, line, reel and rod, made especially in the last century[626]

The earliest information on the use of artificial flies is to be found in Claudius Aelianus' work, *De*

Natura Animalium. It was written in the third century AD, and he there describes the use of artificial flies in Macedonia.[210] Aelianus reports that, in the Macedonian river named Astaeus, in Thessaly, some fish were known to prefer a special type of insect named 'hippuri', flying near the water surface. The inhabitants tried to use these flies as bait, but these insects are so soft and fragile that they are destroyed when touched by hand. Therefore, artificial ones were made of wool, dyed with red wine and completed by small feathers from the head of a cock. This could be the first report about fly fishing, but it was used not for recreation but to get food. Indeed, it seems that this fishing technique was never described before, not even by Oppian, living in the second century AD, who gave a very comprehensive report entitled *Halieutica* about fishing as seen by him or reported by different Greek and Roman writers. Strange to say, this method was not mentioned again until the end of the fifteenth century in the second edition of the famous English *Boke of St Albans* (1496) which has a special chapter – 'Treatise of fishing with an angle'. It has been said that this book was written by an English prioress, Dame Juliana Barnes. Of course, it is a little strange that a prioress should have so much fishing experience. Some people think that a woman at the head of a religious establishment could not have been the author of such a book,[626] and consider that it is based on a French manuscript of the first quarter of the fifteenth century. Nevertheless, in the *Boke of St Albans* not only are rods, lines, floats, leads and hooks mentioned, but so too are twelve artificial flies. Unfortunately, no drawing is given. The first black and white drawing of a fly was published in England not before 1620 and the first coloured one not before 1800. In the sixteenth century and later, artificial flies were mentioned very often. The famous European man of science, Konrad Gessner, describes artificial flies in his *Historiae Animalium*, printed in Zurich in 1551-1558. Even in old Japanese handwritten manuscripts there are descriptions and illustrations of artificial flies. Very often the descriptions of Dame Juliana Barnes have been copied also by Izaak Walton in his book *The Compleat Angler* (1653), of which new editions are printed today. It may be of interest to know that some of the flies mentioned in the *Boke of St Albans* are even used today. Nevertheless modern sport fishermen know of a tremendous number of different flies. They are 'dry', which means swimming like water ticks on the surface, or they are 'wet', which means they are fishing under the surface of the water. There are many famous types distinguishable according to the colour and material they are made from. A rod especially designed for casting artificial flies is needed, and its right selection, not only according to length and weight, will influence success.

Nowadays, the rods of fly fishermen are especially light (ultra-light hollow fibreglass or carbon rods), the fishing line tapers towards either end and is especially prepared to permit its running out easily from the reel (simple automatic fly reel, which takes in the line by a spring). The technique of successful casting in fly fishing must be learned by steady practice; it requires tuition and long and patient exercise, and is the object of special competition among sport fishermen, who today practise their art of casting and exercise their skill in almost every country of the world. This may be also one of the reasons why fly fishing is considered as the most delightful method of all forms of sport fishing.

It has to be mentioned also that there exists a more simple form of 'fly fishing' with larger artificial baits also made of feathers and hairs. Even though these baits are called 'flies' in some countries, they actually imitate not insects but small fishes. Therefore it may be better to use the name 'streamer' for catching larger and heavier fish feeding on smaller ones. Fishing is done in waters with strong currents, with rods made for fly fishing as well as with rods made for spinning.[153]

10.6 Sport trolling

Trolling in a very wide sense can be a form of sport fishing with the same fishing tackle as described before (Chapter 9) for commercial fisheries. When used from a boat, short and strong rods are needed with very long lines and spinning devices, as described for spin fishing. When reels are used they have to be extra large. Otter boards have been mentioned before as being used with commercial troll lines. But it has to be remembered that originally these shearing devices were used for sport fishing in the flowing water of rivers. They were put in the water to tow a line with branch lines and hooks across the water being fished. Later on, more highly developed otter boards were also used from sports vessels to tow lines for trolling over wide areas (*Fig 112d*). Sports fishermen do not only use lateral shearing boards, but also devices for shearing downward. *Figures 115b* and *115c* illustrate shearing equipment used in deep water in sport fishing. Trolling with hook and line is also the method generally practised in big game fishing in tropical seas for shark, tuna, swordfish, marlin and some others. This fishery was not successful before the development and improvement of suitable gear. That means strong lines, rods and reels, operated by a man sitting with the rod in a rest in a 'fighting chair' and secured against being thrown overboard by a sudden jerk of a powerful game fish. Such fish, when hooked, may tow a boat for hours. Sometimes more lures, without hooks, are used only to attract the prey to the catching hook which has a fish as bait.

In some cases, as when fishing for shy sailfish, the bait has to be towed through the water far away from the boat to avoid scaring the fish. It should also be towed near the surface of the water. Therefore, it has been proposed that a balloon or kite should be attached to the line by a cotton thread. When the bait is taken, this cotton line will break and the balloon or kite drifts away.[626] Even today sport fishermen sometimes attempt to use the kite in trolling. The English traveller, Sir Henry Middleton, is said to have been the first of the Europeans to see kite fishing in the South Seas during a visit from 1604 to 1606. He introduced the kite in sports fishing (1616). For this purpose, kites were used flying astern of a moving boat, especially for fishing tuna and other big game fish. The flying fish bait is securely tied to the hook. The fishing line is led from the rod to the kite and then back to the water (*Fig 174*).[356] Thus the hook skips realistically over the wave tops. When a fish strikes the bait, the line breaks away from the kite and the fisherman is free to play the catch, just as it is done in some parts of Oceania.[629] In the Oresund, during the Danish tuna fishing competition of 1947, an effort was made to fish with box kites.[607] However, such efforts as have been made up to the present to introduce this old Oceanic method of troll line fishing have not been successful in other areas of the world. Nevertheless, sportive kite fishing is practised in California and South Africa even today, and kites made of plastic sheets are sold in sports fish-tackle shops.

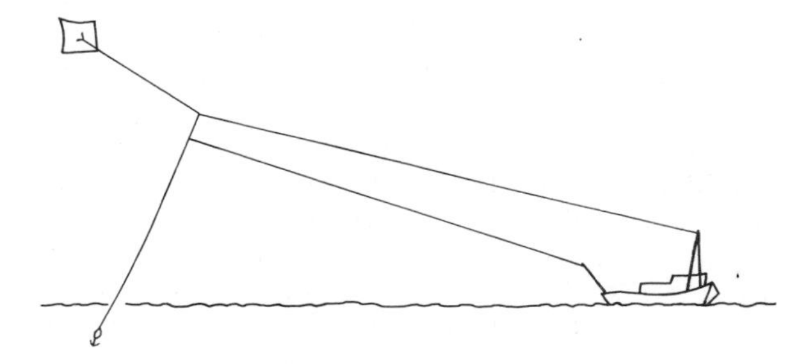

Fig 174 Operation of a handline using a kite. (*de Luna, 1948*).

Chapter eleven

Attracting, concentrating and frightening fish

Sometimes in fishing technology a distinction is made between 'active' and 'passive' fishing gear. As explained in Chapter 1, the meanings of the terms are, that in the first case the gear actively follows the fish to be caught (the gear comes to the fish), and in the other the gear remains passive, waiting for the active fish to come voluntarily to, or into, the gear. Very often an active gear is defined as a towed one, in contrast to the passive gear which is stationary. This definition should be avoided because not all active gear is towed, while some passive gear like troll lines, drift lines, driftnets and even handlines are moved during fishing. For successful catching with any type of passive gear it must be made as acceptable as possible to the prey. To find the most attractive bait, to construct the gear in the most suitable manner, and to operate that gear in the most effective way, needs knowledge of fish behaviour. It may have required many centuries for human beings to learn how to catch fish in any other way than by picking them up and killing them by hand. There may be no objection to saying that most active fishing gears are older than passive ones, and that it needs a lot of knowledge to lure a fish to accept a passive gear. This does not mean that, for active gear, knowledge of fish behaviour is not necessary too. But it is only now that this knowledge has become one of the main ingredients for improving gear construction and devising fishing tactics to be used with the active fishing gear. Many fishing methods are based on attracting prey or concentrating them in an economic quantity. There are also some conditions when it may be desirable to frighten fish into a position where they can be caught.

For attracting and concentrating fish, a bait is frequently offered with the gear. In old and new fishing literature they talk of this as 'bait food', but the enticing element need not necessarily be an edible bait or even a dummy food bait. Other senses of the fish may be exploited to lure them into a fishing gear or to a certain place. Besides food, the fish may have a desire for hiding, for mating, or simply for finding other specimens of its kind, as in the case of shoaling fish. All of these desires can be used, singly or together, to attract or concentrate fish or other aquatic animals near to or into a fishing gear. The term 'bait' is thus by no means restricted to food bait like the lob-worm of the angler, but has a far more comprehensive meaning. The problem is to find the right stimuli influencing the behaviour of a fish or another prey, in a positive or negative manner, as needed for any fishing method, especially with passive fishing gear.

Stimuli attracting fish can be of optical, chemical, acoustical or tactile nature.[399] There are stimuli having either a positive or a negative effect according to their ability to either lure the fish or to frighten it away. The positive and negative reactions of a fish to a certain stimulus can change in the course of that fish's life, and according to its physiological condition. Young fish, for instance, can be attracted by light from which older specimens of the same species would take evading action. They may at first react positively to the photo-tactile stimulus, but negatively at a later stage. Many species behave very differently according to whether they are spawning or not. This explains how it is that long experience is required by practical fishermen for finding out the most effective bait to be used for certain fisheries, as well as for discovering the most suitable fishing gear. Passive gear in particular can be successful only if it is adapted, as far as possible, to the specific behaviour of the animal sought.[86] Very often the problem is that it is not one single stimulus that is decisive for the reaction of the fish but a combination of different ones. This should not be forgotten when reading the following discussion on the main types of stimuli.

11.1 Optical lures

Optical lures may be the first bait originated from the fact that a fish can be attracted by offering food.

Being mostly interested in big game, prehistoric man may have offered small fodder fish to lure bigger ones. Also in prehistoric times, man found out that imitation fish could be used as artificial bait. Some hints were given above (Chapter 6.1, Spearing). Such imitations were originally lifelike, but man then discovered that not only some special design but sometimes also a stronger optical stimulus was desirable. This applies not only to fish-imitating lures but also to the many artificial insects used for bait, especially in sport fishing. Sometimes their appearance is very different from their 'originals', but optically they are much more attractive.

In commercial fisheries, natural living and dead fish or other animals are the most popular bait. But imitation lures are also used. Formerly artificial lures could be wooden imitations of bait fish, carefully painted to attract the fish according to its optical stimulus and whether it is to be considered as prey (*Fig 234*) or as competitor. Man may have found out that it was not only the appearance in colour that was important for the lure to be optically attractive, but that the movement of a lure may be much more likely to cause a fish to snap a supposed prey. Very early it was found also, that any blinking and irregularly moving device could be used to attract fish. The so-called spoons for trolling have already been mentioned as a very old type of artificial lure (*Fig 151*). Any optically striking object, possibly one that is bright or which sparkles irregularly, is often sufficient for that purpose. Frequently a mobile glittering fishing hook, without any addition whatsoever, may be sufficient. It is supposed that the irregular movements given to such a hook convey the impression that a sickly prey may easily be taken. The supposition here, of course, is that the aquatic animal sought to be caught is mainly reacting by its optical sense, through either lying in wait for the prey or chasing it. Therefore, optical lures are especially used to catch predatory fish. As already mentioned, one stimulus may not be enough. The predator has not only to see its presumed prey, its colour and its movement: the effectiveness of a lure may depend much more on its vibrations, which are transmitted to the predator's lateral-line sensory organs.

11.2 Light fishing

Light fishing is a form of optical bait used to attract and to concentrate fish. Since very olden times this method is known to have been effective in fresh water as well as in the seas, for catching single fish as well as shoaling species. Light is used in shallow water by wading fishermen, or by divers hunting in their silent world, or on the sea far away from the coast and down to depths of hundreds of metres. There are, indeed, few fishing areas wherein light is not sometimes used for attracting or concentrating fish, and there is no type of fishing gear which will not be used always or sometimes with light to attract the fish or to lure them nearer to the surface.[31, 542]

The most important fishing methods using light to attract, concentrate and keep the fish in one place till they are caught, may be those used for pelagic fish with surrounding nets like purse seines and lampara nets (Chapter 25, *Fig 558*); with stationary liftnets (Chapter 27) as used in India (*Fig 612*), or the movable liftnets like the 'basnig' nets of the Philippines (*Fig 636*) and the Japanese stick-held dip nets (*Fig 637*). They are also used in line fishing, especially in jigging for squid (Chapter 12, *Fig 220*), and in pole-and-line fishing for mackerel in Japan (Chapter 9). Finally, harvesting fish and other prey with fish pumps may be combined with electrical stunning in a newer form of using light for attracting and concentrating the fish (Chapter 31, *Fig 722*). It can only be repeated that there is hardly a fishing method where light is not used somewhere in the world to attract and concentrate the fish, to keep them at one place, or to guide them into a fishing gear.

As can be seen from this short review of fishing methods operated with artificial light, it is used by small-scale artisanal fisheries as well as large industrial ones. The source of light has changed with the centuries. Torches and fire baskets were used originally, and torches are sometimes also used today, but they will eventually be replaced by more reliable devices which need less handling. Fire baskets attached to wooden boats have been especially dangerous as burning material could fall into the vessel. Therefore a bucket with water should be always at hand.[345] More developed than the hand torch is the famous Hawaiian 'knapsack' type of gasoline torch which allows the hands to be kept free for fishing.[262] Nowadays, transportable or stationary lamps are used, which are operated with fuel oil, acetylene gas, kerosene, generated electricity, or even with batteries. In sardine fishing special lamp boats are used (*Fig 175*) as they are also sometimes by the Norwegians in herring fishing. To spare manpower, unmanned rafts with lights have been developed by scientists,[667] and simpler forms also by fishermen. The Greek purse seiners in the Mediterranean have largely replaced their large numbers of manned light boats (*Fig 176*) by unmanned ones (*Fig 177*).

A special development in light fishing is the

Fig 175 Spanish boats of Benidorm equipped with powerful lights for attracting sardine. (*Photo: J Schärfe.*)

Fig 177 Unmanned rafts with lamps for attracting sardines, used in the Greek fishery of Mythimna on the Island of Lesbos (1973).

underwater lamp as used in connection with pump fishing to attract the fish. It seems that in other branches of commercial fisheries, underwater lamps have not become as popular as might have been expected from their advantage of providing a better light source without loss from reflection of the light from the water surface.

Artificial light, especially from underwater lamps, brings fish into abnormal conditions which these animals do not know by nature. Even today, it is not quite clear just how light does affect fish. Investigations, however, have revealed that the luring effect of light is partly based on a disorientation of the vision of the fish[637]. Nevertheless, this is not considered sufficient to explain the reaction of fish to artificial light. Mostly a positive phototaxis is considered of particular significance. In spite of these explanations there may be unexpected reactions of the fish to light, which are as difficult to explain as are the reactions of fish in an electrical current (Chapter 5). Nevertheless, some basic 'rules' for fish behaviour to light are known. Successful use of light for attracting and concentrating fish requires the night to be dark, without any other disturbing sources of light such as the moon or other lamps in the vicinity,

Fig 176 Greek purse seiner with attendant light-boats preparing to depart from the fishing port of Mytilini on the Island of Lesbos. The smaller unpowered net-boat can be seen on the starboard side of the vessel. (1968).

and transparent water so that the light can extend far without disturbing shades or shadows. But it is not only ecological facts and weather conditions, or the quality or intensity of the light, which influence the success of light fishing; the physiological condition of the fish is also important, and even different fish densities can be decisive in whether light fishery is successful or not. In this respect it must be realised that although stronger light will illuminate a wider area, some fish will try to stay in a lower light intensity, therefore their distance from the light source may become so great that they may not be within the catching range of the fishing gear.

11.3 Chemical lures

Another bait group affects the chemical senses – that is, smell and taste. Like the eye, these senses are used in searching for food. The fishing gear, therefore, may be provided with a suitable bait to attract a particular species of fish by its odour. Sometimes the fisherman himself seeks to have this smell by rubbing his hands with some strong smelling material which is also used for his traps, scoop nets and other gear. (On the other hand gear should not be touched with hands smelling of dark rye bread!) Small or cut up baits are usually used in order to increase their odorous effect. The bait is fixed on a hook, put in a trap, or even on sheets of netting. Sometimes special little bags or other receptacles are used to keep the bait in or near the fishing gear (*Figs 178* and *602*).

Mostly special fish food is used as bait, and this may be changed with the season, to attract fishes or other prey. Sometimes a smelly bait is used which is not normally found by the fish. Certain substances possessing strong odours have always been considered attractive, such as anise, musk, castor, civet, shrimp oil, heron's oil, *etc*. In eastern Germany, longlines for eels have been traditionally soaked in barrels of water with aniseed oil. These strong smelling materials are used even today for manufacturing 'unfailing' chemical bait. Gipsies especially know the secrets of preparing attractive baits like 'muscade de Divio' or 'radio-active balls' which are mostly resin or stones rubbed with strong-smelling oils. The gipsies are also said to be the inventors of artificial lures first made about 150 years ago. But it is very surprising that until now no artificial chemical bait has been used in commercial fisheries. This is a very serious deficiency, because very often the lack of bait hampers commercial fisheries. When artificial chemical lures are offered for this purpose they are based on natural materials. To attract shark, a perforated bag of plastic, filled with chopped up intestines of fish, is moved up and down in the water. For catching tuna, artificial bait with fish oil has been used, but it was not as successful as natural bait fish. Nevertheless, research work is going on in an attempt to solve this problem of the commercial fisheries, especially in line fishing.[271] Fish food can also be used to familiarize fish with a certain place. This means that the fishes are 'trained' to come to a suitable area look for food. Sport fishermen do this for several days prior to fishing. Commercial fishermen, too, know and use this tactic for concentrating fish. Egyptians fishing with lines for sea bream also practised feeding them beforehand. And the French sardine fishermen of the Atlantic coast lure the fish up from the deep into the range of their nets with a mixture of cod roe and groundnut meal.[64] By this means the fish not only rise to the upper water layers, but come near to the surface where the fishermen can catch them.

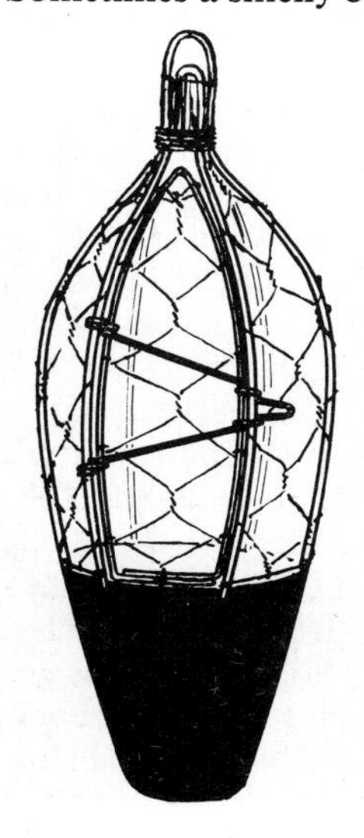

Fig 178 Japanese receptacle for live fishing bait.

There are other fishing methods in which foodstuff is spread to attract and to keep the fish in the range of a gear. An original method is for the fisherman himself to chew the bait and spit it into the water. Fishermen of the Cape Verde Islands know of this method and chew small bait fish to catch *Decapterus* and *Sardinella* with handlines and scoop nets. (*Fig 123*).[81] The fishermen of Hawaii also do this by chewing dried shrimp to catch different fish with pole-and-line.[262]

11.4 Sexual lures

The chemical senses are not only used in search of food; together with other stimuli they may also help in finding sexual partners. It seems that the knowledge that fishes and other water animals can be attracted for catching not only by their sexual partners but also by their sexual competitors is known all over the world. In ancient times it was known that some animals, like males of cuttlefish, could be attracted by their females. Even today this knowledge is used to catch cuttlefish by trolling a female of the same species slowly at the stern of a boat. Male cuttlefish which approach for mating are speared or taken in dipnets.[641] Fishermen in East Asia put female cuttlefish into small baskets in order to attract their males. Mediterranean fishermen in Sicily know of the same method.[54] The Italians place wicker or wire baskets on the bottom of the sea, singly or in strings, 'baited' with a female cuttlefish or a branch of mastic (*Pistacea lenticus*). They catch the attracted male cuttlefish with scoop nets. Not only cephalopods, but also fish, are caught in this way, by luring with sexual stimuli. Formerly fishermen on the upper part of the River Rhine put female salmon into their traps to attract the male fish. Male salmon are also used for luring other males, which will try to fight their supposed competitor and thus become caught in the prepared trap. A dummy fish achieves the same effect (*Fig 234*). A similar method was used when fishing with a stationary liftnet for the same fish. A female salmon was let into the water but tied to a line. When a male was attracted, the female was drawn slowly near to the bank of the river over a net. The male salmon followed and was caught by quickly lifting the net.[331]

In the examples given, chemical and optical stimuli are here acting simultaneously. This also applies to a Japanese method for catching ayus. A living fish of this species is tied to fishing lines beside an unbaited hook; then species of the same type attack the supposed intruder and thus become hooked themselves. Nigerian fishermen use baskets with female catfish to attract the males with their smell in shallow waters. Fishermen in northern Germany put a living burbot into a trap to attract many other fish of the same species to enter the same trap. Characteristically, this method is particularly successful during the spawning season.[385] There may be more examples of fishermen all over the world using this method to attract fish or to frighten away their possible competitors or to encourage them to join others for social reasons, even inside a trap.

11.5 Acoustic bait

Acoustic bait are less frequently used than optical and chemical ones. Moreover, it is often not clear whether the audible sound really has a luring effect or whether the vibrations received by the tactile sense merely excite curiosity. Herodotus tells the story that people had tried without success to attract fish with the notes of a flute. Nevertheless, in some areas the practice obtained of attracting untrained fish by whistling, and the story that fish can be attracted by good vocal and instrumental music seems to have been known worldwide since very early times. Often an unconscious training of fish is mentioned as an explanation. This may be true, because in Mediterranean waters sharks are often attracted to underwater explosions. They are able to hear and, in addition, they may receive the pressure waves created by the explosion by means of the lateral line system.[126] The attraction can be explained by their learning to proceed to a place where, after an explosion, food can be found very easily (Chapter 5).

As explained at the beginning of this section, it is not clear whether it is the audible noise which is attractive, or the sound vibrations, which may be similar to that of a hampered fish which is the usual prey of the predator. It seems that such movements can be imitated by underwater rattles which imitate the noises made by movements of small fish or the noise of crayfish tails flapping.[140] In this respect the shark rattles used in Oceania are very famous. These rattles are made of coconut shells or snail shells and are moved to and fro on the surface of the water. The rattling noise attracts the sharks, which are then caught by loops being slipped over their heads (*Fig 249b*). Rattles are also used to attract catfish in African fresh waters[244] and it is said that the old-time Maori fishermen of New Zealand attracted grouper by dumping a flax bag filled with stones on a deep reef.[140]

Another lure which is often cited as having a supposedly acoustic effect is the 'croakwood' (Quakholz) of the southeast European fisheries, for luring sheatfish between the rivers Volga and Danube.[13, 20, 278, 588] The croakwood is a horn-like instrument made of wood (oak, willow or lime tree) with a long knife-like handle and a plate on its end (*Fig 179*). This plate can be flat and sometimes replaceable, because it can break when used and a new plate then has to be fixed. The plate can also have a hole in its middle, so that it can be considered a small version of the so-called pulse sticks used in many fisheries to frighten the fish by a special noise (*Fig 187*). Such a hollow sound is also produced by the croakwood when it is thrust backwards into the water (*Fig 180*). Formerly a real cowhorn was used for this purpose. Nowadays also the main part of a spoon without a handle can be nailed onto a stick

Fig 179 Hungarian 'Quakholz' for attracting sheat-fish.

and used to produce a sound considered attractive to sheatfish, especially the males. Some people think that this sound imitates the croaking of frogs or the noise of frogs jumping into the water and that this is what attracts the sheatfish. According to other people, these implements imitate noises produced by female sheatfish for attracting the male fish. Doubt attaches to the validity of both opinions and, in point of fact, nothing really is known about the sort of noise made by female sheatfish! It is, however, believed that the sheatfish is aroused by the noise to approach on an investigating mission, and that it then takes the bait of a fish or frog offered with a line. But other baits are also accepted, like gallnuts and Limacidae which never produce any attracting noise! The croakwood is thought to have originated in the Hungarian fishery and spread from there to neighbouring countries.[590] It may be of interest to know that the ability to make a special attracting noise was also known in the Polish fishery for sheatfish.[690] There is also a passage from Homer which is interpreted as indicating that the Greeks already knew about a way of attracting sheatfish by noise.[278]

Fig 180 Operation of a 'Quakholz' during angling for sheat-fish. (*Photo: Solymos, 1965*).

Even though there may be some possibility that in the cases mentioned before the audible sound causes some positive phonotaxis, so the ringing of a bell cannot be considered as a natural lure for fish. An account of the ancient Russian fishery on the Lake of Peipus says[333] that fishing lines, to which were attached underwater bells, were used for attracting fish. But here, too, it may be doubted whether the sound from the submerged bells really did have an alluring effect.

It is understandable that some fish can be attracted by the noise and the movement of the water caused by schools of small fish springing over the water surface to escape their predators. So rattles also cause vibrations on the surface of the water similar to the splashes made by jumping fish. It is supposed that this is a positive phonotaxis, although the waves of vibration may also play a part. A similar effect may be obtained through a technique used in South Asia, Africa and South America to attract fish by splashing or beating the water surface with brushwood.[244, 593] The same effect is also achieved in the tuna line fishery by spraying the water surface with powerful hoses, but it is also desirable here that the vessel and the fishermen should be, as far as possible, invisible to the tuna. Moreover, it seems that the sprays also have the effect of making the lines and hooks difficult to distinguish from the bait scattered on the water surface.[685]

When small fish chased by their enemy come near to the water surface, they attract flocks of birds, which also cause splashing noises when diving for the fish. An acoustic association is presumed for tuna and birds. To catch yellowtail, bonito, mackerel, dolphin (*Coryphaena*) and tuna with troll lines, the Japanese offer a special 'fish inviter' which imitates the aforementioned noises of splashing water (*Fig 181*). This device is towed on the water surface. It dives when the fish is hooked, or if it remains on the water surface with the hooked fish, the splashing stops. Here have to be added some unexpected observations about the behaviour of fish faced with a curtain of air bubbles. It is known that a wall of air bubbles repels fish to some extent and this is thought to be helpful in some catching techniques. But there have also been contradictory observations, that fish are attracted by air bubbles. Russian investigations have found[334] that air bubbles can cause low-frequency noises with the acoustic characteristics of rain, waterfalls and small discharging rivers. The latter may attract fish searching for spawning places in fresh water. The attraction of predators like bonito, tuna, salmon and sea trout to air bubbles is therefore explained

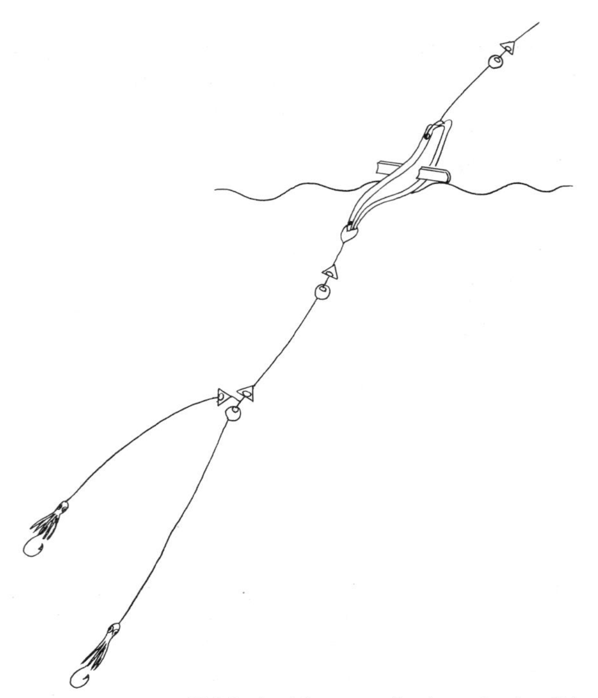

Fig 181 Japanese 'fish inviter' for attracting investigating fish by noises simulating the splashes of birds attacking small fish at the water surface.

by the fact that an acoustic field is produced similar to the splashes of small fish.

The most promising method of using acoustic lures was expected to be the idea of playing back natural noises with the help of underwater loudspeakers. This was reported many times by different people and many optimistic experiments have been tried based on playing back noises caused by fish when feeding, spawning or swimming. The attraction of tuna searching for food, by sounds caused by diving sea birds feeding on bait fish, has already been mentioned with the Japanese 'fish inviter'. It was hoped to get tuna by means of a combination of acoustic attractive signals of a special frequency transmitted through the water from a tape recorder.[458] In 1972 reports came from New Zealand that the problem of acoustic detection and attraction of tuna with the help of an acoustic signal based on natural feeding sounds of bait fish and birds had been solved. Unfortunately, these reports do not yet seem to fulfil the needs of the commercial fishery. From New Zealand came also the idea of a squid lure which was expected to have good attractive properties producing 'musical notes' caused by pressure variations during jigging.[459] This also seems to survive only in the form of a curiosity.

There is another fishing method which is often considered an example *par excellence* of an effective use of noise for the attraction of fish. This is the so-called rattle fishery carried out in winter on the Curiches Haff on the Baltic Coast. There a board is partly pushed through an ice hole while gillnets are arranged in a star-like pattern below the ice. Fishermen then drum rhythmically on the board with two wooden clubs, causing a far-reaching roaring noise which is designed to attract the fish.[357] Here the real explanation is probably that there is no positive phonotaxis, but that the fish are so frightened by the noise and vibrations that they swim madly around and thus get themselves entangled in the set nets. For this reason the fishermen have to change their fishing place from time to time, which would not be necessary if the fish were attracted by this obtrusive and wide reaching noise. Strictly speaking, this method does not use noise to attract, but to stir up the fish by frightening with the help of acoustic and mechanical waves.

11.6 Lure lines and aggregating devices

Some fish, as well as many crustaceans and octopi, can be attracted and concentrated by artificial hiding places. This is especially true for bottom-living animals which need some contact with solid bodies; that means, they show positive tactile reactions. This orientation by tactile senses is called thigmotaxis. Bottom fish and others have a positive thigmotaxis. This behaviour is well known and a special fishery based on hiding places will be described later (Chapter 13).

Other fish, like pelagic fish shoaling under normal conditions, not only keep their distance from their own kind but they also try to avoid touching any solid body, whether living or dead. This can be seen with schools in aquaria or when fishes are encircled by walls of netting. It is known also that this can change with the fishes' physiological condition. Spawning herring, for example, are less careful than non-spawning shoals about keeping a distance of some metres from the netting of a trawl. Their capacity to maintain distance is attained by means of optical and tactile senses. In contrast to bottom fish, pelagic fish in general have a negative thigmotaxis. This is not in contradiction to the fact that pelagic fish are caught in nets in which they are pressed passively or which they cannot see, or that they touch transparent lines or the so-called 'feeling lines' made of fine wire as were used to detect fish before the invention of fish-finding apparatus. On the other hand, this does not mean that some pelagic species of fish would not like to seek shelter or at least to assemble at certain distances from a solid body. The latter aspect can be observed in the neighbourhood of floating bodies of different types. These can be natural stems of trees or bushes, or bunches of drifting plants. They can also be man made materials, used or lost, anchored or free-floating like buoys, kegs or barrels, logs, rafts and boats, or many other things considered as marine debris. The reason for this behaviour of some fish is not quite clear. It can be due to the need of certain species of fish to seek shelter without direct contact, or from the desire for food which is attracted to floating materials. Most people think that it is a need for an optical orientation, or the lure of low-frequency vibrations produced by the movement of the floating bodies.[658] Fishermen have known of this for a long time, and know too that certain species of fish can be attracted to floats, and have used this behaviour to catch them. Well known are the stationary lure lines used by Malay fishermen especially in Indonesia.[682] and Malaysia[487] (*Fig 182*). They are called in Indonesia 'rumpon' (roempon) and in Malaysia, 'unjang'. They are made up of lines on which palm leaves (up to 15 or 20) are arranged one upon another at a distance of one fathom or more. Alternatively, bunches of grass or similar material may be used – the whole line being supported by bamboo floats and anchored in position. The fish, once they are concentrated near those lines, can be caught with other gear as soon as the fishermen reckons it to be worthwhile. Liftnets, surrounding nets, and other gear like seine nets are used for this purpose, but also fishing with handlines and gillnets can be successful in the vicinity of lure lines.[487] In Thailand a special purse seine for pomfret is operated with lure lines of coconut palm leaves.[475] Lure lines can also be used to guide fish into drive-in nets (*Fig 182b*). See also Chapter 26.

A special form of operating lure lines to attract and to catch milkfish fry is practised in Java (*Fig 183*). In this case the lines are exposed in the shallow water to give some shelter for milkfish fry. The concentrated fish are caught along the lure lines with the help of skimming nets, and are then transported to hatcheries.

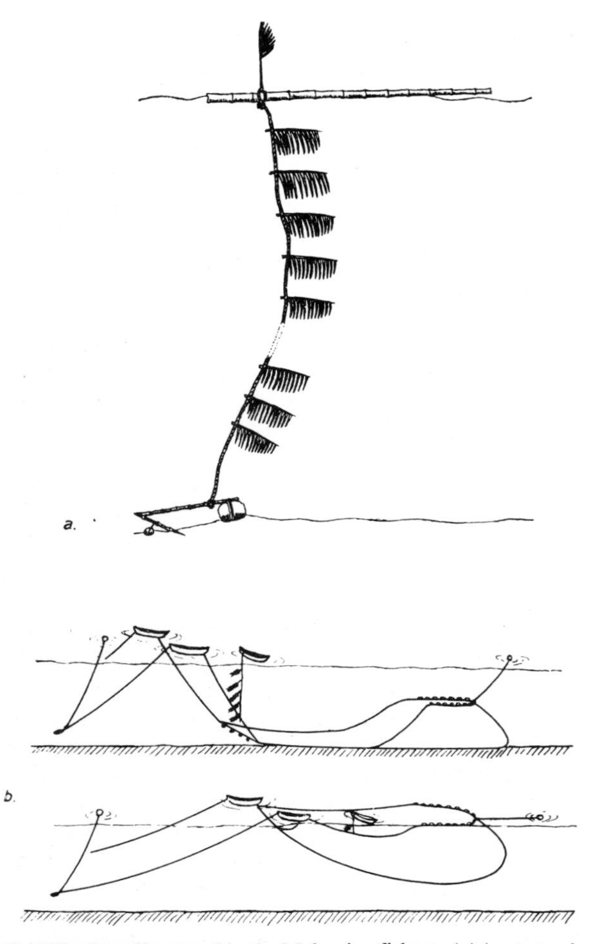

Fig 182 Lure lines used in the Malaysian fishery: (*a*) 'roempon' of the northern coast of Java (*van Pel, 1938*); (*b*) lure lines for drive-in nets in Malaysia (*Parry, 1954*).

Fig 183 Lure lines for attracting milkfish in Java. (*Photo: L Hoss, Eschborn.*)

The association of fish with drifting material in the pelagic environment has been known for a long time in fisheries, and has been widely recorded in recent years. In place of lure lines, other floating objects can also have an attracting and collecting effect on fish. Floating rafts have been used. In the Mediterranean, the so called 'kannizzati fishery' is used for catching *Coryphaena hippurus*. This lure line, used in Malta, is one with a surface float made of two rafts of cork, or more recently, plates of polystyrene foam packed in canvas (*Fig 184*). These anchored floats are set at intervals along a course running out from the coast into water up to six hundred fathoms in depth. The dolphin, here called 'lampuka', are taken with lampara-like nets or caught with floating longlines.[67, 94] Spanish fishermen of Majorca also know of this method, and call the gear 'llampuguera'.[278] In recent years the method of attracting fish with the help of floating rafts and modified lure lines has become more popular for catching tuna, skipjack, yellowfin, and other pelagic fish, especially bait fish for pole-and-line-fishing for tuna. It is known that these fish are not always concentrated in the right place and at the most convenient time, and commercial as well as recreational fishermen spend many hours searching for them. This may be true also for other fish, but in the case of tuna a solution was found from their habit of congregating in the neighbourhood not only of drifting floats fitted out with radar reflectors and radio transmitters, which the fishermen can track and follow for weeks, but also around permanently anchored objects. There are different ideas on how such 'fish aggregating devices' (FADs) should be constructed (*Figs 185* and *186*). As far as is known, the fish attracting devices for pelagic fish could be used successfully in the Philippines, Japan and Hawaii.[373] It seems that by these constructions not only is the quantity of catch increased but also the time for searching and catching live bait for tuna is reduced. Moreover,

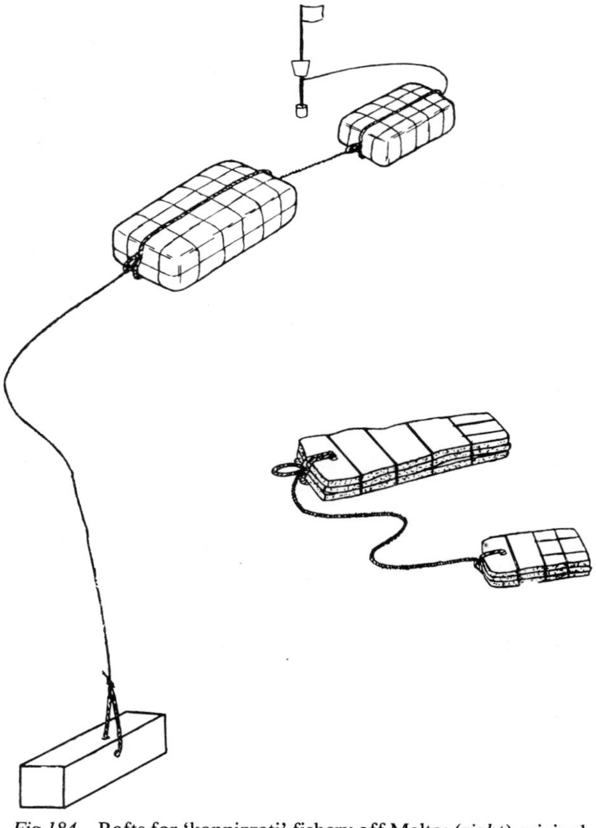

Fig 184 Rafts for 'kannizzati' fishery off Malta: (*right*) original raft made of cork; (*left*) modern raft made of plates of foam plastic (polystyrene) packed in canvas.

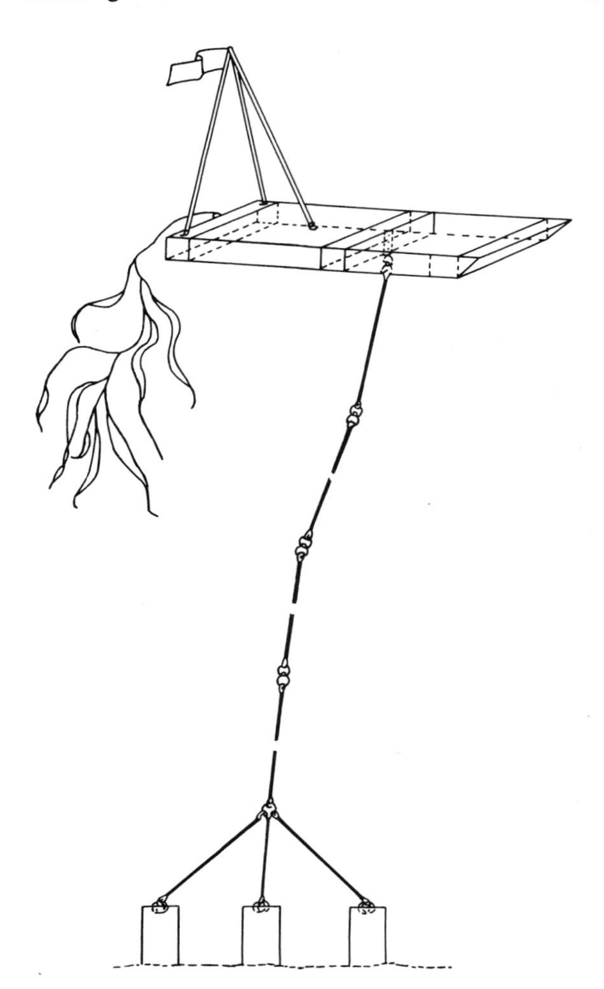

Fig 185 Fish aggregating device, raft-type, as proposed by the Inter-American Tropical Tuna Commission (1980).

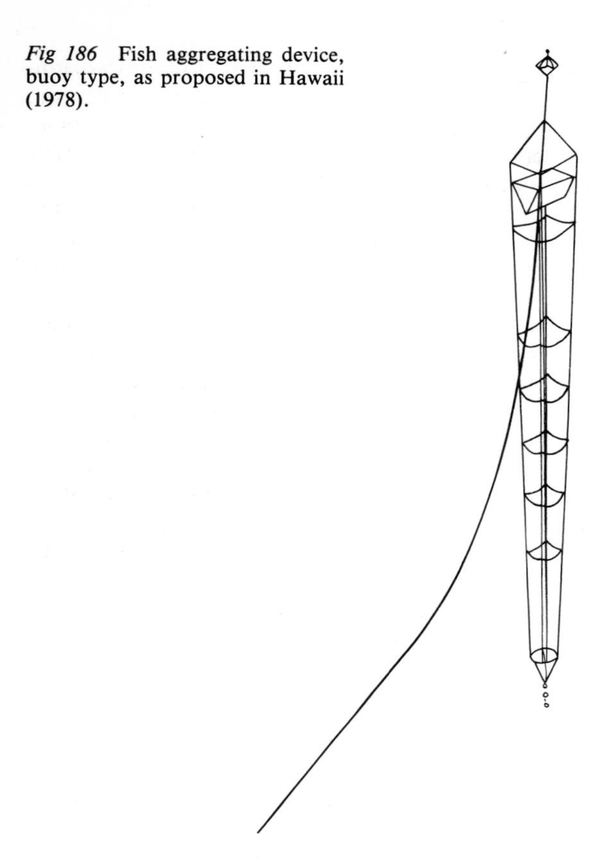

Fig 186 Fish aggregating device, buoy type, as proposed in Hawaii (1978).

it has to be added that aggregating devices are not only of interest for commercial fisheries but also for recreational anglers.

11.7 Fish frightening methods

Sometimes fish have to be kept away from certain places, or frightened to others where they are more easily caught. This is not a new problem. In olden times one method used to drive fish away from certain areas was to spray the water with 'hyssop' (*Hyssopus officinalis* L), well known from its use in the liturgy of the Catholic Church. This strong-smelling labiate flower was formerly cultivated in Europe as a medicinal and spice plant. The fresh green plants were crushed and thrown into the water to frighten the fish away from unsuitable places.[150] Another method of frightening fish away is to use damaged fish, especially their blood. Some species of shoal fish also have an offensive substance in their skin which, when diffused in water after a fish has been injured, causes other fish to leave the place for a time.[182] This fact has apparently not been utilized as much as it might have been, but the thought that there was such a scaring substance is, perhaps, indicated in the earlier reference to the occasional use of fish blood for scaring fish away. It is, however, not as yet proved whether the same scaring substances would not have quite the opposite effect, namely, to attract other species such as predatory fish. Sharks, for instance, are attracted by blood in the water which frightens other fish away.

Fish have always been frightened of noise, so the success of crowds of natives in mass fishing can well be understood. In this they frighten the fish with much noise and commotion and drive them into bights and on to shallow beaches where they can easily be caught. Horses, too, can be led into the water to frighten the fish by their heavy movements. There have been long discussions about whether or not fish can be frightened by the ultra-sound of the various types of echo sounder used in fish finding. There is no reason to believe that the fishes are frightened, but they may perhaps learn that the ultra-sound means danger. On the other hand, it is well known that sea mammals such as whales and seals can be frightened and guided by ultra-sound waves. A description of the fisheries in ancient Russia[333] mentions, in addition to noise, the practices of beating the water, of casting red-hot stones, and of pouring fish blood into the water in order to frighten the fish. To frighten fish by casting stones is very popular, and some conscientious Japanese have found out that the most effective way to drive a fish into a net is to hurl a stone at the side of the fish. . ![432]

Today, a well-known tool for frightening fish is the so-called pulse stick (*Fig 187*), used not only in drive-in fisheries (Chapter 26) but also with seining (*Fig 535*), and purse seining, to prevent the fish escaping by frightening them away from the opening of the gear. More modern experiences have shown that various kinds of fish schools can be startled by playing back dolphin sounds.[228] This method, not so successful for attracting fish, can be used to drive jack mackerel and barracuda into a stationary gear. In sea fisheries it is known that fish can be frightened by intermittent noises, or by those changing in frequency and intensity. Some ideas have been mooted for using this fact to 'persuade' fish that stay near the bottom, but are too high for a bottom trawl to catch them, to shift position by swimming closer to the bottom and so come within the range of that gear. It has been mentioned (Chapter 5) that electricity can be used to compulsorily attract fish so that they can be stupefied and caught. But electrical fields are also used to frighten fish away from certain places, such as the entrances of water turbines.

The knowledge of how to frighten fish, especially

shark, has a practical side, not only for divers and bathers but also for fishermen. Sharks like to attack the cod ends of trawls and it may be necessary at times to scare them away, so special 'shark repellents' are readily available. These are similar to the so-called 'shark chaser', a product of 20% copper acetate and 80% dark violet pigment, used till 1973 by the US Navy to protect swimming men. Even electronic gear has been developed for the protection of trawls. The special problem of driving fish into a fishing gear by movement and noise will be discussed later in the context of the so-called 'drive-in' fishery (Chapter 26).

Fig 187 Pulse stick being used to frighten eels into trammel nets. (*Photo: H Mohr, Hamburg.*)

11.8 Ideas for the future

The idea of attracting, concentrating, and guiding fish by chemical, optical and acoustical influences or other means has inspired science fiction writers more than once. This can be said of sport fishing as well as commercial fisheries. Recently, some ideas were advanced for attracting fish by a very weak electrical field, especially in sport fishing. Equalizing currents between different materials should, it was thought, be sufficient.[572] However, more detailed research is needed in this direction as well as for the use of magnetic fields sometimes proposed for the same purpose. The same can be said of the proposition that sharks and other predatory fish may be attracted by feeling with their lateral organs the weak electric impulses created by the muscle activity of their prey.

There is no doubt that there are good reasons why methods of attracting and concentrating pelagic fish, especially, are mentioned again and again as being of interest to the fishery of the future. It can be seen that areas which once had good pelagic fish concentrations and high fishing activity have disappeared, and have been replaced by more scattered fish in smaller groups. This is contrary to the desired basis of an economical bulk fishery. Therefore, the questions arise of how to concentrate the remaining fish, how they can be exploited by purse seining with light, and how and where small shoals can be brought together to make larger economic ones. As far as can be seen, until now there has been only one new idea for concentrating these fish successfully – and that is with aggregating systems. The idea of using more floating shelters for fish concentration has been discussed[6, 303] as well as how to combine these shelters with a detection system, which would automatically signal catcher vessels when concentrations of fish were apparent. Air bubbles and chemical curtains could, it has been suggested, be developed to keep the fish concentrated and then helicopters could spray chemicals to attract, concentrate, and guide the fish to harvesting machines! Even when there are well-known scientific facts as a basis for such ideas as these, some people think that these concepts may also reveal the helplessness of some fisheries in the face of decreasing stocks. On the other hand, such methods may become the basis of action to keep fish stocks under control in the various national economic zones for future management of fish like herds of cattle. These ideas reveal, at any rate, the concern felt for conserving the resources of the sea for future use.

Last, but not least, a very urgent and previously mentioned problem must be repeated. Very often, line fishing on a large scale is hampered by lack of bait. This can restrict all commercial fishing methods operated with natural bait. As has been shown, with the exception of troll lining, no synthetic, or artificial bait has been able to solve this problem up to now, not even with the help of natural bait fish reared in artificial ponds.[271]

Chapter twelve

Pole-hooks and rippers

In line fisheries the hook itself can act as a bait. Some fish, on seeing the sparkling hook, are attracted by curiosity; they seem to regard it as prey, snap at it, and thus are often caught. Unbaited hooks can, however, also be used on quite different principles. They are then no longer passive hooks taken by the fish, but they are actively guided so that their points hook, spear or rip a fish on it coming within their range. Fish thieves are sometimes caught who cast a line with sharp pointed triple hooks into fish ponds or into natural waters where fish are spawning and, by pulling them to and fro, hope to hook a fish anywhere in its body. Unlike the usual line fishery, in these cases the hook is not used as a carrier of bait, or even as a bait itself. Its movements, at the most, arouse the attention of the fish, may attract it, and then, by a quick movement of the hook, the fish may possibly be pierced and caught. This is not foul-hooking by mistake, but a deliberate tactic to catch the prey. As can be seen from the following examples, catching with 'active hooks' is not only successful with fish but also with other prey, like squid.

In Vietnam cuttlefish are caught by handlines which have at the end a conventional multi-pointed squid hook.[570] Above that a little hook is fastened to hold the bait. This bait (usually a dead fish) attracts the squid to gather round. Then the line is quickly pulled up and the squid, or some of them, are pierced by the points of the ascending squid hook (*Fig 188*).

Ripper-like hooks have been used not only to catch fish and squid but also sea mammals such as seals. In the shallows of northwestern Europe, beams fitted with 20 to 30 long and extremely sharp barbed hooks pointed towards the shore, have been laid in the water channels of the tidal area. The seals come in with the tide, over the hooks, but when they are frightened back during low tide they hook themselves when passing through the channels on their return to the sea.[668]

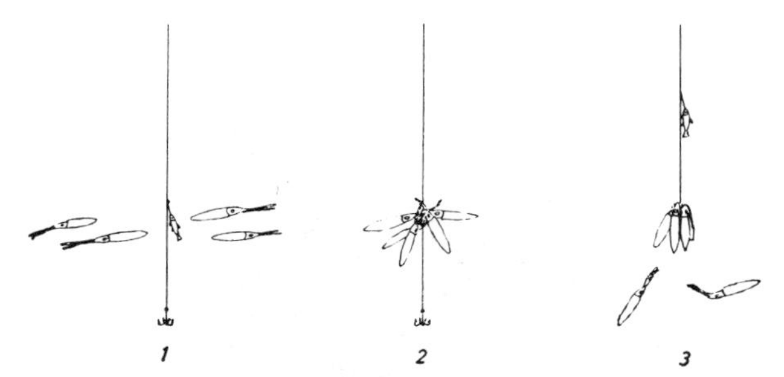

Fig 188 Operation of ripping hooks for catching squid in Vietnam (*Serêne, 1956*).

An essential requirement for such 'rippers' is, of course, that they be very sharp. Several different types of ripping hooks are known. They can be active gear like pole-hooks – better known as gaffs – or multi-pointed implements which can be thrown like harrows over the ground and rip with their sharp teeth, or they can be 'pilks' used for jigging. A special group of rippers are handlines with squid hooks in the form of active gear, as mentioned above, or with single hooks used as passive gear with floating or stationary longlines in sturgeon and other fisheries.

12.1 Pole-hooks and gaffs

Fishing with the ripping hook can be done by fastening a strong single hook, or even several hooks, to the end of a wooden or bamboo pole (*Fig 189*). Certainly, fishing by means of a pole-hook with which a fish is quickly pulled from the water, is much more primitive than fishing with unwatched hooks and lines or with other forms of ripping hooks.

The rod, with its hook ready, is held in the water patiently waiting until a fish passes or until a fish is felt to be touching the rod; then the quick jerk

Fig 189 Arabian pole-hook of Syria.

impales it on the hook and it is pulled from the water. This can be done in open waters and even beneath ice. This practice, with a pole-hook, was formerly very popular in old Russia for catching sturgeon.[278] The method is also considered as probably the oldest form of huso fishing.[527] The experienced Maori fishermen of New Zealand use pole-hooks for gaffing migrating eel during the night when they do not grasp them by hand.

But pole-hooks are, or have been, used for many other fish in Europe, Asia and Africa. This technique, in fact, is so simple that its wide distribution is not surprising. As with the spear, the pole-hook can only be regarded as a lengthened arm of man, with which he can grasp aquatic creatures such as fish, squid, octopi, abalone and sea cucumbers. It may be of interest that pole-hooks belong to the gear operated both in fisheries and for hunting. The hunter uses this gear for taking animals out of their burrows. Small forms of pole-hooks have been already mentioned as tools for hand-picking (Chapter 2). A wooden stick with a small fishing hook tied on the end, can be used not only for dislodging crabs from their holes but also to pick up sand worms and even to catch small eels and trout, although this is considered to be gaffing even though the hook of this gear is only a small fishing hook. But in most cases larger fish have to be caught, which need not only stronger poles but also heavier, long-shanked hooks. Some think that these long-handled hooks are older than the hooks used in line fishing.[16] In this case the pole-hooks are of strong forged metal, without a barb, although there are some exceptions like the barbed gaffs of the Maoris mentioned before. Also Japanese fishermen use strong barbed hooks laid in the bed of a river to await the approach of a salmon.[302, 445] In this case the hook is mounted at the end of a pole of wood or bamboo four to five metres long. With this gear, fishermen wait during the night for salmon to pass. As soon as the fish is felt touching the hook, the fisherman quickly and strongly draws the hook towards himself to hook the fish. When used illegally for catching salmon in Ireland, these ripping instruments also have a barb which enables the fish to be retained more readily.[657] These poles with hooks, especially for catching salmon, are considered a traditional method of river fishing. Until recently they were used by professional fishermen in the estuaries and rivers of England and Wales.[279] The single-barbed pole-hook has been considered a universal implement for the capture of salmon in daytime and during the night with artificial light.

Today, unbarbed pole-hooks are better known as auxiliary gear for landing and lifting fish from the water into a boat, or onto the bank, when caught with other gear. They are then described as 'gaffs' but in reality the gaff hook is a relic of a very early fishing gear. In commercial fisheries, gaffs are needed for line fishing, trapping, even spearing and some other methods, and always when large fish have to be taken out of the water. They are also necessary when many fish have to be picked up in a convenient manner.

In general, the gaff is a simple gear consisting of a short wooden stick with a large specially-made strong hook. Finnish fishermen know of a gaff similar to an eel comb, with six prongs, which is described as a 'fish axe' (*Fig 190*). A particularly interesting form of gaff is used in the Columbia river for white sturgeon (*Acipenser transmontanus*) caught by longlines. In this case the stick of the gaff is replaced by a braided rope. The rope-attached hook is considered less dangerous than one with a stiff wooden handle. Moreover, as with the fish plummets the reach can be enlarged by replacing the pole by a rope. In this connection it should be noted that sometimes gaffs longer than 2.4 metres, or fitted with more than 9 metres of rope, may be not allowed by law.[140]

Fig 190 Finnish 'fish axe', a six-pointed gaff (*Mäki and Pitkänen, 1969*).

Better known, and also better constructed, are gaffs used in sport fisheries. The main reason for using them is because the fishing line may be too fine and weak for lifting larger prey out of the water. This has to be done with the gaff. In this case the gaff replaces the landing net (Chapter 10). Sports fishermen also use a more highly developed gaff called a 'flying gaff'. As with harpoons, the head of the gaff is detachable from the handle, but to avoid losing the hook and prey the hook is tied to the boat with a strong line.[626]

12.2 Fish harrows

As mentioned in the beginning of this chapter, hooks can be dragged over an area for ripping fish. Sharpened fishing hooks may be cast out from the beach, or from a bridge, and pulled in again in the hope of spearing or piercing a fish. This can be done not only with a single or triple hook, but also with a whole row of hooks which is then raked over the bottom like a harrow. In that way it is especially useful for catching flatfish. English fishermen knew such an implement as a 'fluke bar'. This was actually an iron rod equipped with a row of sharp fishing hooks with barbs (*Fig 191*). When that fish rake was towed over the ground, either by a boat or by a man standing up in the water, the sharp hooks cut into the bottom and impaled any fish encountered. The gear was also called the 'murderer' which not only correctly describes its success but also its damaging effect. A similar

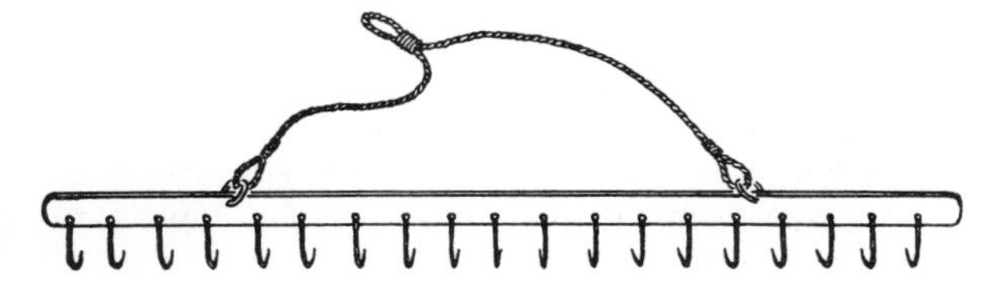

Fig 191 Fluke bar or 'murderer' of southern England (*Davis, 1958*).

method of dragging what looks like a comb with hooks is also known in Asia. In Java, small 'harrows' were used which were similar to the English fluke bar (*Fig 192*). As they were made of wood, stones were normally attached as weights.[285]

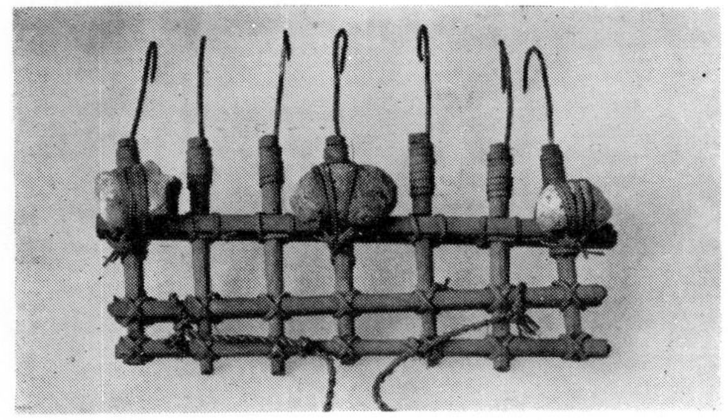

Fig 192 Old Indonesian fish harrow. (*Photo: Ethnographical Museum, Leiden.*)

For piercing fish on the bottom, the Japanese have a similar gear which, although now of a different design, serves the same purpose. Quadruple hooks are fastened with short casts to a transverse rod (*Fig 193*) and the rod is towed by a motor boat. The transverse rod can be up to eight metres in length so that it rakes over a considerable area. This implement, with its multiple ripping hooks, certainly has an adverse effect on fish stocks. The hooks, when towed over the bottom, can also be used for ripping seaweed, sponges and corals. In the modern freshwater fishery of the United States, a similar gear called the 'crow-foot bar' with barbless hooks, is used for lifting freshwater mussels in a commercial fishery.[145] Ancient Venetian fishermen were familiar with such gear

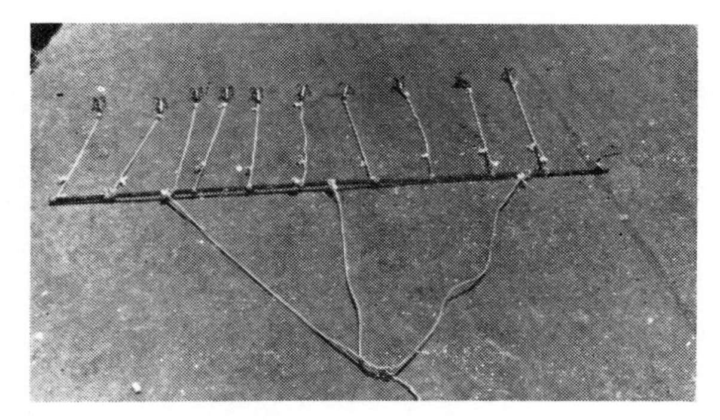

Fig 193 Japanese 'bunchin kogitsuri'.

under the name of 'trezzola' and used it for securing sponges and corals. In the Philippines a similar instrument was used for harvesting siliceous sponges.[369]

It has to be added, that there are some types of dredges (Chapter 20) with long sharp teeth at their openings. Their purpose is to dig out fish, shells, and other animals from the bottom, but they may also cause undesirable damage to their prey. In contrast to fish harrows, dredges have collecting bags, which means that piercing is not the aim of this fishing method.

12.3 Pilking with handlines

Very popular, especially in northern countries, is the technique of catching fish with handlines and ripping hooks. This method is known by many different names, like 'pilking' and 'jigging', and is operated in fresh waters as well as in the seas. The principle is to get the catch by piercing the fish anywhere in its body with an active, mostly unbaited device called a pilk, ripper or jig/jigger. (The name jig or jigger is, unfortunately, also used for other artificial lures including, for example, that used in trolling).

Originally, the pilk was a flashing weight, usually made of metal, combined with one or more hooks. To catch a fish, the pilk is moved up and down to attract it and to pierce it with the sharp hook. That movement can be achieved by casting the line and then quickly hauling it in, or else by raising and dropping the hook with small jerky movements. In the latter case, handlines, with or without rods, are used for jerking the hook up and down. The fish is attracted by these movements of the pilk, comes nearer, and is then foul-hooked in its body. It must be admitted, however, that this fishing method does not always capture the fish by piercing it. There are cases when the hook is actually taken by the fish. The pilk can be an artificial lure like those used for spin fishing (*Fig 173*), but they are mostly more specialised types (*Fig 194*). The pilk must be weighted so that it will sink quickly and also have the necessary force and weight to penetrate a fish's body when it is pulled upwards.

Simple pilks with one hook are used, but some have a transverse rod or two arms like balance lines from which two lines are suspended (*Fig 117e*). Rippers are especially used for the slower-moving spawning fish, or when fishing through ice-holes in the wintertime. With older types of the up and down jerking pilks, the shank of the hook is provided with a fish-shaped glittering lead weight (*Fig 194a*). In many types, hook and weight are of one single piece, with one or two hooks arranged like the flukes of an anchor (*Fig 194b*). Mostly, the pilks for fish are fitted with triple or quadruple hooks. There is one exception, and this is the 'lakekrone' (lake crown) of the Norwegians – used for catching burbot (*Lota lota*).[483] This is a jig similar to the 'umbrella hooks' with many unbarbed hooks, used for catching cephalopods (*Fig 208d*). More modern types of jigs have the hook and weight in two separated pieces[63] although the hook may be combined with the weight through a swivel (*Fig 194e*) or a little chain. Often pilks are home-made, using a lead weight and some normal fishing hooks tied together (*Fig 194c*). The hooks used as rippers are generally barbed. The main requirement of the pilk is that the hooks be sharp. Strange to say, plankton feeders can also be attracted by the movements of the ripper. That is the reason why herring can be caught by this method, as is done in the Bay of Kiel when the fish arrive for spawning.

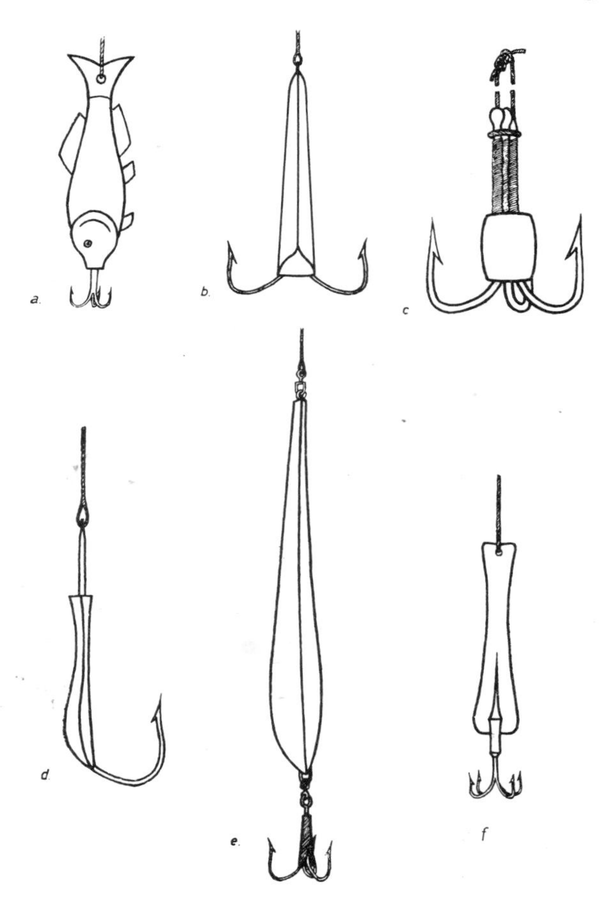

Fig 194 Rippers used in northern lands: (*a*) ripper used in freshwater fishery for perch; (*b*) anchor-like pilk for cod; (*c*) pilk made from three hooks and a lead as used off western Greenland; (*d*) simple Norwegian 'juksa' for cod; (*e*) modern Norwegian 'juksa' with movable triple hook; (*f*) pilk for herring in the Bay of Kiel, Germany.

The technique of catching fish by means of jigging is widespread. In the European freshwater fisheries, rippers are usually used in the wintertime or spring, when the fish are still lazy and not so apt to be frightened away by the moving hooks.[569] In some countries, however, this method is prohibited in fresh water because the fish are caught more or less haphazardly and may be seriously injured. As stated at the beginning of this chapter, this method is mainly used by fish thieves. Nevertheless, jigging is also practised by some sports fishermen. When ice fishing or hake jigging, the Scandinavians use a small rod, sometimes also with a reel.

Jigging is a much more widespread practice in sea fisheries than it is in fresh waters. The cod 'Koppel' and the so-called 'Heringshaue', a herring fishing gear, are used all around the Baltic. Both types of gear are genuine rippers.[238] Even handlines with many hooks are used like rippers in sea fisheries to catch mackerel and other fish. In this case the hooks are fitted with feathers to attract the mackerel; some hook themselves, others are pierced. Nowadays, the feathers can be replaced by bands of split fibres. The handline fishery for cod in northern areas is often more a ripping line-fishery. That is why cod caught by the Norwegian 'juksa' line are often not hooked in the mouth, but pierced elsewhere by the up and down movement of the jig. Ripper fishermen can be found on many coasts.

The Turks have, for many years, maintained a pilk fishery for bluefish (*Pomatomus saltator* L). This fish comes in large shoals through the Bosphorus early in the year (*Fig 195*). To withstand the strong currents of this area, the weights of the pilks operated for this fishing are often as heavy as 1.200g. Mercury is used to polish the pilk to increase its attraction to the fish (*Fig 196*). Large triple hooks, made by the fishermen themselves, usually pierce the dorsal fin of the fish.

Fishing with hand-operated pilks is a simple,

Fig 195 Turkish fishermen pilking for bluefish in the Bosphorus (1971).

inexpensive, but labour intensive method, but nevertheless an effective one. It is, therefore, understandable that efforts have been made to replace the regular and tiring up and down movement of the hand by manually-operated mechanical arrangements (*Fig 197*). Even the use of short sticks can be less tiring. Special short 'pilkestikke' with reels for the line movement are known in sport fishing. More effective were reels fixed on the gunwale of the vessel. Power-operated jigging methods soon followed (see the last section of this chapter).

Fig 196 A pilk for bluefish is polished with mercury to make it sparkle, Bosporus (1971).

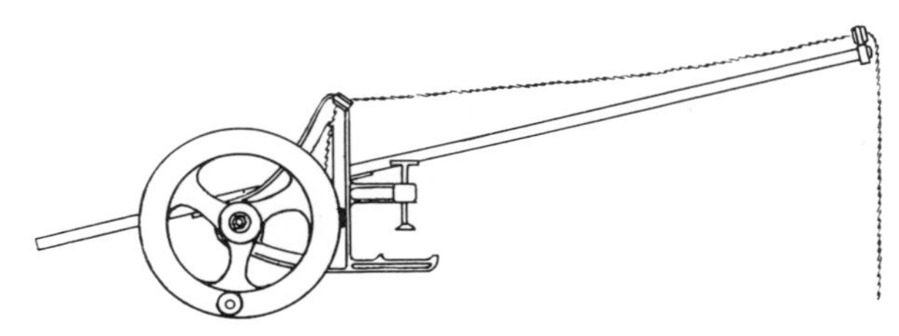

Fig 197 Norwegian hand-reel for 'juksa' fishing.

12.4 Rippers on stationary lines and troll lines

Rippers can also be operated with set lines, especially with stationary longlines. In the Chinese freshwater fishery longlines are known which have short branch lines, each with one sharp hook, tied at short intervals on the main line, on which the fish rip themselves (*Fig 198*). They also have small anchored rafts (*Fig 199*) covered with branches or wheat straw, which offer a good hiding place for some fish. From these rafts more than 20 ripping hooks are hung on short lines on which fish, looking for shelter, hook themselves.[289] The Chinese stationary longlines, with longer by-lines (*Fig 135*), were mentioned in Chapter 9. If the description of ancient Chinese fishing practices[613] is correct, Chinese fishermen used longlines which had whole systems of main and by-lines with sharp ripping hooks set to entangle and hook large fish (*Fig 200*). Here sturgeons, probably from the Amur area, are specially mentioned as being among the fish caught.

Around the Black Sea, longlines with sharp hooks are set to catch sturgeons by ripping. The bodies

Fig 198 Caught by a Chinese longline with ripping hooks. (*Kasuga, 1975*).

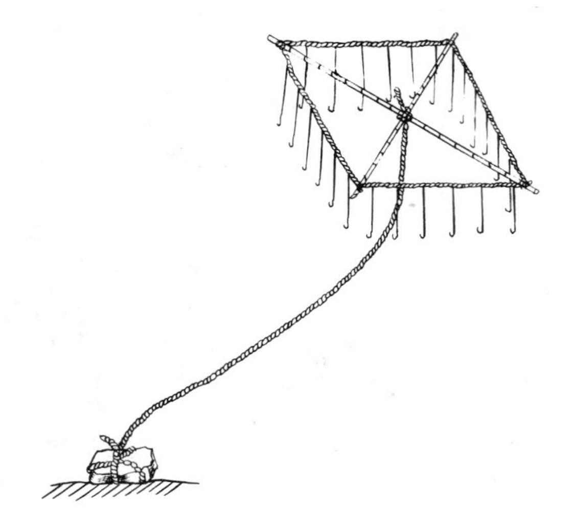

Fig 199 Chinese bamboo raft with ripping hooks. In operation the raft is covered with straw. (*Kasuga, 1975*).

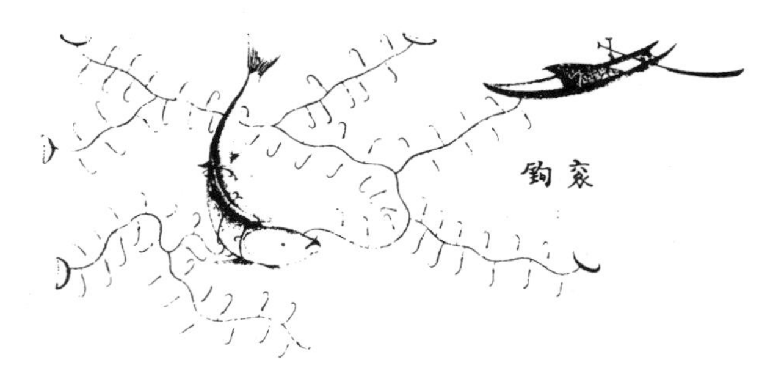

Fig 200 Chinese longline with by-lines. The hooks act as entangling ripping hooks. (*de Thiersant, 1872*).

of these fish are covered with single 'bone plates', the ganoid scales, and the ripping hooks easily catch under these. For this purpose, longlines are set with branch lines fitted with sharpened coarse hooks attached side by side to the main line. This can be done in several different ways (*Fig 201*). Sometimes the line floats and all hooks hang on short branch lines with the points up (*Fig 201b*). This type of line was used in the sturgeon fishery in the Caspian Sea till as late as the fifties of this century (*Fig 202*).

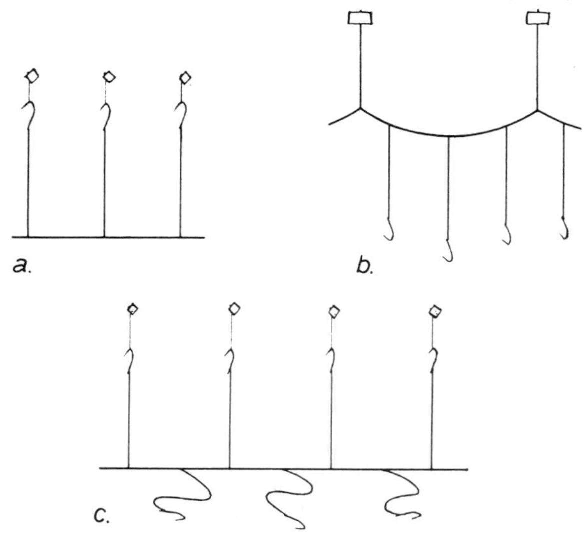

Fig 201 Different construction of sturgeon lines. The branch lines are: (*a*) floating; (*b*) hanging, or (*c*) alternately hanging and floating.

Originally the main lines were set on the bottom, *eg* in the mouth of a river, and each hook was floated by a small float fixed on the bend of the hook. In this case, the point of the hook was turned down (*Fig 201a*). In contrast to the line mentioned earlier, these hooks have small barbs to prevent the line for the float slipping over the point of the hook (*Fig 203*). Finally, the hooks may be set alternately with and without floats. This means that each second hook is floating or hanging down, sometimes resting on the seabed (*Fig 201c*). This type of hook is used in the Black Sea by Turkish and Rumanian fishermen for sturgeon fishing even today. (*Figs 204* and *205*).[69, 383] If a sturgeon swims through such a hook curtain, the sharp hooks are likely to get a grip on the bony plates with ease.[69, 424, 440] There is some evidence that these hooks were originally made of wood and used in the Rivers Dvina and Ob in northern Eurasia.[527] Therefore, pointing down may have been their original orientation. From the north this 'samalow' hook spread to southeast Europe with migrating Turkish

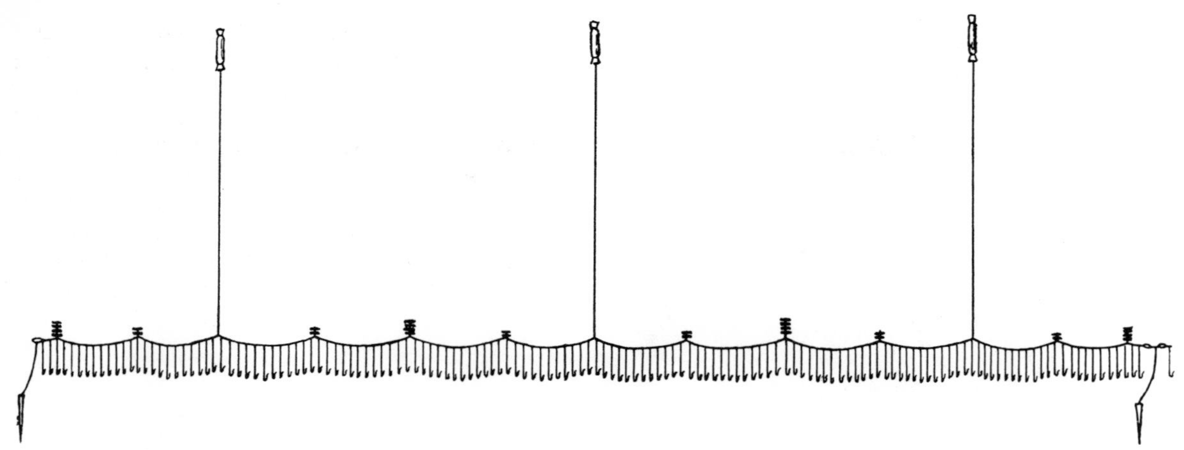

Fig 202 Floating longlines with ripping hooks as formerly used in the Caspian Sea. (*NN, 1951*).

Fig 203 Sturgeon hook from the Black Sea. Between point and bend the hook has a thickening like a barb to prevent the rope with the float attached, (*Fig 201a*) from slipping over the point.

Fig 204 Turkish sturgeon fisherman controlling his sturgeon lines in the Red River (1967).

Fig 205 Rumanian fisherman maintaining sturgeon lines in a fishermen's camp on the estuary of the Danube near Sulina (1976).

tribes in the Black Sea area, covering the lower Danube and Dnieper, the Sea of Azov with the Don, and the Caspian Sea with the Volga. But today it is prohibited in many places (including the Caspian Sea as the sturgeon, though they may be seriously injured, can free themselves by struggling. On the lower Danube, species of fish other than sturgeon have also been caught by fishing lines with just such ripping hooks.

It is interesting to realize that longlines with dense rows of suspended ripping hooks have also been known and are still used in other parts of the world. Longlines with ripping hooks hanging as narrowly as a curtain are known from the River Niger (*Fig 206*). In this case the line, with short branch lines tied at very short intervals, is fixed between sticks

Fig 206 Anchored longlines with ripping hooks are floated some distance above the bottom of the River Niger. (*Photo: Bacalbasa.*)

in such a manner that the unbaited hooks are hanging a short distance from the bottom.[651, 654] Similar ripping longlines are known from the area of Lake Chad,[44] with short branch lines hanging close together. Such lines are stretched across a river to catch fish by them ripping themselves. The branch lines can be very short (*Fig 207*). There is even one type of longline with unbaited hooks which has no branch lines. In this case the hooks are tied directly onto the main line, which is quite extraordinary.

Fig 207 Very short branchlines of a longline with ripping hooks in a village of Benin fishermen near Lagune Aby, Ivory Coast, (1971).

That ripping hooks can also be towed to catch fish can be seen from the example of the various fish harrows. Unbaited longlines with short snoods ending in extremely sharp barbless hooks, which are towed over the bottom are also known in large-scale fisheries. Malayan fishermen of Singapore use a line which is supported, at short intervals, by wooden floats. One end is attached to a raft-like buoy, the other being retained on the boat so that the gear forms a low curtain of hooks just above the seabed. Fish passing through this barrier can be hooked and are subsequently entangled by other hooks in their struggle to escape.[93] The towing of a longline over the ground can also be considered a form of trolling with ripping hooks. In the introduction to this chapter the practice of thieves, whereby rippers are towed through a pond with a dense fish population, was mentioned. An 'improved' variation of this method can be seen in Malaysia, where young people throw heavily-weighted triple hooks into the water and draw them back with violent jerking movements with the help of a rod and a reel like those used in spin fishing (Chapter 10).

12.5 Rippers for cephalopods

For catching cephalopods (squid, cuttlefish and octopus), various types of handlines, longlines and troll lines are used with ripping hooks. Multihooked rippers are considered typical for this fishery (*Fig 208*). Mostly these rippers or jigs are short stems of lead weight painted white and red or wrapped in pieces of white or dyed linen or even velvet. They can also be made from horn and bone.

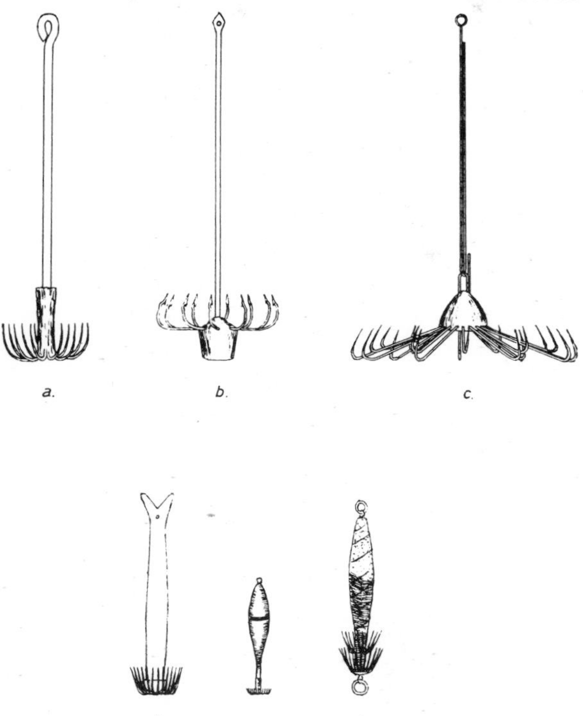

Fig 208 Special hooks for squid: (*a*) long type of Taiwan (Formosa); (*b*) long type of Greece; (*c*) composite hook of Italy; (*d*) usual Mediterranean type; (*e*) small type used in Portugal; (*f*) double hook of Korea.

Modern ones are made of plastic. The colour of these stems is considered important for the success of the catch. In some Japanese experiments, red and orange stems with inserted pieces of shell proved most efficient, whilst white ones and those of silvery metal were the least effective. One end of the stem is fitted with one, two or even three circles of upturned barbless hooks made of stainless steel. In contrast to the rippers used for squid, those used for octopus are simpler in construction and have a single circle of barbless hooks only. The hooks are generally unbarbed but, because some fishermen make their own rippers for squid, cuttlefish and octopus with whatever hooks are available, barbed ones can also be found (*Figs 209a* and *b*). Although rippers are mostly used unbaited, rippers for octopus can be baited when fishing during daytime to lure the prey out of their hiding places and into the range of the gear. There are different sizes of

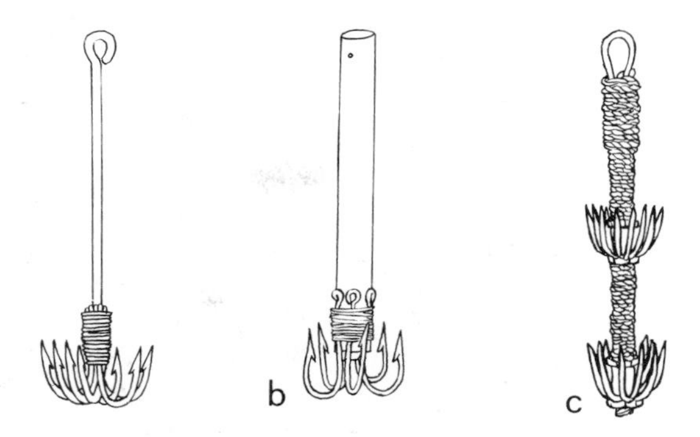

Fig 209 Ripping hooks made by fishermen for cephalopods: (*a*) Madagascar (1964); (*b*) Senegal, for cuttlefish (1971); (*c*) Argentina (1979).

these rippers (sometimes called 'umbrella hooks') used particularly in East Asia, in the Mediterranean area, along the African coasts and also in the northern Atlantic, even as far as Iceland. Nowadays the typical squid hook has many variations. When the squid are more scattered, longer hooks are used and there are some with a small battery-powered lamp in the head of the ripper (*Fig 210*). This hook can be taken by a cephalopod like a passive fishing gear; when it is touched, the sharp hooks rip the

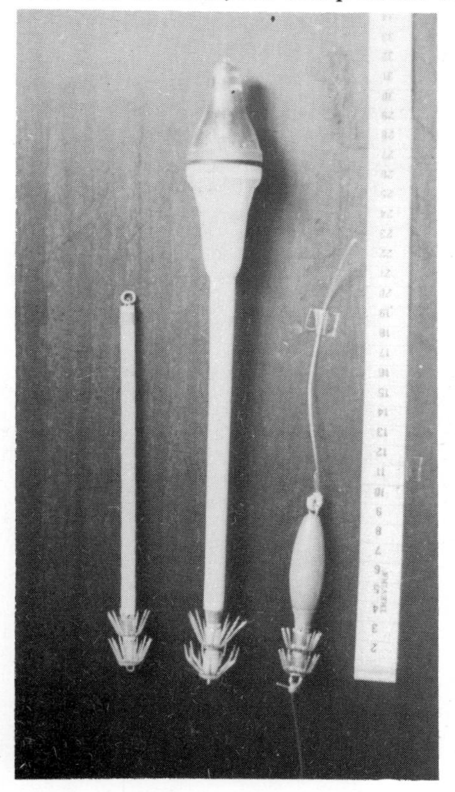

Fig 210 Different types of squid hooks operated in Korea, the longest one with a small lamp.

body or tentacles of the animal. The same implement may also be used like a typical active ripper, hooking when jigged with quick jerks, any cephalopod that comes near.[337]

Simple handlines are considered the original gear for catching squid as well as octopus or cuttlefish. They can be similar to the normal handlines, like those in *Figure 117,* but pole-and-line fishing gear, and even two poles fastened to one wooden handle (*Fig 211*), or a bifurcated pole with two lines, may be operated in this fishery. For fishing in deeper water a gear is used resembling the balance lines for catching fish (*Fig 117e*). An improvement was made by replacing a single ripper with many in a 'chain system' having many ripping hooks in one row – operated like a vertical longline. Manually operated jigging machines were introduced for moving these handlines, with the rippers, up and down (*Fig 212*). These were originally simple rollers, as used when jigging for fish, but more advanced manually operated winding machines soon followed (*Fig 213*). At the same time (about 1950) the chain system mentioned above was introduced, each line often carrying many different types of jigs (*Fig 214*). For this reason the 'umbrella hooks' have an eyelet ring at each end of the stem so that they can be inserted at any desired spacing along the nylon line suspended from the jigging machine (*Fig 210*). With the original hand-driven (later motor-driven) jigging machine, rhythmical vertical movements of the rippers were caused by

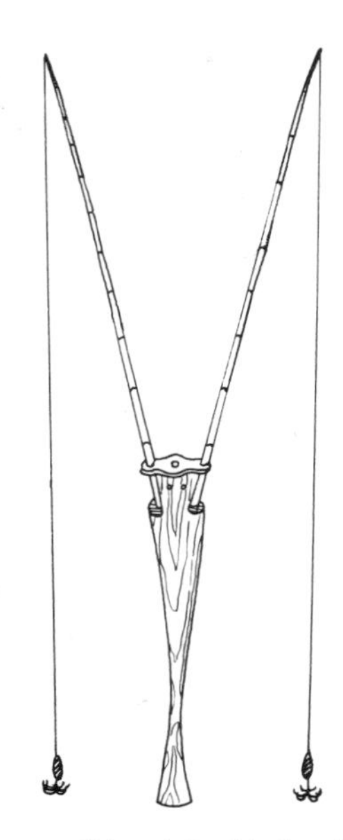

Fig 211 Japanese traditional double handline for squid.

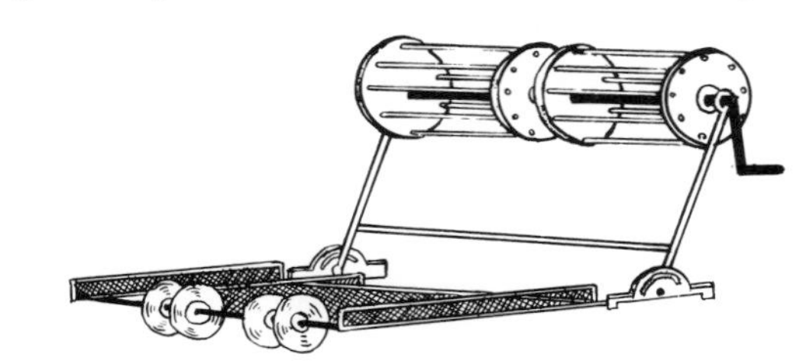

Fig 213 Hand-operated winding machine.

Fig 212 Korean squid fishing: (*behind*) older form with pole and line; (*in front*) newer type with hand-operated jigging machine (1972).

Fig 214 Chain system for different types of squid hooks beginning with an illuminated hook at the top. The longest hooks are near the bottom, Korea (1972).

a reel with an eccentric centre axis, or by an egg-shaped or eliptical form of drum. The next step was the fully automatic squid jigging machine (about 1960) which will be described in the last section of this chapter dealing with mechanization.

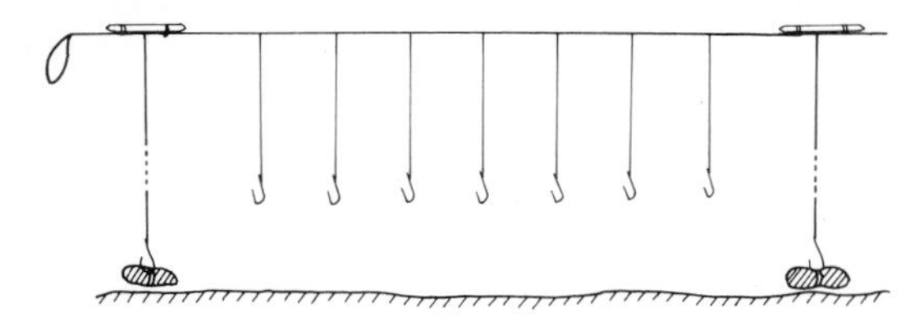

Fig 215 Korean setline with ripping hooks, baited or unbaited, for catching octopi (1972).

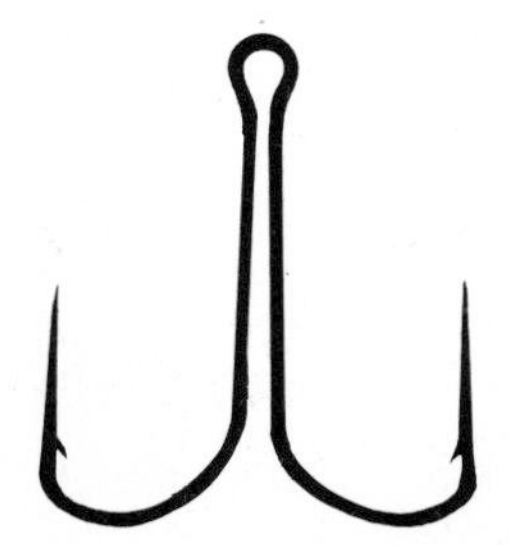

Fig 216 Double hook for ripping octopi. The small barb has to secure the bait (Korea, 1972).

Octopi are also caught with longlines with ripping hooks, baited or unbaited (*Fig 215*). The single or double hooks are considered unbarbed[683], but there is a very small barb at the base of the point to secure the bait (*Fig 216*).

Typical of all longlines with ripping hooks is the short distance between branch lines (compare *Figs 198, 199, 202* and *207*). This is also true for the longlines operated to catch octopi. *Figure 215* is a drawing of a Korean octopus line in correct scale. As often for fish, the main line is kept some distance off the bottom. As soon as the octopus tries to pass between the hooks it will rip itself.[492]

In the Far East, various types of weighted jigs or jig type lures are also trolled in deeper water to catch cephalopods, (*Fig 217*). Sometimes the gear with baited hooks is towed from a vessel over the bottom like a troll line (*Fig 218b*). In other cases single lines with one hook, each connected to an individual buoy, are drifted with the current and/or wind, like a free drift line. When an octopus has taken the ripping hook the buoy stops drifting and the line is hauled up.[681]

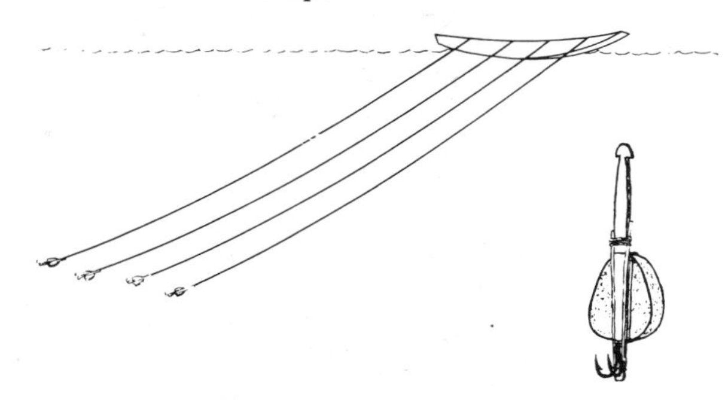

Fig 217 Japanese ripping hooks towed on the bottom for catching octopi.

12.6 Mechanization of jigging

To jerk ripping hooks up and down by hand, maybe for hours as when fishing for cod or squid, can become very exhausting. Therefore, different types of manually-operated winches and reels were introduced to facilitate the up-and-down movements of the pilks in these fisheries (*Figs 195*

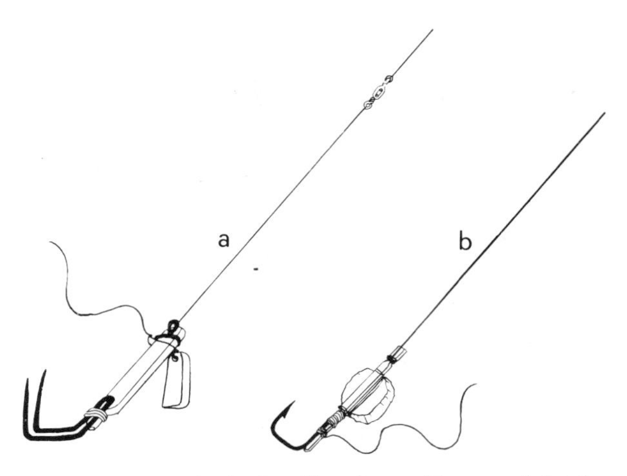

Fig 218 Korean ripping handlines for catching octopi: (*a*) for pilking from an anchored vessel; (*b*) ripping troll line (1979).

and *212*). It was, especially, the Norwegian fishery for cod and saithe which expedited the development of their fully automatic 'juksa' machines working with 10 to 15 rubber-covered hooks (*Fig 109*) mostly unbaited. The automatic jigging machine lets the hook sink down to a specified depth and then starts jigging with an adjustable range of up-and-down motion and at an arranged speed. When the weight is increased by a caught fish, and the pre-set weight is reached, jigging is discontinued and the catch is hauled up automatically; the hauling function stops when fish and hook are on the surface and the fish can be unhooked. Normally one man operates two machines. An adjustable electromagnetic clutch makes it possible to play large fish such as halibut automatically, and to compensate for the roll of the boat in rough weather. It has been said that some of the larger boats in Norway have up to eight such fully automatic jigging machines operating at one time. This is a good example of the type of development in fishing technology which can be expected in the future (see also Chapter 31).

The same problems had to be solved by the squid fishermen in the Far East. The hand-driven squid angling roller system was replaced by one with a mechanical drive. It followed an automatic jigging machine system, which simulated the action of traditional jigging by hand-operated lines or by manually-driven wheels. The line is set by the machine to depths of 30 to more than 140 metres and as soon as the required depth is reached the line is wound in with jerking movements.[120] As in other systems, the jerking action of the line is obtained by winding onto reels with an eccentric axis or on elliptical or egg-shaped reels. It must also be remembered that the line was replaced by a 'chain' with 50 or more rippers. This chain is led over two rollers, one inboard and one outboard of the gunwale (*Figs 219* and *220*). The outboard roller is mounted on a frame with plastic-coated wire mesh, onto which the caught squid falls as the jigs flick over the outer roller. Modern Japanese squid jigging vessels have as many as 20 to 24 or more mechanized double reel jiggers. This fishery for squid is operated during the night with garlands of white or blue glass lamps suspended between the masts of the vessel to attract the squid[32] (*Figs 221* and *222*). The fully-mechanized jigging machines

Fig 219 Japanese squid jigging machine on a Chinese vessel. (*Photo: T F Chen.*)

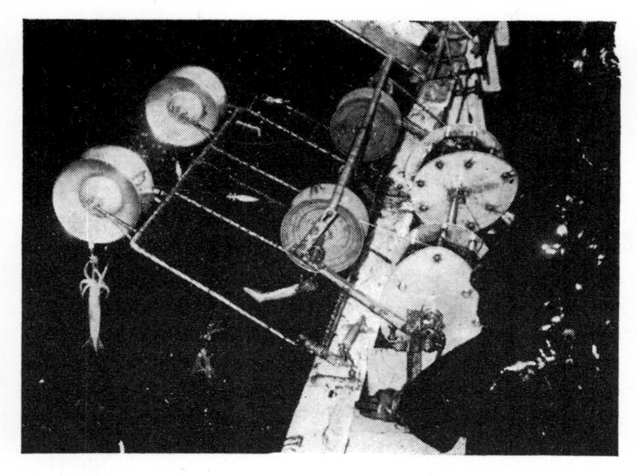

Fig 220 Japanese automatic squid angling machine in operation.

have the important advantage of sparing manpower, because one man can operate up to five automatic jigging machines simultaneously. Unfortunately, these machines can be worn out by 'bad' weather with a wind of Force Two only.

Fig 221 Single automatic squid jigging machine with metal mesh covered frame on a large Japanese vessel in the harbour of Littleton, New Zealand, in 1981. The machine is turned up into its neutral position.

Fig 222 Japanese squid fishers in the harbour of Hakodate (1972).

Chapter thirteen

Natural and artificial shelters

In discussing the methods of attracting and concentrating fish in Chapter 11, it is stated that in contrast to pelagic fish, some bottom fish and crustaceans have a positive thigmotaxis. This behaviour has been used in fishing by offering suitable hiding places. Such safe places can be found in nature under floating vegetation, between stones or water plants, especially below the branches and roots of trees or bushes in flooded areas, or by the banks of natural waters. Man soon found that such places are attractive to fish and crustaceans in search of food and refuge. This knowledge has been used for the installation of artificial 'fish parks', made either by planting vegetation or by placing branches in shallow water to attract fish. This has been done in African inland fisheries, and in West African coastal lagoons, like those of Dahomey, Cameroon, Nigeria and others. In these areas the so-called 'acadja' is known. This is a park formed of a dense mass of branches artificially planted vertically in the muddy bottom to attract fish. These branches are removed after various periods of time and the fish are caught by cast nets (Chapter 28), surrounding nets (Chapter 25), or by other arrangements if the fish try to jump out over the encircling netting (*Fig 375*).[261, 651, 652, 653, 654] To increase the attraction of these installations, regular feeding of the fish can familiarize them with the place. After some time, the area can be surrounded with fences or netting, the plants or branches can be removed, and the enclosed fish caught by different methods.

Today, this method of fish concentration is better known as the 'artificial reef' technique, especially off the sea coast of Japan and the USA. It has been reported that around Japan a million square metres of sea bottom are now covered with artificial structures to attract fish. It is hoped that these will help inshore fishermen acquire fishing places to replace those lost elsewhere. Artificial reefs can consist of simple heaps of stones, possibly covered with a straw mat to lure fish inside. The Japanese submerge concrete blocks for fish shelters. These may be reinforced or not, and are called 'fish apartment houses' or, more recently, 'fish habitats'. At least 50 blocks are required to obtain satisfactory results.[445, 485] Old motor cars and wrecked vessels like the old 'liberty ships' have also been used in different parts of the world as artificial reefs.[137] This is especially interesting in formerly unproductive places which are now becoming suitable for sport fisheries and commercial exploitation.[103] In this way, not only fish but also crustaceans and other aquatic animals can be attracted and later caught, especially with lines and gillnets. In commercial fisheries it is well known that wrecks can be good fishing places and Danish fishermen developed a special wreck fishery with gillnets. There have been some discussions on whether or not artificial reefs are more successful in concentrating fish in clear waters than in turbid waters.[403]

13.1 Bundles of brushwood

A simple method of manufacturing alluring hiding places is to submerge bundles of twigs or branches of trees in suitable waters. In general, the branches are packed flat at the bottom. Stakes keep the branches on the required spot. In Lake Constance and some other Swiss lakes, some such brushwood places are said to date back to the times of the lake dwellers (*Fig 223*). Such untouched brushwood

Fig 223 Structure for a submerged brushwood trap in Lake Constance.

structures could be popular places for snare and line fishing, and also for fishing with gillnets[305] and other gear. At intervals these heaps are shaken or slightly lifted after the site has been encircled by gillnets or traps to catch the fish when they endeavour to escape. Sometimes the brushwood may be completely removed from the water and the fish shaken out.

Such shelters for fish concentrations can also be floating plants, floating branches, or leaves thrown onto the surface of an area of water. These floats are fished in a similar way to lure lines, as mentioned in Chapter 11. This more or less indirect fishery with brushwood is one of those fishing techniques common all over the world. It might have originated from the very beginning of the practice of catching animals, for the method is known to have been used in all parts of Europe,[612] as well as in Asia and Africa. Even the old Indian fisheries of North America knew and used this brushwood method,[528] but there it was used especially in the creation of artificial spawning places for herring, so that the men could afterwards harvest the fish eggs for food. Even today these spawning places for herring are well known off the Pacific coast of Alaska.

Artificial spawning places to get fish spawn, and maybe also spawning animals, are also known in the fishery for cephalopods. As already mentioned with luring methods in the Mediterranean, twigs and branches are set in order to attract spawning cuttlefish. When enough animals are concentrated, fishing is done by raising the whole bundle of branches, and netting the cuttlefish swimming under and around them. The Japanese, on the coast of Kyushu, tie branches to the centre of woven bamboo baskets, and many such baskets are fixed with branch lines some distance from a main line according to the longline system.[445] The baskets are submerged for some days. To take them, the baskets are hauled up and replaced again. This is something like a direct fishing method with brushwood. It is even more so when smaller bundles of brushwood are used in the form of brush traps. Several of these bundles are tied together, also according to the longline system, as explained before (*Figs 224* to *227*). Formerly this method was also used in Europe.[305] As eels like to hide in such bundles, they are called eel tufts in Germany.[513, 644] These brush traps, now prohibited for this purpose, were made of branches of alder trees or beech trees, or of willow twigs about one metre in length tied together like brooms.[569] These bundles, sometimes weighted, were submerged at suitable places for a long time. When the time came for them to be carefully lifted, this was done quickly by keeping a scoop net under the brushwood, or the whole bundle was thrown into the boat before the fish or crustaceans hiding in it could escape. Not only eels can be caught by this method, but also burbot and possibly lampreys. It is well known that these species of fish like to hide themselves. Because eels may sometimes be found in the clothes of drowned people, some have said that the eels fed on corpses. Actually, however, they were using the clothes of such people as handy hiding places.

The use of long rows of brush traps, especially for catching crabs and small fish, is very widespread in Asiatic fisheries.[244, 422, 435, 445, 613] The old Chinese fishery (*Fig 224*) used the method, just as the Japanese still do today (*Figs 225* and *226*). It is also carried out in the Philippines (*Fig 227*), as well as in the fisheries of Indo-China (Burma, Thailand, Vietnam and Kampuchea). In Indonesia, brushwood is used on the large lakes of Sumatra, and the method is also known on Lake Albert in Africa as well as on the lakes of Madagascar.

Fig 224 Chinese brush fishery. (*de Thiersant, 1872*).

Another practice in central Africa is to submerge boxes full of leaves. When small fish seek shelter therein, the boxes are lifted from the water. In Louisiana, on the Gulf of Mexico, brush traps are used for catching soft or shedder crabs. On the Ivory Coast, leaves of coconut trees are put in shallow water to attract shrimps. Every two or three days the leaves are towed slowly to the shore. A fisherman then follows with a scoop net to catch escaping shrimps and small fish. It seems that to use brush bundles as shelter for fish and crustaceans is a very old and widespread fishing technique.

Not only brushes and twigs are used for artificial hiding places. In Oceania, smoked sheepskins are laid in the water to attract fish. Sometimes this shelter is even baited. As with brush traps, the skin is quickly lifted, and a scoop net put under it to secure the fish.[313] In the North Friesian and Dutch

Fig 225 Japanese lines with brush traps showing up during low tide.

Fig 226 Modern Japanese fishery with brush traps. The brushwood is lifted out and shaken over a scoop net into which the fish drop.

Fig 227 Brush traps for shrimps in the Philippines.

fisheries, holes are made in the ice in winter and trusses of straw are put upright into them. This is a widely used way of providing air holes in the strong ice which, when it is covered with thick snow, prevents the light from reaching the water plants that produce the essential oxygen. Eels are expected to creep into the trusses and thus be available for catching – but, for this to be successful, the straw trusses (of which some two thirds of the length are inserted into the water) must be lifted quickly from the hole.

13.2 Tubes for shelter

Because the positive thigmotaxis of the eel is so pronounced, it is used in a special way. When kept in aquaria the animals like to creep either singly or with several others into tubes if they are available. This behaviour permits another fishing method to be carried out, not only for eels but also for some other fish. The method involves attaching to longlines, groups of one, two or three short bamboo reeds and submerging them in the same way that bundles of brush traps are used (*Fig 228*). The eels like to hide in these bamboo tubes. Sometimes the tubes are even baited to make them specially attractive. But to make sure that the eel does not

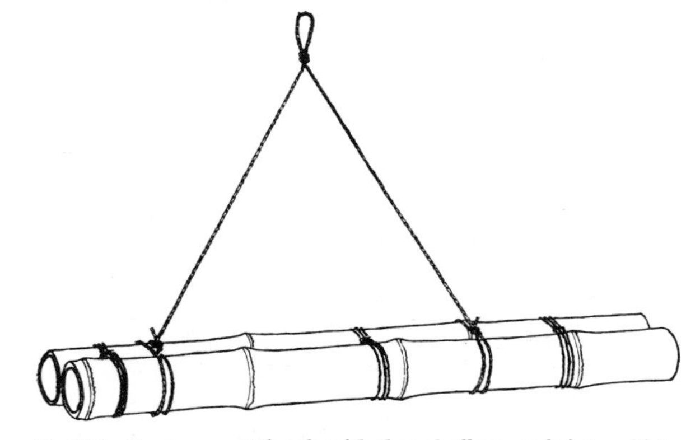

Fig 228 Japanese catch eels with these hollow reeds into which the eels go for shelter.

slip out, great care must be taken in lifting the bamboo reeds. It is also reported that divers sometimes seal the reeds while they are under water – before they lift them.

In European waters, there is no bamboo suitable for such a method, but hollow logs or iron pipes are used in the same way for catching burbots. The stove-pipes are squeezed together at one end to close them, leaving only a narrow slit. The other end of the pipe remains open. The pipes are then fastened on a wire and dropped into the spawning areas of the burbots. After some days, they are lifted out with a quick jerk.[169] The idea is exactly the same as that of fishing for eels with bamboo reeds. This is a fishing technique that is known also in Africa, Australia and other parts of the world. A special method for catching eel with the help of artificial hiding places is known from the freshwater fishery in Madagascar. In Lake Itasy, underwater holes are dug out by divers to form hiding places for eels. The fish are then caught by spearing.[65]

Catfish and other fishes can also be caught with such tube traps. Because strong bamboo became less readily available in some tropical countries, plastic pipes were used, as is done nowadays in Taiwan.[110] Also, other hollow containers can be operated as hiding places, even bottles and drums. Sometimes they are also baited to increase their attractiveness.[361] Also known are bowls of clay and other 'unglazed earthenware pots', better known in the form of octopus pots (see next section).

Tube-like devices are also used as shelters for crustaceans. For catching crayfish in fresh waters, old tin boxes are pressed together to give them a more flattened form and fixed to a line. Some sand and stones should be put into the boxes before they are placed in the water just inside the reeds on the shore. The box has to be placed in good contact with the bottom to be successful. The connection line (longline system) is secured and the boxes remain at the same place until early next morning. Then they are hauled out carefully, but without hesitation, before the prey can escape. Recently[671], artificial shelters for crayfish have been recommended for use in freshwater lakes. The shelters have been made of plastic and concrete in such a manner that the colonies of fabricated 'caves' are attractive to crayfish and also to eels.

In subsistence fisheries, plastic tubes are also used as traps for coastal snails (*Littorina littorea*). The tubes should be without any smell and in a neutral colour, one to two metres in length and with a diameter of about ten centimetres. They are placed among seaweeds and are secured with stones.[577]

13.3 Octopus pots

The discovery that octopi were frequently to be found inside old amphorae and other containers on the Mediterranean seabed soon stimulated man to make unglazed pots of clay specially for the purpose of catching these creatures. Such pots are, or have been, known by Mediterranean fishermen from Italy and Malta, and maybe also from the Iberian peninsula. Earthenware pots are used in east and south Asia much more than in the Mediterranean. They are said to have been known in the Caribbean and the Gulf of Mexico as well.[641] The pots differ somewhat in size and shape; they have handles in Italy, but those used in Japan are without (*Fig 229*). In principle, however, there is no difference, whether these pots are used in Japan, Korea, Italy, Malta or Hong Kong. The octopus likes to enter such shelters for protection and also for spawning.

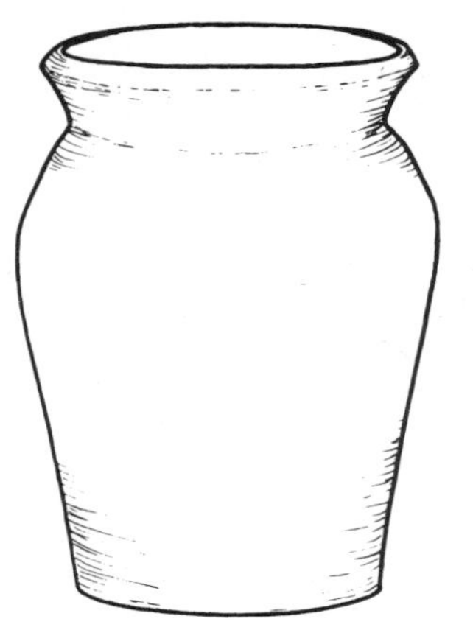

Fig 229 Here are shown an East Asian octopus pot without handles and an Italian pot with handles. The Mediterranean method of catching octopi in these pots is believed to have grown from the fact that in very early times it was noticed that octopi took up their abode in lost Grecian amphora. Today these pots are used either singly or strung together on lines. The same method has evolved in Asian waters.

The animal hesitates in most cases to leave the pot even when moved during hauling. The earthenware octopus pots are set either singly or on the longline system with up to 100 pots strung on a line (*Fig 230*). The Italians fasten 24 or 30 pots at distances of five to six metres on a line. The pots can be so arranged that, during hauling, the opening faces either up or down. In bright light, the octopus is able to rush from its dwelling even at the last moment, so that care is necessary in lifting them. Pots must drain adequately on the surface so that the fisherman does not have to lift a large quantity of water with the pot and the catch.[492]

In some areas, shells of large snails or bivalves are used as hiding places for octopi as an alternative to earthenware pots. In Japan, Korea and south India, the origin of the octopus pots may be large snail shells (*Pteroceras lambis*) which are natural hiding places. The shells are arranged and set in the same way as the pots. In the Palk Straits between India and Ceylon, large quantities of small octopus, which are especially appreciated, are caught by fixing as many as 700 to 900 shells on a longline system which is hauled each morning.[261] Shells have

Fig 230 A string of octopus pots being hauled in the Japanese Inland Sea.

been used in Mexico. Five or more empty shells of *Strombus gigas* are fixed on a line and dragged slowly over the bottom. The shells may be seized by the octopi which are then caught when the shells are hauled aboard.

Working with shells, or even with breakable ceramic pots, may no longer be practicable for large fishing enterprises. So the old useful pots have been replaced, especially in Hokkaido, by wooden boxes (*Fig 231*), which have a better resistance to rough handling and which can be repaired more easily than earthenware pots or breakable shells.[417] Recently, plastic pots of vinyl chloride came into use.[683] It may not be surprising that many other materials are used to catch octopus, even cut tyres, cans and plastic pipes, as well as heavy trawl floats with entrances cut into them, and other objects.[492]

It is a characteristic of all the methods mentioned that a hiding place is offered to the fish, crab, crayfish or octopus, which they accept voluntarily and which they can leave again at any time, generally without difficulty. Even when the pot is hauled, or just as it is being hauled, the animal can still escape. Many efforts have therefore been made – as will be described in the next chapter – to prevent the escape of those animals once they have entered the hiding place (*Fig 239*). Then, however, they can no longer be called hiding places but have become genuine traps, which is the subject of the next chapter.

Fig 231 Wooden octopus box from Hokkaido (1972).

Chapter fourteen

Mechanical fishing gear: traps, lines and snares

A fish that is caught by any method can be regarded as having been outwitted by man and trapped. Nevertheless, in fisheries there is a special conception of what 'trapping' means, in contrast to spearing or line fishing. A trap is a place to which the fish is attracted by any lure or bait (Chapter 11), and from where escape is made more or less difficult for the victim.

Simple traps have to be watched by the fisherman as they are distinct from many other fishing gears. In the same manner hunters and fowlers use cage-like traps which have to be closed by the watchman when the prey has been lured inside. In this sense, some of the hiding places used for fishery, like bamboo tubes used for eel fishing (*Fig 228*) or octopus pots (*Fig 229*), can be considered as simple traps, from which the prey can escape when not prevented from doing so by the fisherman. To stay and to watch a trap may mean waiting for hours and avoiding any movement, and is consequently not very popular with those who are not fishing for fun. Therefore, special mechanisms have been invented to close a trap mechanically, immediately or after a lapse of time, when the prey has, or may have, entered the trap. *Figure 232* shows a Chinese freshwater trap of Taiwan arranged in this manner. The trap is a tube-like cylinder made of a bamboo screens hanging vertically over the water. The fish are attracted by bait under this tube. The cylindrical trap is suspended by a line fixed on the shore. Here the line is pressed between two burning fumigating sticks protected by a small screen seen on the right side of the photograph. When the sticks have burnt down, the line will be burned through – maybe after some hours – and the cylinder, weighted with stones, falls down, trapping any fish which may have been attracted in the meantime. (This mechanism is an old Chinese one, better known from the so-called incense watches, by which burning fumigating sticks release, at intervals, weights which fall audibly into a bowl). The disadvantage of this system for fishing is that the trap is closed whether or not there are fish in it. A better idea is for the gear to close by a special mechanism only when the prey is inside. This is achieved with the mechanical traps used more by hunters than by fishermen. Only those gears in which the victim must release a mechanism in order

Fig 232 Unattended trap from Taiwan. The tube-like bamboo screen is held over the water by a line fixed on the shore behind the screen on the right side. The tube falls down when the line is burned through by smouldering sticks behind the screen.

to be permanently caught or imprisoned can be regarded as genuine mechanical traps.[349] An old hunting and fishing dictionary of the eighteenth century therefore described such a trap as a 'machine' by means of which animals are caught.[433]

Mechanical traps, in this sense, are instruments like the well-known mousetrap, where the mouse must first nibble at the cheese or bacon in order to release the mechanism and cause the trap to shut. Such genuine traps also include fox traps and the box traps, both of which play a part in hunting. The possibilities of designing mechanical traps with a releasing mechanism are relatively limited, and thus it is not surprising that both hunting and fishing traps operate on the same general principles. It is essential that they allow only a single animal to be caught, because the first victim will obviously release the mechanism and so, by being caught, will prevent any further animal being trapped. Other devices as well as traps can be combined with some mechanism released by the victim to make the catch. It is known in line fishing that a jerk from the fisherman is usually needed to make the hook penetrate the jaw of the fish. This can also be done by a mechanism released by the fish. Therefore, lines can be constructed and operated like a mechanical fishing gear. Moreover, snares or nooses are included in this group, following the custom in grouping gear for hunting.[349] In this case, the prey (a fish or crustacean) releases a mechanism which tightens a loop around its body so that it is snared or lassoed. As we will see later, in fishery the snares are seldom tightened by the prey; this is done by the watching fisherman. Nevertheless, for the reason mentioned above, snares operated in fishing are included in the group of mechanical fishing gear[349] in general, even though there may be some justified objections. The different types of mechanical gear, whether for hunting or fishing, will be differentiated according to the principles on which the mechanism is based.

14.1 Gravity traps

Gravity traps, or deadfalls, are those in which a weight is so suspended that it is easily released by the intruding animal, which is then killed or imprisoned by the fall. A good example of this principle used for fishing is the drum gravity trap of Guyana (*Fig 233*). A weighted bamboo reed cylinder of large diameter is suspended in such a way that the suspending device is loosened as soon as a fish pulls at the bait. The cylinder then falls down and covers the fish. An identical method is used in the delta of the Niger in West Africa.[244]

The releasing power of a trap may be supplied by a spring or a stretched elastic tape. Fish traps which have a spring shutter belong to a group which scarcely differs from various metal hunting traps. There is, however, in the fish trap, usually a bagnet so that the fish, once the trap has gone off, is confined in a closed netting bag and not, as with traps used for beasts of prey, between toothed jaws. Such catching devices are used in the European river fisheries, *eg* for salmon in the River Rhine and for huchen in the Danube. *Figure 234* shows a salmon trap from the upper Rhine which has been used until recently.[115] It was mentioned in Chapter 11 that captive living salmon, or dummies, are sometimes tied to longlines near traps to attract other salmon. At first, female salmon were used as bait fish and they attracted males ready for spawning. Also, as soon as there was a spawning hole, male animals, or dummies, were used to attract other male salmon who then sought to fight their supposed competitors – only to become caught in the trap. In figure 234 such a dummy, made of wood and painted like a salmon in its spawning colours, can be seen. *Figure 235* is a similar construction used for huchen in the Danube in Austria even today.[89]

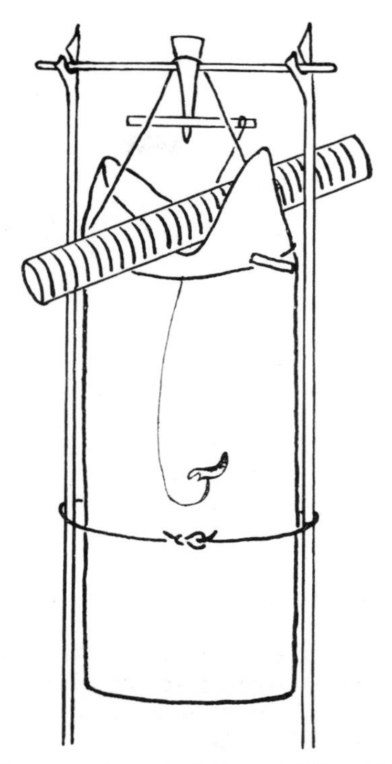

Fig 233 Drum gravity trap of Guyana (*Lips, 1927*).

A small spring shutter trap is still widely used in Scandinavia and Finland for pike fishing (*Fig 236a*), even though prohibited. A small fish is fitted as bait to a horizontal hook. As soon as the pike bites the

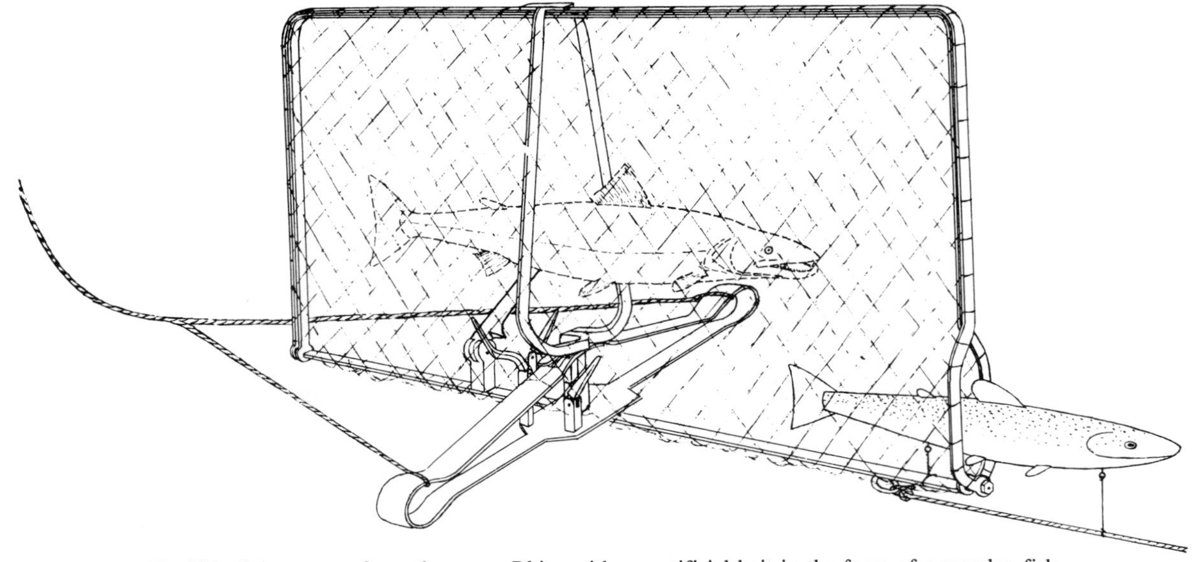

Fig 234 Salmon trap from the upper Rhine with an artificial bait in the form of a wooden fish.

Fig 235 Huchen (Danube salmon) trap from the river Danube. (*Photo: Bruschek.*)

hook, the spring is released and a sharp spike falls down on the head of the pike, killing it or at least gripping it. Several of these mechanized hooks are also used in the form of longlines by commercial fishermen in the eastern part of the Baltic and around the islands of Öland and Gotland (*Fig 237*).[296] Similar instruments were also used in France for pike (*Fig 236b*).[197]

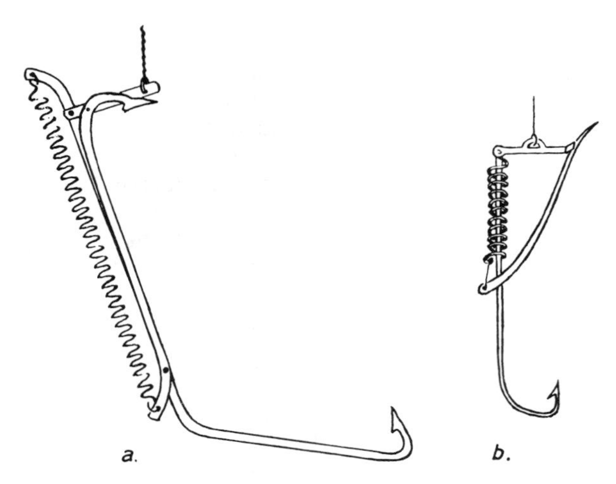

Fig 236 Spring-shutter traps for line fishing: (*a*) from Sweden; (*b*) from France (*Gourret, 1934*).

14.2 Box traps

Box traps also operate on the gravity principle. A mechanism is released by the fish as it enters the trap, and that causes the door to fall down and close the exit. The group includes traps used in the fisheries of southeast Asia, in the Philippines, in Indonesia, Laos and Burma.[200, 261, 630] These traps are ingeniously manufactured in the form of bamboo cages or baskets produced by partly splitting a bamboo reed. A bait is suspended in the trap and when a fish takes the bait, a mechanism is released which closes the door of the trap (*Fig 238*). On the Ivory Coast even sea cows (*Trichechus*) are caught with box traps.[83] The group

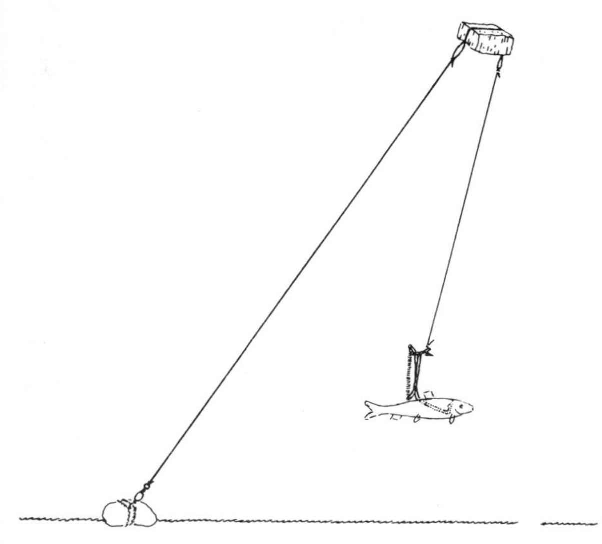

Fig 237 Longline with spring-shutter traps for pike from Gotland Island. (*Kaulin, 1969*)

Fig 238 Fish trap of Indonesia. (*Photo: Ethnographical Museum, Leiden.*)

of box traps in which the closing of the door is activated by the animal being caught also includes a new octopus pot from Japan (*Fig 239*).[290] In the previous chapter octopus pots were mentioned in connection with artificial hiding places. As described, these had the drawback that the octopus was able to leave the pot and escape, even as the pot was being hauled. The mechanical octopus pots have a semi-cylindrical form, are made of cement, and are equipped with a lid. To prevent escape, the circular door is closed by an elastic tape as soon as the octopus touches the bait, which causes a trigger to be released. By this device, the originally simple hiding place has been developed into a mechanical trap. As a consequence, yields have increased so extraordinarily that this very effective gear has had to be prohibited in most areas.

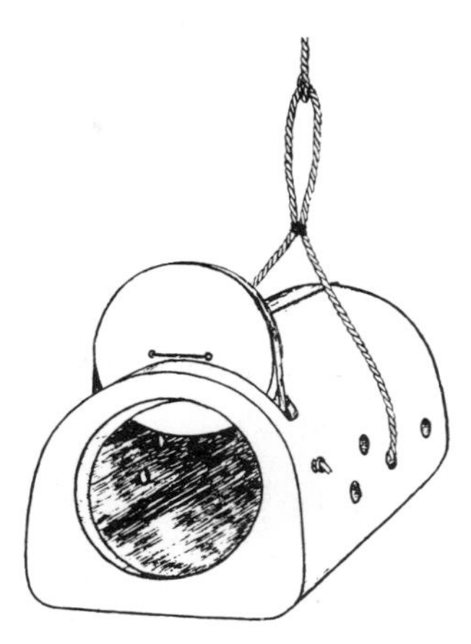

Fig 239 Modern Japanese octopus trap with a mechanical door which is closed by a rubber tape.

14.3 Whippy bough or spring traps

Besides the gravity principle, there are, however, still other principles of power that are used for the construction of mechanical traps which permit the full and voluntary entrance of a fish or crab but which prevent its escape by means of a shutter operated by the action of the animal.[92] These include traps in which the catching mechanism depends on the use of the elastic power of a bent rod. This rod is tied fast in a bent form so that it springs back into its original straight position when the mechanism is released. In such cases they are described as whippy bough or spring traps.[349, 654]

The principle of this trap is used in connection with fishing lines. A fishing rod is bent so that line and hook reach into the water. The cast is fastened or clasped so that the hook lies free. But as soon as the fish takes the bait, the holding device at the cast is released, the fishing rod springs up and effectively hooks the fish by a quick strike which, otherwise, the fisherman operating a hand line would have to do himself. This system has the great merit that the hooked fish is held out of the water, clear of predators. *Figure 240* shows a simple arrangement of this kind from central Java.[612] The cast used here is a piece of rattan with natural barbs. These are hooked on to water plants, *etc*, and so keep the rod bent. If a fish bites, the rattan hooks are loosened and the fish is tossed from the water by means of the fishing rod jumping back into its straight position.

There are many ways of keeping a fishing rod in a bent position until the fish has released the mechanism by taking the hook. Some of these

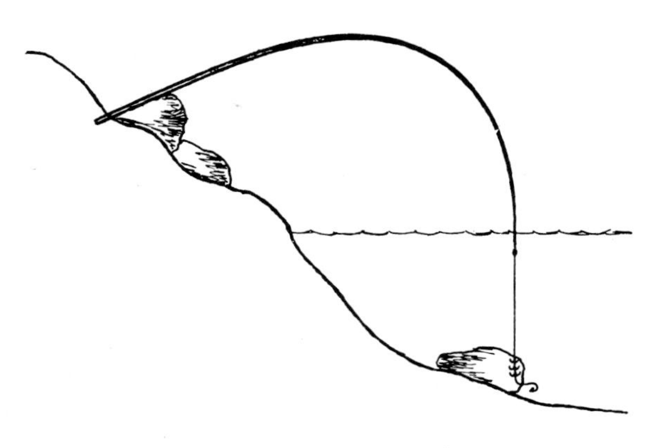

Fig 240 An automatic fishing line of Central Java. (*Thienemann, 1951*).

mechanisms are placed under water. It may be better to place them over water as is done by the Chinese and some fishermen in western Africa. Such spring rods are widely known in Java and are also used in line fishing in the modern Chinese freshwater fisheries (*Fig 241*), as well as in Thailand. They have also been used by some Indians in South America. Bent rods for line fishing are also known in Europe, where they have been used on the Danube for catching salmon – here, however, only by fish thieves. The arrangement is not always as simple as has been described. *Figure 242* shows a fishing line adapted to a whippy bough trap – this time from Thailand.[435] The holding of the bent fishing rod is done by a small transverse wooden stick, just as was previously used in gravity traps (*Fig 233*).

Bent rods and the tension produced thereby are not only used for operating fishing lines, but are also applied to baskets adapted as traps (*Fig 243*). Such a whippy bough trap comes from Brazil. Here, too, the mechanism is released by the

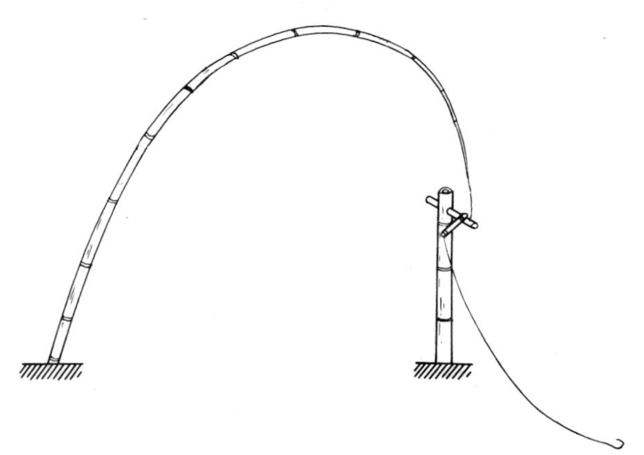

Fig 241 A whippy rod used as modern Chinese freshwater gear. (*Kasuga, 1975*).

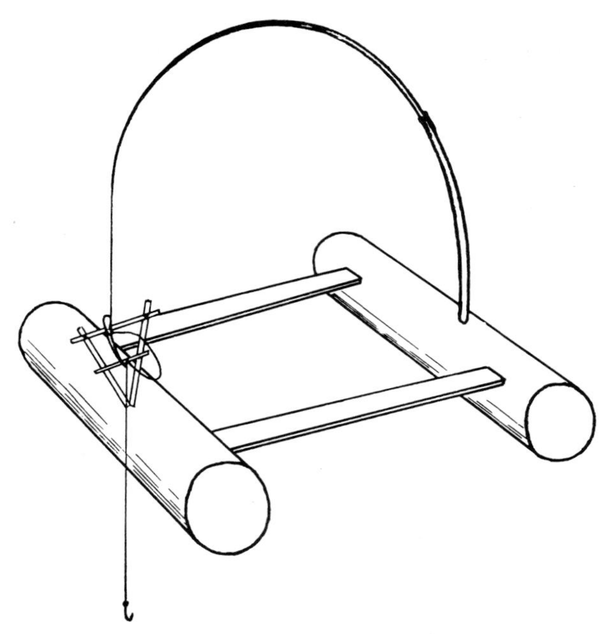

Fig 242 Automatic fishing line of Thailand. (*NN, 1953*).

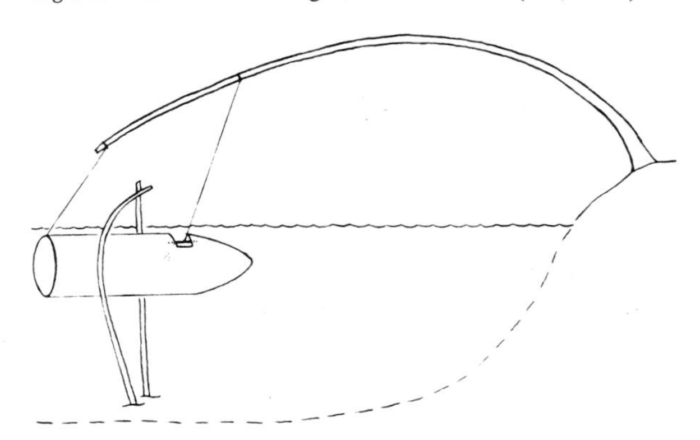

Fig 243 Bent-rod trap of Brazil (*Lips, 1927*).

movement of a little tranverse stick from which the bait is suspended. This same principle of the whippy bough can be used for closing pots or other traps. *Figure 244* shows just such a trap from Cameroon, which closes through the release of a bent rod.[405] They are used for rats as well as for crabs. The same spring traps are known in the Rivers Niger and Chari (Chad and Cameroon) (*Fig 245*).[654]

Spring traps also have a wider distribution. The Indonesians knew and used such automatically closing traps and so did the Indians from Guyana. But there are still other possibilities of successfully using the power that lies in bent rods for fishing purposes. On the Mariana Isles, a crossbow-shaped trap was used for placing in front of the holes in which crayfish lurked (*Fig 246*). If a crayfish entered the tube of the trap and pulled at the bait, an arrow-like rod was shot out to block the exit.

A special type of mechanical fishing gear can be described from the old Russian fisheries and as such gear is relatively rare, it is included here (*Fig 247*). To fish for the white sheatfish in winter on the River Volga, a fishing hook was fastened to the end of a long lever by means of a short line. The lever rested with its centre on a block and had a counterweight on the other end. The gear was so arranged that the lever arm carrying the fish hook was pulled downwards and fastened to a support frozen in the ice. If the fish took the hook, it released the support by its movements and was then tossed by the counterweight onto the ice. Thus the counterweight had the same effect as the power assembled in the bent rod of the whippy bough trap.[333]

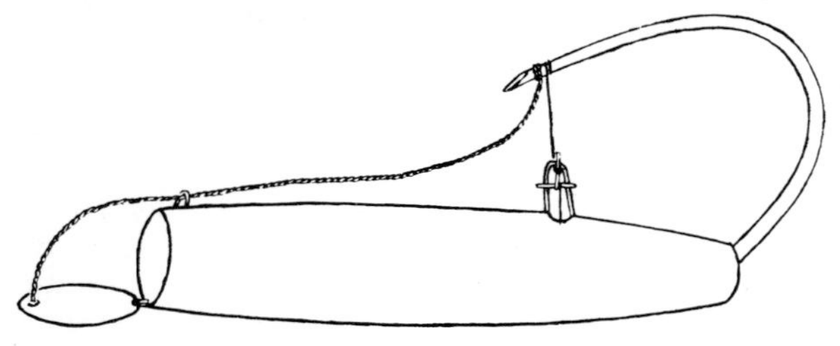

Fig 244 Bent-rod trap for rats and crabs as used in Cameroon. (*Monod, 1928*).

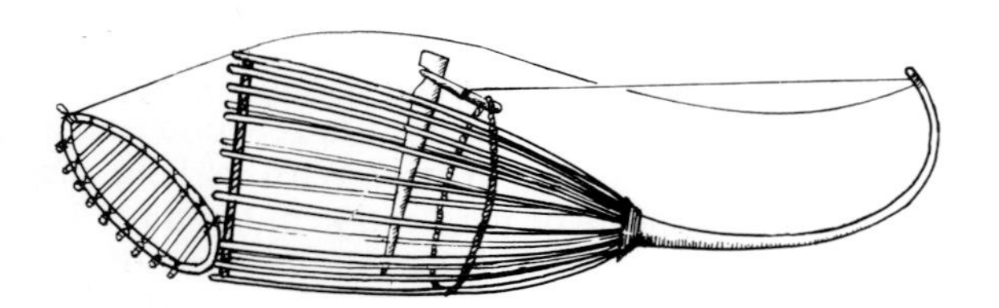

Fig 245 Spring trap used in African rivers like Niger, Chari and Cameroon. (*Welcomme, 1979*).

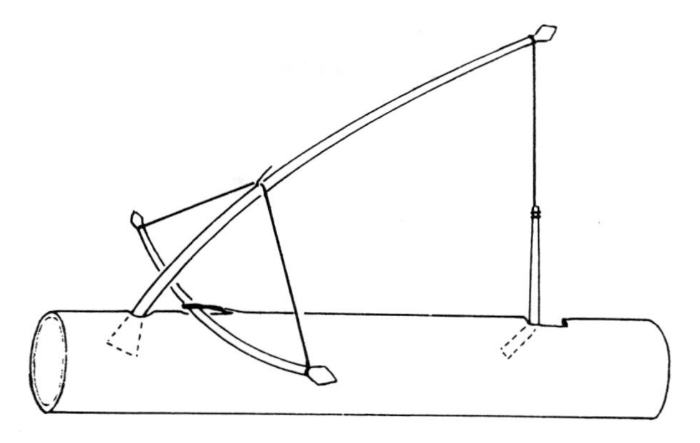

Fig 246 Crawfish trap of the Mariana Islands (*Lips, 1927*).

14.4 Torsion traps

A special group of genuine traps is formed by the torsion shutter traps. As the name implies, the

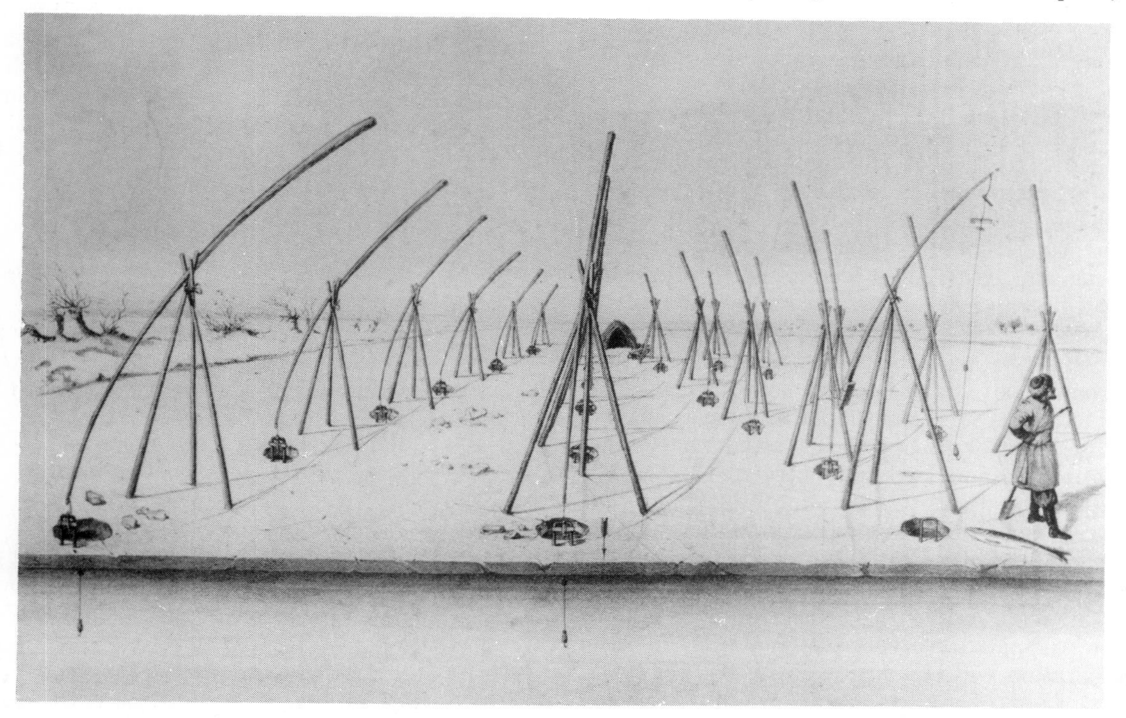

Fig 247 Old automatic line fishing in Russia (1861) for *Coregonus leucichthys* in river Volga.

strength lying in twisted twines is utilized for these traps. The old shape of the carpenter's frame-saw used the strength of these twisted twines to keep under tension the lateral parts which carried the saw blade. The view is held that the knowledge of the power of torsion is a characteristic of the superior cultures of Asia and Africa. *Figure 248* shows a crayfish trap formerly used in south Formosa which operated on this principle. It has two flaps (*a*) and (*b*) fitted into twisted twines. These, therefore, have the tendency to flip over as soon as the safety hook (*c*) is displaced by the crayfish gnawing at the bait on flap (*a*). The flaps knock the crayfish down and hold it on the bottom, upside down.

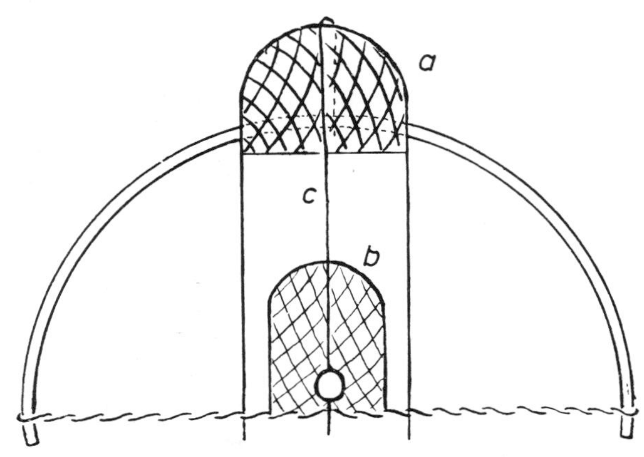

Fig 248 Torsion trap for prawns, used in southern Formosa. (*Lips, 1927*).

14.5 Snares

Snares date back to the basic cultures of mankind.[9] They belong to those old gear used in hunting as well as in fishing. The principle of true snaring is, as mentioned before, that the prey releases a mechanism, tightening a loop of line around the body. In this case, snares are considered as mechanical traps: the prey, by its movement, closes the loop of the snare and so catches itself. This may be true also of the unwatched snares of hunters, designed to take terrestrial animals such as birds in the forest or waterfowl, as well as smaller and bigger mammals. Such passive snares, where the fish has to close the loop to become snared, are not unknown in fisheries. But more often the snare has to be guided around the fish and tightened by the watching fisherman, like a lasso. For this reason it is sometimes said that the fish or crab is lassoed instead of snared. Nevertheless, snares in any form of operation will be considered in this section.

The snare, or noose, is made of a line, forming at its end a loop with a running knot which tightens when the line is pulled. Sometimes the fish may swim through the loop, attracted by a bait, or the watching fisherman may slip the loop carefully around the prey before closing the line with a jerk. In fisheries, smaller snares are mostly made of twisted or plaited horse hair; bigger ones are made from line or soft wire such as brass, and nowadays of PA monofilaments. The different types of snares are known according to the mode of operation (*Fig 249*). Not only fish, but crabs, octopi and even crocodiles can be caught by snares in fresh waters as well as in sea waters. In European fisheries, pike are caught by snaring in the spring when these fish, just before spawning, stay in shallow water. The snare, made of wire, is usually slipped carefully over the head of the pike by means of a rod. This can be a stick up to two metres in length and bifurcated at its end (*Fig 249a*). This forked end is made from wood; formerly, it was also made from whalebone. Originally, the two branches of the stick had to keep open the snare, as can be seen in that formerly used for catching pike in the River Havel in eastern Germany (*Fig 250*). The stick of hazelwood had a length of more than one metre. With its help the snare, made of twine or wire and kept open by the two forks, is brought carefully over the head of the pike and the stick is ripped away very quickly: the noose is loosened from the two points and is closed around the fish.[490] As soon as the wire gets behind the pectoral fin the snare is quickly pulled tight and the pike is thrown, with a jerk, onto the land. Large carp, bream, sea trout and chub can be caught in the same way. In Ireland, snaring was a common method of capturing salmon.[657] Snaring is a fishing

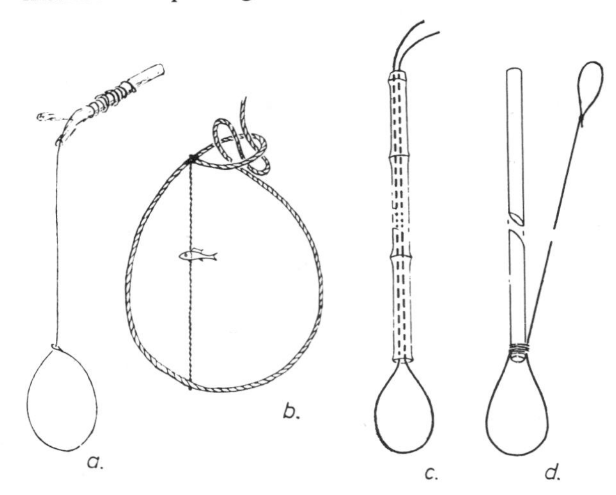

Fig 249 Fish snares: (*a*) Snares for sea trout used in Switzerland; (*b*) shark snare with bait of the Western Caroline Islands (*Eilers, 1955*); (*c*) stick snare of the Admiralty Islands (*Nevermann, 1934*); (*d*) stick snare of the Gilbert Islands (*Koch, 1965*).

method known in many countries and especially used in small subsistence fisheries.[214, 305, 345, 590]

Besides this simple form of snare, another type is known which was specially developed for catching eels. This so-called stick snare looks like an implement for catching snakes (*Figs 249c* and *249d*). Indeed, it is often used to secure eels and moray eels which try to escape. Here, a double line is drawn through a hollow stick, forming a small loop beneath the lower opening. When the fisherman succeeds in putting this loop round the neck of a fish, he pulls the end of the line he is holding in his hand, thus squeezing the fish between the line and the lower part of the stick.[9]

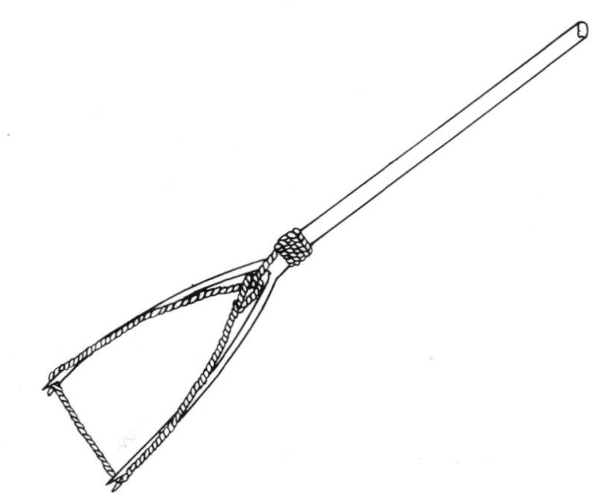

Fig 250 Snare spread in a forklike stick ready for catching pike. (*Peesch, 1966*).

Sometimes, hand-operated snares are also baited to attract the prey into the range of the snare held by the fisherman. Best known are the baited snares for catching sharks (*Fig 249b*), or those in which the shark is lured in an acoustical manner. Such fishing with a shark snare is often described from Oceania. In particular shark rattles are used today to lure the fish (Chapter 11). In shark fishing the snare can be held fast or be free-drifting. In the latter case, the snare is connected to a propeller-shaped wooden float working as a brake or retarder (*Fig 144b*). The loop with the retarder is operated in such a way that the shark swims by itself through the loop. When the fish has passed one third of its body length through the snare, the loop is closed with a jerk. The fish trying to escape is very soon exhausted by the drag of the retarder and can be killed with spears or clubs.[486]

A new description of catching sharks with a baited snare does not differ very much from an old one published nearly 80 years ago. The method, from the Santa Cruz Islands, initially lures the shark by operating rattles in the water.[315] If a shark is attracted, rattling is stopped and some bait fish, fixed on a fishing line, is thrown into the water. When the shark follows the bait, it is towed near to the boat. When the shark is drawn within range the snare is thrown over the fish and is drawn tight. The shark is then killed with clubs. Bigger fish are held and fixed outside the boat in such a manner that the fish, if possible, helps the boat by its movements on the way home!

Simple forms of snares, together with bait, can be held by a diving fisherman in front of a hole where an eel is expected to be. With a stick, a bait is moved up and down near the snare till the attracted fish leaves its hole and swims through the loop – which will be closed immediately.[314] An interesting form of snaring is that used with kite fishing (Chapter 8). In place of the spiderweb towed over the water surface by a kite, a baited snare is attached to catch garfish. As soon as the fish snaps at the bait, the operator jerks the line, thus closing the loop round its upper jaw. The fish's needle-like teeth prevent the loop from slipping off the jaw. Another description from Singapore[93] of this former fishery for garfish with kite and baited snare, explains that the loop was baited with a prawn. This, trailing over the water in response to the movements of the kite, simulated a prawn or small fish seeking to escape from its enemy by a frantic leap out of the water. Garfish were expected to follow their prey, also jumping out of the water to take it. Once the bait is taken, the violence of the attack tightens the noose around the jaw of the garfish. In this case, the fish itself has closed the loop of the snare.

All snares mentioned so far have had a single loop, but snares with two, three or five loops are also known. *Figure 251* shows a tackle from Hawaii with two snares for catching langoustes. The snares are made of fine spring steel wire. A baited hook between the two loops attracts langoustes and a heavy sinker is used to take the line down very fast to the bottom.[262] The attracted langouste can be snared by the fisherman or will snare itself in the loops. Also for fish, snares with more than one loop are known, like those of the 'loop line fishery' for catching snow trout (*Schizothoraichthys progastus*) and others.[575] In this case not only two, but up to five, snares are combined on one fishing line, with a rod as used for pole-and-line fishing. The snare was originally made of horse hair or plant fibres; now often of 2 to 4mm PA – monofilaments. This material is mostly coloured, in clear waters blue or transparent, and multicoloured in turbid waters. There is no hook for bait as with the gear of Hawaii, nevertheless the snares in Nepal are used baited and unbaited. Moreover a small piece of lead hanging under the snare is considered also as a lure. A heavy stone is needed to keep the gear in the right position when fishing in waters with a strong current. The snoods are operated with a pole of five to eight metres in length for swinging out the snares like a fly in spin-fishing. The line is run through rings along the rod but there is no reel fixed on the rod for winding up the line. This is done around a separate board, held in one hand of the fisherman. There are more interesting details with this gear, including a small wooden float by which the size and depth of the snare can be regulated and which works like a retarding device (*Fig 252*). This float and the sinker will support the self collapsing of the snare. Loop line fishing can be done only in waters without underwater plants, as these tend to cause the loops to collapse before any fish can be caught.[575]

Snares for fishing are, or have been, known practically all over the world. But only rarely can they be regarded as genuine mechanical traps into which the fish would be likely to swim without human help, thus catching itself by closing the snare as it pushes forward. Snares, to be really effective in fisheries, generally need human guidance.

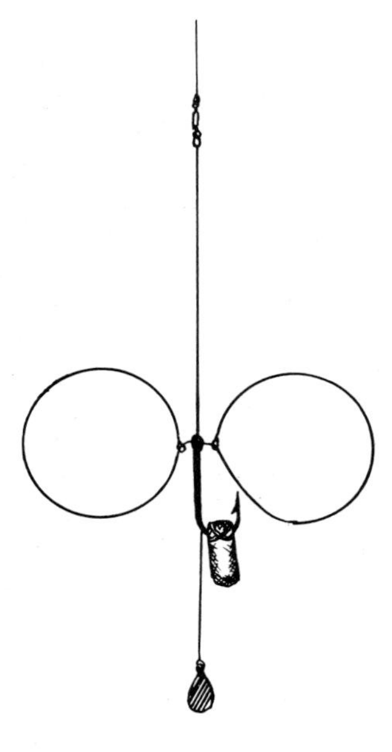

Fig 251 Baited 'lobster tackle' from Hawaii with two snares for catching crustaceans. (*Hosaka, 1973*).

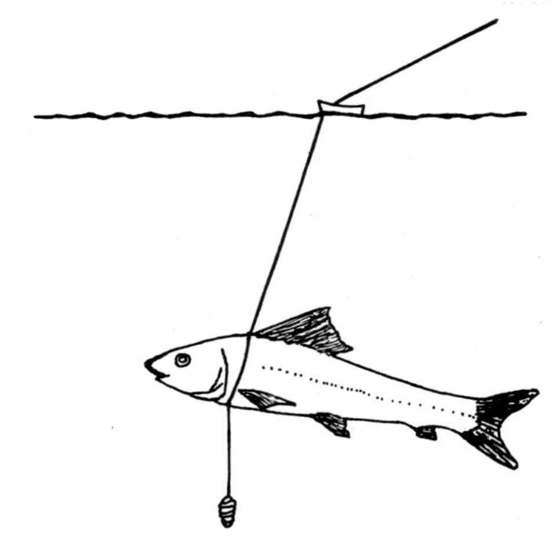

Fig 252 Snow trout taken by 'loop fishing' in Nepal. The loop is operated by the pole-and-line method. A small piece of lead acts as a lure and a small float, swimming on the water surface, supports the closing of the snare. (*Shrestha, 1979*).

Chapter fifteen

Permanent and temporary barriers

Fishing with primitive fishing gear is confined to shallow waters. It was always so in olden times, and is so even today in many parts of the world. Areas with a fluctuating water level attracted old-time fishermen to the inundation areas of fresh waters as well as the tidal areas along the sea coast. In these areas it was not so difficult to obtain good catches. During flood time, fish spread into those freshly inundated areas and, in the main, left them again as the water fell. In the small pools that were left, many fish remained and these could easily be caught. To increase the number of these pools, pits were dug in areas likely to be flooded, and it may be that from this, man invented the first barriers designed to prevent fish from escaping when the water flowed back.

Barriers are made of many different materials. Permanent ones are mostly made of piled-up stones. They can also be made of earth, mud or grass. Barriers can be of very heavy boarding, made of thick trees and thick boards: they can also be light fences, transportable and sometimes only temporary, made of bamboo, reed, shrubs, wickerwork, mats or netting. Modern barriers are now often made of bricks or concrete. In tidal waters, fish and other prey, following the returning water as the tide ebbed, were trapped behind these natural or man-made obstructions, and needed only to be collected by hand. This was done in the past and is still practised today. Barriers were also built in running and static waters to facilitate catching by stopping the movement of fish and concentrating them in places suitable for catching.[361]

The size of the barrier is constructed according to local conditions. It can be a straight or curved wall, and fences ending in a spiral increase the efficiency of this form of construction (*Fig 260*). The fish are caught behind the barrier in shallow water with any type of gear. Often such barriers have narrow passages where the fisherman awaits the catch. If he cannot catch the fish by hand[654], he tries to get them with a spear, scoop net or other hand-operated gear. Some barriers, made of fences, are set in the form of a large 'V' with a passage at the apex providing a place for the fisherman to lurk with his gear. Such passages with a catching place can be very comfortable, as are those of the freshwater fishermen in Madagascar, where, behind the passage on the upstream side, a shelter for the fisherman is made (*Fig 253*) in which there is a catching chamber from which the fish (eel) cannot escape, and where they are killed. Strictly speaking, this is not catching but simple killing, known also in other parts of the world. It has been reported that at some African barriers fish are killed with spears, and also axes.[666] In Europe it is recorded that migrating salmon were killed in the River Duna (which runs into the Baltic) with clubs and lead balls tied onto a rope.

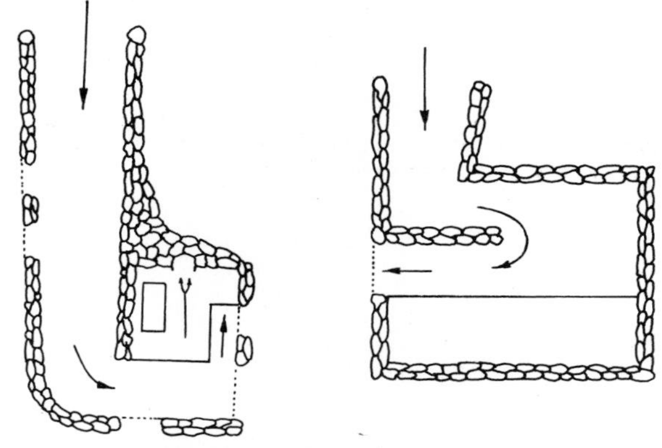

Fig 253 Buildings with chambers for catching eels in the outflow of the Lake Ithasy in Madagascar: (*left*) according to Kiener, 1963; (*right*) according to v Brandt, 1964.

Barriers can be constructed in such a way that they not only stop migrating fish but also catch them with additional fishing traps (*Figs 254* and *255*) or stow nets (Chapter 19). They can also work as guiding arrangements for different types of fishing gear not considered in this chapter. Here it may be added that fishing with barriers, especially when they are made of wooden fences, is considered

Fig 254 Permanent barrier in the river Eider in northern Germany at the outlet of a lake (Westensee), with baskets made of iron.

Fig 255 Temporary barrier made of mud and stones combined with a trap (Thailand, 1960).

in Europe as a typical fishing technique of Finno-Ugrian populations.[13, 278, 580]

15.1 Stone walls as tidal weirs and traps

Stone walls, simply made by piling up stones, are used in different ways in many parts of the world. They are known in the fisheries of east and south Asia[427, 428], of Polynesia and Melanesia, in Australia[618], Africa[111, 361] and last but not least in Europe. In all these places, fishing with stone walls is considered a very old fishing method, and some of the stone walls existing today date back to early neolithic times, and even to the pre-*sapiens* phase of human evolution.[427] Therefore, some of the stone walls can be considered as 'living fossils of the oldest fishing gear' (a description used in Japan)[428] and as 'the only work of permanent character known to have had its origin among aboriginal workmanship' (used in Australia).[618]

In most cases, stone walls are used as barriers in tidal areas. Here the stone walls can be more or less permanent arrangements, sometimes named 'tidal weirs'.[431] They are flooded at high water when the fish can enter them. But as the tide falls, some fish remain behind the dams if they are correctly arranged. To keep back the fish, the tidal weirs are made in a semi-circle or in the form of a horseshoe (*Figs 256* and *383*). The walls are of different lengths. It seems that the longest tidal weirs, hundreds of metres long, can be found in Japan. Here there are stone walls more than 1,000 metres long, built centuries ago.[431] At low tide the water can run easily through the piled-up stones, but the larger fishes cannot follow and are retained behind this barrier, from where they are collected. The Japanese stone walls may have outlets to increase the speed of drainage, and these outlets can be good places to catch the fish with simple fishing methods.

Stone walls in tidal areas can be used in a similar

Fig 256 Stone dam built off the coast of Guinea to capture fish as the tide falls.

manner, as is done in Indonesia (Western Flores). There, a wall is built in the shallow water parallel to the sea shore. As in some of the Japanese stone walls, there are passages through which the fish can enter with the flood, but they are prevented from escaping on the ebb tide. The outlets are closed and the fish remain in the water-filled channel behind the walls until they are collected (*Fig 257*). To build large stone walls requires a 'community spirit' or some pressure from outside powers. Now stone walls are not used as much as they were before, and the loss of that community spirit may be the main reason for this. Therefore it may be that tidal stone walls have fulfilled their historical and economic role.[431]

Stone constructions are not only used for tidal

Fig 257 Pond in the tidal area of Indonesia used for catching fish. (*Photo: Kollmannsperger, 1973.*)

weirs – they can also be used as fish traps.[431] That is a passive fishing gear into which the fish is guided, in contrast to the tidal weirs in which the fish enters by itself. But to build real traps with stones may be difficult in comparison with the construction of genuine traps from wooden materials. It seems that fish traps made of stone have to be combined with other materials to become an effective gear. *Figure 258* shows a trap made of stones for catching small fishes swimming upstream against the water falling in a cascade over a small barrier. The fish cannot overcome this barrier and so swim to the sides of the arrangement where the water current is limited in such a way that only a fine but uninterrupted flow comes over this barrier. Under the cascade is a wooden semi-circular pipe conducting water from just below the weir to a fish box, or bag made of netting. Fish trying to overcome the barrier fall into the pipe and are guided into the catching box. This method is used not only in Japan but also in Taiwan, where it is considered to be an aboriginal fishing method.

In this section, only stone walls have been mentioned, but it must be remembered that when stones are not available, walls may be made of other materials, like earth, which can be used in the same, or similar, manner. Here again the famous Maoris of New Zealand have to be mentioned as using, even today, stone walls for their eel fishery. These are not artificial, but built by nature by the strong waves of the sea. The estuary of Lake Forsyth in southern New Zealand is mostly separated from the sea by high barriers of pebbles. Some water may flow through but the eels can not escape. The Maoris dig in this wall of pebbles a trench ten to fifteen metres long and one to two metres wide (*Fig 259*). The eels following the current when migrating in the night, are concentrated in the trench and can be caught with bare hands, by gaffs, or by other gear.

15.2 Fish fences

Earth walls and stone walls are permanent constructions, sometimes operated in fisheries for many centuries. This does not exclude the use of stone walls as temporary barriers but in this case the permanent walls are mostly replaced by more or less durable fish fences, which can be easily removed and transported when necessary. Such non-permanent fish fences are still operated in many fisheries of the world. They may consist of carefully plaited mats, strong bamboo walls, or robust hedges made of brushwood. Such fish fences can be operated as tidal weirs, like stone walls. Often the water does not flow over the fences, but the fish come in with the current and swim behind the fence which is set at an oblique angle to the shore.

To increase the efficiency of such fences they are set in a semi-circular form, and often the ends have spiral forms to prevent the fish from following the falling water round the end of the fence (*Fig 260*). In this case, the fence sometimes guides the fish into the specially arranged ends where they are trapped. This may have given rise to the idea of using fish

Fig 258 Barriers to catch small fish swimming against the current near Taitung in Taiwan. The fish are not caught in the middle cascades with strong currents but in the slower water on both sides.

Fig 259 Artificial trench built by Maori fishermen to concentrate eels behind a barrier of pebbles in Lake Forsyth, New Zealand (1981).

Fig 260 End of a fish fence in the tidal area near Majunga, Madagascar.

fences to construct independent catching facilities, as we will see later. Large fences can be set in a straight line or in a zigzag pattern across the tidal current, as was done formerly on the North Sea coast of Britain. On the side of the fence facing the shore, a flat water channel is dug out, which serves as a catching chamber from where the fish are removed. Small fences can be used very simply, by setting them as a semi-circle or three-quarters of a circle at the end of a water channel flowing into another channel or pool (*Fig 384*). The fence also serves as a catching chamber where fish may have concentrated. In this case, a watch must be kept and the chamber must be closed when fish are inside it to prevent their escape. More will be said about watched gear in a later section.

Nowadays fences are usually permanently combined with traps, and sometimes with stow nets as well (Chapter 19). In this case they are no more than a guiding arrangement. Moreover, home-made wooden fences are no longer widely used. They are replaced mostly by more easily-handled netting when this is less expensive than home-made fences made of mats or rough wickerwork made of local materials. Netting can provide better gear for tidal waters. On the North Sea coast of Britain, special nets have been developed which are suited to the conditions of high and low tide.[555] They are so constructed that they let the fish pass with the flood tide, but retain them when they try to follow the water out again on the ebb tide (*Fig 261*).

15.3 Gratings in flowing waters

There are special types of barriers with arrangements for filtering out fish migrating with

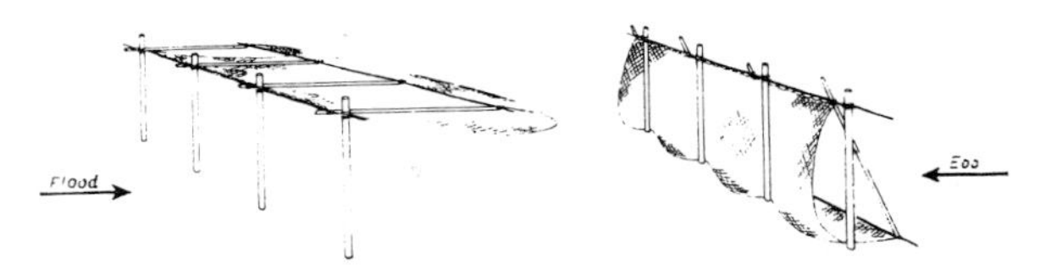

Fig 261 English 'baulk net' which operates automatically during flood and ebb tide. It swings up to let the fish in and then down as the tide flows out. (*Davis, 1958*).

the current in a river. A relatively simple and useful construction, especially in stronger currents, consists of a sloping grating screen constructed in the river and ascending in the direction of the current. The screen can be operated either with or without a watchman. Strong side walls are built at each side of the screen, and the fish, swimming with the current, are thus guided onto the screen so that they actually run aground while the water disappears through the slats of the screen. The construction of this screen is similar to the grating (called a 'rake') that is installed before the entrances of turbines, *etc*, to catch drifting objects. However, the rods are set more closely together, depending on the size of fish to be caught. *Figure 262* shows such fish rakes from Mexico and from the old Indian fishery of northwest California. The strongly flowing current presses the fish against the obliquely sloped grating and washes them upwards. Trout and salmon are caught in this way. Fish screens of this type are also very well known in Japan (*Fig 263*). There, companies operating such gear catch the

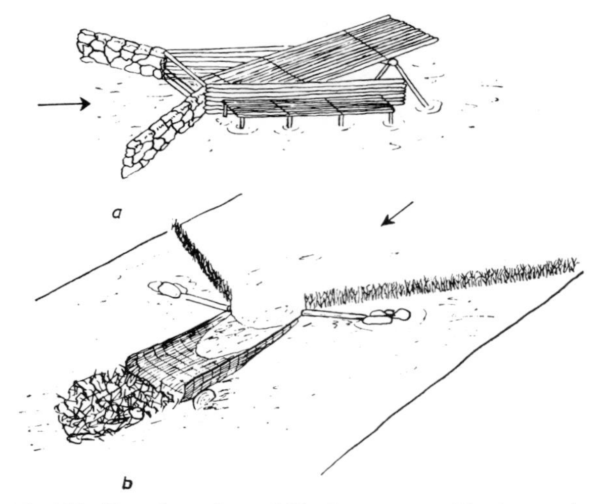

Fig 262 Trough gratings of filtering mats used in rivers – the water filters through but the fish remain on top: (*a*) Mexico (*Sanchez, 1959*); (*b*) Indian fishery of northwestern California (*Kroeber and Barrett, 1960*).

much appreciated ayu and eels, as well as other freshwater fish. Sometimes openings are cut in the screens or filtering mats and net bags are hung below them, so that the fish fall into them but cannot escape. In such instances the catching equipment operates automatically and does not need to be guarded. Such barriers, where the fish are stranded on a sloping grating, are known also in the fishery of Kampuchea.[244]

Fig 263 Japanese 'yana' for catching ayu fish and eels by the filtering method.

Catching fish, especially eels, by leading the running water against a rake is also known in Europe. *Figure 264* shows such a gear (similar to one in Japan; *Fig 263*), formerly in the German river Sauer (Eifel). The gear has an ascending grating made of wood, and walls of piled stones to guide the fish, which indicates how old this gear might be. *Figure 265* is a schematic drawing showing how this type of gear can be constructed, sometimes enclosed in a building, to guide the fish, after stranding, into an unattended catching box. The reservoirs for mills, or the outlets of lakes, only need a small grating assembly (*Fig 266*). Very often these smaller assemblies have a roof over the catching chamber. Instead of an ascending gear, a descending one can be installed, over which the fish glide into a fish box (*Fig 267*). With this type of gear they remain in running water until removed.

Fig 264 Wooden grating ascending with the current and with long stone walls for guiding the fish onto the grating. Formerly in the German river Sauer (Eifel). (*Photo: G Jens.*)

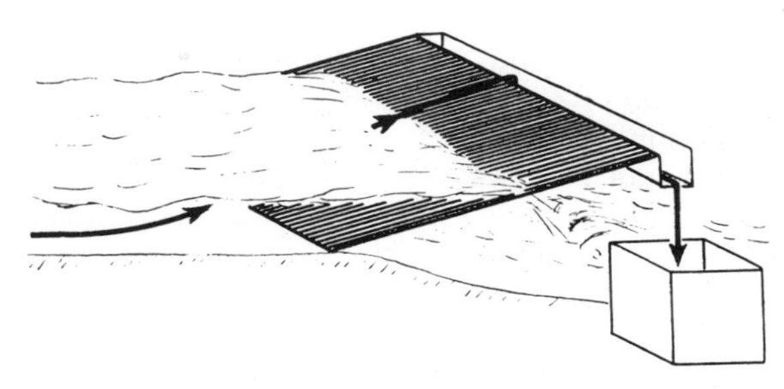

Fig 265 Weir for eels in northern Germany. (The protecting building has not been drawn).

Figure 268 shows a similar installation in Scotland. Here the size of the grating can be adjusted according to the quantity of the running water, by covering the grating with boards. The fish slide into

Fig 266 Gratings for catching eels in the outlet of a mill-pond in the Eifel/Germany. (*Photo: G Jens.*)

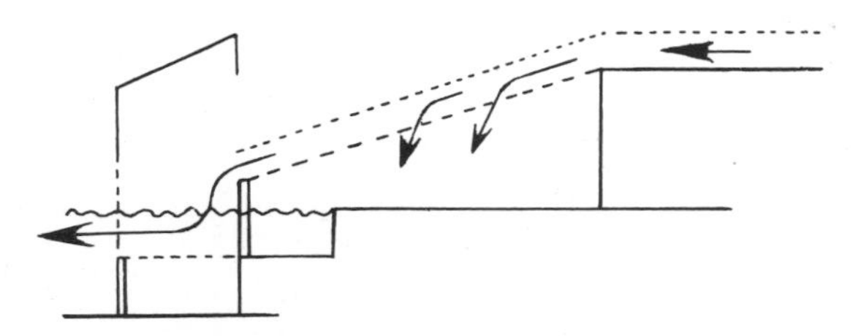

Fig 267 Sketch of a filtering barrier for catching migrating eels.

Fig 268 Scottish arrangement for filtering fish migrating with the current over a grating (*left*), falling into a channel to guide them into a collecting box (*right*), at Ballater, near Aviemore (1974).

a water channel along which they are guided into a catching chamber. *Figure 269* gives a total view of this arrangement with the fish collecting box in the foreground.

The concept of separating fish and water by a filtering arrangement descending in the direction of the current seems to be known also in other parts of the world. *Figure 270* shows an old Rumanian gear made of wickerwork in a slipper-shaped form.[13] This gear is called a 'leasa' and is placed in the current between stone walls which guide the fish into the gear.

Fig 269 Overall view of the arrangement for catching fish swimming with the current. Behind the filtering part in the middle is a wooden channel for guiding the fish into the catching box in the foreground.

15.4 Watched catching chambers

The simplest way to catch migrating fish is to set a barrier in their way, like a large open chamber into which the fish have no cause to hesitate to enter. Such chambers are known in many different forms and are simple to make, but they have to be watched, and some arrangement has to be made to close the entrance quickly as soon as the fish have

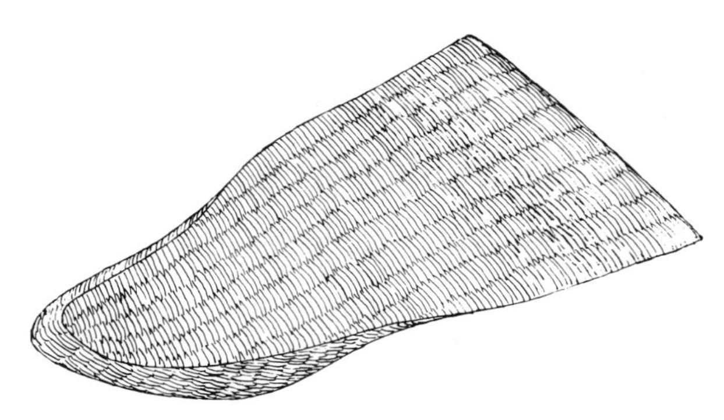

Fig 270 Old Rumanian wickerwork to filter fish swimming with the current. (*Antipa, 1916*).

entered the gear. This principle has already been mentioned with simple earthen walls and fences. *Figure 271* shows such an arrangement made of fences in Thailand. In this case the catching chamber functions in both directions. The method of watching a catching chamber, generally during the daytime, and closing the gear when fish have entered, is used even today with large chambers made of netting, provided that the catches are good and sufficient manpower is available!

Fig 271 Barrier in Thailand with large catching chamber and entrances from both sides.

One of the oldest forms of this type of fishing gear may be the chambers used in the Mediterranean for catching tuna swimming near the coastline on their way to spawning grounds. The catching places known and used today are thought to be very old and used by the Phoenicians, Greeks and Romans. In those times the catching places were owned by temples and other holy places. It is not quite clear how the catching chambers were constructed, or of what material they were made. But there are, even today, simple chambers consisting of nothing more than a rectangular place surrounded by netting. One side is bounded by the shore, the opposite one is formed by a length of netting, as is the smaller length on the third side of this large catching chamber. The last side is open and set in such a way that the fish expected to be caught can swim into the surrounded area without difficulty. The fish are usually shoals of sardines or tuna or other migrating fish. As soon as it has been ascertained from a lookout (*Fig 272*) that the expected fish have entered the chamber, the open side is closed by netting lying ready on the ground. The catch itself is then secured by other means. In some cases the catching chamber has a bottom netting which can be lifted to concentrate and scoop the fishes.

More complicated than the simple chambers are those sub-divided into different sections and completed with a long guiding part. Examples are the tuna traps used in the Mediterranean fisheries. They are known by several different names, including 'tonnara' in Italy, 'madragues' or 'tonnaires' in France, 'almadraba' in Spain and 'amicao' by the Portuguese. It may be that the Sicilian tonnara is the oldest existing forerunner of modern pound nets, specially invented in prehistoric times for the capture of tuna and other migratory fish in the Mediterranean. Today such gear consists of a barrage, or leader, in the form of a wall of netting stretching out more or less at right angles from the shore, which bars the way to the fish and leads them off in the direction of the impounding device. This is a gear with several different chambers, in which the fish are gathered and concentrated (*Fig 273*). The last chamber is the 'death chamber' (in Italy the 'camera della morte'), where the catch takes place. This chamber is also named 'leva', which means 'liftnet', because the chamber has a bottom made of netting which is hauled to close the chamber and to concentrate the fish (*Figs 274* and *275*).[173] There is not much difference between the Italian type of gear and the now-forbidden madragues of France and those operated in Spain and Portugal, in Morocco (off the Mediterranean and Atlantic coast), and in Tunisia. The Portuguese introduced this effective gear into Angola (*Fig 276*).

In the Mediterranean area there is one more gear which may have originated in the ancient tuna fishery. It is not much more than a large catching chamber like that known also on the Yugoslavian coast (*Fig 272*). This is the Turkish 'dalyan'. In this case, it seems clear that its original catching chamber was made of fences because there are, even today, such gears made of wooden material and operated in the same manner. This gear also has to be watched. It is used in the eastern Mediterranean by the Turks, and also by the Bulgarians. It is also known in the Russian fishery. The modern dalyan is made of netting and is held by sticks in such a

Fig 272 Yugoslavian barrier for tuna in the Adriatic Sea with two look-out posts.

manner that a tonnara-like chamber is formed with an opening on the side from which the fish are expected to come. A watchman (or two) must stay during the day-time on one or two wooden towers, to control the entrance of tuna or schools of other fishes, like mullets (*Fig 277*). In this case, the chamber is closed by lifting the netting (*Fig 278*). Tuna are caught with hooks and spears, smaller fishes with scoop nets or by hand after 'drying up' the netting.[382, 384] Those types of fishing gear with a look-out probably originated in the eastern part of the Mediterranean. Here, and in the old fisheries of Russia, such watched chambers have been known, maybe, since Phoenician times.

The idea of fishing with large watched chambers made of netting is not only known in the Mediterranean area. There is even a floating form of this gear – the Japanese 'kaku-ami' or herring square set net – a large net box with an entrance through which the fish are guided by a length of netting (*Fig 279*). When herring or sardines have entered the gear, the entrance is closed by netting and the fish are concentrated and caught by lifting up the netting on one side of the gear.[445] The great disadvantage of watched chambers is that the large and more effective ones, in spite of their simple construction, are nowadays very costly to build and maintain. Great numbers of helping hands are needed for their operation (*Fig 275*) and often when good catches cannot be predicted. During the fishing season the fisherman must always be present to do the catching. This is, of course, a burden that is not suitable for a modern fishery, and, consequently, endeavours have been made to

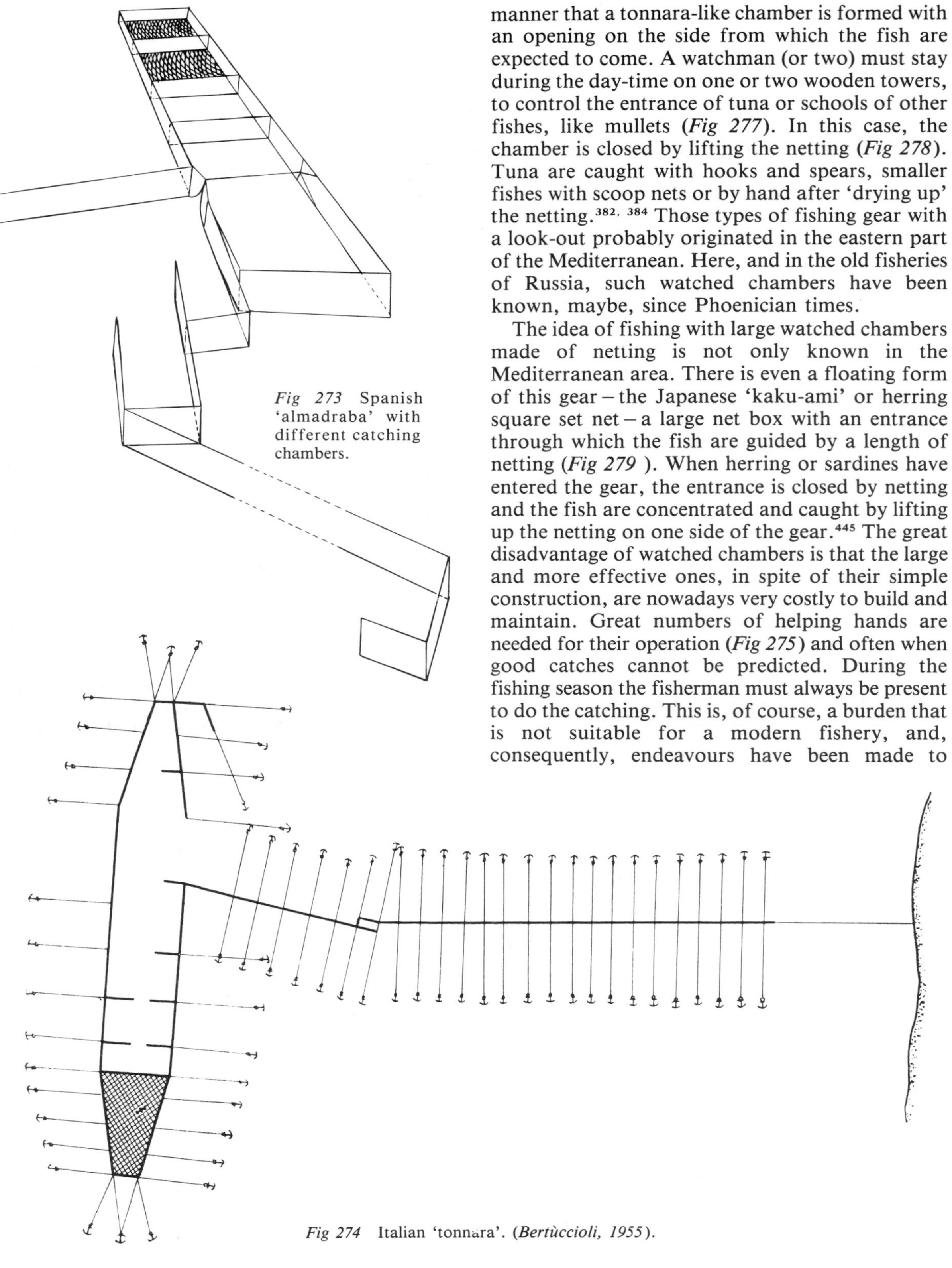

Fig 273 Spanish 'almadraba' with different catching chambers.

Fig 274 Italian 'tonnara'. (*Bertùccioli, 1955*).

Fig 275 Hauling up the death chamber of a Sicilian 'tonnara'. (*Photo: Schärfe.*)

Fig 276 Hauling the catch of a 'madrague' off the coast of Angola.

Fig 277 Watchman on a Turkish 'dalyan' near Beykoz in the Bosphorus.

remove the need for watching by providing automatic fishing barriers which do not require any permanent guard. On the other hand, modern barriers made with netting of synthetic fibre are often owned and operated by communities of fishermen. Set up in good places, this type of gear can be very successful for catching migrating fish.

15.5 From barrier to fish trap

As has been shown in the third section of this chapter, transportable light barriers can be made from fences, and are used especially in tidal areas. It has also been shown that fences can be constructed with spirals at their ends (*Fig 260*). These spirals cannot prevent the escape of the fish completely, but they hamper them from finding the way out. Such arrangements, with intricate winding passages, are considered as labyrinths and they have been used in many fisheries (*Fig 280*). Simple forms of such labyrinth fences can be simple spirals, or

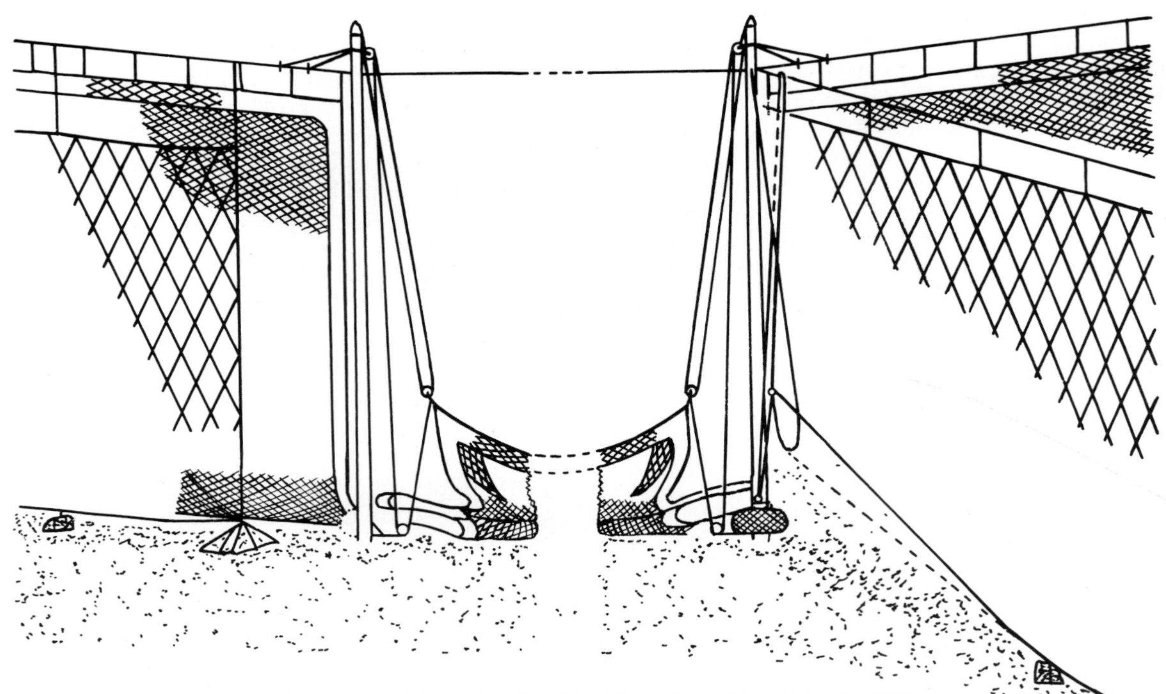

Fig 278 Entrance to a Turkish 'dalyan' which can be closed by lifting the netting. (*Mengi, 1977*).

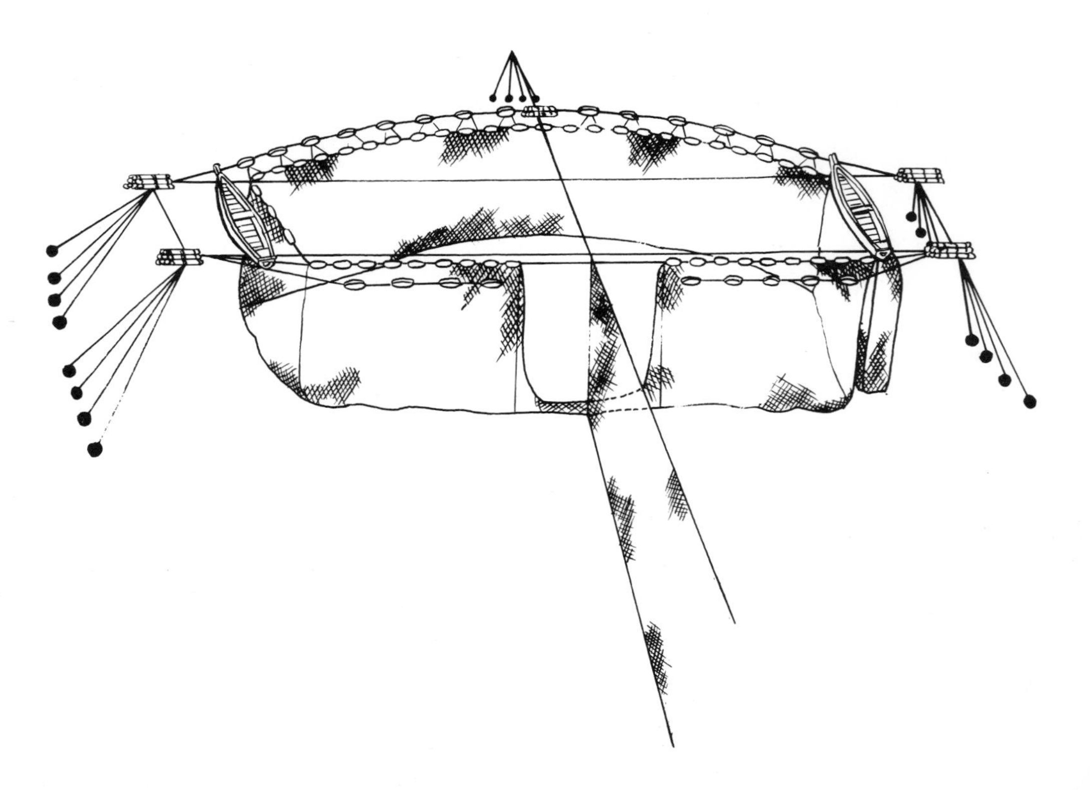

Fig 279 Japanese 'kaku-ami' for catching herring and sardines after closing the entrance and lifting the netting. (*NN, 1959*).

kidney or heart-shaped chambers. Some of them can become complicated when combined with leading nets. A very sophisticated construction is known in Japan for setting in fish runs (*Fig 280d*). In some cases the fish may find the way out. The chance of this happening will be decreased, not only by a more complicated arrangement of the fences, but also when catching chambers are combined with each other so that one runs into another, and maybe the second one is followed by a third (*Figs 281b* and *281c*). Theoretically, the fish can still find the way out, but it becomes more and more difficult and unlikely. The way out can be made even more difficult if the large entrance of the first chamber becomes smaller with the second one, and the third may be only a slit. The fish has to press through to get into the next catching chamber and then there is no more chance of finding the way back. In this form we have a real trap with a non-return device, but this transition from fences and other materials used for barriers, to fishing gear considered as real traps, will be discussed in the third and fourth sections of the next chapter which deals with trapping.

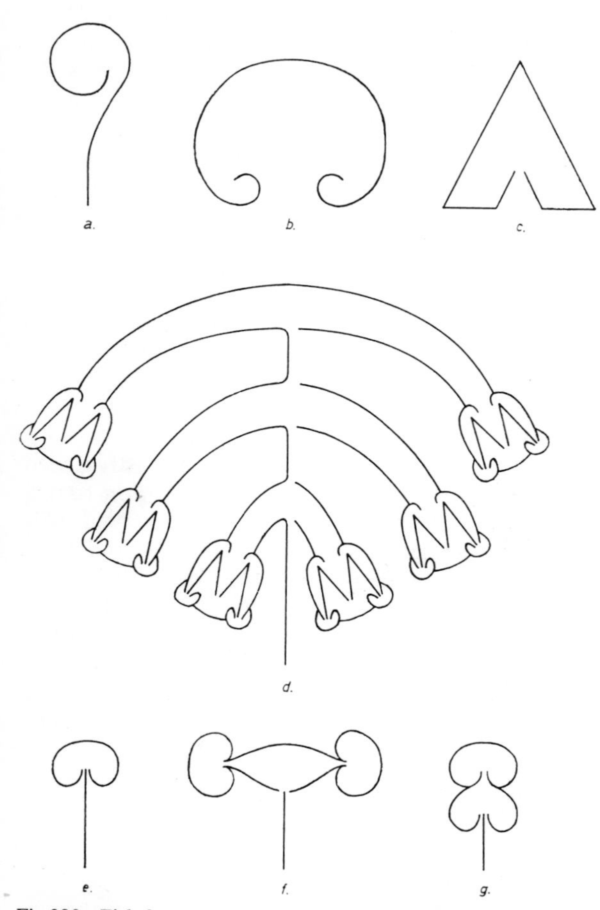

Fig 280 Fish fences set in the form of labyrinths: (*a*) fish fence of Finland (*Jankó, 1900*); (*b*) Korean fish fence; (*c*) fish fences in triangular form; (*d*) Japanese labyrinth used in big lakes (*NN, 1959*); (*e*) heart-shaped form from the estuary of the Danube (*Jankó, 1900*); (*f*) Swedish fish fence (*Herman, 1900*; (*g*) fish fence of northeastern Europe (*Jankó, 1900*).

Fig 281 Big weirs made of wood: (*a*) bamboo weir of Thailand (*NN, 1953*); (*b*) menhaden weir of the North American coast (*Sundstrom, 1957*); (*c*) sardine weir of the Philippines (*Umali, 1950*).

Chapter sixteen

Trapping

Generally speaking, in fishery and hunting trapping means that the wanted prey enters a catching chamber from which escape is difficult or even impossible. The prey enters the trap voluntarily, maybe when searching for a shelter, or when lured by some bait, or when frightened and guided by fishermen or hunters. Mechanical traps of this type (Chapter 14) are most effective in hunting, but have the disadvantage, for fisheries, that the trap is closed as soon as a single fish has entered and so no more catching can take place. As has been shown in the last chapter, there are some methods by which fish are trapped in catching chambers, including some with large entrances, which have to be watched and closed by hand as soon as fish are seen to enter. It has also been said that this may be an effective way to operate a fishing gear even today, but for the fact that it is labour-intensive. The solution was found by making the entrances smaller and smaller, finally in such a manner that the entrance itself became a non-return device, allowing the fish to enter the trap but making it practically impossible for them to leave the catching chamber again. Today, non-return devices are considered typical for fishing traps. This is the same for all traps whether used for fish, crustaceans or gastropods. The form and size of a catching chamber can have many variations but the principle of catching is always the same. But in fisheries, as in hunting, there is also another, possibly older, principle by which the prey can be prevented from escaping. These are gears, looking more or less like a long funnel, which the fish enters and then becomes jammed between the narrowing sides of the gear. This is another solution based on the principle already mentioned, but it also has the disadvantage that, in general, not more than one fish can be caught at a time. Nevertheless, we have to begin this chapter with the so-called tubular traps.

16.1 Tubular traps and thorn-lined traps

Tubular traps are funnel-shaped gear, mostly closed at the smaller end and without any non-return device. They can be made of split bamboo reeds (*Fig 282*) or of slender branches (*Figs 283, 284* and *285*); they can also be made of plaited smooth bast or from netting yarn (*Fig 286*). In non-tropical countries the tubular traps are made of rods of hazel, linden, spruce or willow. They are slender elastic funnels which the fish enter, maybe voluntarily searching for shelter, or lured by bait.

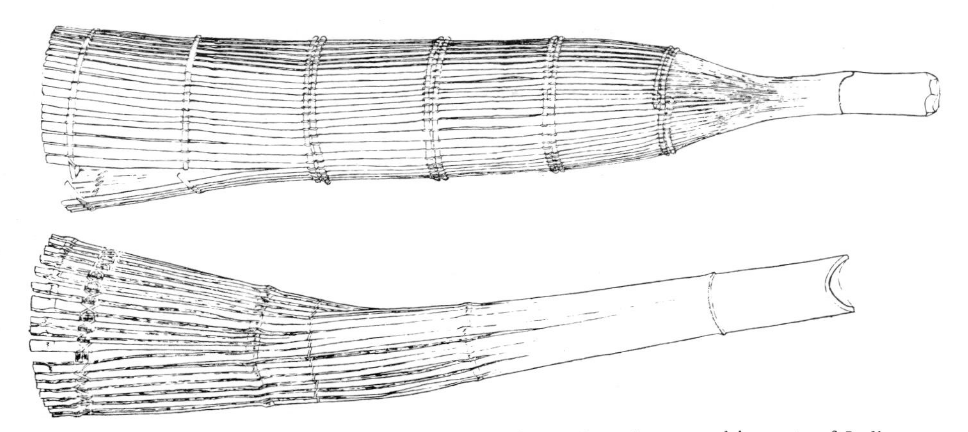

Fig 282 Tubular traps made of split bamboo, without funnels, as used in parts of India.

Fig 283 Tubular traps of the Wagenia fishermen in the Zaire River near Kisangani. (*Photo: B Konietzko.*)

Fig 284 Tubular trap used in the Zaire River, near Kisangani. (*Photo: FAO. R Kreuzer.*)

Fig 285 Fishing place for tubular traps in the Bandama River, Ivory Coast (1971).

Fig 286 Smooth tubular trap made of netting (Thailand).

The fish creeps into the gear, gets stuck, tries to move back, but is prevented by the backward-angled rays of its own dorsal fins. Tubular traps are used especially to catch catfish in this manner in the swamp fisheries of Africa.[244] There, the baited trap may be combined with a fence to guide the fish into the gear.[666] Obviously the long, narrow fish is unable to turn round because there is no room in the smooth, loosely plaited tube. Traps of this tubular form are familiar from the fisheries of Europe, Asia and Africa, as well as from the ancient Indian fishery of the New World.[328, 345, 580] They are characterized by their length and small width. In the Indian fishery of California, these fishing tubes sometimes ended above water level. Their length was given as up to fourteen feet, that is, over four metres, so that fish could proceed a long way up them but as they did so, their return, because of the narrow width, became more and more impossible.

Some people think that tubular traps are typical fishing gear for rivers with strong currents.[361] In this case, the traps are set in large scaffoldings, particularly where the flow is concentrated, and are set with their openings against the current in such a way that the fish may be swept into the gear. Such traps are sometimes set vertically below an artificial waterfall, so that the water carrying the fish falls into, and through, the gear. Escape for the fish is then impossible. A fish, however, can get slightly damaged by this method. Tubular traps of this type, set both vertically and horizontally, are known in Asia, Africa and South America. They can be placed on the bed of a shallow stream like a barrier. The fishermen or fisherwomen proceed upstream for some distance and return downstream, driving the fishes into the open mouth of the traps.[261] Tubular traps are operated today in some rivers of western Africa. A well-known example of tubular traps used in rivers with a strong current, are those of the Wagenia fishermen in the Zaire River near Kisangani (*Figs 283* and *284*). At a place where the mighty river narrows into rapids, the local fishermen build long scaffolds of poles lashed together with wires. From this rickety pier they hang tubular traps three and more metres in length and up to two metres in diameter at the mouth. The principle of the device is that fish, passively swept into the narrowing gap between palisades by the swift current, are dashed against the poles of a palisade-like structure. The fish, perhaps stunned, are carried by the force of the current into the tubular traps, from which they cannot escape. Every day the traps are checked and the contents emptied out.[244] The old European fishery also used quite a number of such traps without non-return devices: they were called 'Anschläger' in German-speaking countries.[580] In Scotland such gear is made of whitethorn or hazel twigs and, more recently, of aluminium. In the Severn district of England, the gear was called 'putcher' or 'butt' and was used for catching salmon.[127]

In the southern Asiatic fishery, yet another way was found of retaining fish in such tubular traps. On their interior side, thorny twigs of rattan or other plants were fastened. These are pointed inwards like barbed hooks and thus prevent the fish, once it has entered, from retreating. Here, as in the smooth tubular traps mentioned before, bait is put into the innermost part of the gear to attract the fish into the funnel. These thorn-lined traps are especially used in Indonesia, but are also known in Indo-China (Burma, Malaysia), in the northern Philippines, and as far away as Australia, Taiwan and Melanesia.[9] There are also variations of them in use in East Africa. It is supposed that this type of trap, equipped with thorns, may have originated in the pre-Austronesian cultural area[315] known for fishing as well as for hunting. *Figure 287* shows two thorn-lined traps, of which the larger one is a typical tubular trap. The smaller one is suspended from a float and, when operated, wrapped with some leaves. As soon as the fish has entered and tries to get free, a weight is released and the trap then rises (with its catch) by means of the float to the surface of the water.

Before ending this section, it has to be added that tubular traps can be used in another manner. On Lake Chad, tubular traps are used to filter fish which are drawn out with the water from a pond. This method of catching fish by drawing out is also known in other parts of the world, where fish ponds are drained off and the fish scooped out through a sieve in the form of a reed box or a pocket-shaped basket.[361]

16.2 Non-return devices

The method of catching fish by the use of complicated catching chambers has been improved by the development of non-return devices (*Fig 288*). In the final section of the last chapter, one type was mentioned which had an entrance like a 'V' with a small slit at the narrow point, through which the fish can force itself as it will do when making its way through water plants. There is very little chance of the fish returning the same way (*Fig 288a*). This type of non-return device is used especially for traps with a catching chamber made of any form of fence or fence-like material. Another very simple way of preventing an escape, or making it more difficult, is to install a step, if possible with a ramp, as in *Fig 288b*. This step guides the approaching fish from the bottom up to a higher level. As soon as it has passed over the step it will drop down to its former depth. Thus it does not usually find its way out of the trap again by the way it came in – even though it could easily swim over the step if it knew it was there. In many fisheries, *eg* in the sea of Azov[441] or in the coastal waters of Japan,[445] entrapment gear with such a step is operated. These ramps can guide quite large shoals of sardine-like fish into the enclosure (*Fig 349*). Non-return devices in the form of a step or ramp are used when the gear is made of netting, and large catches are expected.

Fig 287 Thorn-lined traps of Oceania. (*Photo: Ethnographical Museum, Leiden.*)

With smaller gears, the entrance with the non-return device is formed like a funnel (*Figs 288c, d* and *e*) whose tapered end is directed away from the opening of the gear into the catching chamber. Such a funnel-shaped valve is often called the throat.

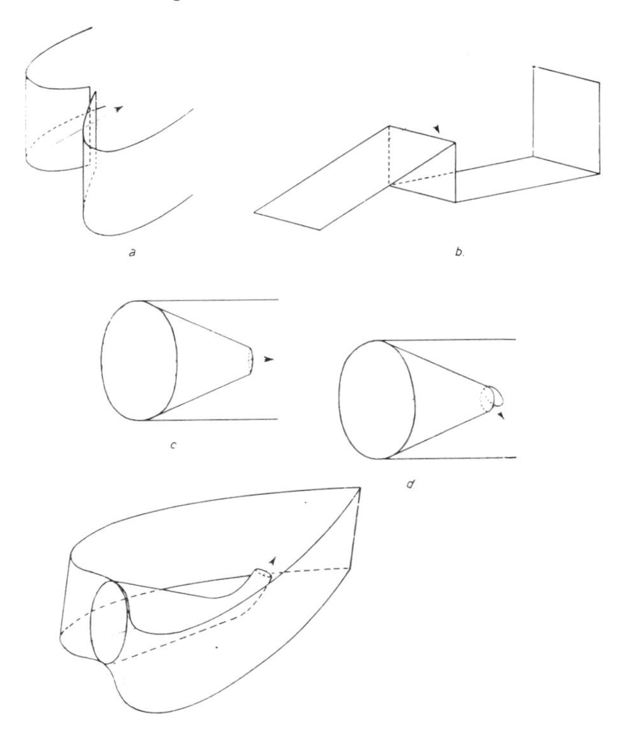

Fig 288 Entrances of traps: (*a*) in the form of a slit; (*b*) in the form of a step; (*c*) and (*d*) funnel with hinged flap; (*e*) turned entrance of a trap used in the Antilles.

Throats are typical for smaller traps made of wood, wire or netting. With the original wooden baskets, such a funnel-shaped valve can be formed in a simple way by fitting two pointed baskets, one into the other. With fyke nets made of netting, the construction of a funnel-shaped throat becomes more difficult. Therefore, the manufacture of well-formed funnels is properly included in the training of young fishermen. In the case of baskets made of wood or wire, sometimes single elastic rods are allowed to protrude from the funnel into the inner part of the trap, into its first chamber, sometimes named the parlour (*Fig 289*). The fish, lobster, or crawfish may be able to press these rods apart when it enters the gear, but the points bar the way out when it tries to leave the trap. Nevertheless, to ensure that any fish caught cannot escape through the funnel, a flap may be fastened in front of the opening so that it swings open only towards the interior of the trap (*Fig 288d*). There are such iron

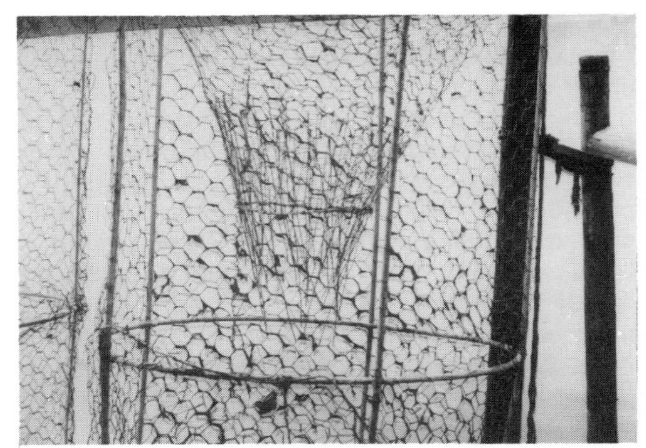

Fig 289 Fishing pot made of wire with elastic spikes around the opening of the funnel to prevent fish escaping. Lake Lucerne, Switzerland (1954).

flaps in lobster pots and wooden shrimp baskets, *eg* of the type which were formerly used exclusively on the Friesian coast. The Japanese close some wooden traps in the same way, with a curtain of slanting bamboo sticks which can be lifted only when coming in from the outside. Finally, the funnel-shaped throat may not be made straight, but may be bent to make it even more difficult for the fish to get out. In this way a kind of step is combined with the funnel in that the entrance to the funnel and its outlet into the enclosure are not on the same level. *Figure 288e* shows such an arrangement as used for some types of wooden baskets. In some traps several enclosures are often set one after another, with the openings of the entrances becoming more and more narrow. With fyke nets, the first opening of the funnel on the entrance of the trap may be a square, the opening of the next funnel may be triangular and that of the last a narrow slit only.

The principle of these different forms of non-return device is to keep the fish away from the entrance. As has been said of the non-return device in the form of a step, the fish, returning to the bottom, has little chance of finding the entrance again even when it is very broad. What happens with the slitlike or funnel-shaped entrances is demonstrated in *Figure 290*. The fish entering the trap is guided as demonstrated. Swimming in circles, the single fish or the fish shoal has virtually no chance of finding the way to the entrance. This is a known fact used in other fishing gear, *eg* purse seines. Moreover, non-return devices are arrangements which are fitted to other types of fishing gear, like stow nets, trawls and seine nets. They are one of the basic elements of fishing gear construction.

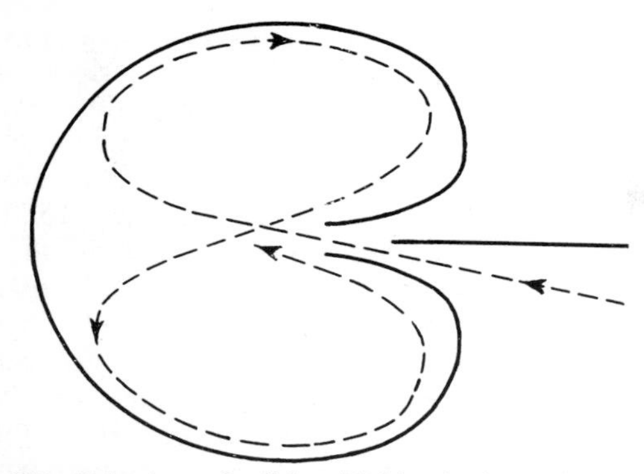

Fig 290 Behaviour of a fish guided by the funnel into a trap.

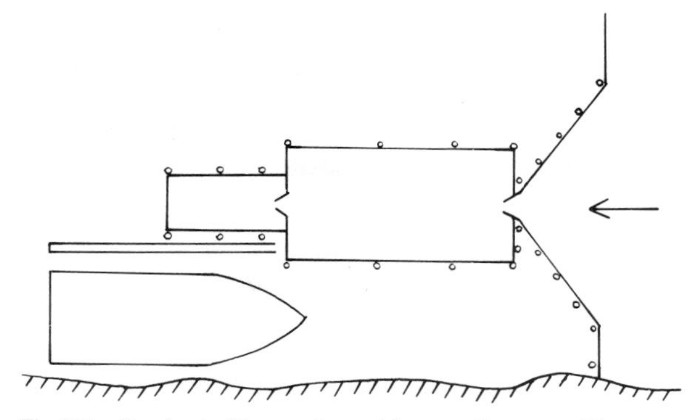

Fig 291 Barrier in Kampuchea with a small passage like a slit leading the prey into a catching chamber. (*Fily and d'Aubertin, 1965*).

16.3 Trapping barriers made of fences

As shown before, barriers can have small passages to facilitate catching. When these are made in the form of a slit leading to an enclosed catching chamber,a fishing gear is formed which is considered a true trap. *Figure 291* shows such an arrangement in a river of Kampuchea.[167] In this case the barrier is made of a strong wood frame covered with fences made of mats. The whole barrier has a 'V'-like form with a small passage. The large opening of the 'V' by which the fish pass into a permanent enclosure, faces the current. From here they can be guided or driven into a smaller movable container, which can be pulled out of the water by a pulley system. A sampan is slipped underneath and the fish are emptied into the vessel through an outlet in the bottom of the container. In this example, a strongly built barrier was incorporated in a trap-like fishing gear. This can be done more easily by flexible fences as shown in *Figure 280*. This facility has been utilized in many fisheries to build real traps with slit entrances as a non-return device.

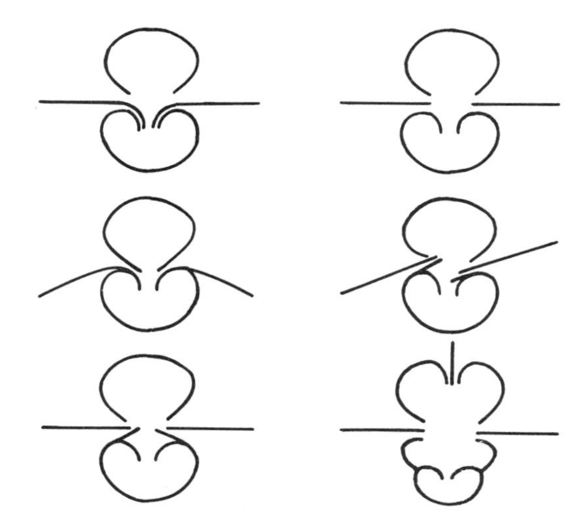

Fig 292 Barriers with catching chambers made of fences with slitlike entrances in Rumania. (*Antipa, 1916*).

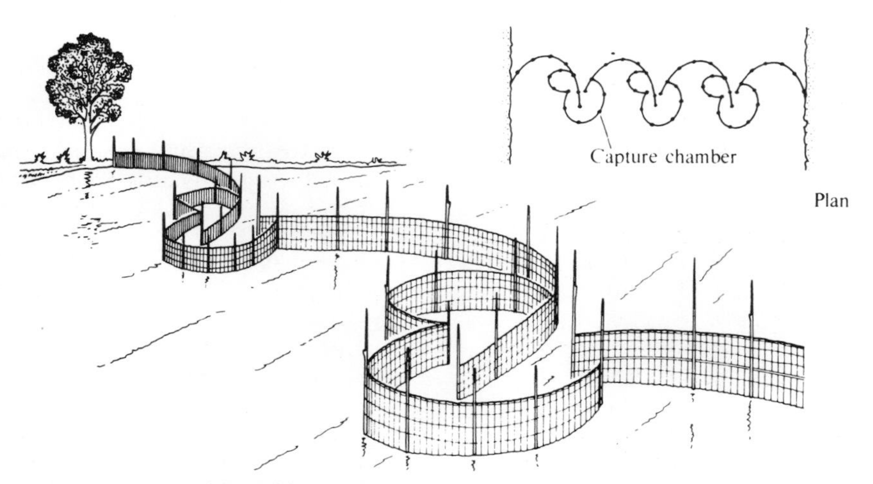

Fig 293 Barrier with catching chambers made of fences in a lagoon in Benin. (*According to Welcomme, 1979*).

Figure 292 shows barriers of fences set as traps in heart-shaped form from Romania[13], which do not differ very much from a barrier crossing a lagoon in Benin (*Fig 293*).[654] Such arrangements do not always need to have round forms. *Figures 294* and *295* show the principle of a similar Turkish arrangement.[384] But there may be no place in the world where fences have not been set as traps with slit-like entrances as non-return devices. These may be long barriers which include traps or small barriers set in a trap-like manner. *Figure 296* shows a barrier with a long row of connected traps made of fences off the Ivory Coast. *Figure 297* shows a similar fishing gear from Indonesia, but these are large-scale traps which will be mentioned in the last section but one of this chapter.

Fig 294 Turkish barrier, so-called 'wooden dalyan' with catching chambers. (*Mengi, 1977*).

Before ending this section, one of the most famous barriers made of fences has to be mentioned. This is operated in the Italian fishery for eels between Ravenna and Venice with the main centre in the Valli di Comacchio (*Fig 298*).[11] These barriers were originally made of reeds (*Fig 299*) with an entrance in the form of a slit. During experiments, some parts were made of plastic tubes but the modern barriers are made of concrete with slit-like non-return devices made of steel (*Fig 300*). *Figure 301* shows the principle of this method for catching eels migrating from the sea into the lagoons. The fish move from the sea towards the saline lagoons through the open entrances of the barrier (1). Good-sized fish will be caught in the chamber between the two fences, because the openings in the next and later catching chambers (2) become smaller and smaller until only small elvers can escape into the lagoons. On the other hand, eels coming from the lagoons through the openings in the direction of the sea (3) will be caught in the chamber (4) because at this migrating time all other openings are closed.[11] These trapping barriers for eels are similar to those made by the Italians to catch mullet (Mugilidae) (*Fig 302*) and also those operated in Ireland to catch salmon in the River Shannon (*Fig 303*) near Limerick.

16.4 Wooden pots

It is typical of traps that the fish or other prey enter a catching chamber from which escape may be difficult, especially when the way out of the trap is secured by a non-return device (*Fig 288*). This

Fig 295 Turkish 'wooden dalyan' (1963).

Fig 296 Fences arranged like traps off the Ivory Coast. (*Photo: Steinberg, 1965.*)

Fig 297 Traplike arrangement of fences in Indonesia. (*Photo: Kollmannsperger, 1976.*)

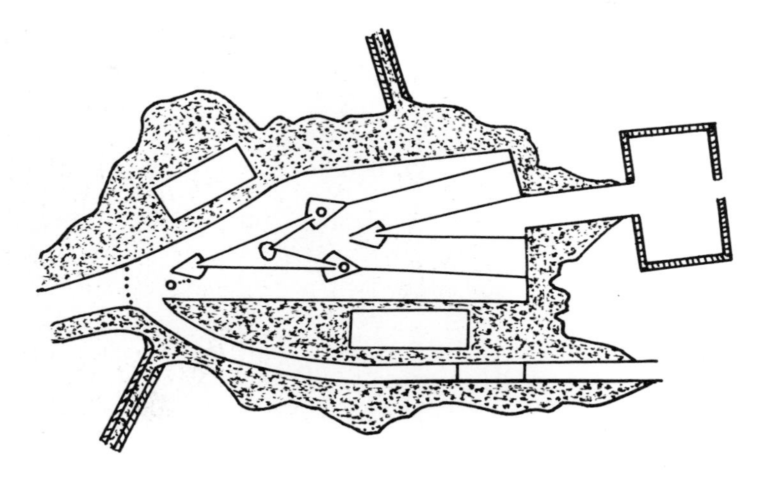

Fig 298 Barrages for catching eels in Valli di Comacchio, Italy. (*According to Hornell, 1950*).

Fig 299 Catching chamber in Comacchio made of reeds (1975).

is also true of wooden traps, generally known as fishing pots or baskets.

Fishing traps made of fences have open chambers which are two-dimensional[406], and it is sometimes necessary to let the fences rise well above the water surface to prevent fish from escaping by jumping over the fences. In contrast to these traps, pots are three-dimensional in that they have completely closed chambers, with the exception of one or more entrances secured by non-return devices (*Fig 304*). As with traps made of fences there can be one or more of these catching chambers one after the other, each with an entrance in the form of a funnel (*Fig 309a*). All pots are transportable movable fishing gear. Wooden pots, together with other types of fishing gear made of this material, are early stages in the development of fishing technology. Of course, they are older than other traps made of netting. Nevertheless, even today some types of wooden pots have an important place in some fisheries because of their great stability, especially in rivers and coastal waters. The large quantities of

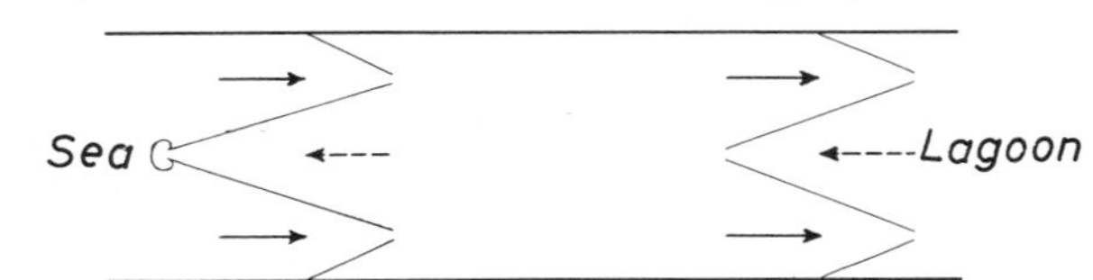

Fig 301 Plan of the Italian method for catching eels between the sea and lagoon in Comacchio. (*de Angelis, 1959*).

Fig 300 Modern catching chamber in Comacchio (1975).

Fig 302 Modern Italian arrangement for catching mullet near Ansedonia, Tyrrhenian coast of Italy (1971).

Fig 303 Salmon trap in River Shannon, Ireland (1956).

Fig 304 Small Turkish pots as operated in the Bosphorus to catch smaller fish (1971).

wooden pots operated for catching crustaceans in the offshore fisheries of Norway, Great Britain and France are a good example of their usefulness in industrial fisheries today. Pots can be made of wire, plastic or other hard material as well as the traditional wood.

Traditional wooden pots are made from strips of reed, split bamboo, rattan, or wood laths. They may be plaited in a similar manner to the early agricultural wicker baskets (*Fig 305*) or carefully woven like mats. They can be made of parallel strips of wood, like European crayfish pots (*Fig 306*) or of parallel sticks, sometimes with large square meshes, as in some African fisheries (*Figs 307* and *308*). They can also be plaited in a complicated hexagonal shape (*Fig 385*) or a seldom used pentagonal shape. Due to the materials used and the techniques by which pots are made and their world wide distribution, it is not surprising that varying shapes of pots have evolved. *Figure 309* gives a small selection of examples only. It is understandable that, because wooden pots are transportable fishing gear and because of the material from which they are made, they can have only a limited size. When soaked with water, large wooden pots can be very heavy. Wooden pots with an opening of a man's height are rare, because they are difficult to handle. Nevertheless, a few are still operated (*Fig 307*) because their weight is reduced by partial construction of lighter-weight material. In this respect the large, and sometimes heavy, 'bubus' of the sea fisheries of South Asia have to be mentioned. These are operated at great depths where they remain for a long time. The bubus vary greatly in size and construction. Their entrance can

Fig 305 Turkish fish basket made of wickerwork. (Lake Van, eastern Turkey, 1974).

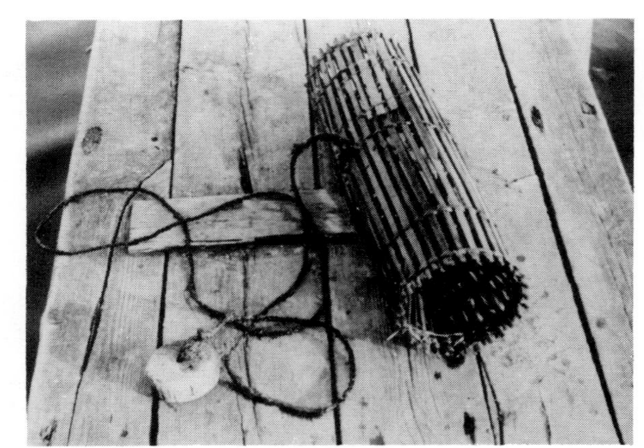

Fig 306 Pot made of strips of wood for catching crayfish in German fresh waters.

Fig 307 Large wooden basket of Shaba. (*Photo: C P Halain, 1966.*)

Fig 308 Wooden basket with square meshes made of palm leaves; from Nigeria. (*Photo: Baçalbasa, 1970.*)

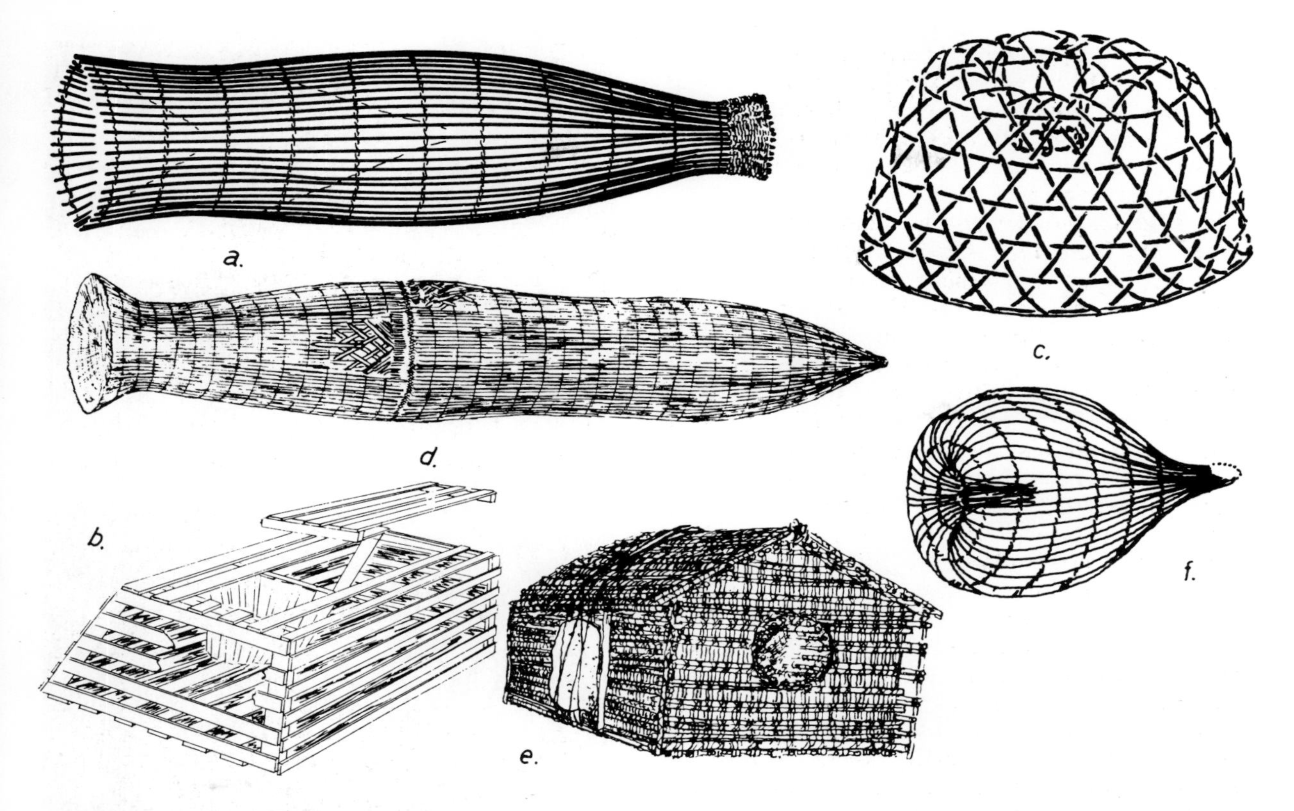

Fig 309 Different types of basket: (*a*) basket for eels, northern Germany; (*b*) box-like basket for spiny lobsters of Florida (*Sundstrom, 1957*); (*c*) shrimp basket of the Philippines; (*d*) basket of Thailand with lateral entrances; (*e*) house-like basket from the Gilbert Island (*Koch 1965*); (*f*) basket with square meshes from Lake Chad (*Blache and Miton, 1962*).

be a simple slit or a curved funnel. Originally these traps were made of woven bamboo or rattan. Nowadays a framework of wood or wire is used (*Fig 310*), covered with chicken wire. Larger pots as used in sea fisheries can have the form of a beehive, but then the entrance is from below, which means that they have to lie on the side when fishing (*Figs 311, 312* and *313*). Smaller forms of wooden pots, like the French lobster pots, have the entrance on the top (*Fig 314*). A French dictionary of fisheries terms compares their form with 'champignons sans pied' and the English speak of 'inkwell pots'.[149] Pots in this form are also used for catching whelks in England (*Fig 316*).

Some pots are like barrels or drums, originally developed in France for langoustes. They are made

Fig 310 Frame of a Malaysian trap, called a 'bubu', with an entrance like a slit. (1978).

Fig 311 Beehive fish traps in the harbour of Santa Cruz, Tenerife (1968).

Fig 312 Beehive fish traps in the harbour of Mar del Plata, Argentina. The traps are baited and set according to the longline system to catch *Pagrus pagrus* (1979).

Fig 313 Small vessel (firilla) of Malta with large bottom traps (nassi tal-arznell) which can be neither folded nor stacked. There are two fishermen on board the vessel! (1966)

Fig 314 French lobster pots in Portsall, near Brest in Brittany (1977).

Fig 315 Australian rock lobster pots made of wood and strong wire in Stanley, Tasmania (1981).

Fig 316 English 'iron whelk pots' so-called because the bottoms of these pots are made from plates of perforated iron. (*Photo: Archives.*)

of wooden laths. Nowadays the two ends are closed by netting or wire (*Fig 317*). This type also has the entrance on the upper side. Other pots are bottle shaped, like the eel traps operated in Europe and elsewhere (*Figs 309a* and *318*). The entrance is in front and more than one funnel prevents the escape of the prey. Only some very tube-like pots of Thailand and Nepal have secured entrances on the side (*Fig 309d*).

Fig 317 Portuguese traps made of wood and wire; for spiny lobsters.

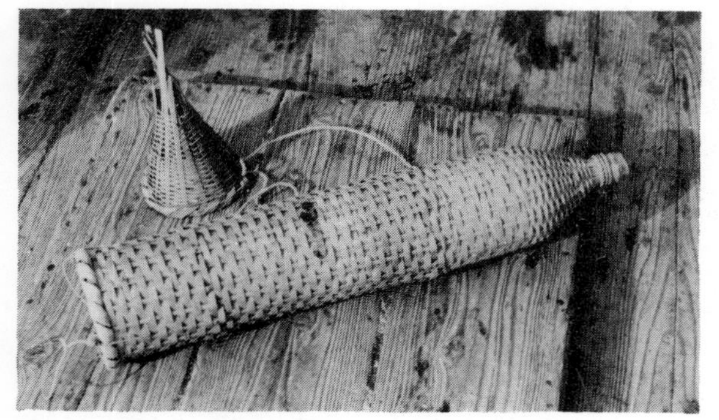

Fig 318 Korean basket for catching eels. The valve can be separated (1972).

An interesting wooden trap is the so-called 'Madeira trap' from which the 'Antilles trap' has been developed. This was originally heart-shaped and made of hexagonally plaited rattan strips (*Fig 319*). Its history of distribution is more or less known. These traps are supposed to have originated in India and Sri Lanka and to have been brought back by the Portuguese after sailing round southern Africa to the Seychelles, Madagascar and Madeira, and later to Brazil and the Caribbean. Originally the heart-shaped traps had one central entrance only (*Fig 319*): now the West Indian or Antilles traps have the form of a single or double 'Z' with two or four opposed valves (*Fig 320*).[91, 370, 678] There are many variations in form and size of wooden pots. Some strange house-shaped types used in Oceania (*Fig 309e*) are built according to the special secrets of different families and are used to catch moray eels.[315]

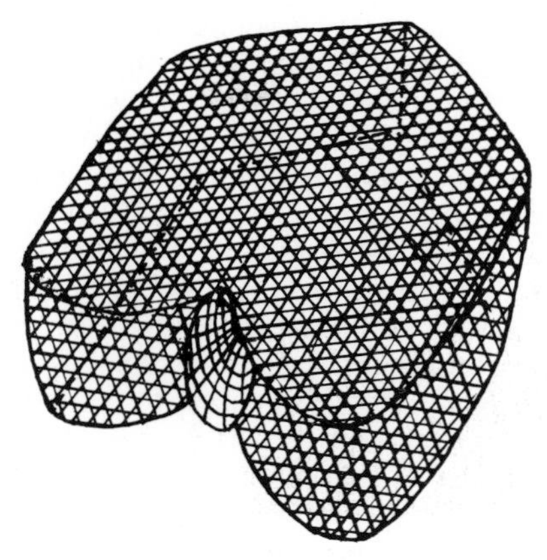

Fig 319 So-called 'Madeira trap' made of rattan with hexagonal plaiting.

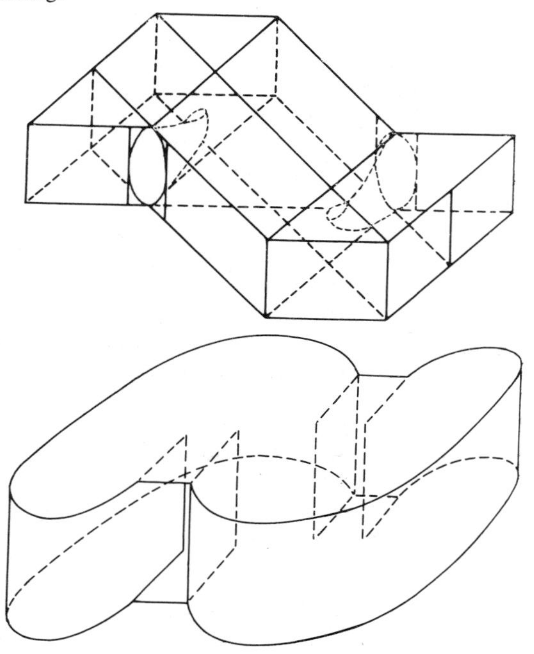

Fig 320 Traps of the Caribbean.

There are many different types of wooden traps but it is hoped that those mentioned will indicate the very many forms they can take. As mentioned before, wooden pots can be very heavy. In order to reduce their weight, use of heavy hardwood can be restricted to the framework only. This is then covered with lighter material such as netting or textiles. Large and small traps are constructed in this manner (*Figs 311* and *317*).

Pots – not only the wooden ones – are mostly used as bottom gear without any other arrangements for leading the prey into the trap, but in most cases they are baited. This is also so when pots are set according to the longline system, as in the example in *Figure 321* for traps operated for shrimp fishing off Majorca in the Mediterranean.[371] This longline system is also used in fresh waters, *eg* for eel traps in rivers. As with other gear, the longline system facilitates the easy handling of the gear. The disadvantage of this system is that single pots can be placed more efficiently than several joined together. This is the reason why, *eg* for rock lobsters in Australia or New Zealand, the pots are set singly after checking the ground with echo sounders.

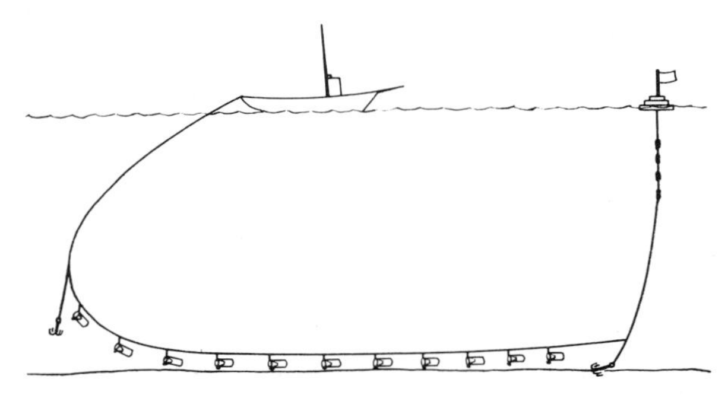

Fig 321 Longline technique for operating shrimp baskets off Majorca (*Massuti, 1967*).

Pots can also be operated in combination with barriers (*Fig 254*), usually as interchangeable gear in the outlets of a barrier. In this case the passages of the barrier need not be watched by fishermen to catch the passing fish with spear, gaff or scoop net. Unwatched traps in the passages will catch the prey automatically. Here it has to be added that there is a relationship between the strength of a current and the number of traps. Each gape of a trap reduces the force of the current, and its power to swirl fish along is thus lessened.[82] For this reason not too many baskets should be built into a barrier. On the other hand, there is no doubt that a combination of traps in any form with barriers increases their catching efficiency considerably. An interesting and unusual example are barriers with pots operated even today by the Maoris in New Zealand for catching lamprey during their upstream migration. In the strong current of a river, a barrier with some passages is placed which the lamprey try to swim through. In many cases this will not be possible. By the jet-effect of the gap, the fish are pressed back and driven into the traps placed before the barrier. In this case the fishing gear is a wooden

Fig 322 Lamprey pot, operated by Maori fishermen in the Waganui River in New Zealand. The fish migrating upstream attempt to swim through the gap, but the force of water flowing through the narrow opening washes them back into the funnel-like opening of the pot. (*Todd, 1979*).

pot with an opening enlarged by a funnel made of large-meshed netting (*Fig 322*).[624]

Pots can also be used to catch pelagic fish. In this case the basket does not stand horizontally, as on the bottom, but vertically. The Javanese use small baskets set vertically for catching freshwater shrimps.[612] In Malta, egg-shaped baskets are used (*Fig 323*). They are baited and two are fixed on a main line, held by a float above and by a weight below.[67] Finally, baskets made of wickerwork can be made as floating gear when fixed on the underside of a raft.

Fig. 323 Egg-shaped basket for pelagic fishing gear Malta. (*v Brandt, 1966*).

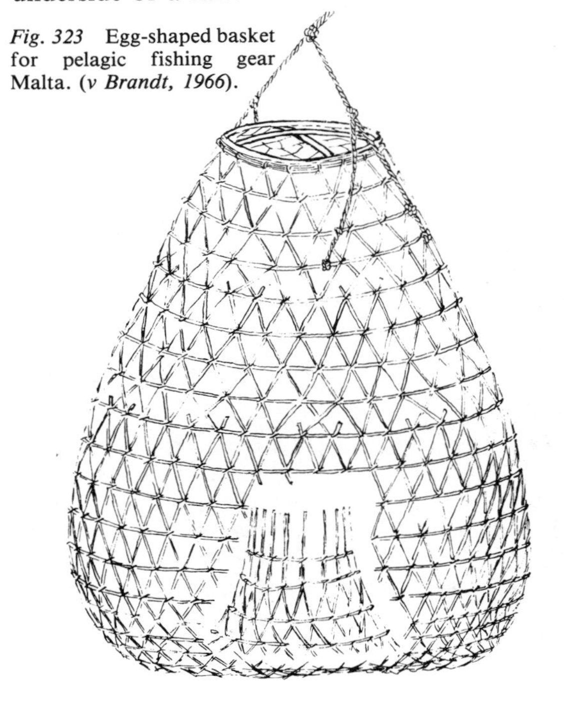

16.5 Pots made of wire

Pots are three-dimensional traps, which means that their catching chambers are completely closed with the exception of the entrance. Such traps can be made of many materials other than wood. An early method of making traps for catching fish, crayfish or even beavers, was to use hexagonal chicken or poultry wire in different forms. The disadvantage of traps made of wire is that they are vulnerable to rust, even when galvanized. Nevertheless, they are well known in freshwater fisheries (*Figs 324* and *325*) and in sea fisheries like that in the Persian Gulf where wire baskets as high as a man are known (*Fig 326*). In sea fisheries, wire traps are sometimes protected by zinc and aluminium anodes which are placed in the traps. The anode generates an electrical current, inhibiting the corrosion of the wire and increasing the value of the trap.

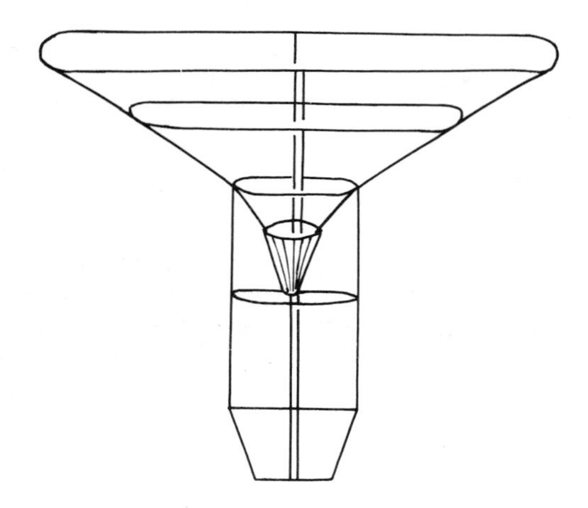

Fig 324 Modern wire trap with broad and also high entrance opening.

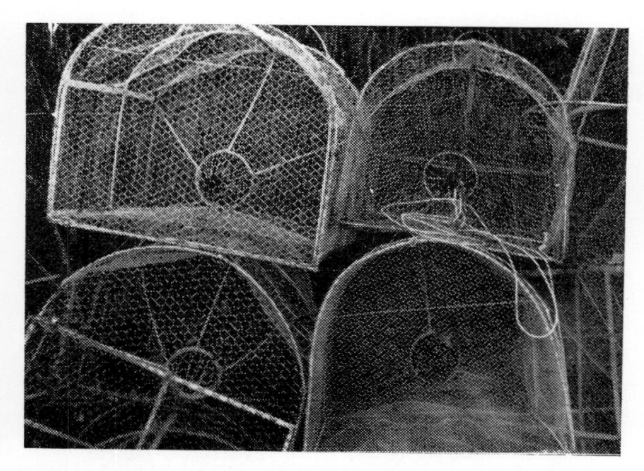

Fig 325 Swiss traps made of wire with elastic rods in the funnel, used in Lake Geneva.

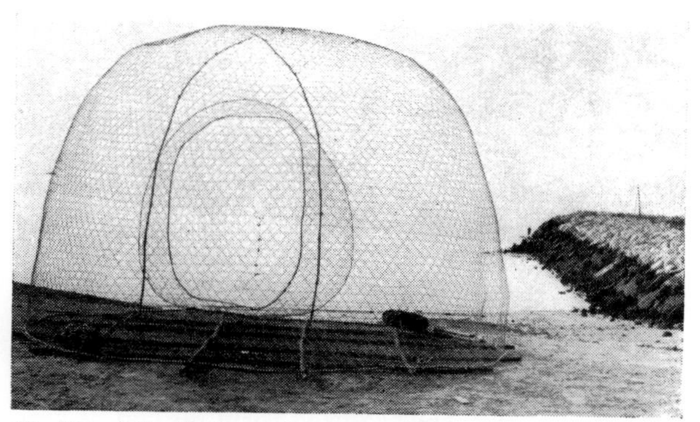

Fig 326 Wire baskets of a man's height in Kuwait (1970).

In most cases well-known pots made of wood have been the model for wire pots. Even the famous Antilles traps, in a 'Z' form with two or four entrances (*Fig 320*), can be made of wire instead of split bamboo. In the Mediterranean the Greeks and their neighbours use very flat round wire traps with the opening at the top. When fishing, such a trap will be camouflaged with seaweed (*Fig 327*). This flat wire trap may be an old type of basket trap and is known in Saudi Arabia and in the Persian Gulf, where a similar trap is considered a traditional fishing pot. But this type is, or was, also known in the western part of the Mediterranean.[186]

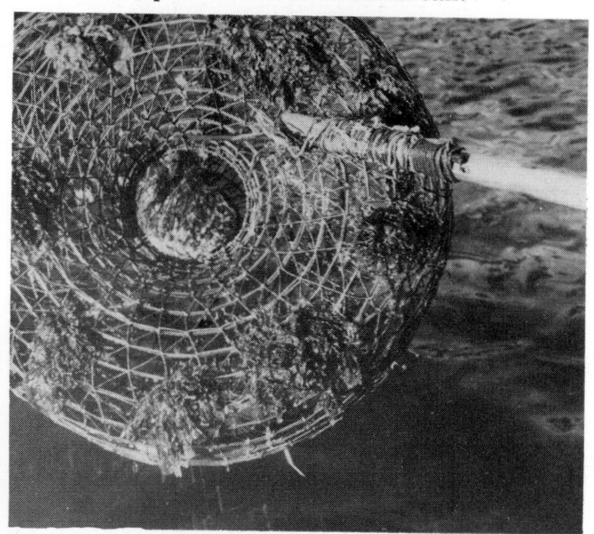

Fig 327 Round Greek wire trap camouflaged with seaweed before setting.

Many experiments have been made in an effort to overcome the difficulties of the rusting of wire pots in sea water. Traps have been made from seawater-resistant aluminium wire or of iron wire coated with plastic. Sometimes the valves of wire traps have been made of plastic or even of sheet metal.[337] A successful idea – and also an economic one – may be to replace the wire with a stiff PE netting which, especially in France, will be used more and more with wooden traps (*Fig 328*). In the USA, thick 'plastic-coated steel wire' or 'plastic coated galvanized welded wire' is offered for traps. When using wire, especially chicken wire, for the construction of a fishing pot, it is generally necessary to first make a frame of stronger material to give the trap the right form, as with some wooden pots. But when using stiffer or more rigid wire mesh it may be possible to construct the fishing pot in any desired form without such a frame by folding the wire mesh in the required form, as can be seen in *Figure 329*. The new American plastic coated wires can be used to form crab pots without any frame. Finally, it may be added that sometimes old wooden pots of half rotten, weakened, but still very effective, sticks of bamboo are covered with wire netting to give them an added life, which the Australians also do in their lobster fishery.[266]

Fig 328 French shrimp traps in Guilvinec, Brittany, with stiff PE-netting (1977).

Fig 329 Trap formed of wire mesh without any frame. Lagune Aby, Ivory Coast, (1971).

16.6 Traps made of netting

In contrast to wooden pots and some wire traps, those made of netting require special supporting arrangements to keep them in the correct horizontal and vertical form. Whilst fish pots made from solid materials have their special forms, the netting used for traps must be kept under tension by frames. Fyke nets are spread by rings or hoops (*Figs 330* and *331*). Poles driven into the bottom (*Fig 330c*) or spreading sticks (stick stretchers) (*Figs 330a* and *330b*) keep the fyke nets in a horizontal position. But fyke nets are not always operated horizontally. In the Baltic there have been fyke nets for turbot which were hung by a long central leader vertically from the ice surface.[628] There are hooped nets with two entrances, looking like a drum with an entrance at each end. Known world-wide are the conical fyke nets with at least one, but sometimes more than ten hoops, as used by the Danes. The first hoop can be replaced by a horseshoe-shaped frame or by a square one (*Fig 331*). They have at least one funnel-shaped non-return device, sometimes three.

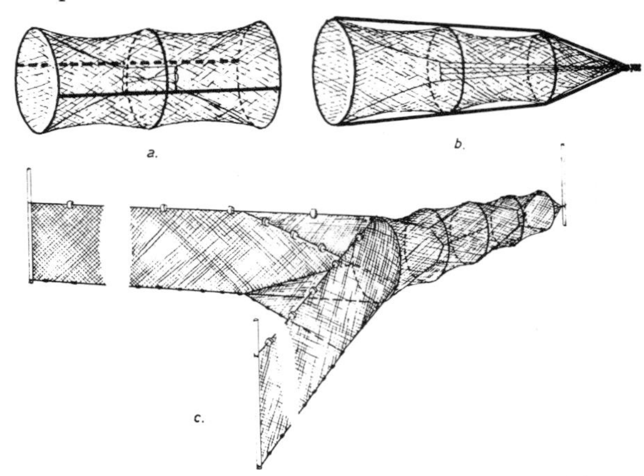

Fig 330 Hooped nets and fyke nets: (*a*) hooped net with two entrances and spreading sticks; (*b*) fyke net with spreading sticks; (*c*) fyke net with wings.

Fyke nets can be used alone when they replace wooden eel traps, and are often fixed like the longline method in a river. Often fyke nets are combined with walls or fences. Most of them are combined with leaders and wings (*Figs 331* and *350*). Their effectiveness is increased considerably by such additional arrangements as will be discussed in the last section but one of this chapter. Traps made of netting, like the conical fyke nets and the drum-like traps, are small-scale fishing gear. This means that they are of limited size, and that a single trap can catch only small quantities of fish. Even though most of these traps are small in size, there are some exceptions in which the first hoop at the

Fig 331 Fyke nets with two funnels, four rings and a central leading net. The first ring is horseshoe-shaped.

entrance of the trap is as high as a man. On the other hand, there are also small traps made of netting, like small fyke nets, for catching fish such as a single trout in a mountain brook (*Fig 330b*), or like the small drum-like Italian traps, not more than 30cm in length, for catching Gobiidae in the lagoons of Venice (*Fig 332*). Both traps have spreading sticks and a single valve only.

Commercial fisheries need a very large number of small traps if their operation is to be economically viable. To catch Gobiidae, for example, vessels operate about 200 traps. Transportation may not be a problem when the traps are small and if they collapse when the spreading sticks are removed, or when conical fyke nets (which are usually stretched horizontally between sticks rammed into the bottom) are stored folded together. However, transportation of a large number of traps becomes a big problem when large quantities of bulky traps, like pots, which are neither collapsible nor can be folded, have to be brought from one place to another and cannot be stacked (*Fig 313*). Therefore progress was made when traps made of netting with wire frames were introduced in a collapsible form (*Fig 333*) or made of plastic (see next section) in such a way that they could be stacked by 'nesting' (their bottoms being made of netting which can be loosened) like plates or cups (*Fig 334*).

Fig 332 Small traps with spreading sticks. Near Venice, (1975).

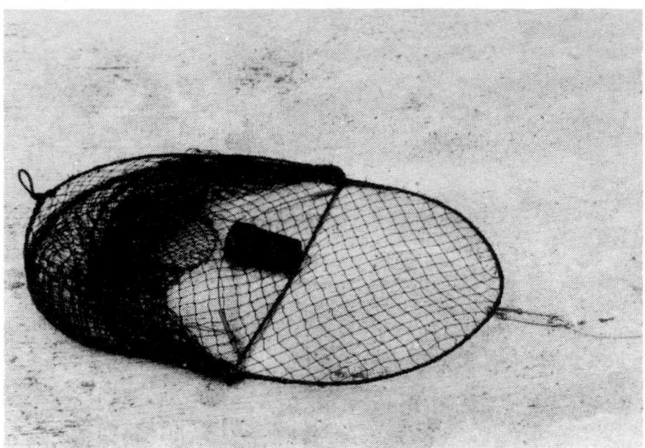

Fig 333 Foldable Japanese trap: (*above*) ready for the catch; (*below*) folded for transportation. Japan, (1972).

Fig 334 Stackable Japanese traps for crab fishing. Banba, Kanakawa-ken, Japan, (1978).

There have been many transitional stages between wooden pots and those made of netting. In order to decrease the weight of wooden pots, the heavy part of the wooden frame was made as small as possible and covered with netting or chicken wire.

Fig 335 Lobster trap. Hermanus, South Africa, (1965).

Also the wooden frame was replaced by steel or even plastic tubes (*Fig 335*). Many traps used for catching crustaceans, and also fish, are made in this manner – like narrow rectangular boxes with steel frames covered by wire or fibre netting. The small lobster pots used by the fishermen of Heligoland are made in this manner (*Fig 336*). The traps of the fishermen of South Africa for catching rock lobsters in the southern Atlantic, *eg* on seamount Vema, are also constructed in this manner; as are those for rock lobsters in New Zealand (*Fig 337*). Here also a similar type is used to catch blue cod (*Parapercis colias*). Large traps of this type are operated to catch king crab in the northern Pacific Ocean (*Fig 338*).

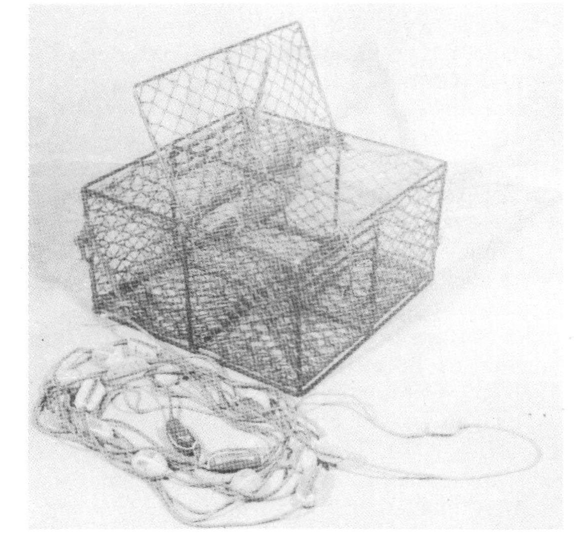

Fig 336 Modern lobster trap of Heligoland, Germany.

In this connection the so-called 'creels' of the British fishermen have to be mentioned.[149, 614] These

Fig 337 Hauling a rocklobster pot near Akaroa, New Zealand. To prevent the prey escaping long spines are welded around the entrance of the trap. The arrow shows the escape vent on the back of the trap (1981).

Fig 338 King crab pot for Alaskan waters. Seattle. (*Photo: J Schärfe, 1968.*)

creels are longer than they are broad, with a strong frame and a 'U'-shaped cross section (*Figs 339* and *340*). The frame can be made of wood, iron or plastic. This frame is then covered with strong netting, formerly tarred cotton but now synthetic twine or plastic-coated wire lattice. Mostly these pots have two entrances, one on each of the longer sides (*Fig 339*). The size of these creels varies greatly in the different fishing areas of Great Britain and neighbouring countries. The Scottish types are

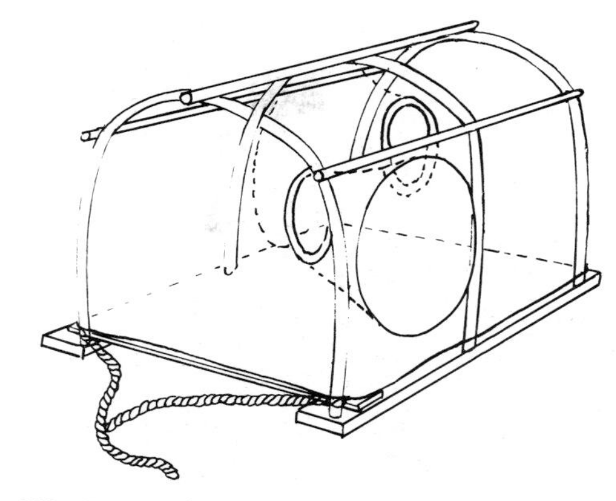

Fig 339 Frame of an English creel with two entrances.

Fig 340 Creel with one entrance only. Portnacross, Ireland, (1956).

considered the smallest. Small creels are recommended as being more economic in lobster fishing. Mostly they are operated not singly but in the longline system as explained before. Creels are said to be operated in fleets. Single creels, used in shallow waters, can be set more carefully and bring higher yields per trap. On the other hand, fleets with more traps set in deeper water can bring higher total yields.[614]

16.7 Plastic pots

As far as is known, the first plastic traps were made for sport fishermen wanting light transportable and collapsible traps to replace, to some extent, the glass bottles with pierced bottoms traditionally used for catching bait fish (*Fig 341a*). Although interesting for sport fishermen, plastic traps are too expensive for commercial fisheries which in general need larger traps in greater quantities and at a lower price.

The first plastic traps to be introduced into commercial fisheries were eel traps (*Fig 343*).[401] The

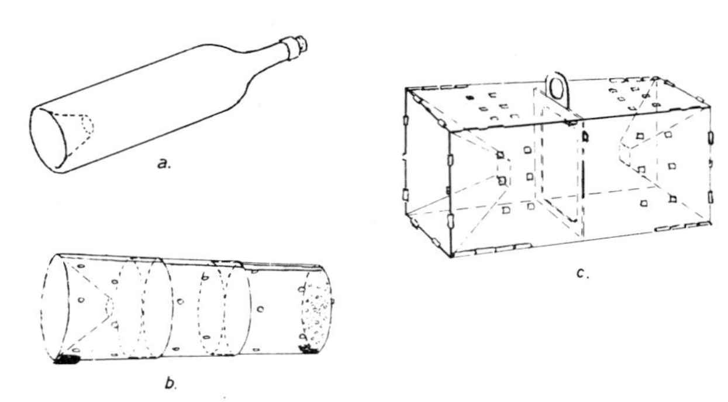

Fig 341 Transparent traps for catching bait fish for sport fishermen: (*a*) glass bottle with bottom section removed; (*b*) French bait trap, made of plastic, which can be telescoped; (*c*) transparent trap from Switzerland which can be folded.

construction of the trap itself was not changed. To mould complete traps of high density PE, as wanted by commercial fishermen, can be economical only when large quantities are produced. Therefore, plastic traps have been made especially for catching crustaceans and eels in commercial fisheries. Here the Norwegian lobster pots without netting have to be mentioned. They consist of two parts which nest very easily in each other. Others can be dismantled for easy transportation. The Spanish have made large beehive fish pots consisting of eight or ten moulded sections with an easily removable conical entrance for ease of transportation (*Fig 342*).[532] In northwestern Europe, plastic eel traps found a wide distribution.[308] They were constructed in such a manner that they could be put together from six or more parts, moulded separately. One well-known type has metal rods for weight on the lower side, and a cover on the upper side (*Figs 343* and *344*). The principle of this trap is not to filter the eel out of the current or to guide the migrating fish into the trap by wings or guide lines, but to offer a shelter which will be voluntarily accepted by the eel. Therefore, this trap with two valves can be

Fig 342 Detachable plastic beehive trap. Costa Brava, Spain, (1963).

Fig 343 German eel trap made of plastic according to masterfisherman H Köthke: (*a*) upperside with a plate for shelter; (*b*) underside with two iron sticks for weighting. (*Photo: G Klust.*)

Fig 344 Hauling a plastic eel trap in the River Weser.

considered more as a tube for shelter (Chapter 13).

Simpler than the eel traps mentioned before, and more like the original eel pots used by German river fishermen, is another modern plastic pot (*Fig 345*).

Fig 345 Plastic eel trap. (*Courtesy of Norddeutsche Seekabelwerke A G, 1979.*)

The trap has two valves and a closing cap at the narrow end, which is removed to get the catch. This trap is operated on the longline system as are many other traps in commercial fisheries.

Plastic traps have good stability, can be operated for a long time with little maintenance, and rarely need repairing. They are easy to handle and need little effort to operate.[331] Plastic traps, like those made of wire, also have a high resistance to damage caused by crabs like the Chinese mitten crab (*Eriocheier sinensis*) and other gnawing water animals which destroy netting. Traps made with a frame of welded tubular polythene and covered with netting of synthetic fibre are often called 'all plastic pots'. These are special round pots for catching crustaceans (*Fig 346*) but are similar in operation to the British creels (*Figs 339* and *340*).[149]

16.8 Ghost traps

All traps have the advantage that the prey caught remains alive for some time, and therefore the catch is generally of good quality, it being taken for granted that the traps are inspected at regular

Fig 346 French lobster pot with frame made of plastic. Audierne, Brittany, France, (1977).

intervals. When they cannot be lifted due to bad weather conditions, or when they are lost and cannot be found, they may continue to catch for a month before they deteriorate enough to cease fishing. In such cases people speak of 'ghost fishing'. This is defined as the ability of a fishing gear to continue fishing after all control of the gear has been lost by the fisherman.[584] It will be seen later on, in Chapter 29, that there are not only traps but also gillnets which can continue to catch as ghost nets.

Ghost traps became a special problem in the crustacean fishery following the introduction of non-rotting synthetic net materials. Many pots can be lost in stormy weather and by entanglement of the lines in rocky grounds. This is especially possible when traps of light material, higher than they are broad and therefore with a low stability, are operated in waters with strong currents or where wave motion reaches the seabed. In this situation the higher traps fall over and will roll, winding up their lines with the floats so that they cannot be found again. This is why the beehive lobster pots formerly used around Heligoland have been replaced by a boxlike trap with lower weight but a broader base (*Fig 336*). Nevertheless, the loss of traps cannot be prevented completely. King crab fishermen of Alaska estimate their annual pot losses at about ten per cent. The crustaceans caught in lost pots can injure each other by cannibalism and, having no chance to escape, they finally die. Their carcases then act as bait for other crustaceans. In other words, the lost pots are self-baiting death traps which continue to catch for several years and could be responsible for higher mortality and reduced yield of a crab resource. Therefore, efforts have been made by different methods, to prevent continuous fishing by lost traps. In traps made of stable frames covered with synthetic netting, the interior netting yarn is made of natural fibres. When this material rots, after a short time, the catching room of the trap collapses and crabs can no longer be caught by this gear. This method is also decreed by law for bottom fishing pots in the State of Washington in the USA.

A better means of preventing ghost trapping has been found by using pots with escape vents.[584] The escape vents are made in such a manner that they allow lobsters under the legal minimum size to escape (*Fig 337*). This may decrease ghost fishing mortality but does not solve the overall problem. This perhaps can be achieved by a new proposal – to design the opening into the pot so as to allow any prey to escape after a specified time. In this case the opening is made as a hinged door with a timed release mechanism combined with the legal escape vent mentioned before. The release mechanism can be a door kept closed by a latch made of degradable material which will rot in a short time.[46]

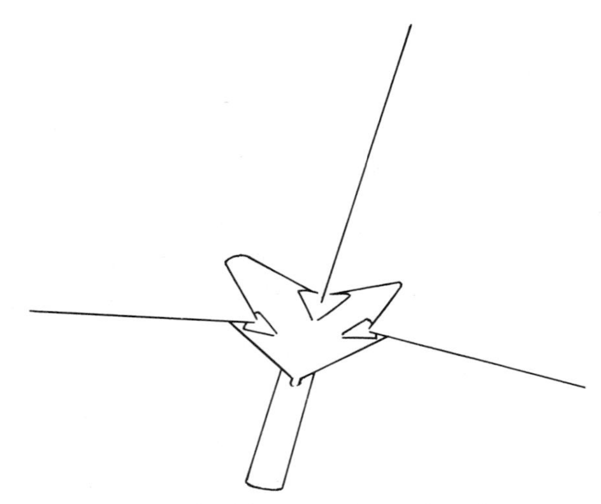

Fig 347 Traps made of fences can be very large like this one from Kampuchea with leaders, catching chamber with non-return devices as slits, and a large chamber (below) to keep the catch. (*Fily and d'Aubertin, 1965*).

16.9 Trap systems, weirs and pound nets

As with other fishing gear, attempts have been made to increase the efficiency of fish traps, especially those made of netting. This has been tried in many different ways, not only by improved construction and use of better materials, but also by increasing the size of single traps and by combining many traps with catching systems supported by leading arrangements such as the so-called wings and leaders. As has been shown before, the increase in size of three-dimensional traps made of wood, wire or plastic, or of netting held by hoops and frames, is limited by the increase in weight and difficulty in handling. As mentioned earlier, in the eastern Baltic there were hooped nets made of netting with rings taller than a man, but with their increasing size, their handling became more and more inconvenient and labour-intensive. In contrast to three-dimensional traps, the two-dimensional ones, made of fences of different materials and fitted out with non-return devices in the form of slits or steps, can be enlarged in a theoretically unlimited manner (*Figs 347, 348* and *349*). In this case, it is helpful if the catching room is fitted with bottom netting which can be lifted to get at the fish caught.

An indirect enlargement of a trap can be made by its combination with leaders and wings, especially when these end in other traps of the same size (*Figs 350a* and *350e*) or smaller (*Fig 350b*). By this method, very effective trapping systems can be built, like the double fyke nets (*Fig 350a*), which can be combined in rows some hundreds of metres long (unfortunately, sometimes named in a

Fig 348 In this large bamboo weir of the Philippines a slit, as a non-returning device (see above), gives entrance to the catching room from which the catch is secured with scoop nets at low tide (see below). (1960)

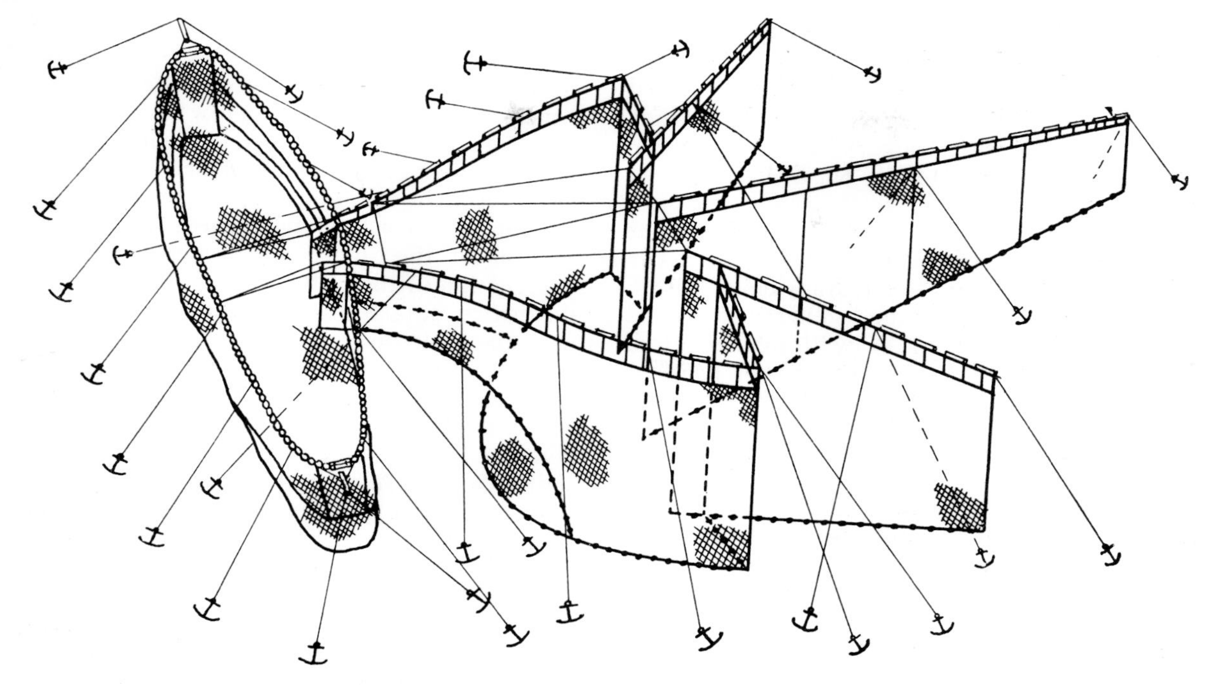

Fig 349 Japanese pound net for sardines. (*NN, 1959*).

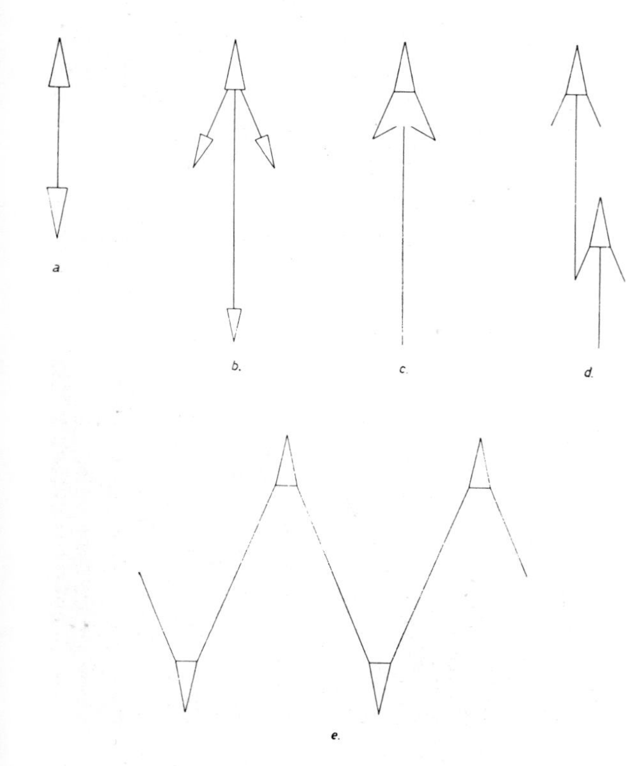

Fig 350 Arrangements for fyke nets with leaders and wings: (*a*) double net; (*b*) cross net; (*c*) hook net; (*d*) fyke net weir; (*e*) scissor net.

misleading manner 'trawls' by the Americans). Also popular are the combined single traps (*Fig 350d*), as well as the combination of many traps set in a zig zag line as a barrier (*Fig 350e*) off sea shores and in large lakes. In such cases, the construction of a single trap in the form of a fyke net with one or more funnel-like entrances remains unchanged.

To increase the effectiveness of a trap, its construction can be altered by combining a three-dimensional trap (a completely closed one) with a two-dimensional one (open at the top). In other words, a closed trap is enlarged by its combination with one or more open catching chambers before

Fig 351 Old herring weir of Kappeln on the River Schlei, Schleswig-Holstein. Big wooden leaders guide the herring into fyke nets made of netting.

its entrance. These additional chambers can be so extensive that the original traps, pots or fyke nets with funnel-like entrances, appear as small appendices only (*Figs 352* and *353*). In the drawing to scale of a Danish 'bundgarn' (*Fig 352*) the two fyke nets are difficult to see, but their length can be more than ten metres, which demonstrates just how large the additional catching chambers are. The advantage of this combination is that the catch can be got by hauling the genuine traps only. It is no longer necessary to catch the fish in the additional chambers with other gear, or by lifting the bottom netting if there is any, or by driving the fish into a corner for scooping, as is still necessary with some large traps when catching bulk fish.

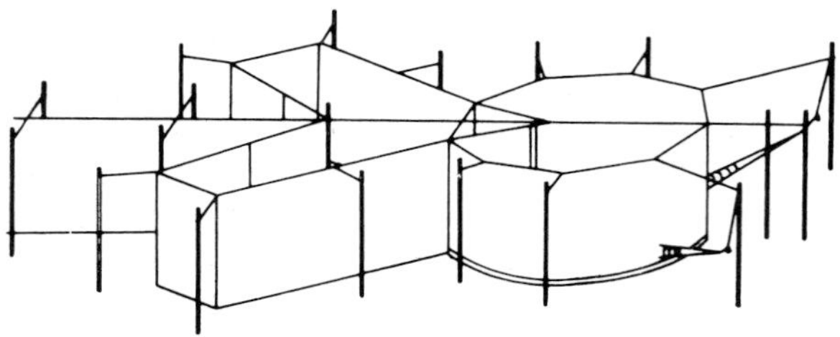

Fig 352 Danish 'bundgarn' with small fyke nets on the Baltic coast (*Klust, 1965*).

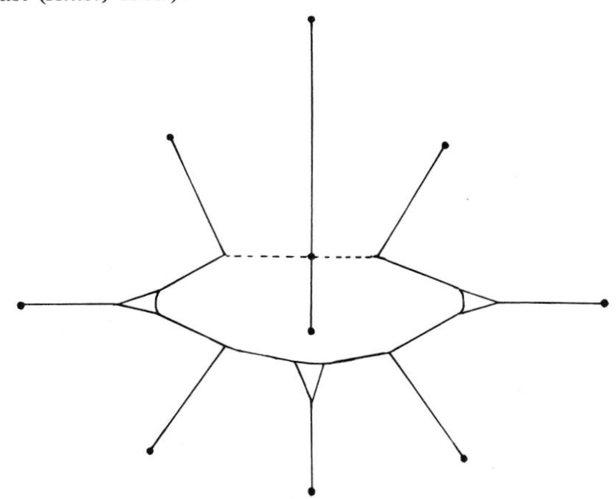

Fig 353 Japanese anchored pound net with three conical fyke nets for catching shrimp. (*Shigueno, 1974*).

Such large catching arrangements with big collecting chambers are called weirs if made of non-textile material, or pound nets if they are made of netting. Weirs made of wickerwork or mats, as used on all the coasts of Asia, North America and in several parts of North Europe, might be of greater importance for a bulk fishery than the small pots and fyke nets. *Figures 281* and *348* show some examples of weirs. It has already been mentioned, in Chapter 15, that sometimes the entrances of successive chambers gradually decrease in size, so that they can be considered as non-return devices in the form of slits which can be passed in one direction only. *Figure 281a* shows a weir operated in Thailand with interesting leaders consisting of waving rods pushed singly in a row into the bottom. These guide the fish through a slit into spacious catching chambers. It is not difficult for a fish to swim through the leading sticks, but it will not do so unless it has been frightened. The swinging motion of the stems is considered to be the explanation of their obedience.[658] From the weir, the fish can be taken or caught by other fishing gear, once the encircling room has been narrowed.

Wooden weirs are replaced more and more by pound nets made of netting (*Fig 354*). These can be arrangements with a sophisticated system of wings and leaders, and with step and ramp as non-return devices. Also, in this case the leaders need not be very dense. Even nets with large meshes, through which the fish may easily swim, actually do have a guiding effect. This applies, too, even to the stretched ropes or twines which are sometimes used for leaders instead of netting. It is believed by some people that the vibrations of the lines prevent the fish from crossing the leader and swimming away, and thus induce them to keep within the bounds desired. For the same reason, air-bubble curtains have been used to contain fish and to direct them into traps. Here, in contrast to large meshed netting and the rows of lines or rods mentioned before, the guiding effect is an optical one and, to some extent, also an acoustical one. The bottom of the catching area of the pound nets is made of netting which can be lifted so that it is easier to collect the catch, as with the watched tuna trap mentioned in Chapter 15. Large quantities of salmon and tuna, as well as herring, sardines, cod and other bulk fish, may be caught with pound nets.

Fig 354 Scottish salmon trap. A fisherman walks on ropeways along the leading net to the catching area in the background. (*Photo: British Resin Products Ltd., London.*)

The large pound nets are set by stretching them between stakes driven into the bottom (*Figs 354, 355* and *356*). When the water is too deep, or the ground too hard, the traps are anchored (*Fig 349*). The Alaska salmon trap is an example of an anchored trap. This is why this gear is also called 'floating salmon trap' (*Figs 357* and *358*).

It seems that there is some tendency to replace large pound nets, made of netting and held by stakes, by anchored and floating ones. Anchored pound nets are considered to have a higher elasticity and, consequently, greater resistance to the influences of bad weather.[609] Anchored traps are known even in large lakes. In the Great Lakes region of North America, anchored deep-water traps are used. It is a curious thing that the same type of anchored trap is known in Lake Constance between southern Germany, Switzerland and Austria. The local name is 'trapnet' (mistakenly written 'Trappnetz') and most people do not know that this is a simple English word used by the fishermen who imported this gear at the beginning of this century from the Great Lakes.

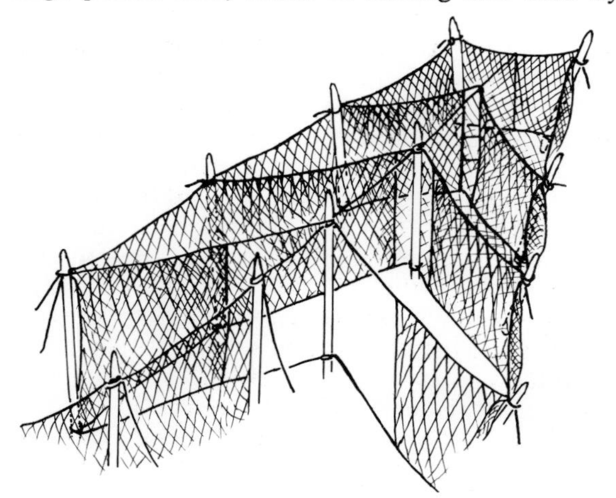

Fig 355 Last part of a Scottish salmon trap. (*Garner, 1976*).

Fig 356 Slitlike entrance in the last chamber of a Scottish salmon trap. Montrose, Scotland, (1974).

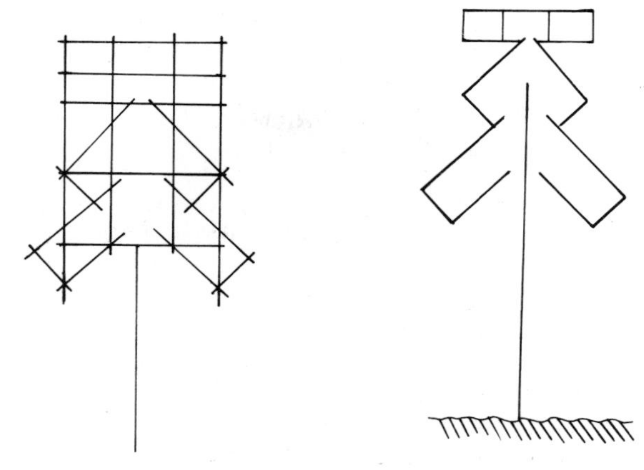

Fig 357 Salmon trap: left, floating and right, fixed on sticks in Alaska. (*Dumont and Sundstrom, 1961; Bartz, 1950*).

Pound nets can be among the largest of all fishing gears and are known in many different forms. The types of pound nets used in Japan are so numerous that their description occupies quite a big place in the literature dealing with Japanese fishing gear. Also famous are the larger pound nets used by the Americans off the Atlantic coast, as well as off the coast of Alaska in the Pacific. Widely known too are the Danish 'bundgarn', which means 'bottom nets', operating in large numbers off the Baltic coast of Sweden, Denmark and the Federal Republic of Germany, especially for eel fishing (*Fig 352*). As for weirs, there is also an inherent disadvantage in the use of pound nets. This is the high purchase cost and the need for a large crew for setting and hauling the gear. Moreover, these large nets can be damaged in bad weather. This may be the reason why, in contrast to the small traps, the number of large pound nets and weirs is decreasing in the world. Nevertheless, some technical progress has been made with weirs and pound nets even though their number is decreasing. As mentioned before, handling and maintenance of the large traps is expensive. Even when fish worth the money are

Fig 358 Close-up view of a floating salmon trap in Alaska. (*Courtesy of Fisheries Research Institute, University of Washington, 1974.*)

caught, the season can be limited and very short in relation to the long time spent in preparing a pound net and removing it. For large traps held by stakes, the vessels can have special pole-drivers replacing hand-operated devices for setting them. This work can also be supported by arrangements for washing out a hole in the bottom before setting the stake.[18]

To save time in controlling the catch, the Japanese propose to place acoustic implements in the pound nets to calculate the quantity of the catch from the noise caused by the trapped fish. Ice in northern areas and heavy storms in tropical parts of the world can damage weirs and pound nets or even destroy them completely. There have been some discussions about lowering the gear automatically under the water surface during stormy weather. One idea was to replace the floats by pressure tubes which could be blown up by compressed air or deflated as necessary.

16.10 Mechanization in trapping

Traps, especially three-dimensional ones for catching crustaceans and high-priced fish, have always been singled out for improvement, though more in sea fisheries than in fresh waters. The trend to increase the number of set traps and to fish in deeper water can be hampered by the need for more labour to operate them, which is costly. In commercial fisheries, small or large pots are set, as far as possible, not singly, but on the longline system. That means many pots are tied, with branch lines at intervals, on a main line (*Fig 321*). To haul the pots with the main line, anchor and buoy lines, needs a lot of manpower. Even though some fishermen continue to avoid special pot haulers powered by hydraulic motors, and continue to use a general purpose hauler, such as a capstan[97], for fishing in depths of up to 2,000 metres, special hauling machines cannot be avoided. They can not only save manpower but can also simplify pot line fishing by reducing the manual labour of hauling miles of incoming ground lines and heavy anchor and buoy lines. They are especially necessary with the heavier pots such as those used for king crabs (*Fig 338*).

With the help of advanced high-speed hydraulic winches and new over-the-side handling techniques, pots can be operated in a much shorter time than before. This also means that an economic number of pots can be retrieved, hauled, re-baited and re-set in deeper water, faster than ever before. It is estimated that, by the utilization of longline techniques for handling pots with high speed winches, up to 300 pots per day could be successfully fished in water depths exceeding 200 fathoms.[674] Different types of haulers or pot line coilers are used, some davit-mounted. A light and portable creel hauler driven by an outboard motor is available especially for small-boat fishing. Hydraulically-driven haulers are mostly in use but have modified mechanically-driven differential assemblies. Practically all haulers are driven from the main engine but occasionally, on larger boats, an auxiliary engine is used. Another labour saving device for operating pots is an arrangement which not only hauls the pots but also swings them on board. By this means a small boat can be operated by only one man: generally at least two are needed. Of interest also may be a Japanese development which has the hauling device mounted in such a manner that it can be used anywhere on the boat (*Fig 359*). As mentioned before, sometimes the pots have to be set singly at favourable sites. To find these places in lakes or along the seashore, echo sounders can be used, as in the rock lobster fishery of New Zealand.

Fig 359 Movable hydraulic pot hauler on a Japanese vessel in Banba, Kanagawa-ken (1978).

Chapter seventeen

Fishing in the air

'When, during the months of August, September or October, on beautiful nights the stars are sparkling and the moon is pouring her milky light over the quiet waters and the calm lakes; when you then see long narrow boats twinkling in the light; on board, a man bent over his rudder and trying to manoeuvre his boat as quietly as possible – that is a fisherman who has nailed a board to the one side of his boat, from one end to the other, at an angle of 45 degrees, and painted it with a bright varnish and who, moreover, has fixed on the opposite side of his boat a strip of netting of three to four feet in height with very small meshes. . . .'

In this way, but in much more detail than is given in this shortened translation of a much longer sentence, the French consul, de Thiersant[613], who was stationed in China during the second half of the last century, describes what are today called the 'white board catch boats' of Asia. Not only he, but also many other travellers in China during the previous centuries, described these boats into which the fish jump on moonlit nights so that they only had to be collected! That fish are able to jump out of the water is, of course, widely known. Some species of fish jump more than others; some not at all. The jumping species, which can often be observed, include the salmonids and cyprinids, or carp-like fish, in freshwater areas, as well as the grey mullets in the estuaries of the rivers or the sea. On the sea coasts, there are the scombroids or mackerels, and carangids or horse mackerels, all of which frequently jump. More famous in warmer seas are the different families of flying fishes, which got their name from their behaviour. This jumping can be in the form of a brief jerking from the water, or a gliding flight of from one to several seconds as in the case of the so-called flying fish. The flying fish interest and intrigue all travellers on the warm tropical and sub-tropical seas as they suddenly see one or more fish jump from the water. At the beginning they leave traces of their motion on the surface of the water, but then they quickly rise clear and skim away airborne for considerable distances. Large fan-shaped and strengthened pectoral and ventral fins enable the fish to 'fly' in this way. Strictly speaking, even for the 'flying fish' this really cannot be called a genuine flight. A flight, in the true sense, can occur only if there is specific propulsive power, like that provided by the flapping wings of a bird. That is usually not the case with these fish. Their flight is nothing but a glide after they have once jumped clear of the water. With the flying fish the starting, or take-off, speed required is attained through quick, powerful wriggling movements of the tail fin. As this develops, the body and the spread pectoral fins of the flying fish rise out of the water, while the tail fin is still submerged. Thus the well marked tail traces on the water's surface show up in the beginning of the gliding flight. The other fishes mentioned before can only jump out of the water and then fall back after a certain distance.

There are many reasons for fish jumping from the water. The jump may be a single one for the purpose of securing aerial food, such as can be seen in the evening on any trout pond. It can also be a more or less voluntary and deliberate effort to escape from an enemy. On European lakes, whole shoals of small minnows may sometimes jump across the water in flight from a predatory fish, and in tropical areas even shoals of larger fishes may suddenly jump out of the water to a height of one metre or more and fall back with the noise of a cascade. Finally, fish jump to overcome obstacles on their migrations. In this connection, the actions of salmon are especially familiar, for they are able, by their leaping powers, to pass over high natural waterfalls and artificial barriers in journeying to their spawning grounds in the headwaters of rivers.

It is not so well known that some species of shrimp are also able to jump when aroused or alarmed. They then jerk themselves out of the water with great leaps – and this is especially true of some of the species of shrimps caught on the southern

Asiatic coasts. It is also not so well known that some small squid are named 'flying squids' because they can shoot out of the water and glide through the air for considerable distances.[337] But as far as is known, no attempts have been made to catch flying squids in this situation for commercial purposes. Also none have been made for the true eagle rays which can jump and glide through the air for a short distance.

As with any jumping activity, the direction of the jump cannot be changed once the jerk or jump has begun. Neither the jumping fish nor the shrimp, nor even the flying fish, can swerve away from any obstacle while in flight as can a bird, or even a beetle. Knowledge of this is essential if the jumping activity of some species is to be utilized as a method of catching them. These methods are known as 'fishing in the air', but this description also includes the way the fish or other water animals are caught when occasionally migrating out of water. The jumping habit of some fishes may be quite an undesirable activity in a fishery, and so steps have to be taken to combat it. A net wall, too, it will be appreciated, is only an obstacle for some species of fish, as many species will attempt to avoid it either by swimming under it or by jumping over it. To prevent that, seine nets used for catching large East European coregonids are provided with special wide meshed strips of netting which fold to the inner side.[675] To catch mullet, which are especially fond of jumping, net walls are equipped with strips of netting which float on the water's surface towards the fishing side, so that the nets look rather like the type of fence (usually seen around a prison or some factories) which slopes inwards in the upper part in order to make it more difficult to climb or jump over from the inside to the outside. Sometimes even straw or sawdust is spread on the water's surface to prevent grey mullet from jumping over the nets.[534]

17.1 Salmon traps

Fishermen in many parts of the world have learned to use the jumping habit of fish to catch them. They have even learned how to induce the fish and shrimps to jump so that they may be caught in a trap. To catch ascending salmon, so-called salmon boxes are built on their migration routes up rivers. This is a well-known device in the salmon fisheries of northern Europe and in the Indian fisheries of the New World. The salmon jump over the supposedly simple obstacle and then find themselves in a box which is provided with a roof at the other end so that they cannot move forward by jumping out (*Fig 360*). In the Rumha cataract

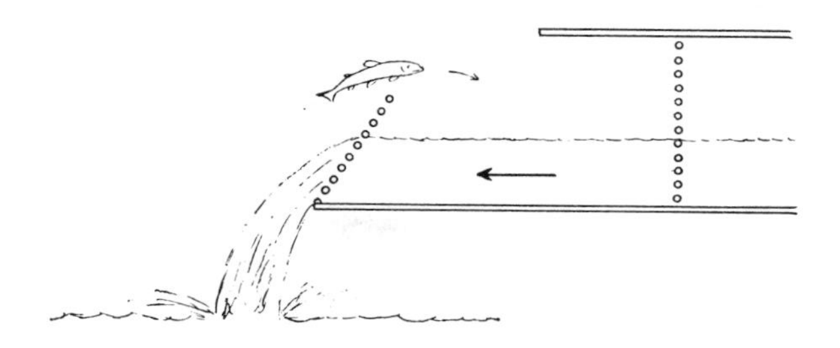

Fig 360 Outline of a box trap for catching jumping salmon.

of the River Windau (Venta) near Goldingen (Kuldiga) in Latvia, to catch salmon and also other fish like *Abramis vimba,* or zanthe, baskets were hung in a waterfall, which the fish tried to spring over during their ascent of the river.[345] They usually ascended in such great numbers that many salmon which did not at first successfully clear the obstacle fell back into the suspended deep baskets, from which they could not escape (*Fig 361*). This catching arrangement, near Windau, has been known since the seventeenth century. The same method was also used in southern Sweden and in northern Finland until 1940.[639] In Ireland, too, a large scoop net was often fixed below waterfalls to catch salmon,[657] and the use of baskets in waterfalls was also formerly well known in Scotland.

Fig 361 Jumping salmon caught by baskets near Windau in Latvia. (*According Thiel, 1949*).

17.2 Fishing with rafts

The fish that are most fond of jumping, and which are caught today by means of aerial traps in many parts of the world, are the grey mullets already mentioned. As can be appreciated, this particular fishery must be related to the habitat of the fish. Mullet occur off the coasts of tropical and subtropical lands. They live especially in the Mediterranean, Indian and Pacific Oceans, but they are also caught in the Atlantic. In the so-called raft fishery, the jumping of mullet is used to catch them. Rafts, floating on the water surface and casting a shadow on moonlit nights, are regarded as obstacles by the sea mullet and so they attempt to jump over them. As the rafts are relatively wide, extending from 1·5m to 3·5m, the fish do not always succeed and so fall onto the floating rafts. To prevent them wriggling off, the edges of the rafts are bent upwards by about a hand's breadth, and brushwood and netting are also put on them in which the fish get entangled. Previously, this method of fishing by raft was spread over the whole Mediterranean area. The Portuguese allowed rush rafts to float down the Mondego River, into which the grey mullet penetrate from the sea.[24] The fishermen followed with their boats to collect the fish from the rafts.

In Malta, a raft fishery was still practised until the end of the 1920s. There the Maltese not only utilized the shadows cast by the rafts anchored in bays or bights, but they also fitted barrier nets below the rafts to prevent the fish from swimming under them. Several boats then set to work to scare the fish with much noise, and drive them towards the rows of rafts and make them jump. Then they were caught in the straw or brushwood on the rafts.[261] Till recently, however, the raft fishery existed only in the eastern area of the Mediterranean, in the Black Sea, the Sea of Azov and in the Caspian Sea. In the USSR the rafts were considered among the most important fishing gear for the grey mullet fishery in those seas.[424] On bright nights the grey mullet shoals are encircled by large rings consisting of many rafts (*Fig 362*) and the fish are then driven towards those rafts by much noise so that great quantities of fish are caught.

Another centre for the fishery of mullet with the help of rafts is India, where this method is still practised in the Rivers Ganga and Yamuna near Allahabad. There the rafts are constructed of plantain trunks; their surface is also covered with twigs to prevent the escape of the jumping fish. These rafts are either moored or allowed to drift free. The fish are driven towards the moored rafts, but it is hoped that the free drifting rafts will pass in the way of jumping fishes.[192]

17.3 Boat traps

For grey mullet, and also for other jumping fish, boats are very often used as a trap. This can be done in a simple manner. In Yugoslavia a boat is fixed transversely and slightly obliquely into the shallow outlet of Lake Varna.[586] The grey mullet, as they come from the sea, attempt to jump over this obstacle and then simply fall into the boat (*Fig 363*). Anchored boats are also used in Lake Chad to catch a jumping fish (*Hydrocyon brevis*) descending some rivers. For this purpose three or four canoes are anchored across the river behind a wooden barrier. To prevent the fish jumping over

Fig 363 Catching grey mullet with a boat in the outlet of Lake Varna, Yugoslavia. (*Soljan, 1956*).

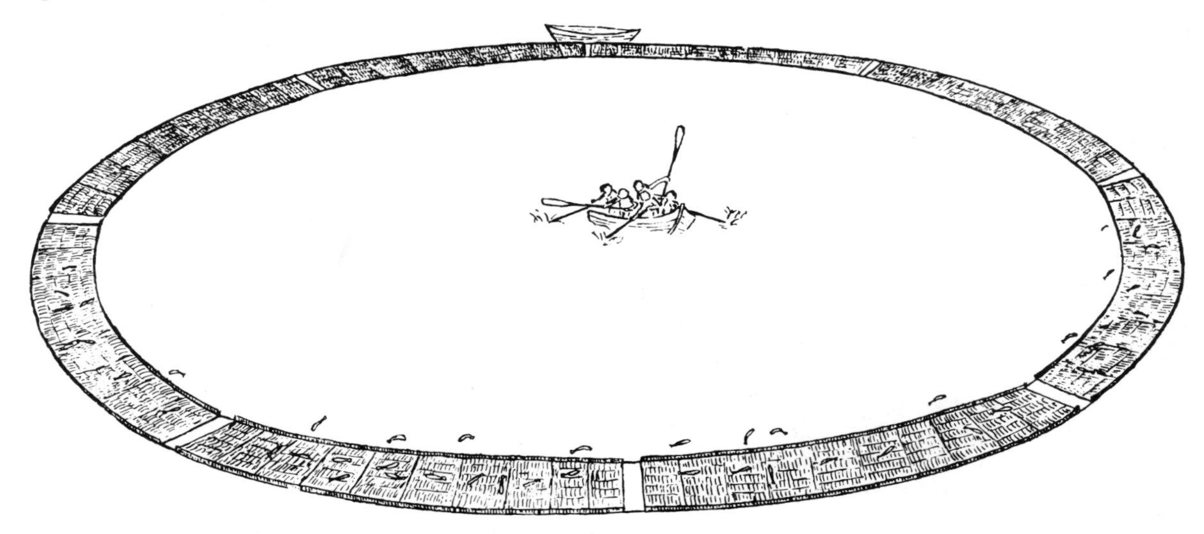

Fig 362 Russians fishing with floating mats in the Caspian Sea. (*NN, 1951*).

the boat, screens up to two metres high are set along the length of the canoes. The fish jump against the screens and fall into the canoes[44] (*Fig 364*). This catching screen is a great success for catching jumping fish by boat.

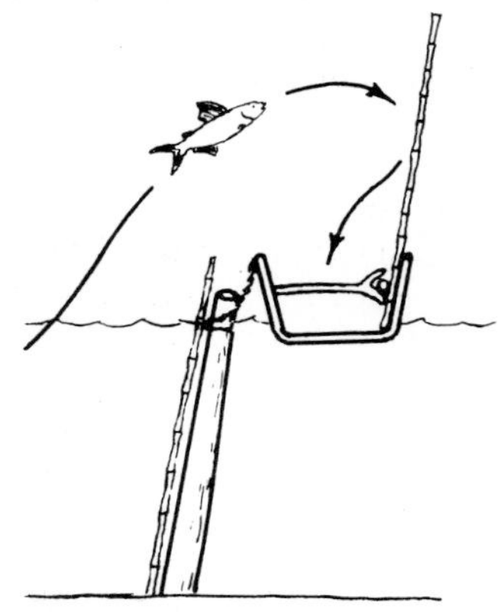

Fig 364 Catching jumping fish by boat on Lake Chad. (*Blache and Miton, 1962*).

Another essential characteristic of the boats that are specially equipped for catching jumping fish has already been described according to de Thiersant (1872)[613] at the beginning of this chapter: a white board is fitted to one side of the boat and this encourages the fish to jump[206, 347] (*Fig 365*). Each boat is manned by one fisherman sitting, not in the centre of the boat but more on the side of the white board, so that the boat has an oblique position and the white board is mostly or entirely submerged. The fishermen row slowly in daylight or by night in the moonlight, or even with torches or lanterns, not far from the beach in shallow water, where they expect to find jumping fish. They then beat the water with their oars or bang on the boats' sides with a rod. The fish and shrimps, frightened by the noise, flee from the beach towards deeper water and, coming upon the bright board, jump to overcome the presumed obstacle. They then strike the screen and fall into the boat, as mentioned for the similar system used in Lake Chad. To ensure that the fish do not jump out of the boat again, palm leaves, straw or brushwood is spread in the bottom to entangle the fish. The holding screen may also be made of coconut leaves or, to be quite modern, of wire mesh, and they can have a pocket at the lower edge in which the fish will remain hanging. Boats of this kind for catching jumping fish are to be found over the whole Indo-Pacific fishing area. They are used even today in the Chinese fishery, Taiwan and Hong Kong included, as well as in the Philippines and Indonesia, and off the coast of Indo-China, Malaysia, Thailand, Burma and the southern part of India. It may be supposed that this ancient fishing technique originated in China. The Chinese also know of a stationary method of fishing with the white board.[289] In this case the fish are guided, with the help of fences, towards the gear, where the boat is replaced by boxes designed to collect the fish frightened by the white board into jumping against the screen (*Fig 366*).

Fig 365 Catching boat used in Thailand with a white board to frighten jumping fish or shrimps and a screen to prevent the prey from jumping over the boat (1960).

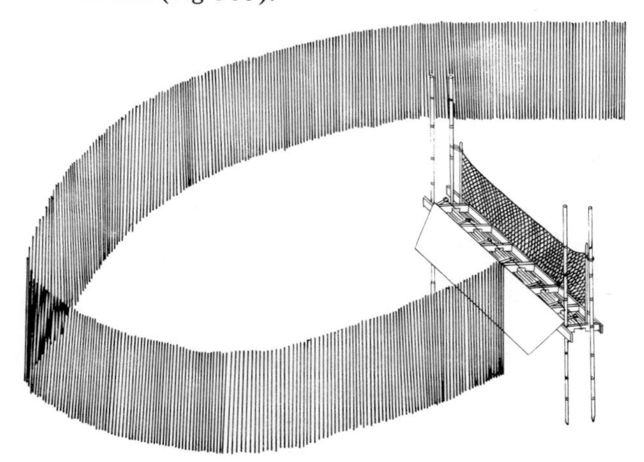

Fig 366 Modern Chinese barrier with stationary white board arrangement for catching jumping fish. (*Kasuga, 1975*).

There are many variations on ways to catch fish springing, for any reason, voluntarily into a boat. In Hong Kong a pair of canoes may work together side by side, each with a white board, facing each other. The fishermen try to bring a shoal of fish (anchovies or grey mullet) between the two canoes so that the frightened fish dart away in all directions and many jump into the canoes. The boards are also considered as a way of preventing the fish from escaping under the canoes.[353] Nevertheless, there are also boats without white boards. The reason is that scaring the fish can be achieved by a scare sweeper fitted vertically on to a boat and pushed slowly through the shallow water by a wading fisherman.

The scare sweeper consists of a bamboo pole provided with a row of rattan roots suspended like a curtain[107, 530] (*Fig 367*). These pass lightly, like a brush, over the bottom and frighten the fish and shrimps. In this case, the white boards may be omitted and also the screen designed to prevent the fish from jumping over the boat. This sweeping method is practised in the Philippines and Thailand. A similar method is reported from the South American Indian fishery, in that the Indians there wade in shallow water towing their boats after them. As they proceed, they beat the water with twigs and the frightened fish begin to jump and many fall into the boats.[151]

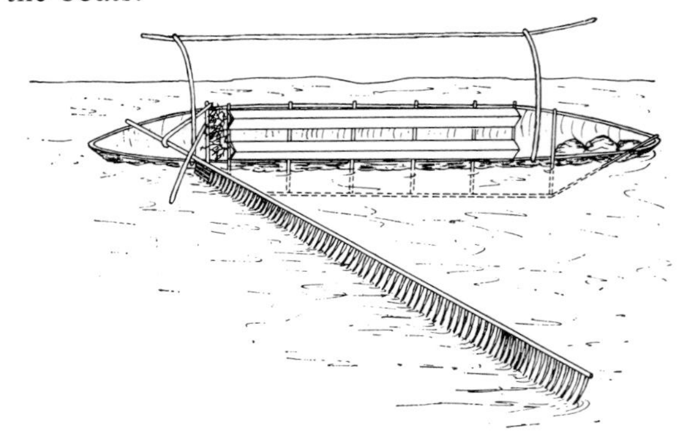

Fig 367 'Kalaskas', a catching boat of the Philippines with devices to scare fish and shrimps. (*Montilla et al., 1959*).

In a scaring method known in Kerala, South India, two canoes are needed for catching jumping prawns during the night. The boats are tied together at the stern at an acute angle of about 30°. Moreover, the canoes are held by a framework, made of bamboo, in a position inclining towards each other (*Figs 368* and *369*). Inside the angle, between the two boats, a kerosene lamp is placed to attract the prawns. To frighten them up from the bow of the canoes, an iron chain is dragged along the grounds which causes the prawns to jump out of the water and maybe also into the boats which, by their list towards each other, facilitate the landing of the jumping prawns into the vessels.

Many other similar types of boat traps are known for catching jumping fishes. The frames spanned with hanging netting which are used on the Ryukyu Islands[439] show a transitional stage in the transfer of this activity from rafts to boats. The aerial trap that they use is towed by two boats over shallow water and the frightened fish and shrimps jump upwards, many thus falling into the net. This method is practised by older fishermen during the night and they are so successful that they can produce up to 200 kilograms of fish in a night's

Fig 368 Boats ready for prawn fishing. (Kerala, 1973).

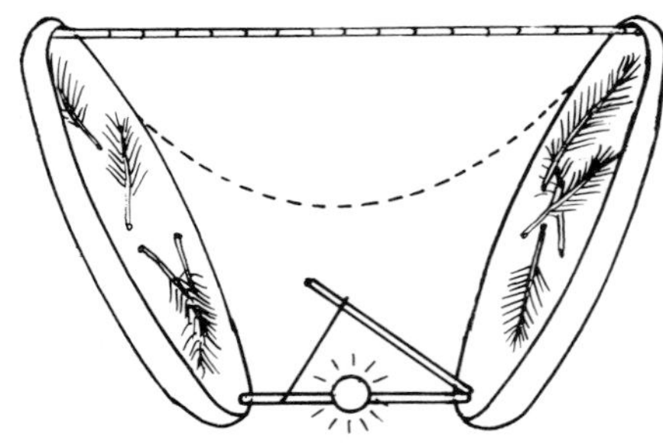

Fig 369 Plan of the arrangement of two boats with light and frightening chain to catch jumping prawns in Kerala, southern India.

fishing. It is very surprising to find that the fishermen of Madagascar used a similar method, which is called 'pêche à la tente'.[497] A group of canoes with outriggers, with netting stretched horizontally between them and carrying vertical barrier nets in front of them, may encircle a shoal of grey mullet (*Fig 370*). Then, scared by noise, the fish will jump into the nets or even into the boats. This method is not operated any more. When netting of transparent monofilament was introduced and used as a barrier, it was found that the fish did not jump but, by attempting to swim through the net, became caught by the gills. So the

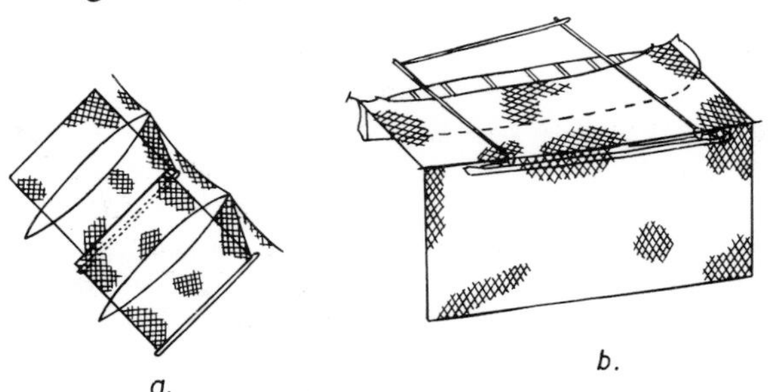

Fig 370 Different methods of rigging the nets for catching jumping fish in Madagascar: 'pêche à la tente'. (*a*) *Angot, 1961;* (*b*) *v Brandt 1964.*

fishermen found it was easier and simpler to use the nets as gillnets and the old method was abandoned.

17.4 Verandah nets

This trick of making fish jump into a trap – an aerial trap as it has been called[92] – can also be achieved by stationary gear. The French author mentioned in the beginning of the chapter showed, in his book, a drawing of a Chinese fishing gear used for securing jumping fish. In principle, this fishing arrangement resembled the boat traps mentioned in the former section – but without the white board. A net is set in the way of migrating fish which attempt to jump over the obstacle: but this is not possible. The fish fall back into bags made of netting hanging over the water. These bags replace the inside of the boat, in which the fish were collected (*Fig 371*).

Fig 371 Old Chinese installation for catching jumping fish. (*de Thiersant, 1872*).

A variation of this system is the so-called 'verandah net', known in the Mediterranean area (*Fig 372*) as well as in China, Indo-China and India, and also some parts of Africa. In this method, the barrier netting and the collecting bags are made of the same piece of netting, arranged as shown in *Figure 372*. The net forms a vertical barrier which encourages the fish to jump, and also an almost horizontal apron or verandah onto which the fish fall. The barrier can be set in a straight line or in a more or less open circle formation. In the latter case, guiding nets are used to direct the fish, usually mullet, into the catching enclosure. The Italian name for this gear is 'saltarello'. A similar one was known in Portugal.[24] It was set like a large spiral but without guiding nets. Also, in the saltwater lagoons of Egypt a stationary type of verandah net is operated, as well as in Mauritius.[244] It may be that the origin of the stationary verandah net is the old freshwater fishery of China, where this fishing method is still used today.[289] *Figure 373* shows a modern form of this fishing method in today's China.

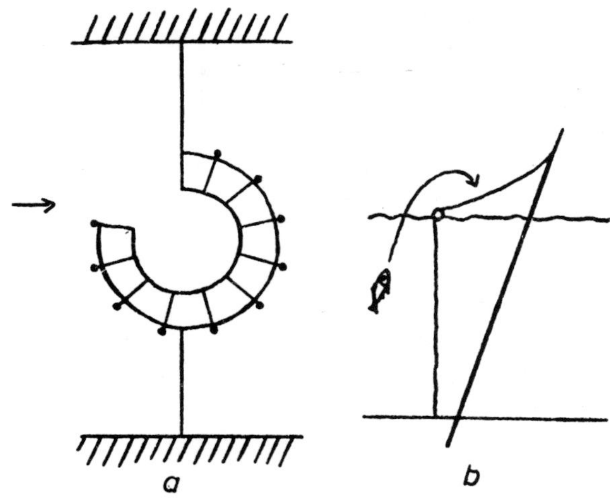

Fig 372 Fixed Italian verandah nets, Adriatic Sea: (*a*) from the top; (*b*) from the side. (*Grosskopf, 1942*).

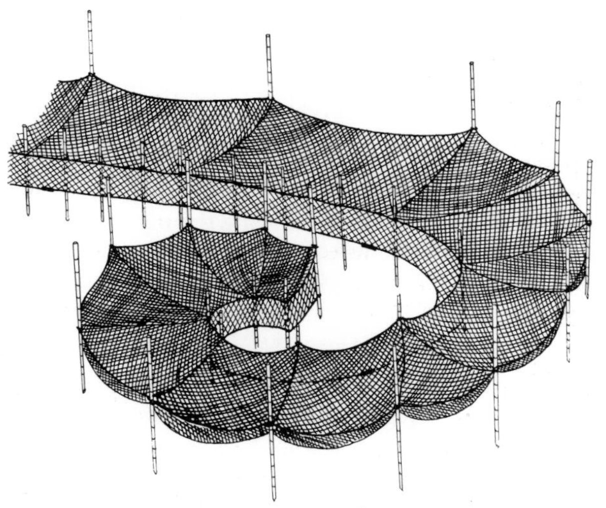

Fig 373 Modern chinese verandah net for catching jumping fish. (*Kasuga, 1975*).

Many forms of fishing gear from old China spread over southern Asia; therefore it is not surprising that the stationary verandah net is also known in the modern freshwater fishery of western Bengal.[192] The Indian gear forms an open circle with guiding lines constructed by fixing water hyacinths between the twists of a rope. Such a guiding line (refer to the scare lines discussed in Chapter 26) can have a length of several hundred metres. The principle of catching is as before (*Fig 374*). In this case, the catch are mainly major carps. A similar method is known from Kampuchea. The variation is only that the netting, in which the jumping fish will be caught, is hung at an angle of 45° above the fencing on the outside.[167] In this case, it is intended to catch jumping fish which try to escape some of the capture chambers. The same intention is also the reason for using such a gear in Benin.[653] Here, fish in parks (Chapter 13) are caught trying to escape when the shelter-giving branches of the park are removed and the area, surrounded by fences, is gradually diminished (*Fig 375*). Such methods are also known in other areas of Africa. It has been reported that in the swamp fisheries of Zambia, spawning areas for cichlids are surrounded by fences with the exception of a few openings. The fish swim in, concentrate during the night, and try to come out in the morning. The openings are then closed and at daylight the fisherman enters the pool to spear and club the fish. The fish try to escape by jumping over the shallow fences, but they land on a rack of reed and grass above the water level and encircling the whole pool outside the fences.[82]

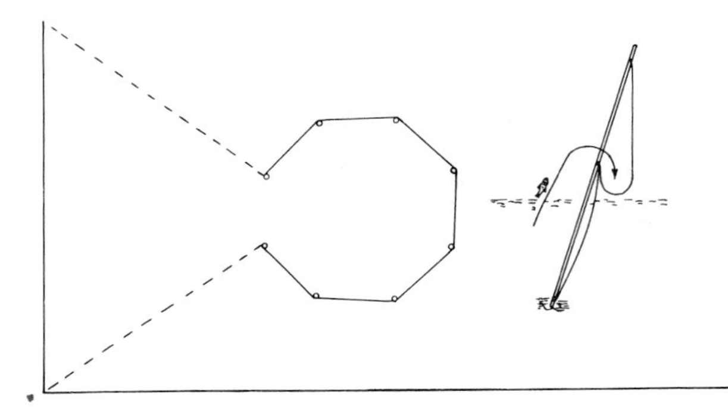

Fig 374 Indian type of verandah net for catching carp. (*George, 1971*).

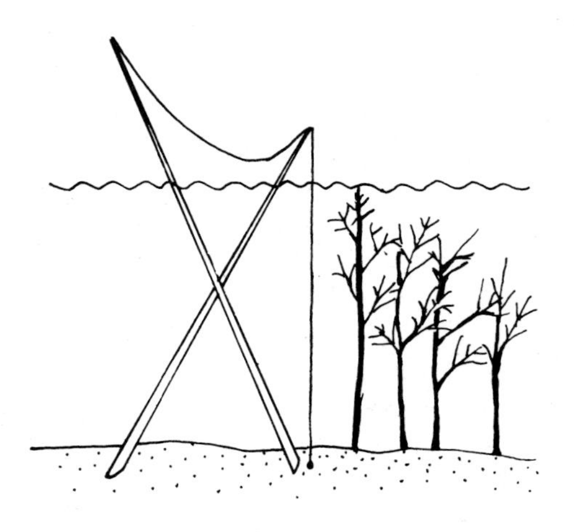

Fig 375 Installation of verandah nets around a fish park in the coastal lagoons of Benin. (*Welcomme, 1972*).

It seems that the stationary verandah net, constructed as described, became less popular than the movable form – operated without a boat, but like the old rafts mentioned earlier. In this method, a fish shoal is encircled by a transportable net wall, forming the barrier which the fish tries to overcome. On the upper edges of this vertical encircling net, horizontal catching nets are fitted, held by bamboo rods (nowadays often by closed plastic tubes) floating on the water (*Figs 376, 377* and *378*). These catching nets consist of trammel nets (Chapter 30). The barrier part and the catching part may consist of one piece and can be set simultaneously. Alternatively they can be separate nets, joined once they are set.[63] When this is done, men in a boat inside the circle frighten the fish by noise and, in endeavouring to escape, the fish meet the obstacle formed by the nets. This they try to jump over, landing in the catching nets floating outside and quickly becoming entangled. That type of verandah net is familiar all over the Mediterranean, in the eastern part as well as in the western part for catching grey mullet in daylight. As it is a very successful method, it has also spread into neighbouring areas. According to old prints these nets, in former times, have even been towed by rowing boats to increase their effectiveness. But this can also have another reason. As mentioned in the beginning of this chapter, there can be some difficulties with jumping fish with seining. To prevent their escape, seine nets were sometimes equipped with reed trays as platforms to catch the fish when they tried to jump over the more or less vertical netting. This method in seining was known in the Mediterranean[261] and also in southern Africa.[361]

17.5 Scoop nets for jumping fish

The catching of jumping fish and shrimps with these aerial traps requires very good knowledge of their behaviour – and a high level of technical development. But even greater skill is needed if flying fish are to be caught with scoop nets directly from the air. This is a method practised by fishery co-operatives in Oceania.[313] At night (without moonlight) the flying fish are encouraged to jump by a display of torch lights. They tend to jump towards the lights, and are then caught by scoop nets held on long rods – more than three metres in

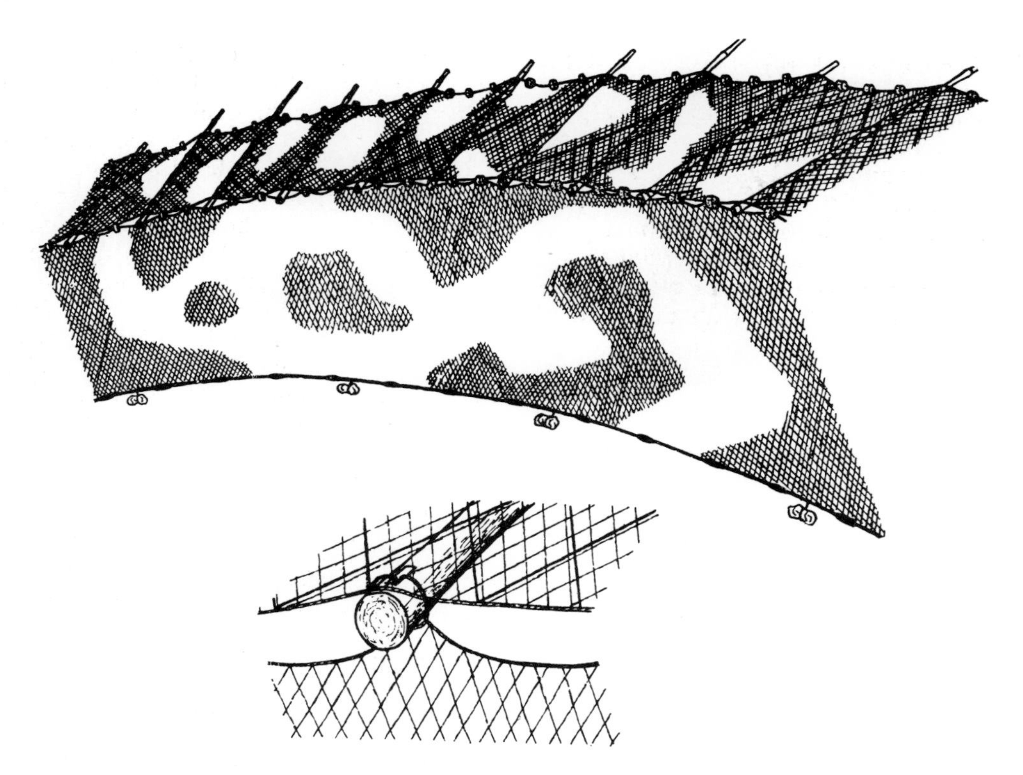

Fig 376 Part of a transportable verandah net as used in the Greek Bay of Hera at Mitilini Island.

Fig 377 Greek verandah net in the Bay of Hera. The fish are frightened by fishermen beating the water and so jump onto the net.

Fig 378 View of a portion of the floating trammel net, a section of the verandah net.

length and used in the same way as butterfly nets. The same practice of catching flying fish by the light of torches is also carried out by the Yami tribe on the island of Botel Tobago (Lan Yü) southeast of Taiwan (*Fig 379*). This is a co-operative fishery in which up to ten families participate.[288] A large torch is held high over the heads of the crew, who kneel on the edges of the boat, and their aim is to catch the fish with scoop nets as they fly through the air. That is real 'fishing in the air'. But, as in Madagascar, this method has been replaced by

Fig 379 Catching flying fish by torchlight with long-handled scoop nets by Yami fishermen of the Island Botel Tobago, (Lan Yü) in the south of Formosa. (*Kano and Segawa, 1956*).

gillnets made of polypropylene. Nevertheless, torch fishing for flying fish remains, even today, a ceremony of the Yami at the opening of the fishing season in spring time. At other places it may occasionally occur that fish, while jumping over an obstacle, can be caught in the air by scoop nets. *Figure 380* reproduces such an activity from an old Japanese manuscript which was found at Mya in the Archi Prefecture. A number of fishermen are shown standing in the water, behind a barrier, with antiquely shaped scoop nets, and they are catching jumping fish while they are in the air. This ancient illustration is remarkable because the Japanese fishermen of today do not otherwise have any practical knowledge of fishing with aerial traps, as have the Chinese and their scholars of fishery.

17.6 Angling in the air

As has been shown in the previous sections, fishing in the air is the interception of the prey as it falls back into the water from its jump. Catching with scoop nets was considered, in the last section, as real fishing in the air. There is another method known in the modern freshwater fishery of continental China and this is the angling of jumping fish (*Fig 381*). In this case, baited hooks on a long line are hung some distance above the water and the fish, jumping for the bait, hook themselves when doing so.[289] Insects, shrimps and little frogs are used for bait.

To explain this in terms of fish behaviour may be difficult. It is known that fish jump for insects near the water surface, but the insects are flying and the fish may have learned to jump at the right moment to get the food out of the air. From a holy spring in Madagascar, strong eels can be seen taking meat in the air from a priestess who holds it over the surface of the water. This can be explained by learning. But what is the explanation for fish acting in a very unnatural manner and taking a bait, even when it is wriggling, from a hook held over the water?

17.7 Pitfall traps for fishes

Fishing in the air, in contrast to fishing in the water, can also mean fishing on land. That this is possible has been explained in Chapter 2 with hand-picking along the beach. But it has to be remembered that some fish do migrate over dry land. We are not considering the famous eels which are said to steal peas from the farmers' gardens during the night, nor the octopi which, according to the Greek poet Oppian (about 149 to 179 AD), climb during the night into the vineyards to steal grapes and olives from the holy tree of Athena. Nevertheless, it is

Fig 380 Catching jumping fish with scoop nets in the Kinugawa River, Tochigi Prefecture, shown in a Japanese manuscript of the beginning of the last century.

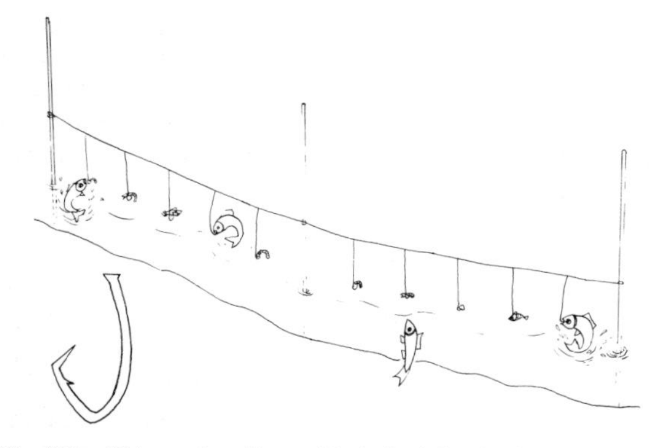

Fig 381 Chinese longline with baited hooks hanging some distance over the water. Fish jumping for the bait can hook themselves. (*Kasuga, 1975*).

known that some fish can migrate during the night over dry land to move from one water to another one with a better situation. This is known in African swamp fisheries and also of some fish living in Asiatic rice fields.[244] To catch such fish crossing over land, fishermen in Burma arrange entrapments which consist of a barrier with a pit dug near each end, into which some fish fall in trying to make their way round.[92] This method has also been known by the Chinese[613] and it seems to be known in other parts of Indo-China.[244] To catch animals in pitfall traps is an old hunting technique. It may be a good example of the close relation of hunting methods and those of fishermen as mentioned in the first chapter of this book.

Chapter eighteen

The art of net-making

To be typical of a fisherman's village, any picture or any photograph must show fishing nets hanging out or spread out for drying. In our conception, nets and fishing must go together. But that has not always been the case. On the contrary; compared with the age of fishing, the net is a recent invention, although it may still be some thousands of years old. Like other primary textile techniques such as plaiting and weaving, the art of net-making dates back at least to the Mesolithic – that is, the end of the period of gatherers and hunters. That again presumes that men had learned how to obtain net-making material – whether it came from plant fibres, bast, leather strips, silk threads or animal hair, eventually to be spun and twisted. It also had to be available in adequate quantities. Certainly that must have been difficult in the beginning, so the first handmade nets would almost certainly have been only very small ones. The large sheets of net required today by some large-scale fisheries for bulk fishing have become possible only through success being achieved in making nets on machines. But that did not happen until the second part of the last century. Up to that time every bit of netting had to be made by hand, and fishermen spent much time in producing raw material for net making; then they had to process it themselves by spinning and twisting before they could make the netting. In many parts of the world this is necessary even today. Therefore it will be understood that the fishing net is a relatively recent invention among the many types of fishing gear.

Many signs indicate that, with some nations, the net was introduced in hunting before it was used for fishing. How young the invention of the net is may also be demonstrated by the fact that in Europe the symbol of fishing is not a net but a fishing spear, namely the trident of Neptune or Poseidon. This trident is nothing but the ancient tuna spear of the Mediterranean. Thus the spear, not the net, was considered by the Greeks and Romans as representative of fishing gear. It was so important that it became the symbol of the Sea God. Even today nations are known that have a high cultural standard, where net fishing plays a secondary part as compared with other fishing methods. Moreover, the relatively late introduction of the net into fishing is also indicated by the fact that in the myths and tales of the nations living around the northern seas as well as of those living on the coasts of the Pacific and Indian Oceans, gods and heroes are described as teaching men how to make nets. The knotting of nets is a particular art, like boat-building and the forging of swords. The myths reveal that the art was not known to all men when they (the myths) came into existence, but that the knowledge of how to make nets had to be learned by each apprentice fisherman. Previously it was praised in myths and tales as being a special skill taught to men by superior powers. But it has to be admitted that in highly developed industrial fisheries this knowledge is decreasing and that on a highly sophisticated trawler today there may be only a few people with experience of how to make and mend netting.

There are many terms used in literature for the meshed webbing used by fishermen to construct fishing gear. According to a decision of the International Organization for Standardization (ISO) in Geneva, Switzerland, the official term should be 'netting'.[274] A netting is a meshed structure of indefinite shape and size, which is the raw material for the construction of many types of fishing gear, especially for fishing nets, but also for some gear used by hunters and bird catchers. There is no limitation either by the material from which the netting has been made, or by the size or shape of the single meshes of which the netting is composed. Here it must be remembered that nets have not been invented only by men. Long before the gods taught men how to make nets, animals used nets for their own purposes. We all know about spider webs. But the wheel-shaped nets of a certain spider family are not the only nets that exist in nature. Devices used for obtaining food, which may be called nets, are also manufactured by many other animals. Some species of aquatic animals produce such catching equipment in order to harvest plankton. The net made by the larvae of the caddis fly (*Hydropsyche*) (*Fig 382*) are of a particularly regular pattern. Construction and use of these catching devices, which were developed by nature long before man invented them, correspond to our stow nets (*Fig 435*).

Fig 382 Section of a 'net' made by a caddis larva of the genus *Hydropsyche*. (*Sattler, 1958*).

Certainly man did not learn how to make nets for hunting and fishing from any natural models. His technology of netting is quite different, and has changed greatly and become perfect only by repeated trial and error over a long period of time. Many fishing populations even today have not gained the knowledge of how to make nets for themselves. In our time, however, new independent invention is no longer necessary because net-making is now widely known and taught. Now the machine-made net can be delivered without trouble to even the most remote islands and is frequently replacing the home-made article, just as machine-made fishing hooks are displacing hand-made hooks in all parts of the world.

18.1 Stone walls, fences and netting

As in hunting, the original problem which led to the making of nets was to prevent fish from getting away in the water and to filter them or extract them from the water. For that purpose, fishery does not require textile netting in the modern sense. Stopping or barring the way of the fish in a bay or bight, or in running water, can also be done by earth and stone dams (*Figs 256* and *383*). As has been shown in Chapter 15, stone walls are known in many parts of the world. Mostly they are used in tidal or flood areas to retain fish during ebb tides. In this case the walls are permanent barriers. But they can also be erected during fishing, as the Oceanians do.[313] Fish encircled in shallow water by a large number of people, sometimes more than a hundred, can be enclosed by a quickly-made wall of coral stones so that their chances of escape are negligible. By that

Fig 383 Stone dams built off the coast of Guinea to retain fish as the tide falls. (*Sahrhage, 1961*)

means they are caught.[92] Stone walls can also be built in complicated labyrinths as the aborigines of Australia have done.[529] Therefore, it may be right to consider stone walls as 'living fossils of the oldest fishing gear'.[428] Stone walls have been replaced later in many areas by light transportable fish fences made of twigs, reeds, bamboo, *etc*.[62] These may be either simple fences or mats (*Figs 260* and *384*), or ingeniously plaited work in, for instance, the hexagonal technique used today for making baskets, especially of split bamboo and similar material (*Fig 385*).

Fig 384 Transportable fish fences used in a Philippine fish pond. (1960)

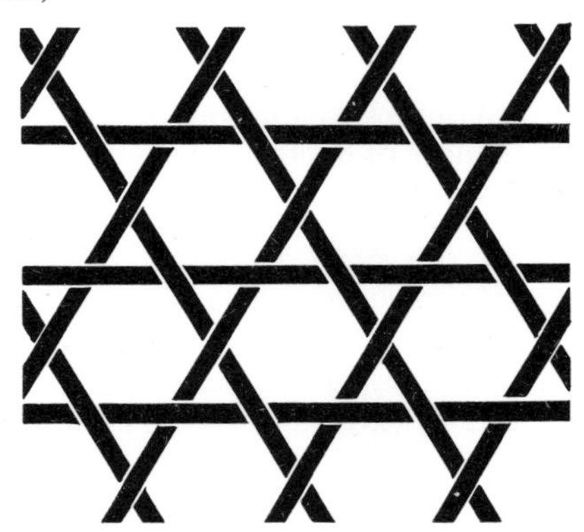

Fig 385 Hexagonal technique used for the construction of fish pots.

Just as the coarse stone dams have been replaced by plaited fences which are manufactured more easily, handled more simply and operated more efficiently, these again are being replaced by net fabrics made of various fibre-like materials, especially from plants, more rarely of animal origin. This development is still going on. But in spite of that trend, in many fisheries where sufficient material for plaited gear is available, (wood, bamboo, rattan *etc*), and where wages are low, there is still a preference for stable wooden gear instead of netting. Moreover, textile nets made of natural fibres require much care and maintenance, unless very cheap materials such as grass or straw have been used. The Japanese made some traps from rice straw, and this material is used for bigger forms such as leading netting. The Sicilian fisheries use special types of esparto grass for their tuna traps, which are so cheap that they can be left in place until they have rotted, before being replaced by new ones. Natural fibres as net materials have been used for centuries – possibly for thousands of years. In modern times, however, they too are being replaced by the better man-made fibres. These synthetic fibres are known under different trade names and include the following chemical groups: Polyamides (PA), Polyesters (PES), Polyethylenes (PE), Polyvinylchlorides (PVC), Polyvinyl alcohols (PVA) and others.[310] These fibres have many advantages which allow the manufacture of more effective fishing gear. Among the most useful properties are high resistance to rotting, the high breaking strength and favourable tenacity, low visibility in water, and low water resistance. Moreover, some of these properties can be varied according to the needs of the different fishing methods. This can be done also by mixing different types of synthetic fibres in one netting yarn. Man-made fibres offer fishery possibilities which may not yet be fully utilized. Unfortunately, the synthetic fibres can be too expensive for non-industrial countries. In their case, there is no neutral control of the properties of netting materials, and no training of fishermen in how to decide which material may be the best one for their purposes. Moreover, to the practical, but not instructed, fisherman inferior netting material may be offered, which by its low-class properties can hamper the use of any synthetic fibres. Originally, high prices for netting yarn made of synthetic fibres in comparison with those made of cotton or local fibres, hindered a worldwide introduction of netting materials of new synthetic fibres. Decreasing prices and increasing knowledge of how to use the new materials in the best manner, lead to wider use of this material, but there is still some uncertainty about the price development in the future. This may prevent the use of the best synthetic fibres available, in all fisheries, as wanted.

18.2 Primitive knotless netting

The basic design of textile netting is a mesh, usually of rhombic or square shape. According to a standard definition, a mesh is a 'designedly formed opening, surrounded by netting materials'.[274] The size and shape of the meshes regulates the sizes of those fish to be prevented from passing through and determines whether the fish shall be caught by mechanical filtering or by sticking in the meshes according to the circumference of their bodies, as shown for gillnets in Chapter 29. It is, therefore, understandable that right from very early times the consistency of size and shape of the meshes has been considered most essential.

How such meshes of equal size and constant shape can be obtained depends on the material used. As long as the material was rigid and rough this was relatively simple. *Figure 386* shows a primitive form of netting made by using bast twines and simply hanging each mesh on one in the previous row. Such 'knotless' meshes remained constant only as long as the net was firmly stretched in a frame or fastened over a rack, like the old baskets made of lime tree bast used in the north European fishery.

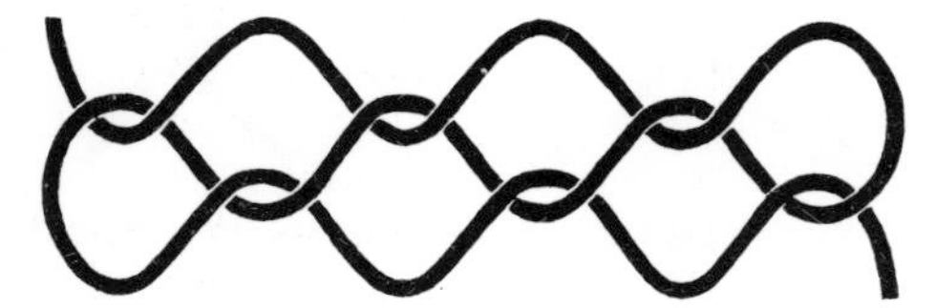

Fig 386 A primitive form of net-making achieved by hanging bast twines on each other.

Knotting was not necessary. The netting was kept together by its own roughness. A more permanent form of netting is obtained by twisting the bars of the meshes with each other, once or several times, at the joining points (*Fig 387*). In Scandinavian museums there are on display, relics of such twisted meshes made from lime tree bast that were originally found in Danish moors or fens, as well as some from old fish traps – and these last were even used until modern times. Compared with simple hanging (as in *Fig 386*), the twisting of the bars to form net meshes, (as in *Fig 387*), represented a significant development. As long as only rough materials were used for manufacturing these net-like forms, the technique of simple or multiple twisting as described was sufficient. That method is used even today when the netting is held stretched in a frame, like that made to cover or close the openings of baskets used by the fishermen of Malta,[67] (*Fig 388*) or of the Canary Islands. This method of building a mesh can even be helpful today with netting made of wire, as used for traps, dredges and also liftnets. The single twisting of the wire is sufficient to give the mesh some stability and consistent size, as can be seen from the beehive rock-lobster pot of Tasmania, the bottom of which is made of stiff wire which cannot be formed into a mesh in any other manner (*Fig 389*).

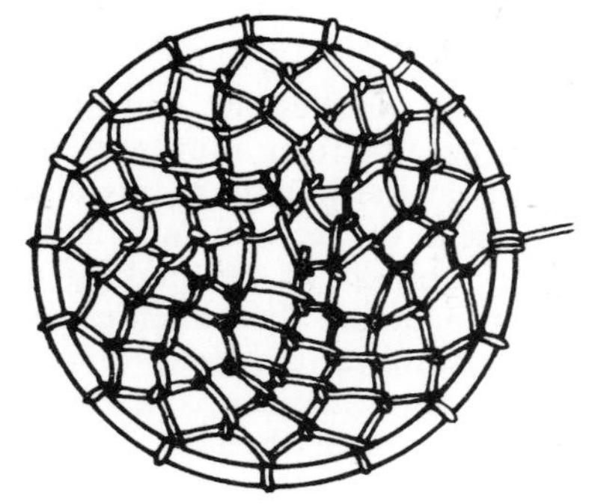

Fig 388 Cover for the top opening of a wooden beehive-basket in Malta. The cover is made by a simple twisting technique.

18.3 Knotted netting

As soon as man became settled, and agriculture was beginning, the conditions for cultivating fibre plants like linen, hemp, ramie, and many others, was created. Man learned how to obtain the fibres from various wild or cultivated plants and to spin and twist them into netting yarns. As mentioned before, as long as this yarn was rough it was not so difficult

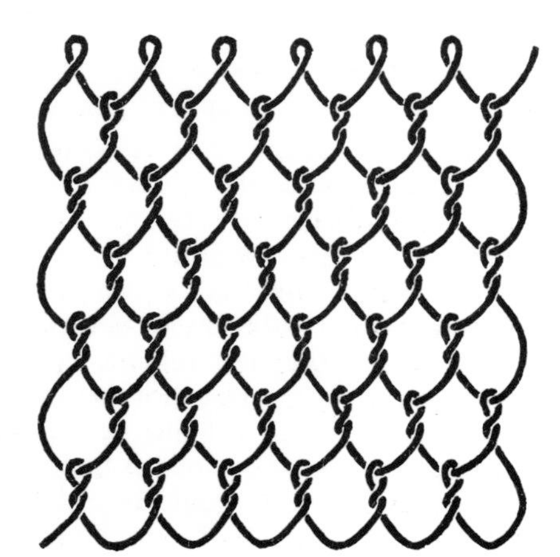

Fig 387 Simple knotless netting with low stability of the mesh size made by single or double twisting of the netting yarn at the joining points.

Fig 389 Australian rock lobster pot made of wood and wire in Tasmania. The mesh of the base is of very stiff wire and is therefore made by simple twisting, without knotting.

to get consistent meshes for netting. When the netting yarns became finer and smoother, twisting of these yarns at the joining points alone was no longer sufficient to get constant and fixed-size meshes. The method of net-making had to be improved by replacing the hanging technique by knotting the netting yarns at the previous mesh row (*Fig 390*). As that technique was first found in relics of nets discovered near the lake dwellings on the shores of Lake Constance, the knot – maybe the first used in net-making – was called the 'lake-dweller knot'. That technique of manufacturing fishing nets, however, is far more widespread than

Fig 390 This illustrates the net-making technique used by lake-dwelling fishermen in Switzerland.

has ever been supposed. The ancient African fishery in the area of the Zaire River, as well as the fisheries of Oceania and the Peruvian coast of South America,[71] knew how to manufacture meshes in that same 'lake-dwelling' technique. With that method of net-making there is produced no longer a 'knotless' but a 'knotted' netting. The knot does not slide, and the mesh remains constant, especially when the netting yarn is not too smooth. But when the material for net-making became finer and more smooth, this technique of net-making was no longer sufficient. The knot could be moved to and fro on the smooth loops of the previous row of meshes, which meant the mesh did not remain of a constant size. This unwanted slipping also applies to the method of knotting, which may be mentioned now, often known as the cow hitch (*Fig 391*) which can be considered as a loose form of the following knot. This cow hitch, too, remains fixed only as long as the net material is rough. Nets manufactured in that manner are known from the ancient African fishery. But nets from Peru have also been found to have been made in this way, and these date from times before Columbus. Because this knot is found very often in excavations in Peru, it has been named the 'Peruvian knot'.

Fig 391 Netting made with the help of a kind of 'failed' reef-knot, also called the 'cow hitch'.

The better the material became from which netting was manufactured – that is, the smoother and more uniform the twines became – the less did the meshes remain constant. The knots were found to slide, the meshes became distorted, and it became necessary to make serious efforts to find new methods of knotting to produce netting with meshes which retained their uniform shape. The development of the technique of net-making thus runs parallel to the development of manufacturing yarns and twine. The technique of net-making last described is so interesting because it already includes the knotting of nets, which even today are of great importance – that is, the manufacture of nets with the reef knot (*Fig 392*), which is widely distributed in the Asiatic fishery. This is identical with the

Fig 392 Netting made with the well-known reef-knot.

knotting on *Figure 391*, but the thread in the knot is placed a little differently so that the slings on the preceding rows of meshes are actually included in the knot. In this way, relatively constant meshes are obtained, which are sufficient for their purpose in many cases and are typical of the Asiatic fishery.

In the old fishery literature, that type of knot is very often called the 'Chinese knot'. But, according to Japanese statistics, that method of making nets is steadily diminishing from year to year. The reason for this is that this knotting technique is no longer sufficient for manufacturing nets from synthetic fibres. Their use is steadily gaining ground; in particular, in the form of twines of silk-like continuous fibres which call for non-sliding knots. This is the reason why the so-called 'weaver knot' has become more and more popular. The manufacture of nets with the weaver knot (*Fig 393*) has been known in the fishery of northwest Europe from very early times. Nets from the Stone Age, possibly four or five thousand years of age, found in a moor in Finland about 50 years ago[581] and recently in a moor in Schleswig-Holstein, show the weaver knot.[71] It may, therefore, be supposed that the weaver knot for making nets was developed in the ancient North Atlantic fishing area, including as well the native fishery of North America even before the day of Columbus. There, too, the weaver knot was known and it is hard to believe that such a complicated thing can be said to be a duplicate invention and that no connection existed between the use of weaver knots in northern Europe and North America.

Fig 393 Weaver knots are used for making this netting.

Nowadays the weaver knot is the most widely distributed type of knot for making nets in the European and American fisheries, and most of the modern, fully automatic net-making machinery, no matter whether it is built in Asia, Europe or America, is making netting with this knot. Compared with them, net-making machines which use reef knots play only a local and secondary part, and are restricted to East and South Asia. But even the weaver type of knotting is often not sufficient for the very smooth modern net twines made of continuous synthetic fibres. So the single weaver knot is being replaced by double knots of various types or, where their mechanical manufacture is too expensive, the single knots are fixed by thermal and chemical treatment of the netting.

Mentioned here are only some of the more important types of net-making. Fisheries, especially the traditional ones, know many more techniques for making netting, both woven and knitted. An example can be seen in *Figure 407*. Moreover, there are different techniques to get the same joinings for meshes,[62, 80] and fishermen know techniques for hand knotting without any auxiliary tools, as well as with different types of needles (*Fig 394*) and mesh sticks. Most of the knotted netting can bemade by machines, and machines can also make knotless netting.

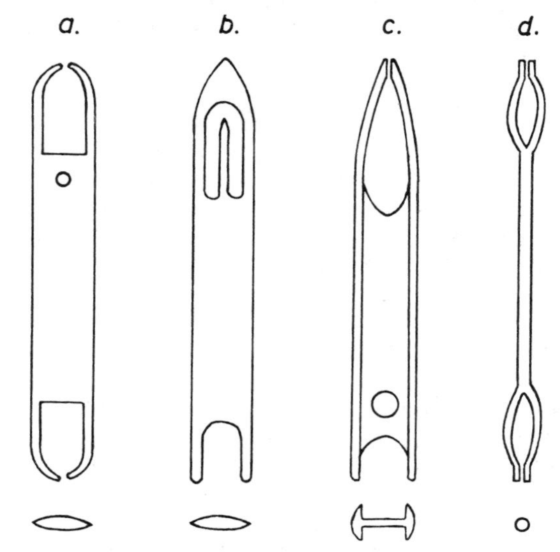

Fig 394 Main types of net needles: (*a*) filet type; (*b*) tongue type; (*c*) Icelandic type; (*d*) Mediterranean filet type.

18.4 Modern knotless netting

As has been mentioned above, ancient people did know knotless netting. There are other more complicated types. Even in modern fisheries, as with Canadian shellfish dredges, very simple knotless netting may be used. In this case, the meshes are formed by joining the netting twines with cramp-irons (*Fig 395*). But modern fishery knows and uses much more complicated machine-made knotless netting. Since the beginning of the fifties, modern knotless netting has been used in many fisheries. It is made either according to the Japanese technique, together with twisting the netting yarns (*Fig 396a*), or after the Raschel technique developed in northwest Europe (*Fig 396b*). Both techniques can be realized only by machines. Some years ago a third method was developed in the German Democratic Republic. In this case the meshes are formed by plaited, not twisted, netting yarns (*Fig 396c*).

Knotless netting has the advantages of lower water resistance and lower weight. This depends on the method of manufacture. Weight of the netting, breaking strength of a single mesh, and diameter of the bars are decisive for judging the value of knotless netting. But there are some properties more of interest for specific fisheries, like the fact that knotless netting is less bulky than a knotted one.

Fig 395 Netting made with clips as used for Canadian shellfish dredges.

Moreover, it has been found that knotless netting made according to the Raschel system can have, by virtue of its longer 'joining points', meshes with an hexagonal opening (*Fig 397*). This seems to provide a better flow of water through the netting and therefore brings better catches.[481] A disadvantage of knotless netting with large meshes is that it can be more expensive than netting of the same mesh size made by knotting. Finally, it should be mentioned that since the appearance of synthetic fibres the idea has grown that it might be better not to knot the nets, but to weld or to stick them together, or even to mould them as ready-made

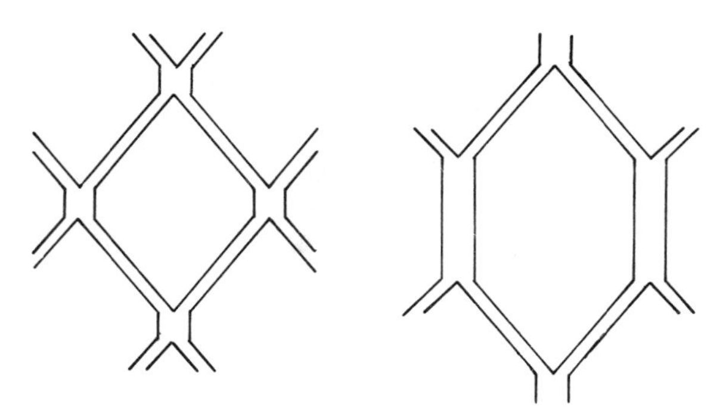

Fig 397 Knotless netting (Raschel technique) with rhombic or hexagonal mesh opening.

sheets. If the sticking of threads for making nets developed, we would once again have reached the techniques used by spiders or the larvae of caddis flies for making their nets.

The foregoing descriptions demonstrate how intricate is the history of net-making and how it has never come to a standstill. The very beginning of the technique can only be imagined. Owing to the poor keeping qualities of all textiles made of natural fibres, remnants of nets from remote times have very rarely been preserved up to the present time. There may have been various origins. But, whatever the origins were, all the efforts down the ages have led steadily to great and intensive development, which is now being accelerated more than ever by the invention and increasing availability of synthetic fibres. Stone dams and fish fences were created at a very early stage. They were replaced by woven fences or knotless nets manufactured by simply hanging the threads of one mesh on another. These in turn were displaced by knotting net fabric. The lake-dwellers' knot was invented and survived in

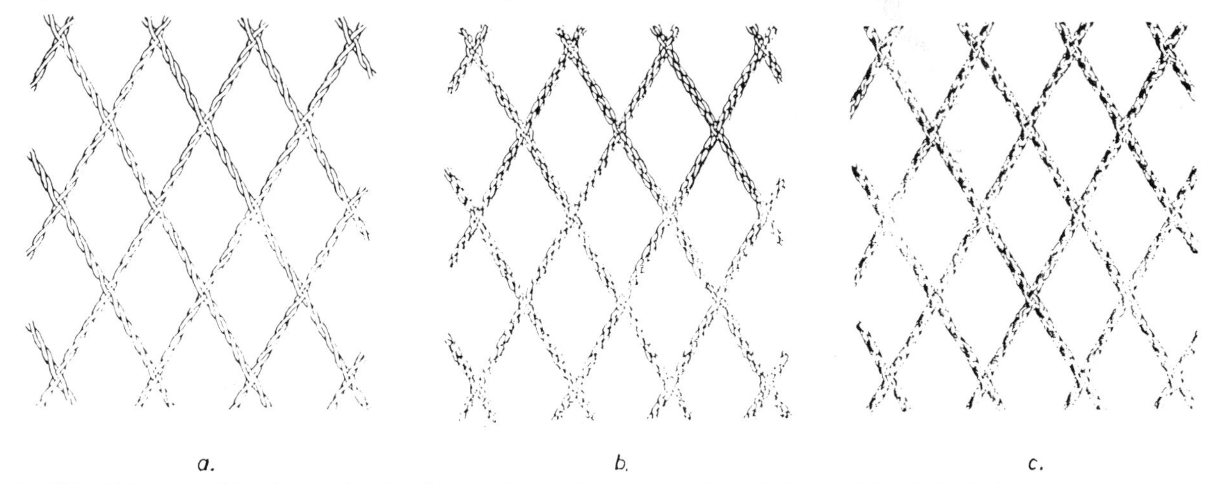

a. b. c.

Fig 396 Main types of knotless netting (machine made): (*a*) Japanese twisting technique; (*b*) Raschel technique; (*c*) double braiding or Reichel technique as used in the GDR.

Africa until modern times. The reef knot was adopted by the Asiatic fisheries and developed for making nets, even mechanically. The northern fisheries invented the weaver knot which displaced the two others. With synthetic fibres now available, the knotless technique has been revived because it has certain advantages in some fishing techniques. But there are already to be heard meddlesome voices predicting an early end to the use of fishing gear made of netting and claiming that it will be replaced by methods like electrical fishing (Chapter 5), or by harvesting machines (Chapter 31). But very often electrical fishing is a fishery with electrified fishing gear made of netting and also some harvesting machines will still need netting, even if it is only for scoop nets.

Chapter nineteen

From the scoop basket to the stow net

The first fishing gear was made of wooden materials like sticks and flexible branches; maybe also from grass and bast. Later on, net-making was invented, and netting of various different fibres has been used for gear construction right up to the present. The technique for making netting for fishing has been known for several thousand years. On the other hand, knowledge of how to knit nets is still not so very old, so that even in highly developed fishing countries, fishing gears made of wood only, without any textiles to supplement them, have remained in use until the present time. It may be supposed that these wooden gears date back to those ages when the art of knitting nets was still unknown.

The previously mentioned fish baskets, considered to be the predecessors of fyke nets, are an example of the transformation of a gear of plaited wooden material into one made of netting. In the construction of other traps, and of barriers, there has also been a transition from plaited wooden material to netting – just as happened with much other fishing equipment. This development is also true for the type of fishing gear discussed in this chapter. In their smallest forms these 'bagnets' are hand-operated devices for scooping fish and other prey out of the water. Originally made of wood, like flat baskets, these are now more or less deep bags made of netting of different materials. Typical of this gear is that it is held open by a frame around the opening of the bag. This gear, today usually made of knotted netting, may be called a framed bagnet even though, as shown later, the frame can sometimes be replaced by some other arrangement. Very different forms and methods of operation of this gear are known in fisheries. Small scoop baskets or scoop nets can be used for handling or transporting caught fish – like the landing nets of sport fishermen or the brail nets for scooping large catches out of other gear in commercial fisheries.

It has to be remembered also that scoop nets of different sizes, which are typical in pond fisheries, are sometimes the only fishing gear in this branch of fisheries. Moreover, transportable scoop nets can also be used for the direct catching of fish in many waters. In this case, the framed bagnet is no longer a supplementary gear but a true fishing gear. This is much more true for the stationary stow nets which are considered as one of the most important gears in the river fishery. But they can also be operated in the outlets of lakes or in coastal waters with some current. This will show, too, that these gears, insofar as they are made of netting, need some current in order to operate in an effective manner. That means, the current has to stretch the bag in the horizontal, downstream, direction while the frame holds the entrance open.

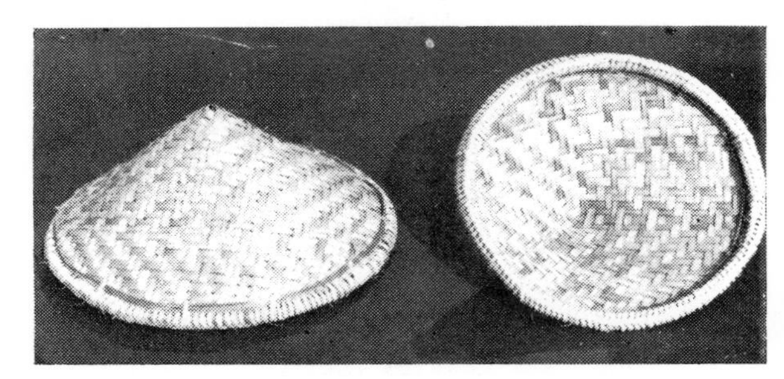

Fig 398 Scoop baskets used in the Bena Lulua area of Zaire.

19.1 Scoop baskets

Scoop baskets are examples of an old fishing gear made of wooden materials. Originally, they were shallow plaited plates (*Fig 398*) or shovel-shaped wickerwork implements (*Fig 399*) and they are still used in that form in the Asiatic fisheries to filter fish from water. As these scoop implements are small, they are quite easily and capably used by women and children wading in the water, sometimes working together in a line. With scooping movements they catch small fish and shrimps. They can also be used for screening out of the mud small animals like mussels, worms and crabs which may be needed for bait. This can be done by moving the gear up and down only, or by stirring up the mud by hand, or, as is mostly done when fishing in breast-high water, with the foot (*Fig 400*). When used in this way the basket is pressed against the bottom and the mud is shovelled by foot into the basket before being screened out through the mesh.

Fig 399 Japanese boy fishing with a shovel-like type of basket used in agriculture.

Fig 400 Thai woman using her foot in a basket to wash small animals out of the mud (1960).

The form and operation of the scoop basket – long known and widely distributed – differs very much from area to area, like all gear manufactured individually and not mechanically mass produced. An interesting form of scoop net is known from Thailand. Made of bamboo and called a 'leh', this gear can be considered an old type of 'multi-purpose gear' (*Fig 401*). It is a basket, open on its upper side, and equipped with a non-return device, which can be used also as a trap by setting against the current in

Fig 401 Thai multipurpose basket called a 'leh' (1960).

narrow waterways, or which can be operated to scoop small fishes in shallow waters like rice fields. Very often, catching by scooping demands rapid action for successful results. Therefore the scooping implement must be able to be guided easily through the water; that is, it must not be swollen and bulky in form and, when lifted, the water must run out quickly to leave the filtered catch behind. This, therefore, requires that the scooping gear be plaited as lightly as possible and be not too large. Strong wooden gear can, especially when wet, become heavy and tiring for the operator. One solution to this problem may be to use light mats for the construction of fishing gear for scooping as is done in Madagascar (*Fig 402*). Fishing with scoop baskets is also popular in Black Africa. As in Asia it is normally a fishery for women, working in a collective. In this case, a line or circle of vociferous

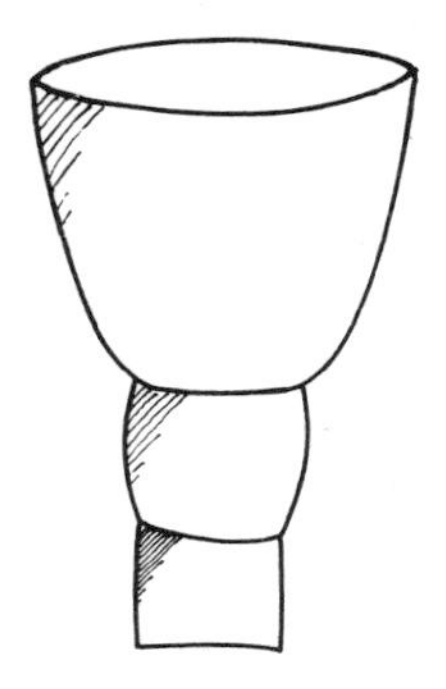

Fig 402 Special form of plaited basket used for scoop fishing in Madagascar.

women – it can number several hundred[361] – crowds into the water to place their scoop baskets in the flow, opening downstream, or, by pushing the gear with the opening forward, the lower and larger edge of the basket upstream. One woman alone would not catch anything, as the fish could easily swim out of the way of her basket. So, after some steps forward, the basket is pushed up by all the people at the same time; the caught fish are put in a collecting container, and the line of women goes on again.[82] Boys can join the women. When the current is too strong, men take over this basket fishery from the women. Large scoop baskets can be operated by two women.[361] The women can also stand in a line with their baskets touching side by side and wait till helpers drive the fish into their baskets. It has to be mentioned that some of the baskets can be temporarily operated as cover pots (Chapter 28). There are also some observations that large wooden baskets can be fitted out with a long handle and pushed forward over the bottom (*Fig 403*).[651]

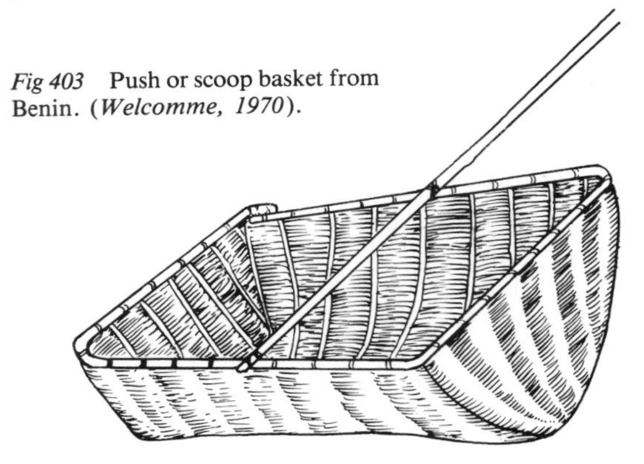

Fig 403 Push or scoop basket from Benin. (*Welcomme, 1970*).

19.2 Scoop nets and skimming nets

Even though wooden scoop baskets have the advantage of high stability, and can be operated for a long time without deterioration, efforts have been made to decrease the weight of the gear by using lighter materials, especially by making the catching bag of plaited mats, woven textiles or of netting, instead of wood. Many other materials have been used to transform a scoop basket into a scoop net. An interesting example is the replacement of the filtering area of the bag by natural spider webbing (*Fig 404*). These scoops have practically no weight, or only that of the frame, and the water filters away quickly. There are some spider webs found in Papua-New Guinea, in Jamaica, the Bermudas and Brazil which are so strong that they can be used for making baskets. It is known that spider webs are also used in fishing in Papua-New Guinea[504] and the Solomon Islands. The webs are collected when many insects have been caught in them; they are fixed in a frame and set into the water. The insects work like bait, attracting small fish which entangle themselves or can be easily landed by the 'baited scoop net'. It has been reported that scoop nets have been operated with a filtering area made of spider web with a diameter of up to two metres and strong enough to catch frogs or even fish the size of a trout.

Sometimes loosely woven cloths are used for making the bags of scoop nets, but in general netting is preferred. Sometimes only very small pieces of netting are needed for hand-operated scoop nets. On the basis of probability, it may be supposed that the first netting used in fishing could be manufactured only in small quantities and therefore could only be used for making small scoop nets. To keep open the bags made of different materials they are framed, but under certain conditions even hand-operated bagnets can be used like scoop nets, without frames (*Fig 405*). How old and widespread this type of fishing gear is can be

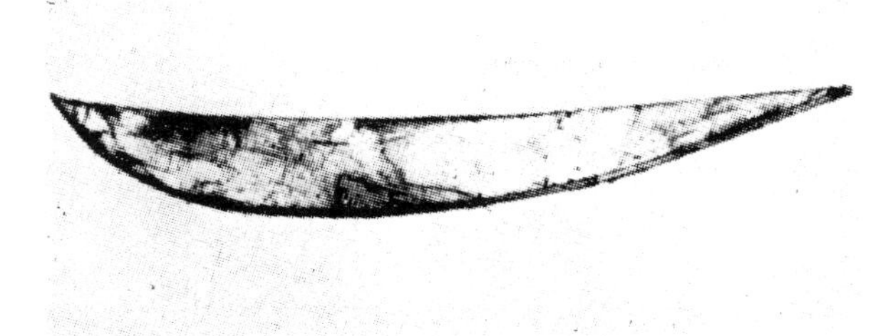

Fig 404 Remarkable and unusual scoop net made of strong spiders' web as used in New Guinea. (*Photo: Überseemuseum, Bremen.*)

Fig 405 Indian boys fishing with scoop nets without frames for mussel shells on the Malabar coast.

seen not only from the drawings of Inca fishermen in Mexico (*Fig 406*) but also by the fact that sometimes scoop nets are found with a netting made by a very old technique (*Fig 407*).

Fig 406 Fishing with scoop nets. Illustration in an old Mexican manuscript.

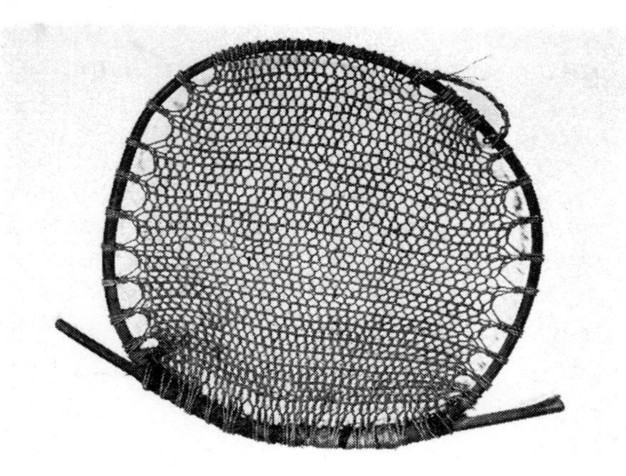

Fig 407 Flat scoop net from Geelvink Bay, New Guinea.

The scoop nets include the many other hand nets regularly used in all parts of the world. Their shape depends on the form of the frame (*Figs 408* and *409*). The most common form for small nets is a round frame with a net bag attached. As *Figures 408*(*a*) and (*b*) show, they can be more or less of circular form. The filtering bag can be either stretched flat or allowed to hang in the form of a bag. The round scoop nets can be without a handle, like those operated by women and children as a device for collecting small fish (*Figs 407, 410* and *411*).

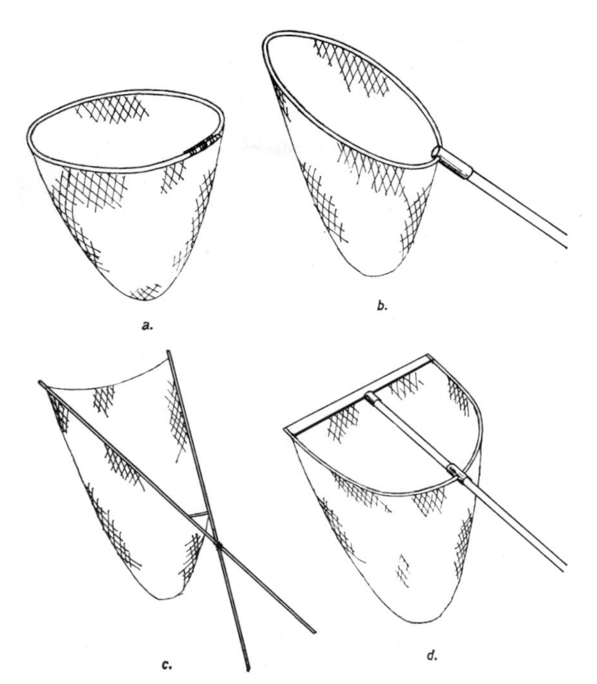

Fig 408 Here are shown the usual forms of small scoop nets; (*a*) without handle; (*b*) with handle; (*c*) skimming net; (*d*) push net.

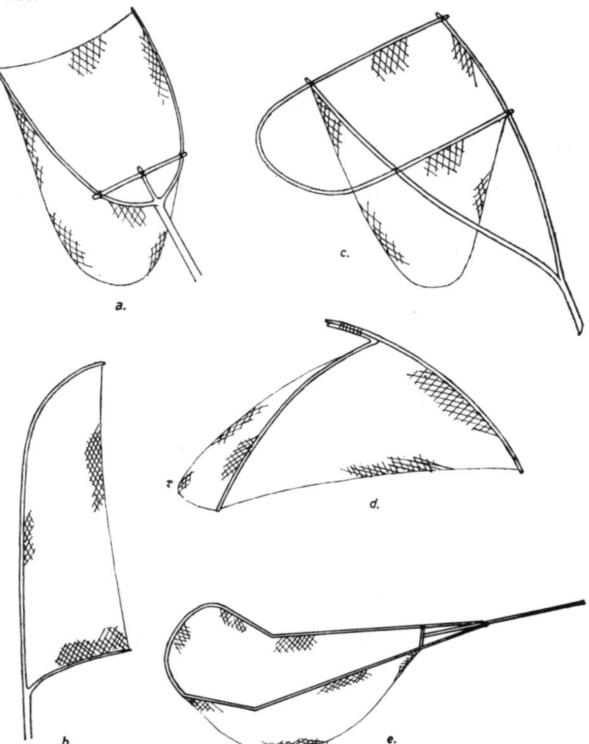

Fig 409 Some special forms of scoop nets from different islands in the South Seas: (*a*) Yap; (*b*) Luangiua; (*c*) Yap; (*d*) Truk; (*e*) Ponape.

Fig 410 Tilapia fishing in Guinea. (*Photo: FAO. A M Wirtz.*)

Fig 411 Thai woman fishing with scoop net in a klong in Bangkok. (1960).

Another basic form of small hand-operated nets are the skimming nets (*Fig 408c*). These are V-shaped scoop nets with two crossed mobile or fixed rods to keep the net open. The mobile poles can be clapped together to close the net bag, which is therefore also called a clap net with movable branches. Skimming nets are, as we will see later on, not so limited in size as the round-framed scoop nets. A special form of the V-shaped skimming net is the Indian triangular net with a 'V' frame made of three sticks of equal length. With one type of this Indian gear the opening of the bag is covered with a large-meshed triangular netting, mounted on the three sticks of the frame. Because of this large-meshed netting, small fish can enter the net but the entrance of unwanted seaweeds is prevented.[192] This is an idea which can be found again with dredges and beamtrawls (Chapter 20).

In addition to the round and triangular scoop nets, there are also others, sometimes of rather strange shape. *Figure 409* shows only some of them. Among these, the butterfly nets are quite famous, as used by the Mexican Indians of the Tarascan tribe on Lake Pátzcuaro (*Fig 412*). The frames, shaped like butterfly wings, gave the name to these large oval scoop nets. Another striking form is a large scoop net from the island of Penang (Malaysia) with an oval rattan frame more than twice as long as it is high (about 2·6 × 1·1 metres) (*Fig 413*).

Scoop nets in whatever form, used as direct fishing gear, will be operated in a different manner by men, women and children. The usual method is a scooping movement when wading in breast-deep water, as mentioned before for scoop baskets (*Figs 410* and *411*). Sometimes the gear is also operated

Fig 412 Mexican fishermen with 'butterfly nets' at work on Lake Pátzcuaro. (*Photo: FAO, H Ortiz.*)

Fig 413 Large scoop net from Penang (Malaysia) operated from the side of a sailing vessel. (1973).

from the shore, or from a boat as described for the gear of Penang. In the Samoa Islands, palolo worms are scooped from the water surface with small nets during the night, just as fishermen do in northwestern Europe when collecting bait worms after stirring them out of the bottom mud (Chapter 2). A peculiar form of scoop net fishing is known in the sea fishery of the Cape Verde Islands. To catch small fish, mostly mackerel (*Decapterus* sp.) during sunset, the fishermen place their canoes in a long row in the open sea, luring and keeping the fish near the boats by spitting chewed raw fish into the water. The attracted fishes are then caught either with small hooks or with flat scoop nets.[81]

When larger quantities of small fish, prawns or squid, or large single fish have to be caught, a bigger gear is needed maybe with special handles some metres in length. This can be very large fishing gear, which needs not only great skill but also some considerable energy; therefore the so-called 'pole net fishing' is special work for men only. One of the largest scoop nets known is from Lake Tanganyika[326] (*Fig 414*). This gear has a diameter of 2 to 2·5 metres, a pole of about 3 metres, and a very large net bag.[417] For scooping, the fish are attracted and concentrated with light during the night. In most cases, however, the hand-operated scoop nets are smaller in size (total length about 2 metres), like the triangular nets operated in Malaysia for catching mullet during the rough weather of the northeast monsoon (*Fig 415*). To operate this gear the fisherman has to stay deep in the surf, like the Chinese do to catch eels with small round scoop nets during bad weather surf on the Penghu Islands (Pescadores) (*Fig 416*). When heavy storms press the waves onto a small beach, the fishermen stay behind protecting walls with scoop nets, observing the water surface. As soon as they see an eel swimming more or less exhausted by the waves on the water surface, they jump into the shallow water to catch the fish with their scoop nets.

A special form of the operation of large round scoop nets is known in the Bosphorus (*Fig 598*). When fish (*Engraulis*) are observed swimming near the quay against the current, a large scoop net is placed behind them in the water and they are then frightened back into the net with the help of a white stone fixed by a short line to a long pole.[384] This method of frightening fish with the help of a 'white (marble) stone' we will find again in use with Greek gillnets used for drive-in fishery (Chapter 26). Another strange form for operating large scoop nets has already been mentioned, and that is the catching of flying fish in the air (Chapter 17) (*Fig 379*).

Sometimes bigger scoop nets and skimming nets are used for working in muddy water. When the

Fig 414 One of the largest hand-operated scoop nets used in night fishery with light in Lake Tanganyika. (*Photo: FAO, H Kristjonsson.*)

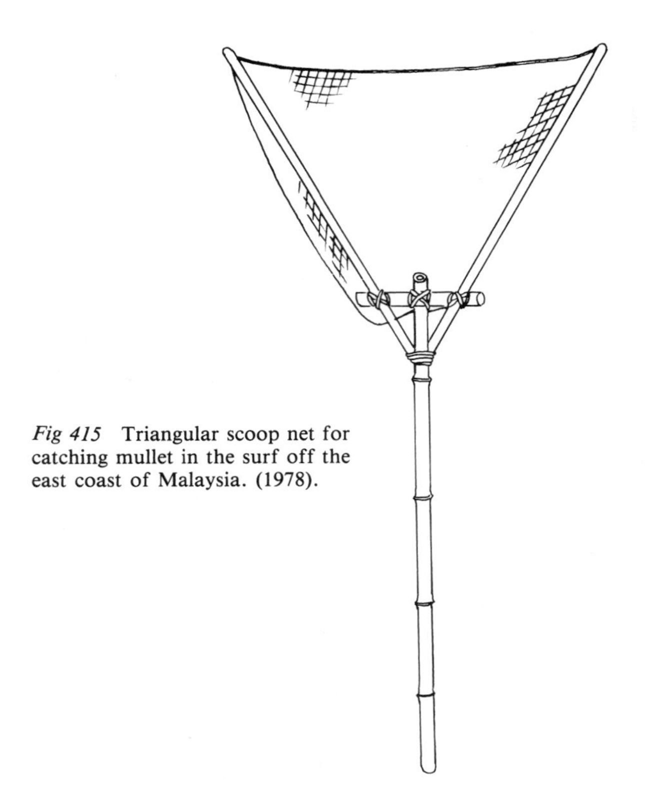

Fig 415 Triangular scoop net for catching mullet in the surf off the east coast of Malaysia. (1978).

fisherman feels a fish strike the net, he quickly lifts it out of the water. In this manner, in Ireland, salmon have been caught in strong currents.[657] Simple round scoop nets can be used as catching gear, as the Indians on the northwest coast of North America have done in their salmon fisheries (*Fig 417*). Their scoop nets had very long handles and great skill was necessary to catch the jumping salmon in the foaming water. The artificial platforms from which the gear was operated were considered typical for this fishery.[625] This 'pole net fishing' of the Indians in the river cascades of North America is considered an age-old method of salmon fishing. To catch salmon – and also shad – with the help of long-handled scoop nets is considered an inexpensive fishing method as well as a most selective one! The diameter of this gear is about 1·75 metres. The bag is made of monofilament and is up to 2·5 metres deep. There must be a pole long enough to handle the gear from a scaffold high over the strongly running water. To hold the gear in the strong current, its frame is connected to the scaffold by a fine steel wire. Moreover, a 'feeler line' (*Fig 434*) runs from the bagnet to the upper end of the handle held by the fisherman. When a fish hits the bag, he can feel this touch, which is the signal to raise the scoop net hand-over-hand to prevent the escape of the fish from the net bag.[460] The scaffold

Fig 416 Chinese fisherman catching eel with a scoop net during the bad weather season on Penghu Islands, Taiwan. (1978).

Fig 417 Indians fishing for salmon with scoop nets at the former Celilo Falls on the Columbia River. Chinook salmon in particular were caught here before the area was flooded by the construction of the Dalles dam. (*Photo: M H Naggiar.*)

is a temporary platform only and has to be rebuilt every year because it is often washed away with the winter rains.

A similar fishery for catching salmon with scoop nets existed formerly in England and in Finland. Also the Finns have known the fishery from scaffolds, but the Finnish scoop nets were relatively small, 0·9 × 0·6 metres and only one metre deep. The pole of elastic pine wood had a length of 4 to 5 metres.[639] There the salmon were caught in artificial channels built in front of the barriers where the fish paused to rest. In Finland also white fish (*Coregonus lavaretus*) have been caught with scoop nets from scaffolds over rapids.[581] In England the fishermen had no artificial platforms, with the exception of 'standings' on huge blocks of stone, set up centuries ago, on an ebb channel into the sea. At low tides the tops of these standings were exposed and there the fishermen watched, with their scoop nets, for the salmon coming downstream.[279]

These examples are given to show that simple scoop nets can be useful as catching gear not only in small-scale collecting fisheries, but also in more lucrative ones. As mentioned before, scoop nets are better known as additional implements with which to scoop the catch out of large fishing gear such as stationary traps, or purse seines (Chapter 25) and other gear, but they are also useful in many other fishing activities, particularly in pond farms. The most well-known type of scoop nets may be the landing nets used by sport fishermen in fresh water and sea water. They are collapsible and are used when there are no lines with free hooks which may entangle in the netting. When large fish are caught, gaffs have to replace landing nets.

19.3 Brail nets with purse lines

In general, scoop nets are bagnets with a closed, sometimes strengthened, bottom. For brailing out large catches from purse seines (Chapter 25) and for the direct catching of squid, scoop nets are used with a bottom which can be opened and closed to facilitate the emptying of the bagnet. Such scoop nets are made like a tube of netting kept open at one end by a strong iron hoop one metre or more in diameter, connected to a handle several metres in length. At the other end of the tube of netting, small purse rings are sewn on to hold a purse line

(*Fig 418*). For brailing large catches, or for catching squid attracted and concentrated by light as in California, at least three men may be needed.[293] One guides the brail by the handle and holds the purse line for opening and closing the bagnet. A second man operates a winch for lowering and lifting the brail, and a third one tows the bagnet through the catch (*Fig 584*). It is, however, possible that two men or even one man could operate the gear.

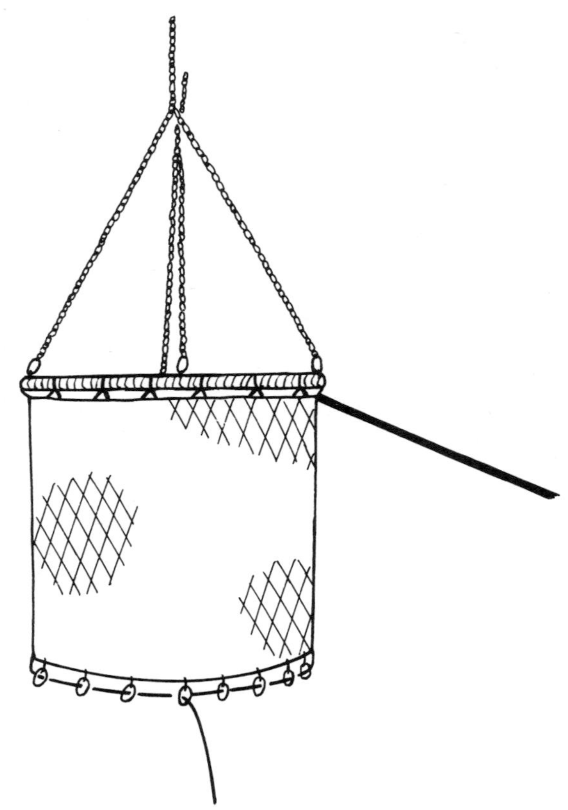

Fig 418 Brail net, or brailer, for emptying purse seines. The bottom of the bag net can be opened or closed with the help of a purse line drawn through the rings.

19.4 Push nets and dragged scoop nets

Scoop nets can be used in quite another way. They can be pushed over the bottom in shallow water. In this form of operation, push nets are widely used by fishermen and their wives. They wade up to the waist in the water and push the nets forward ahead of them, especially to catch shrimps. For that purpose, the frames that keep the nets open must have a straight edge so that they can be pushed along the bottom like a snow scraper (*Fig 408d*). The prey is collected by pushing or thrusting the net, and caught when it is raised from the water (*Figs 419* and *421*).[93] Such gear, when made of wood,

Fig 419 A skimming net used on the Pacific coast of Taiwan.

must be weighted enough to prevent it rising onto the surface of the water. Not only are scoop nets with a more or less round frame used as push nets, but so too are those with triangular fixed and movable frames like the skimming nets already mentioned. Skimming nets can be used as scoop nets but they are mostly used for pushing according to their construction. The triangular push nets are handled in the same manner as the usual scoop nets, by pushing forward to catch shrimp, prawn or milkfish fry. To ensure that the points of the scissor-like cross sticks of the skimming nets glide smoothly over the bottom they can be provided with runners. These can be hoe-shaped shoes made from hardwood, pieces of coconut husk,[93, 299] (*Fig 420*) or cow horns. In the early river fisheries of England, a square piece of leather was nailed on to the ends of the sticks of the skimming nets to facilitate their

Fig 420 Another skimming net used in Manila Bay, Philippines.

sliding along the river bed during shrimping.[279] As has been mentioned before (Chapter 2), even today in France there are, in the 'pêche à pied' fishery, semi-professional people who use push nets of different types when fishing for 'crevettes'. Skimming nets are also used, especially those with the slender curved ends which glide easily.[577] In the Malaysian fishery, the extremities of the sticks of the skimming nets are sometimes connected by a rope. This limits the gap between the collapsible poles, but it also causes the shrimps and prawns to leave the bottom. However, it does give the fisherman warning of obstacles which might otherwise damage the net.[93]

Skimming nets can also be guided through the water near the surface by a fisherman wading forward (*Fig 421*). Large skimming nets, which are attached to a vessel, are also operated (*Fig 422*). They resemble the scraping nets which will be

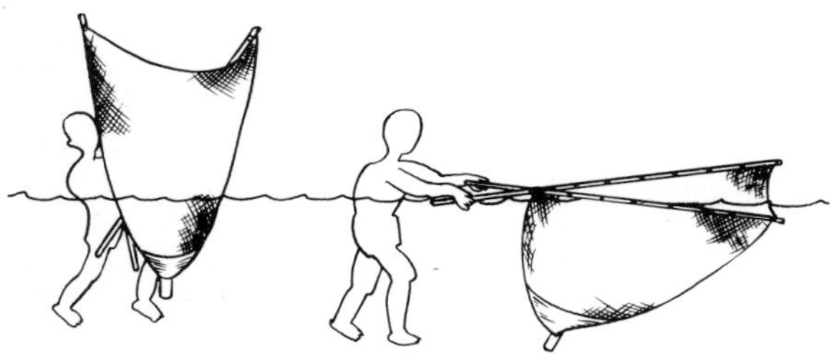

Fig 421 Fishing on the water surface with skimming nets in Taiwan. (*Chen, 1973*).

discussed in the next section. However, large gear of this type, pushed along the sea bed with an engine-propelled boat, is forbidden in some countries (*eg* in Malaysia).

Bagnets can also be dragged or towed towards a fisherman staying on shore or in an anchored boat. The smaller forms of these nets are often trilaterally pyramidal.[30] The bag is sometimes made not of netting but of loosely woven canvas (*Fig 423*). This operation of bagnets is a link with another fishing method – that based on dragged nets. There is a particularly remarkable type of bagnet, with a square or triangular frame, which is dragged behind a fisherman wading through the water (*Fig 424*). Ancient descriptions tell how it was also dragged by horses. In this way, larger and heavier bagnets with an iron frame in the opening, could be towed. Reminiscent of this fishing method are the famous 'garnallvissers te paard' of Oostduinkerke in Belgium (Chapter 21) (*Fig 490*). The original gear was like a triangular scoop net with a bottom board of about four metres in length and a stick in the middle to keep the bag of netting open.[40] The rear end of the bag could be opened to take out the catch. Since 1940 this gear has been replaced by a small trawl with otter boards. This indicates that these framed drag nets are the predecessors of the dredges and trawls which became so important in some industrial countries. When these bagnets became larger and the fishery

Fig 422 Philippine skimming net fixed on a motor boat in Laguna de Bay.

Fig 423 Dragged bagnets made of woven manila fibres as used in Taiwan.

moved to deeper waters, such gear as this could no longer be dragged by men, even on horses, but needed to be pulled by sailing boats, steam or motor vessels, as will be described in Chapter 21.

Nevertheless, some so-called 'manpower trawling', which may be identical to dragging bagnets, can be found even today in some parts of the world. In a net reported from Benin, the frame is reduced to two sticks, about two metres in length, which are towed by two fishermen (*Fig 425*).[651]

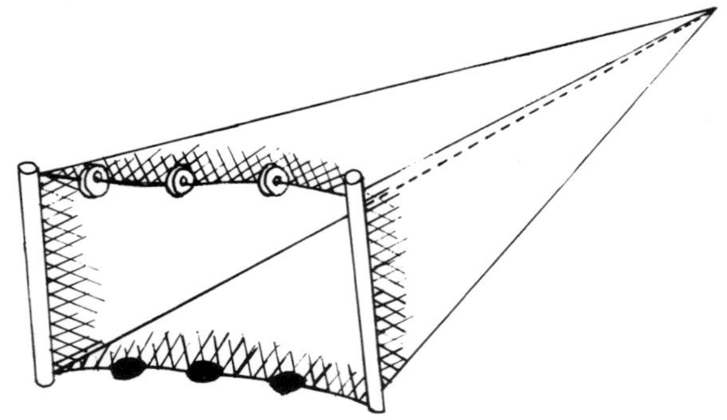

Fig 425 Drag net from Benin which would be towed by two fishermen. (*Welcomme, 1970*).

Figure 426 shows the so-called 'soppevod', which means 'splash net' – used in Denmark even today for catching eels and bait fish in shallow waters.[511] The gear is a simple net bag with the frame of the opening replaced by floats and sinkers. Two fishermen, with a small boat to hold the catch, tow the gear for a short distance. They then come together, and one of them takes the two towing lines whilst the other frightens the fish into the far end of the towed net bag by splashing (hence the name of the gear). This gear resembles a mini-trawl. There are more examples of 'manpower trawling' but – as with the Belgian shrimp fishery using horses – the original bagnet with frame is now largely replaced by a trawl with wings and otter boards.

19.5 Scrape nets

Bagnets, especially of the skimming net type, can become such a size that they cannot be operated by hand, nor can they be pushed or towed. Instead they

Fig 424 Dragged scoop nets, the predecessors of trawls. (*Duhamel and la Marre, 1776*).

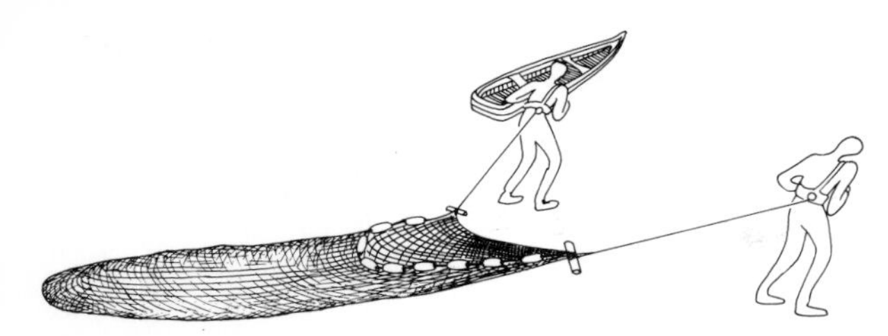

Fig 426 Danish fishermen towing a net bag in the so-called 'soppevodsfiskeri', which is still operated today. (*Rasmussen, 1975*).

are mechanically operated according to the lever system, from a vessel, by using the edge of the boat as the pivot. A simple form of such a large gear, previously used in northern Germany for eel fishing, had scissor-like crossed rods more than five metres in length. They were held from the boat against the current and were lifted by leverage over the boat side at short intervals. Such nets are also used in the fisheries of Asia and of Africa as movable gears operated from boats (*Figs 427* and *428*), or as stationary ones operated from the bank of a river or a suitable beach by installing them on a special platform (*Fig 427c*). Because this gear is operated by lowering and lifting like liftnets (Chapter 27), they are often included in that group of fishing gear. Strictly speaking, however, scrape nets, as they may be called, are quite different in construction and operation, and are nothing more than large (sometimes very large) scoop nets which are operated in a different manner. They are frequently so large and heavy that counterweights have to be

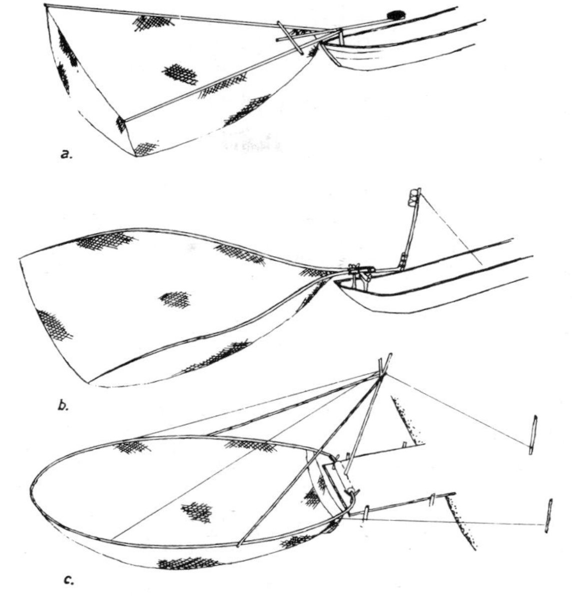

Fig 427 Fixed scraping nets in boats or on the beach in: (*a*) Japan (*NN, 1959*); (*b*) Lake Chad, Africa (*Monod, 1928*); (*c*) parts of Cameroon (*Monod, 1928*).

fitted to them so that they can be handled more easily (*Figs 427a* and *427b*). The scraping nets from Lake Chad in Africa are especially well known.[44] They are found in Africa only in the areas of Lake Chad and the River Niger and became such a symbol that they were printed on the stamps of French Equatorial Africa and have also been adopted by the Republic of Chad on her own

Fig 428 Scrape net on the Ganges in Bangladesh. (*FAO Photo: FAO W Williams, 1952*).

stamps. These may be the largest skimming nets used in fisheries. Similar types are also known in East and South Asia (*Figs 427a* and *428*).

Here may be included a gear which can also be considered as a scrape net. For catching elvers in the River Severn (UK), fishermen use special hand nets like a long stretched scoop net of a curious construction[279] (*Fig 429b*). The handle of the gear passes through the bag (nowadays made of a webbing of terylene (PES) or nylon (PA)) almost to the end of the gear, with some smaller branches which keep the bag open like a hand. A similar gear, but one more complicated in its construction is known only from the lower River Danube and is called, in Rumania, 'sacovistea' (*Fig 429a*). There are also other names like 'billeg'[569] or 'billing'. The sacovistea has the similar unusual construction described earlier.[20, 21] Smaller sizes of this gear are hand-operated anywhere from the shore (*Fig 430*); larger ones need special platforms (*Fig 431*).

Fig 430 Rumanian fisherman handling a 'sacovistea' in the lower Danube. (1976).

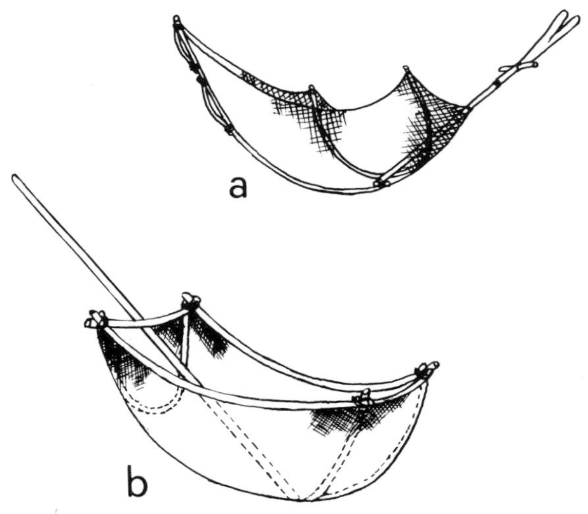

Fig 429 Hand scrape nets: (*a*) 'sacovistea' from the lower Danube (*Nédélec, 1975*); (*b*) elver fishing equipment in the lower river Severn. (*Jenkins, 1974*).

Fig 431 Rumanian 'sacovistea'. (*Photo: Bacalbasa and Pectu, 1969.*)

19.6 Stationary stow nets in rivers

In previous sections, different types of bagnets have been described. Some are very small, operated by hand and easy to transport; others are large, separated from the shore, and transportable only when mounted on a boat or raft. Common to this gear is a frame around the opening to keep the net bag open at its mouth, and they all need a current of water flowing through the net bag to keep it extended. To be successful the gear must be watched permanently, otherwise it will not work. But there are other types of bagnet, important for river fisheries, which do not need to be watched. These are large bagnets with the typical frame for the opening, fixed firmly in running waters against the current, and they are known as gape nets or stow nets. This gear, too, is derived from older models constructed of materials other than netting. In the fisheries of eastern and southeastern Europe, there existed wooden constructions built in running waters in the shape of large funnels with rectangular openings of wooden rods arranged in parallel. Today this gear is made of netting and is operated in many running waters, particularly in large rivers and estuaries, but also in the open sea when a current is available to keep the gear in a catching position. Often these bagnets are set in barriers, as in Europe for catching eels, and elsewhere for catching fish and shrimps. In this case the gear is usually designed for long-term operation (*Figs 432* and *433*).

Fig 432 Barrier for stow net in the lower Danube near Braila in Rumania. In the middle of the barrier, there is a gap for the fishing gear; on the right side, an opening for passing boats (1976).

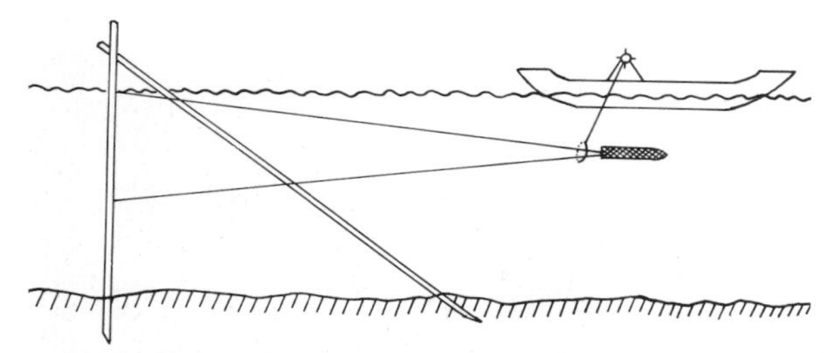

Fig 433 Stow net ending in a wooden trap behind a barrier in Kampuchea. (*Fily and d'Aubentin, 1965*).

With gape nets there are two problems: how to control the entrance of fish into the gear and how to prevent them from escaping. To detect that fish are in the gear, warning strings – so-called 'feelers – 'are used. One of the ends is tied inside the net bag; the other is held by the watching fisherman so that he can feel the fish if it touches one of the lines as it enters the gear. *Figure 434* shows an old Russian drawing of the entrance of a stow net with eight feelers, as operated in the sea of Azov during the last century. Such warning lines were known in many parts of Europe,[279] and although used mainly with gape nets, they can also be used as messenger lines with other types of fishing gear. When a fish is located by feeling, the gear has to be hauled quickly because, originally, there was no retarding device in the gear. As with the archaic tubular traps (Chapter 16), the fish is pressed into the stow net on the current. To prevent fish escaping, stow nets are now often fitted at the end with a fishing trap, fyke net or basket (*Fig 433*) which retards the fish by valves or a funnel-shaped throat of netting inside the gape net. This is the reason why, in fishing gear classification, gape nets are sometimes grouped together with traps. But in contrast to fishing traps, all bagnets, including gape nets, need some water current flowing through them to be effective.

Stow nets can be stationary gear, fixed for a long time at the same place in rows. They can also be operated from a vessel, when they become movable gear which can change the fishing place very easily when wanted. The simplest form are single stow nets kept open by a complete frame (*Fig 434*). When set in a row the frames are replaced by stakes (*Figs 435* and *436*). There are also 'stake nets' with cross-shaped split bamboos in their opening, as described from the 'kona jel', a common stow net row of the lower River Brahmaputra.[282] Bagnets can also be used without the typical frame. The entrance of the bag is held open in another way. This is also possible with large stationary gape nets when rigged in a special manner. *Figure 437* shows a row of frameless stow nets in the River Mosel. The nets are set before the outlet of a barrier and, with the help of lines, the net bags can be towed to and fro like a curtain to bring them into a fishing position in the river and to tow them back, with the catch, to the shore. The setting of stow nets on stakes becomes difficult where deep water and hard bottoms are found. Here the development is the same as that already described for the use of trap nets. The stakes are replaced by anchors. Such bagnets, anchored at the bottom and floating free, are known in many countries, like the English swing nets formerly operated in the River Thames (*Fig 438*). Other types will be mentioned later in the context of stow nets used in sea fisheries.

19.7 Stow nets with vessels

Very often one or two stow nets are fastened to a vessel, from which they are operated.[309] This has

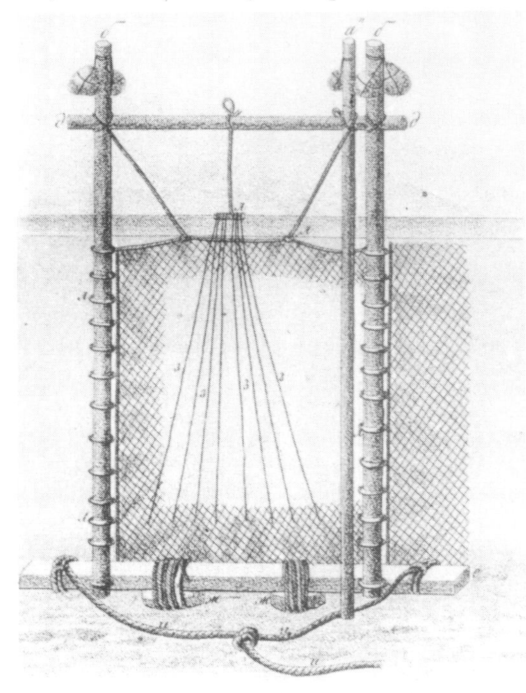

Fig 434 Old Russian drawing (Azov Sea, 1871) showing the opening of a stow net with eight feeler-lines for controlling fish entering the gear.

Fig 435 German stow nets as used in the river Weser. (*Photo: G Klust.*)

Fig 436 Indian stow nets from Kerala, South India. In the foreground, stow nets are drying and behind, in the river, the sticks for fixing the nets can be seen.

Fig 437 Set stow nets not fixed on sticks or anchors but mounted on lines which allow them to be towed to the shore and back like a curtain in the River Mosel, Germany. (*Photo: G Jens, 1979.*)

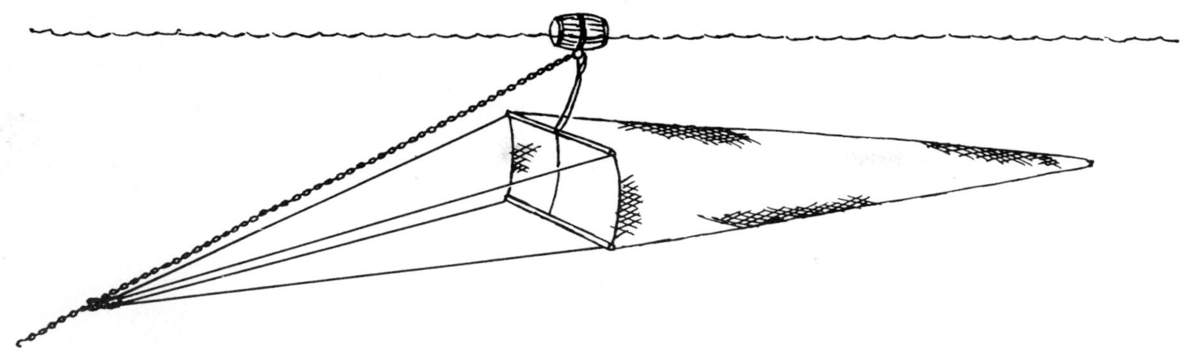

Fig 438 The English swing net. (*Davis, 1958*).

Fig 439 Full-framed stow net in the River Mosel.

some advantages when fishing in rivers and river estuaries with much traffic. In this case, the gape net vessels are able to avoid transport vessels and convoys if necessary. Stow nets operated from vessels can be kept open by a complete frame as used with the stow nets of the River Mosel and Elbe (*Figs 439* and *440*). One of the famous river stow nets is the so-called 'Ankerkuile' or 'Schokker net', named after the vessel from which this gape net is operated in the River Rhine and some other large rivers in Europe. This gear originated in the Netherlands and the lower part of the River Rhine for eel fishing. About the year 1900, the gear spread from the middle Rhine to other rivers of northwest Germany. By the introduction of this gear, the commercial fishery boomed in the first decade of this century.[331] As with other bagnets, the gear has a reduced frame – in this case consisting of floating upper beam and a weighted under beam only (*Fig 441*). Moreover, it is remarkable that the vessel equipped with the 'Schokker' is not mechanized. The vessel is anchored by long cables and is shifted simply by these cables being shortened or extended.

19.8 Stow nets in sea fisheries

Generally speaking, stow nets are fishing gear for fresh waters, especially for rivers and river estuaries. In the open sea, gape nets are rarely used because they are too much affected by the weather. Moreover, a permanent current is necessary. A favourable site for marine stow net fishery exists around the south and west coasts of Korea. Here the Koreans use anchored gape nets held by boats; the openings of the nets are not kept apart by a

Fig 440 German framed gape nets as used on either side of a vessel on the River Elbe.

Fig 441 'Schokker' on the River Rhine. The net is hanging from the mast for drying.

frame but, like the Schokker nets of the River Rhine, by two beams only – a bamboo bundle at the top and a weighted beam below (*Fig 442*). Originally, one net only was operated by each boat but for some years now the operation of two gears, one on each side of the vessel, has made this fishery more effective.[312] The Korean stow nets are now set with an anchor each and are no longer connected to the vessel. By this method each vessel can operate up to four stow nets. Moreover, the vessels are now motorized, and the formerly hand-driven capstan has been replaced by a powered one, driven from the main engine. The hauling of the gear is now much quicker and less labour is needed. Finally, the bulky bamboo bundle used as float and upper frame of the net bag is replaced by a closed steel tube, not because of the increasing shortage of bamboo, but because it is more convenient to handle, being

Fig 442 Korean stow net used in sea fishery. The beams (an upper bunch of bamboo and a lower one weighted with stones as can be seen at the left) are hauled and the catch is set onboard (1960).

smaller and lighter. The lower sinker beam is also of steel. Of great interest is that pieces of clothing are used as underwater sails or kites to increase the opening of the gear (*Fig 443*).

There are more place in Asia where stow nets are operated in sea fisheries, maybe with the help of the tidal current. The 'pompang' of Malaysia is a completely frameless stow net for fishing in deeper water and is held open by floats and bottom stakes (*Fig 444*). In Malaysia and Indonesia also, stationary arrangements for long time fishing are known in sea fisheries. In Malaysia these platforms are called 'kelong' and can be combined like the 'ambai' in Indonesia with a frameless stow net (*Fig 445*). However, they are mostly used for fishing with lift nets (Chapter 27, *Fig 626*).

19.9 Gape nets with wings

All types of stow nets mentioned up till now are typical bagnets, with an opening held by a more or less complete frame and a bag stretched by the water current. But there are some types with wings also for guiding fish or shrimp into the bag. As has been shown in connection with traps (Chapter 16), such guiding arrangements can be fences made of different materials, including netting, but they can be a row of stakes only, which guide the prey into the gear. In Malaysia, Singapore and Indonesia, such stow nets with swinging guiding lines can be placed miles away from the coast. In this case they have to be combined with a working platform and houses to give shelter for the fishermen, who need a cooking place for their own food and also for cooking the catch before drying it (*Fig 445*). A hand-operated winch is installed on the platform for operating the gear. The stow net hangs from the platform for fishing operations and a frame is no longer necessary.

This is also the case with other winged stow nets. In North Carolina (USA), such a winged gear is used for shrimp fishing in tidal currents (*Fig 446a*). The origin of this so-called 'channel net' is said to have been a trawl set between two anchored boats.[216] This became such a success that trawl-like stow nets with wings were specially made for this purpose. This explains why, sometimes, stow nets are defined as 'stationary trawls'.[654] As with modern trawls, the anchored gear is held open not by a

Fig 443 Korean stow net with underwater sails to keep the gear open. (*Photo: Kwan Soh Ko, Busan*).

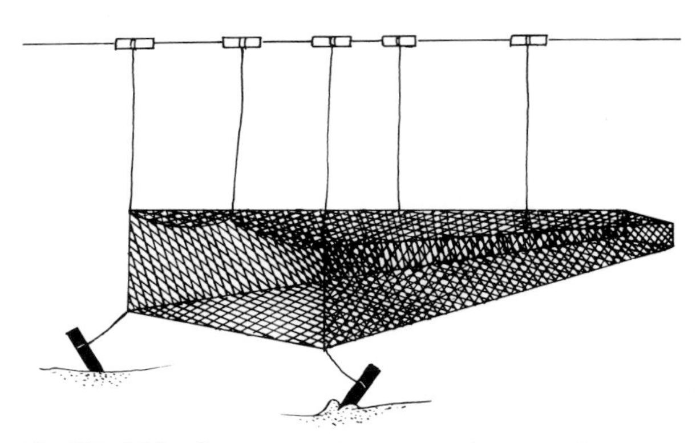

Fig 444 Malaysian stow net known as a 'pompang'.

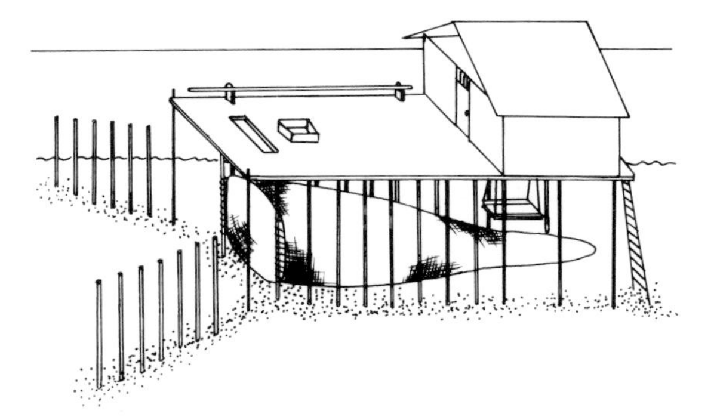

Fig 445 A watched Indonesian stow net ('ambai') with guiding sticks set under an artificial platform in the open sea. (*Yamamoto, 1975*).

complete or partial frame, but by a system of floats and sinkers, and sometimes also by spreading sticks as known from other types of fishing gear (*Fig 483*). Such winged stow nets are also used in other parts of the world (*Fig 446b*).

Highly developed types of winged stow nets are the otter board stow nets.[319] This gear, used without vessel in the Rivers Elbe and Weser, can be used to fish in a shipping channel and yet be able to avoid hindering the shipping, which is not possible with other types of winged stow nets on stakes or anchors. The gear consists of a bagnet with two wings added to the net in order to cover a large area of the river to be fished (*Fig 447*). One wing is connected to the river bank while the other is attached to a large otter board which is kept floating by large tin containers. The use of otter boards in currents has already been mentioned in connection with line fishing (Chapter 8) as being one of the elements typical of the effective construction and use of fishing gear. The board, set obliquely towards the current, pulls the entrance of the bagnet wide open and thus takes over the function of the frame. In this case the otter board has a controlling wing which can be operated from the bank. By shifting it, the otter board's position can be changed. It then no longer shears away from the bank and stretches the net, but is pressed by the current in the opposite direction, namely, against the bank, thus closing the net. In that way, the otter board stow net can, if necessary, be moved out of the way of shipping and be returned again to the current once the vessel has passed. This is an ingenious method of fishing with stow nets, with relatively little effort, in waterways where there is much traffic. At the same time, the otter board stow net must be regarded as the most advanced gear of that type. It is very effective, but its efficiency is threatened by water pollution which is causing trouble for all types of river stow nets and many other fishing gears used in the rivers of industrial countries.

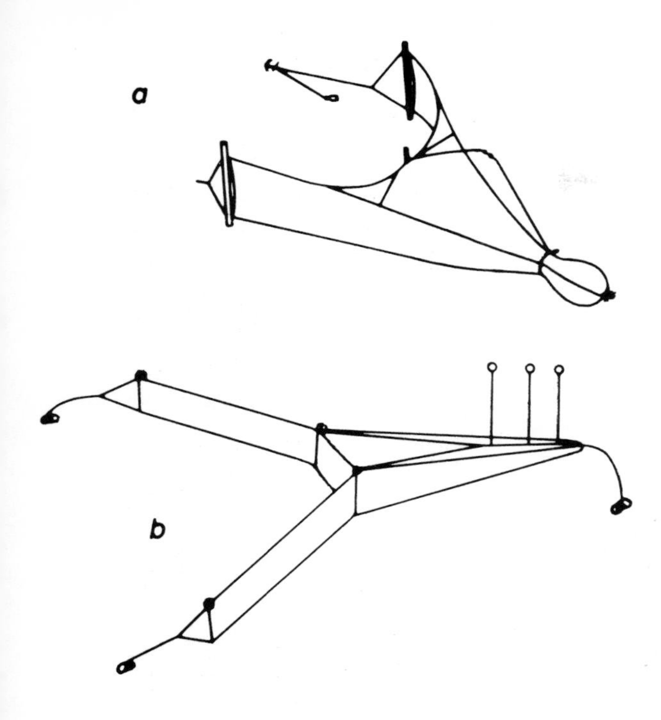

Fig 446 Stow nets with wings: (*a*) American channel net (*Guthrie, 1966*); (*b*) Korean 'long bag' stow net (*NN, 1968/70*).

19.10 Closeable stow nets

Before eel fishing with 'Schokker' nets was introduced in the fishery of the River Rhine, another type of gear was typical of this river. The net can be considered a 'closeable stow net', and was designed specially for catching salmon during the night. This was the so-called 'Salmenwaage' (salmon balance). It is an endemic gear developed a long time ago, and was already known in the fifteenth century. The 'Salmenwaage' was a large bagnet operated from a pontoon-like vessel (*Fig 448*) anchored broadside on to the river at places behind barriers where the salmon like to rest in the counter-current. The bag was kept open by counterweights but could be closed with the help of two, three or four levers (*Fig 449*) as soon as the

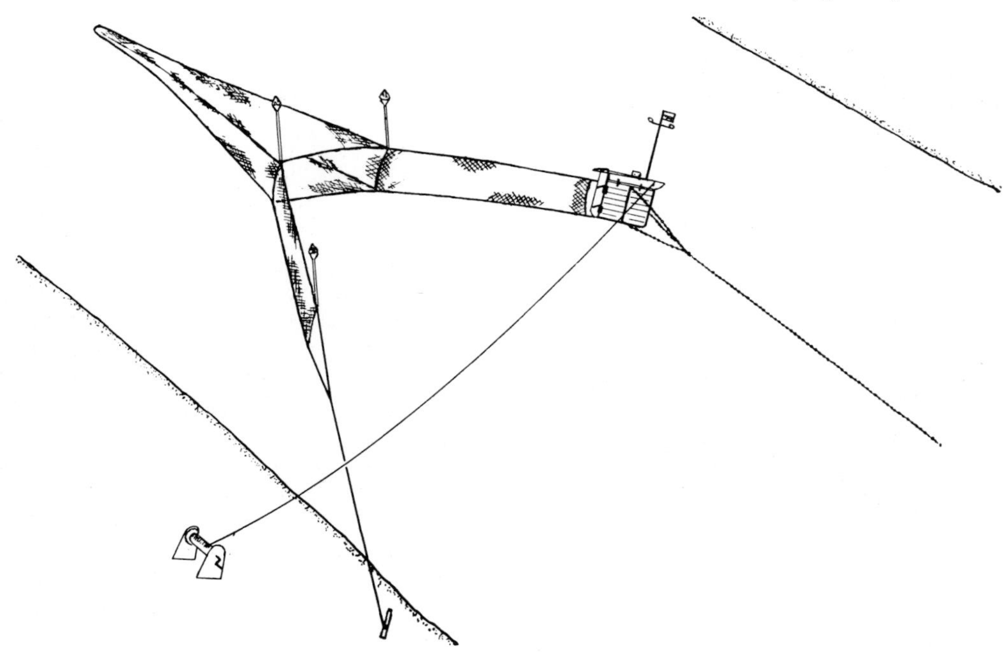

Fig 447 An otter board stow net, as introduced in European river fisheries by master fisherman Hugo Koethke in 1936.

watching fisherman, keeping some part of the netting in his left hand, could feel a fish touch the netting. The gear is no longer used today. The fishery stopped at the end of the thirties when the salmon fishery collapsed completely in the River Rhine.[49, 50]

The idea of using a closeable and watched stow net is also known in another part of the world, where it is still used today. For catching hilsa, (*Clupea ilisha*) an anadromous clupeid, in the River Ganga, a transportable stow net, with some variations in its form, is operated.[192, 261] The gear is constructed of two sheets of rectangular or polygonal netting, resembling a very large old type purse for small coins (*Fig 450*). This bag is suspended with two ropes from a dinghy drifting down with the current of the river. Its opening is framed with bamboo and can be closed by a closing-cum-hauling rope as soon as fish have entered the bag. This can be controlled by a feeler rope, branching in two to four lines, connected with the surface netting of the gear and held taut in the hand of a fisherman. As soon as a signal is felt, the net will be closed and hauled for emptying. The boat is then paddled upstream and allowed to drift down again. During the season, sometimes two of these nets may be operated by a single vessel.

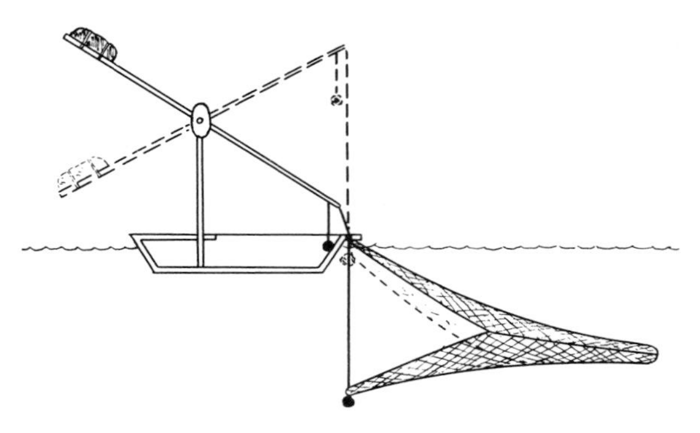

Fig 449 Principle for opening and closing the bag of a 'Salmenwaage'.

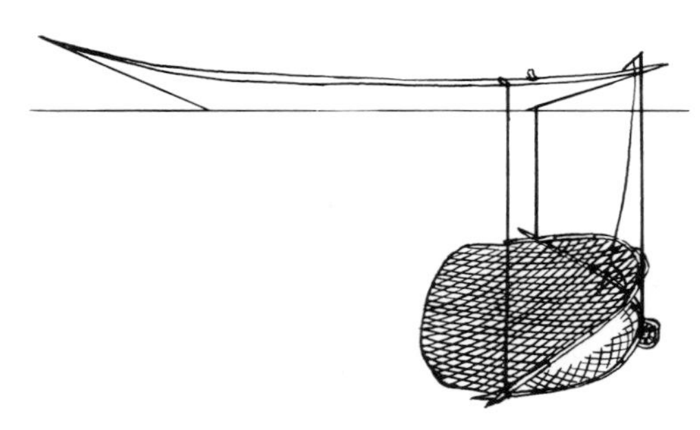

Fig 450 Closable stow net for catching hilsa in the River Ganges. (*Hornell, 1950*).

Fig 448 'Salmenwaage' (salmon-balance) formerly operated in the River Rhine with four balanced-beams operated near Xanten (till 1949). (*Böcking, 1967*).

Chapter twenty

Dredges and beamtrawls

In the last chapter it has been demonstrated that bagnets can not only be pushed over the bottom before a wading fisherman or before a slowly moving boat; they can also be thrown behind them onto the seabed, especially when more power is needed for scraping or scratching the surface of the bottom. This is especially true when digging into the bottom for shellfish living on, or in, the seabed deposits. This can be done not only with towed bagnets or scoop nets but also with iron rakes which, according to their type of teeth, are especially suitable for removing animals living deep in the seabed. But rakes have the disadvantage that the prey dug out has to be collected later on, usually by hand, unless the rake has a special form (*Figs 89b* and *89c*) or is combined with a bag made of netting to store and secure the raked-up catch until it is brought out of the water (*Fig 89d*). In this case, such combined gear is considered as a scratcher or dredge, even when the tines or teeth are replaced by sharp edges of a strong frame at the opening of the bagnet (*Fig 451*). Different forms of such towed bagnets, and other developments like dredges and beamtrawls, are used in fisheries to drag out sedentary and bottom-dwelling animals like mussels, snails, sea cucumbers and sponges, and also some crustaceans and flat fish in shallow or deep water. Here also a dragged gear of an unusual construction has to be mentioned; that is the runner net (in German 'Kufennetz'), used for catching near-bottom fishes in shallow waters in eastern Europe. The gear was popular till the beginning of this century (*Fig 733*).[30, 343, 381, 589]

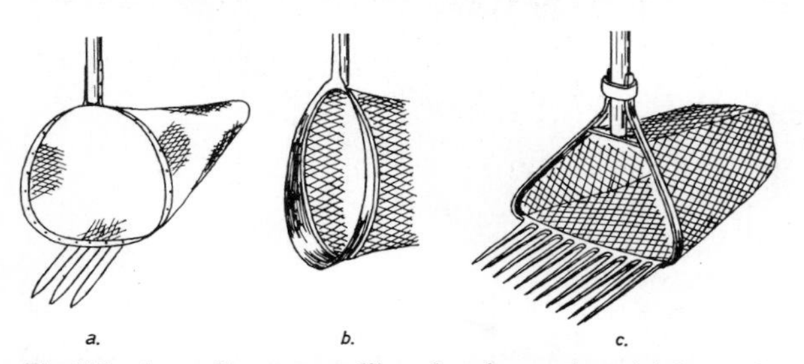

Fig 451 A small scoop net like a hand scratcher: (*a*) formerly used in Malta with three prongs only (*Burdon, 1956*); (*b*) with a sharp edge on the frame; (*c*) Japanese form with a wire prong (*NN, 1959*).

20.1 Hand-operated scratchers

Hand-operated scratchers are types of fishing gear that can be found all over the world in different forms and with various methods of operation. They can be small baskets made of branches or wire, as used by Malaysian fishermen to separate cockles from the mud during low tide (*Fig 452*). For this, no vessel can be used, nor can the fisherman wade over the soft and very deep bottom mud. Here, mud sledges are used, as they are all over the world – even in areas of neglected fishing technology – to catch prey in this dangerous ground and transport it to the shore.[429, 516, 517] Gliding with the mud sledge over the ground, the fisherman draws the small basket by hand through the surface of the mud to dig out the cockles and wash them free of mud and sand (*Fig 452*).

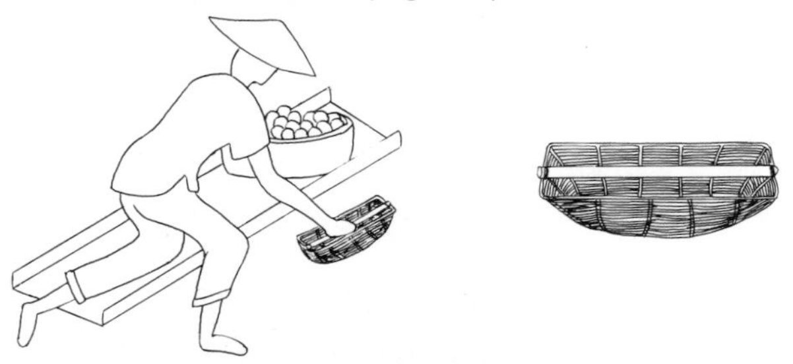

Fig 452 Hand-operated scratcher gear for separating mussels out of the mud in Malaysia, west coast. The fisherman operates the gear from a mud sledge (1978).

In general, the scratchers used in fisheries are large ones combined with a long stick (*Fig 453*), resembling long-handled scoop nets with a strong framed opening. The so-called pole scratchers used by biologists for scratching organisms from the bottom, from stones, from poles, *etc*, are designed in that manner. Their fishing bag consists of netting or strong fabric or, in the case of heavier gear like the American clam rakes used by commercial fishermen, of rigid material – in particular wire mesh. That is especially necessary if mussels with their sharp edges are to be gathered, as otherwise they would soon destroy the netting. The fishermen operate these devices by means of long handles, which enable them to push the rake or scratcher into the bottom as far as can be reached from the beach or from an anchored boat. The gear is then dragged back in such a manner as to scratch over the bottom. For deeper water, the handles of these scratchers can be very long, even up to six or seven metres in length. Iron-framed hand scratchers of that type can be found in use in many fishiers, especially for shellfish digging, or for collecting small mud-dwelling animals needed for bait.

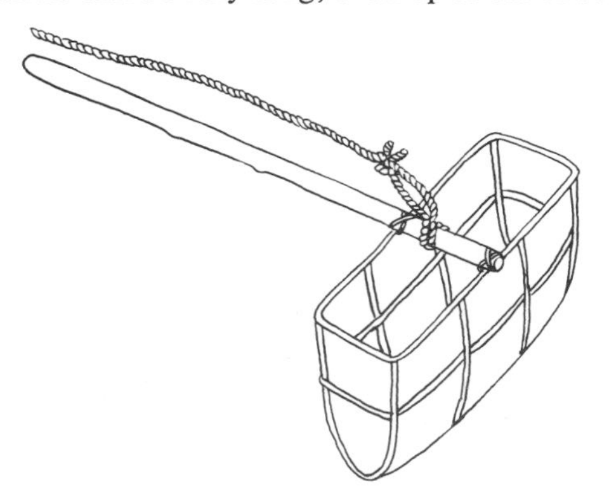

Fig 453 Dredge basket made of wire with supporting line. (Malaysia, west coast, 1978).

20.2 Boat dredges

The handling of larger and heavier scratchers, by means of long rods or sticks from a fixed place or boat, is rather tedious. It also becomes impossible to simply drag them over the bottom with the hand. Then, a better way is for the scratcher to be pressed against the bottom while the boat itself is driven forward. Almost the same gear is used as for hand operation, but the implement can be heavier and the bag larger. Some of these boat-operated scratchers have frames like push nets, like the 'qoofa' gear used for shrimp fishing in Kuwait with each side 3·5 metres in length (*Fig 454*). This gear, with its wooden frame and the long handle, is similar to the hand-operated dredges. The same can be said of the Italian 'draga a rastrello', even though the handle of this dredge is a short one. For operating the gear when digging wedge shells (*Donax trunculus*) out of the mud, a small hand-operated winch is used. With increasing depth and heavier gear, the stick for handling the scratcher is completely discarded, or retained only for guiding purposes. The gear now becomes a real dredge – towed by a vessel and characterized by a

Fig 454 Shrimp vessel with two long-handled dredges in the harbour of Kuwait. The push-net-like frames are to be seen, the net bags hang for drying on the left side (1970).

frame opening low in height in comparison with its width (*Fig 455*). The lower opening edge is often sharpened or provided with rake-like teeth (*Fig 456*). The upper edge can have a pressure plate at an angle of 30° to 35° in order to press the gear close to or into the bottom as it is towed.[365] The shape of these dredges can vary quite a lot, as they are known in many parts of the world and are locally manufactured (*Fig 455*). Their size, shape and construction will also vary according to preference, size of operation, and also type of bottom. For the same reason also, the material from which the collecting bags of the dredges are made varies widely. Smaller types are made of netting (*Fig 457*), heavier ones of wire or iron rings held together with clips. The Dutch shellfish dredge (*Fig 458*) used in northwest Europe, has an upper part made of nylon netting and a lower part made of iron rings.[160] At the end of the bag, an iron rod is fastened for better handling of the gear. Also, a hollow iron roller is fixed on the gear to give it support when gliding over the ground. Generally, this type of dredge has no teeth, but heavier ones, with teeth, are known (*Fig 456*). The dredge for the American scallop (*Placopecten magellanicus*) is similar to a large-sized Dutch dredge,[141, 536] and, until recently, was almost exclusively operated by boats in this fishery. Sometimes these dredges are of very heavy construction.[496] The narrow rectangular frame is made of steel and has a sharp underbar which scrapes the bottom, digging out the shellfish which pass into the collecting bag. The upper part of the frame is connected with the towing arms. The lower part of the collecting bag and the rear end of the

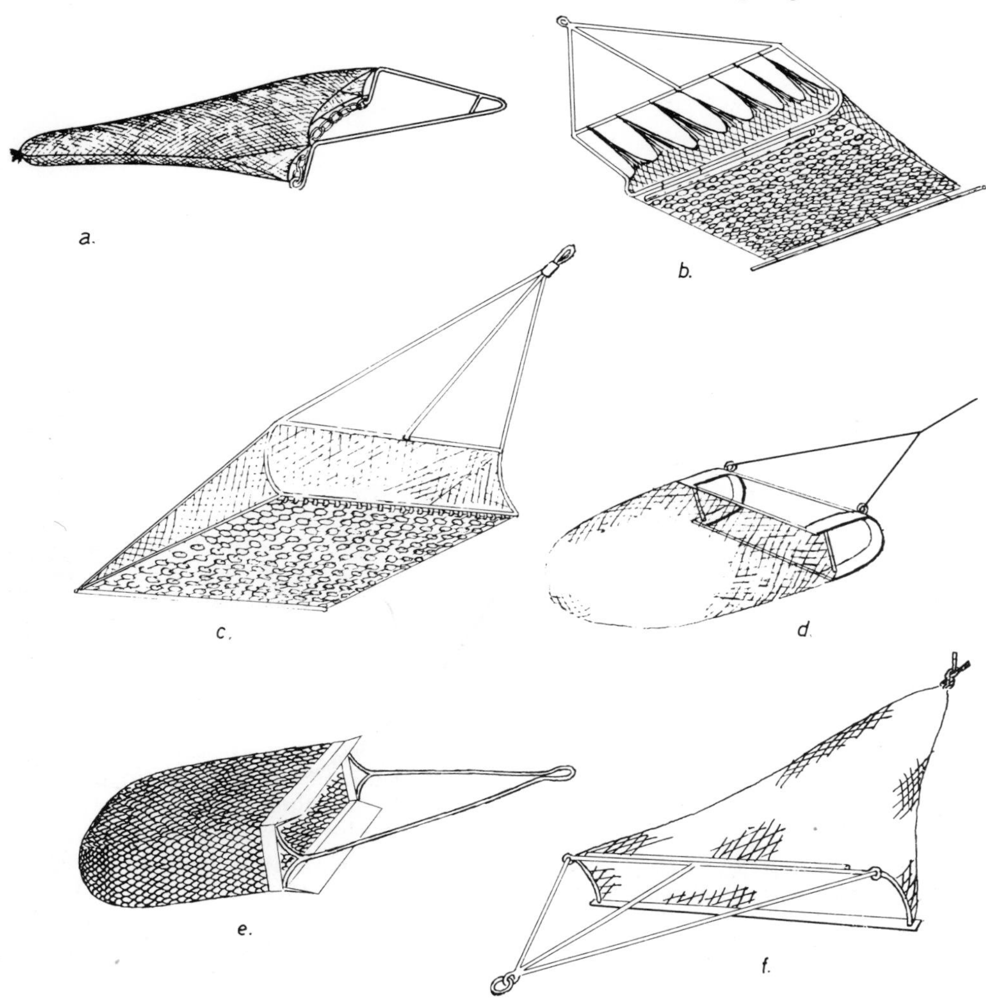

Fig 455 Different types of dredges: (*a*) small German 'trynet' for shrimp; (*b*) Dutch mussel dredge; (*c*) French type (*Boudarel, 1948*); (*d*) Japanese 'manga' net; (*e*) Russian type of the Black Sea (*NN, 1952*); (*f*) shellfish dredge of Ireland.

Fig 456 French dredge, Dutch type, with teeth for the collecting of venus-shells. (*Photo: R Piboubes, Brest.*)

Fig 457 Icelandic 'kúhfiskplógur' for dredging *Arctica islandica.* (*Photo: G Thorsteinsson, 1968.*)

upper parts are made of steel rings. The rest is made of strong netting yarn.

Quite another type of boat dredge is operated on the French Atlantic coast. For catching mussels, scallops and venus long box-like dredges are used, made of long iron rods (*Fig 459*). Smaller types can end in a bag of strong netting. On the light outside curved lower part of the opening, teeth can be fixed, but they are forbidden in some places and they are then replaced by a sharp blade, shearing downwards (*Fig 460*). Smaller types of boat dredges are dragged by rowing or sailing boats. Sometimes the boat is pushed forward by hauling with its winch along a line fastened to a pole which is driven into the ground ahead or is attached to an anchor. The dredge can also be towed by the winch of an anchored vessel. An original idea for moving the boat forward, and consequently also a fishing gear, is to use a submarine sail. Such sails were known in Europe 200 years ago. The French encyclopaedists of the eighteenth century reproduced in their illustrations submarine sails such as were used by the French coastal fishery to set before vessels and nets. These real sailing cloths, suspended from a beam, floated on the surface of the water and were driven forward by the current, slowly dragging after them both the nets and the boat.[133, 554] Even today in Far Eastern underwater operations, sails are used for towing dredges and other gear (*Fig 492*).[294] The fishermen of the Tanshui River in northern Taiwan use for sails flat plaited baskets (*Figs 461* and *491*). The boats are towed broadside by five or six such baskets in the tidal waters as they tow long-handled scratchers through the mud to catch small mussels (*Meretrix meretrix* L).[73, 108]

Fig 458 Dutch shellfish dredge, upside down, with netting on the upper side and a mat of rings on the lower side.

Fig 459 Large French dredge for catching venus shells with gallows and arrangement for the operation of the gear. Erquy, Baie de St. Brueuc. (*Photo: R Piboubes, Brest.*)

Fig 460 French dredge without teeth, which are replaced by a sharp-edged blade shearing downwards. (*Photo: R Piboubes, Brest.*)

In modern dredging, powered vessels usually tow two dredges, one on each side. Sometimes more may be operated from a single vessel (*Fig 462*), in which case special arrangements are made to tow the dredges with beams, and to haul and shoot them by means of hand-operated or, nowadays, mostly powered hydraulic winches. As mentioned before, dredges are considered especially suitable for mussel fishing by digging the animals from the bottom and separating them from the mud. In this manner, boat dredges are used in the mussel fisheries of East Asia, North America, Australia and western Europe. Mussels have a good market all over the world and this fact may have encouraged the improvement and modernization of dredging. Powered vessels made it possible to use larger and heavier dredges, but heavier dredges also need mechanical handling. The Italian dredge operated in the area of Venice is an example of a heavy but good mechanized dredge operated by a special gallows from the bow of the vessel (*Fig 463*). When fishing, the boat is anchored with a long wire and, after setting the dredge, the vessel, together with the gear, is towed backward

Fig 461 Mussel dredging in the Tanshui River, North Taiwan. The boat is towed broadside by underwater sails made of bamboo as can be seen behind. On the boat, longhandled dredges are fixed; three of their sticks can be seen. (1969).

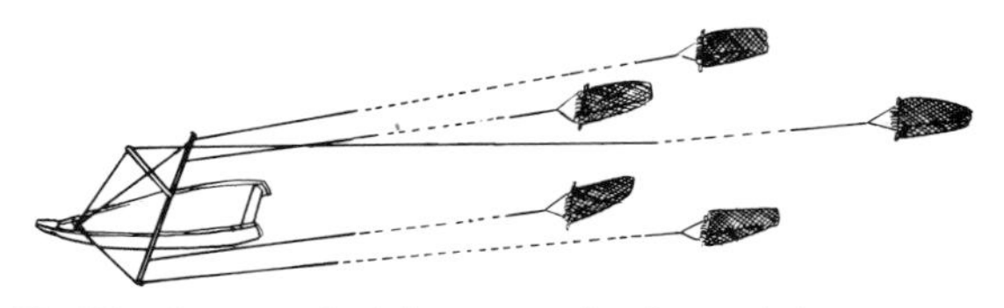

Fig 462 Japanese dredging system for clams, shrimps, prawns, flatfish and sea cucumber. (*NN, 1959*).

by a small winch (*Fig 464*). This is a technique very often used in dredging. Moreover, water jets from two tubes connected to the dredge, wash out deeper-sited shells, which are collected in the wire basket of the dredge. The catch can be brought on board the vessel when the dredge is hauled in, by a system which is often used with trucks which are emptied very quickly by lifting one end of the platform. The shells are washed in a washing machine on the vessel and packed into bags for the market. A similar dredge is used in fishing for scallops in Australia (*Fig 465*). In this case, the old system of towing the vessel to an anchor is abandoned, and the dredge is towed from the stern of the vessel like a trawl.[417]

A disadvantage of dredges is that they are not highly efficient harvesters. Tests have shown that they collect only a small proportion of the shells in their path. Moreover, many are badly damaged.[283] Dredges are also ineffective when the shells sit deeper in the mud – like some mussels do when, for example, the salinity is decreased in rainy seasons. The problem of digging out shells more carefully and in greater quantities when they are deep in the mud has been solved, to some extent, by using high pressure jets of water with the dredge. When large quantities of mussels are caught, other systems of hauling the catch out of the water are by suction pumps or conveyer belts. By these improvements the dredge becomes a quite different type of fishing gear. It is no longer a simple fishing gear as described at the beginning of this chapter but has become an integrated fishing system like a harvesting machine, which will be discussed in Chapter 31.

Finally, it has to be added that not only living mussels can be gathered in this way; dredges are also used for collecting mussel grit for producing lime. In Sao Vicente, one of the islands of Cape Verde, the inhabitants use simple hand dredges to collect coal from the bottom of the harbour in Mindelo.

Fig 463 Italian mussel dredge in the area of Venice during transport from or to the fishing place. (1975). The dredge is mounted on the bow of the vessel.

Fig 464 Italian mussel dredge in the area of Venice during fishing. The boat is towed backwards on a wire towards an anchor. (1975).

Fig 465 Australian scallop dredge mounted on the stern of a vessel. (*Photo: R Wawrowski, 1979*).

By this technique, marine snails, *Murex* sp. are also caught and used for bait and food.

20.3 Beamtrawling

Bottom fish can also be caught by means of dredges but, generally speaking, dredges cannot be regarded as specific gear for catching fish as distinct from shellfish. The opening of the dredges used for shellfish is too small, and the towing speed so low, that even a lazy fish can escape with a slight movement. This means that to catch fish the gear should have at least a wider and a higher opening. Then, those fish which stay on the bottom, as some flatfish do, may be caught. There are dredges that have been specially developed to catch flatfish. The principle used is the same as that in mussel or shrimp dredging: a frame keeps the bagnet open and special implements, such as rake-like prongs, can be fitted to the lower edge for digging the fish from the bottom and rousing them (*Fig 466*), as already described for the dredges. The only difference is that the rectangular frame is much larger than for dredges used in shellfish fisheries, and the bag is longer and more slender.

In towing, however, a square frame is a hampering implement, particularly on uneven ground or when a high towing speed is necessary (*Fig 467a*). Therefore, the lower transverse beam of the original frame, which kept the net open in a horizontal direction, can be removed and also the teeth or digging blades, but the remaining upper beam is retained along the upper edge (*Fig 467c*) or is fitted more into the centre of the net opening

Fig 466 Italian beamtrawl used to catch flatfish. The gear is shown upside down. The lower part is visible and beneath it is the upper part with a board for pressing the gear to the bottom.

(*Fig 467b*), as is done with the so called 'plumb staff type' of beamtrawl operated in Alaska and northern America for catching shrimp.[417] The two shorter lateral parts of the frame are usually still retained in their places to keep the net open vertically; these can, however, be converted into guides (called shoes, or iron runners, *etc*) to secure easier movement by sliding over the bottom (*Figs 467d* and *468*).

The horizontal transverse beam is considered to be typical of these nets and therefore they are called 'beamtrawls' (*Fig 468*). The beamtrawls are the simplest type of modern bottom trawls. Several models of them are employed in the northwest European fisheries as well as in the Mediterranean. The first European trawlers used beam trawls for capturing flatfish. Beamtrawls are also used off the African coast and in North American waters, although to a lesser extent. They have been, and are even now, sometimes widely used in the Far East. There have been, also, some other ideas to facilitate the movement of a beamtrawl over the bottom. One of them is to fit the gear with wheels. This idea is not new. It has been proposed from time to time, but without success – with two exceptions; the Turkish 'kankava' beamtrawl with two or three wheels, used for harvesting sponges, and the Taiwanese three-wheel beamtrawl for shrimp fishing. In contrast to the gear operated in Taiwan, the Turkish beamtrawl with wheels seems to be an old endemic invention. This gear generally has two

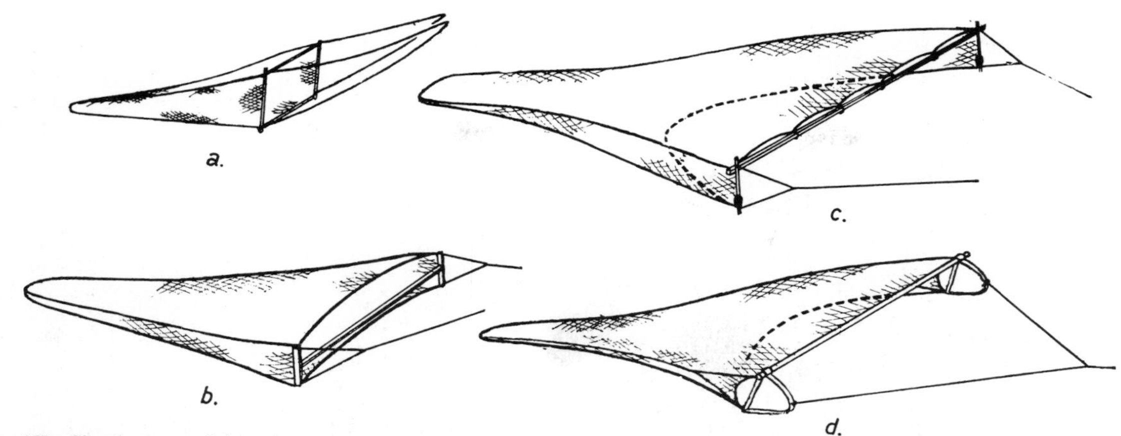

Fig 467 Simple types of dragging gear: (*a*) towed stow net; (*b*) 'Keitel' of Curishe and Frische Haff (both are lagoons on the southern coast of the Baltic); (*c*) Japanese beamtrawl; (*d*) modern European beamtrawl for shrimps.

Fig 468 German double-rig beamtrawls for shrimp fishing.

iron wheels, one on each end of the beam, a steel tube of four to ten metres in length (by law no more than nine metres) (*Fig 469*). With the longer beams, two bags of netting can be operated and three wheels may support the beam (*Fig 470*).[384] The Chinese beamtrawl with three wheels was introduced into the fishery of Taiwan some years ago. The wooden wheels have only a small diameter of 20 to 40 centimetres and the beam has a total length of ten metres. The wheels are fixed on both ends and in the middle of the beam (*Fig 471*). Two bagnets are towed with one beam, but they can be constructed differently. It may be operated with two simple net bags or two traditional shrimp beam trawls with two codends each. Some of these beam trawls can be electrified (*Fig 472*) to chase up the shrimps, especially in daytime fishing (see the last section of this chapter).

Beamtrawls with a single upper beam supported by a gliding shoe on each end, are mostly operated for fishing and shrimping. Originally, the net bag of the beamtrawl was a completely uniform bag, possibly composed of congruent upper and lower parts and maybe also of two lateral sections, like the net bags of stow nets and dredges. More modern patterns have a receding notched edge at the lower net, or a protruding upper net which is typical of all modern bottom trawls (*Figs 473b* and *473c*). It is through the beams that the net can be kept open in a horizontal direction. But as mentioned before that extension is limited, in that the gear becomes more and more unwieldy as the beam becomes bigger and longer. Thus, in practice, the beam without wheels can scarcely be much longer than six to eight metres. Nevertheless, the longest used for flatfish extends to twelve metres. In Europe, the smallest are operated by rowing boats on the River Tejo near Lisbon. Here the beams are not more than two metres in length. Sometimes the beam is placed more forward of the net opening (*Fig 473*). In this case the bagnet can have wings, to the points of which the beam is fitted (*Fig 473b*). The beam may even be set further forward yet and so spread

Fig 469 Turkish vessel with a beamtrawl ('kankava') with two nets and two wheels for collecting sponges. (*Mengi, 1977*).

Fig 471 Chinese beamtrawl with three wheels for shrimping; in the harbour of Kaohsiung, Taiwan, (1978).

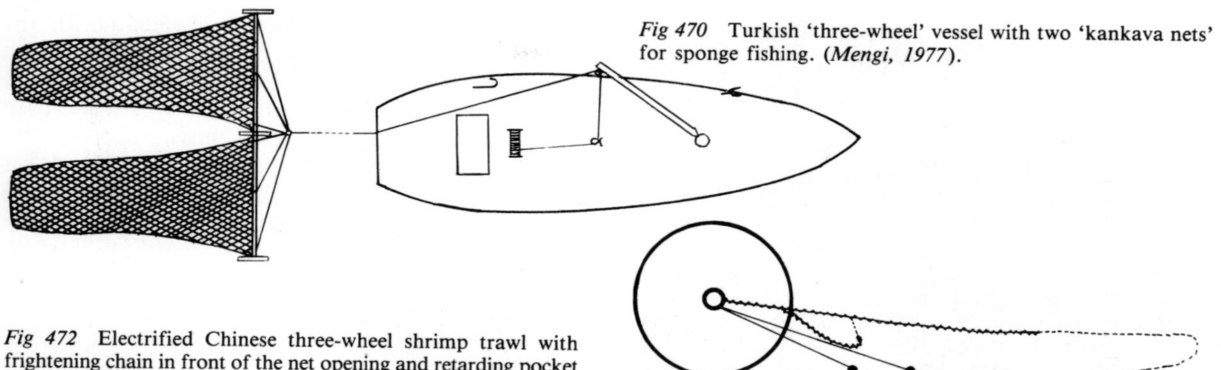

Fig 470 Turkish 'three-wheel' vessel with two 'kankava nets' for sponge fishing. (*Mengi, 1977*).

Fig 472 Electrified Chinese three-wheel shrimp trawl with frightening chain in front of the net opening and retarding pocket near the headline.

the drag lines, as was formerly done in the Baltic (*Fig 473c*). But there may be some doubt as to whether these are true beamtrawls or whether they are regular trawls additionally spread by sticks or beams. Modern beamtrawling is done according to the double-rig system, *ie* one beamtrawl on each side of the vessel (also called twin-trawling or twin-rig trawling) (*Fig 468*). Formerly the nets could be of different sizes but today they are always equal. Sometimes a smaller third beam trawl or a try-gear (*Fig 455a*) is operated from the stern of the vessel. Some attempts have also been made to tow beam trawls for shrimping in shallow water by tractors. In the UK, shrimp nets have also been towed by cars and trucks. Because it is not possible to fish with these vehicles beyond a certain depth of water, amphibious vehicles have been used successfully to tow beamtrawls in shrimping.[449]

In the shrimp fishery off the continental North Sea coast it is the beamtrawl that is nowadays mostly employed (*Fig 468*),[52] but less so for the capture of fish, with the exception of flatfish. For this purpose the beamtrawls have been altered. They became heavier, as with the big beamers of the Netherlands (*Fig 474*). The reason is that rows of 'tickler' chains (sweep chains) are added in front of the ground-rope of the beam trawl to scare up the flatfish, especially soles. This was done, originally, by the teeth and blades of the earlier dredge-like type of beamtrawls. Another interesting variation of the beamtrawl, looking like an American scallop dredge, is also used by the Dutch and some German fishermen to catch whelks.[72] In this case a large-meshed netting, made of chains, is fixed before the net opening to deflect stones (*Fig 475*). Fixing a square meshed netting before the

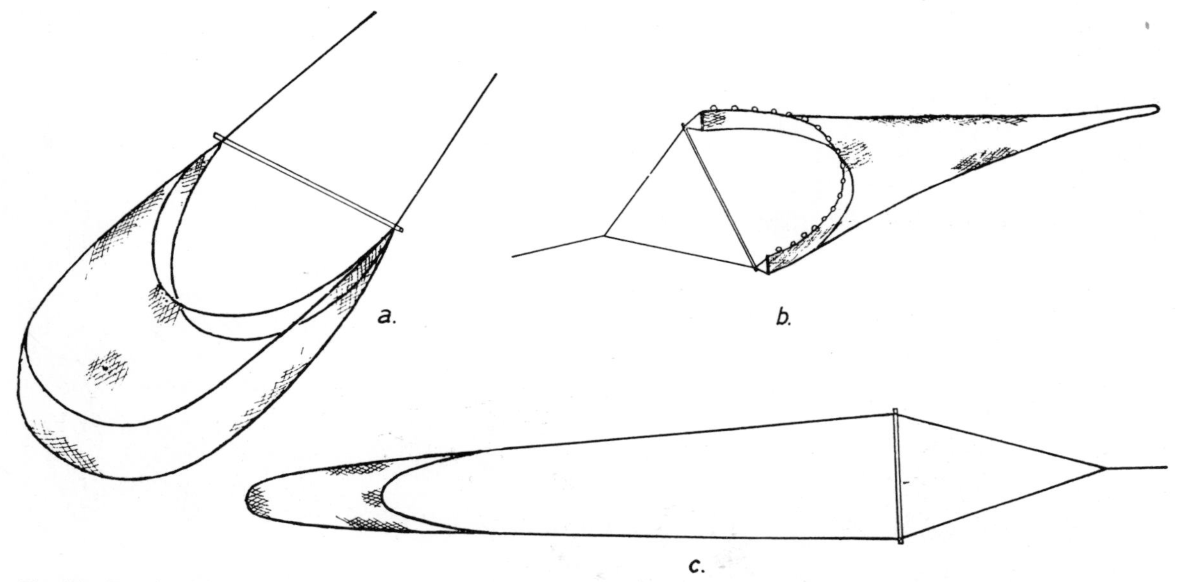

Fig 473 Trawls with the beam pulled forward: (*a*) 'gangui' of the Mediterranean; (*b*) old type of beamtrawl of California (*Scofield, 1948*); (*c*) old type of Baltic beamtrawl.

Fig 474 Heavy Dutch beamtrawl for sole fishing. (*Photo: R Steinberg.*)

opening of a dragged gear made of chains is also known with the American scallop dredges and, to some extent also with the Indian stow nets which have large meshed netting before their opening to repel seaweed and other unwanted matter. Using large and heavy netting made of chains before beamtrawls requires strong motors to deflect the stones. This is not possible for smaller vessels with low power, which would be stopped by such stones. However, the heavy chains used as tickler chains or as stone-repellent netting raised many objections because they were considered responsible for the destruction of the bottom of the sea and its fauna and vegetation.

Gear similar to dredges or beamtrawls is also used for fishing at a great depth, maybe deeper than 2,000 metres. In most cases, this is done for scientific investigations only. Such dredges are constructed in such a manner that both sides are the same and the dredge can fish regardless of which side is up or down. Some of them are well known in marine biological research work like the 'Agassiz-trawl' for catching demersal macro-fauna (*Fig 476*).

20.4 Electrified beamtrawls

As mentioned before, beamtrawls are used for catching fish, especially flatfish, and shrimps of different species. In both cases the wanted prey has to be stirred up off the bottom to come within the reach of the net opening. For this reason, so-called ticklers, tickler chains or sweep chains are placed before the net opening. In the fishery for soles these can be heavy steel chains. In the Netherlands up to eleven rows of chains with a total weight of more than two tons are used, towed by vessels of up to 3,000hp or more. It is thought that such a heavy gear towed across the bottom may be responsible for some destruction of the seabed, and this caused many objections, with the result that the gear was banned from some fishing grounds.

In shrimp fisheries electrified beamtrawls are operated in many areas of the world, such as northwest Europe, East Asia and North America.[55, 475] Therefore an electrical stimulation system for

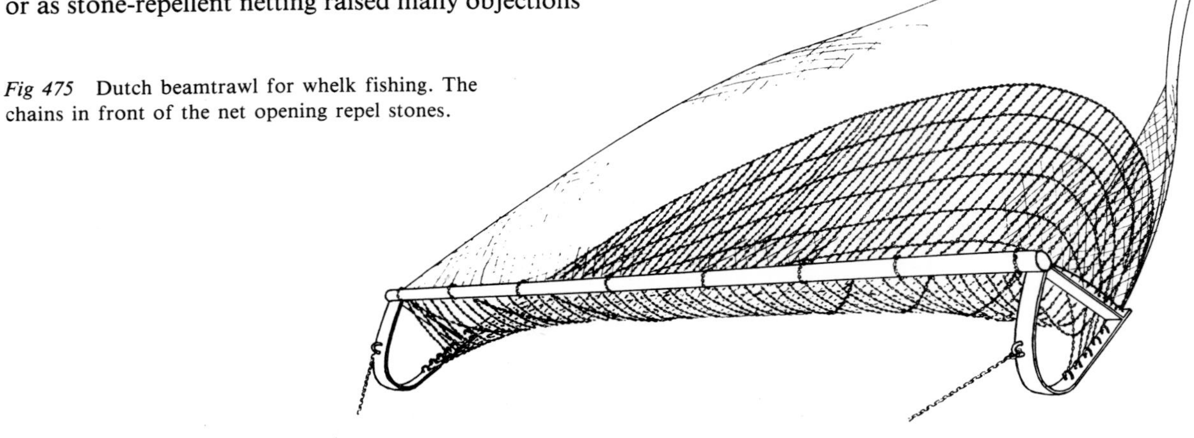

Fig 475 Dutch beamtrawl for whelk fishing. The chains in front of the net opening repel stones.

Fig 476 Agassiz trawl for making scientific catches at great depths. (*Photo: H Thiel, Hamburg.*)

stirring up flatfish has also been produced – so reducing the number and weight of the transverse tickler chains needed. Now only one single light chain is placed half a metre before the ground-rope of the beamtrawl. The electrodes are a few iron chains plaited together with a copper braid and running in the same direction as the towing direction. The electrical stimulus is delivered from a pulse generator mounted on the centre of the beam or placed on the deck of the vessel. The power is transmitted from the towing vessel via an armoured cable. By this electric tickler system the fish are induced to move off the bottom. The fish attempt to swim ahead of the ground-rope, but this zone is rendered frightening by the electric field. The fish react by dropping back into the beamtrawl. This system is considered not only less destructive to the seabed but reduces gear drag and, hence, towing power. But it is also more selective, by catching larger fish with a higher average weight.[253, 254, 602] The problem of fishing with electrified otter trawls, and the question of how to separate fish and shrimps during fishing, not only to avoid work and unwanted catch, but also to preserve juvenile fishes, will be discussed at the end of the following Chapter.

Chapter twenty-one

Fishing with bottom trawls

There are arguments about which gear is more important to fisheries trying to feed the hungry world; the trawls or the purse seins. But the answer is influenced by the question of whether bottom and mid-water fish are to be caught, or whether the target is large concentrations of fish near the surface of the water. Both trawls and purse seins are gear for bulk fishing and the operation of both needs a lot of experience and skill to be successful. Moreover, both gears need highly specialized vessels, especially when operated in large-scale sea fisheries. Therefore, there are some doubts as to whether trawling and purse seining can be combined on a so-called multi-purpose vessel without some compromise, as this always means some loss of efficiency for both methods.

Trawls are considered to be further developments of towed bagnets (*Fig 424*), dredges and beamtrawls, as discussed in the previous chapter. These are gears especially operated in fisheries for bottom fish or, at least, near-bottom fish, but also for cephalopods, sponges, some shellfish like shrimps or prawns, and different types of molluscs. Trawls are used in sea fisheries and to a lesser extent also in fresh waters where there is sufficient space for towing. The importance of this fishing method can be seen by the fact that many special variants of bottom trawls have been developed. There are very small 'baby trawls' and very large ones, with an opening higher than a house, which have to be towed by high-powered vessels. Until the end of the 1970s, the introduction of trawling was considered to be one of the main features of fishing development. But trawling in most cases is a fishing method needing high energy for towing a gear with sufficient speed. Moreover, it has been found that the efficiency of a trawl increases with the size of the gear. Larger gear also means greater energy requirements. For the heavy, highly developed modern trawls, powerful sophisticated vessels are needed if trawling is to be economical. This may create difficulties in further development of trawling through the increasing price of fuel. Further, it may be that in about ten years' time not enough oil will be available for the operation of effective trawlers.

21.1 Trawling with outriggers

As mentioned before, trawls can be considered as a further development of dredges and beamtrawls. By their construction, these latter gears have the disadvantage of their net opening being limited. To catch more fish, it became necessary and desirable to operate a broader gear than that permitted by the maximum length of the frames of dredges and beamtrawls. A relatively early solution to this problem was to tow a net bag without any frame in its opening, from a vessel sailing broadside, or at least in a slantwise direction, so that the two warps were fastened to poles protruding from the bow and the stern at the greatest possible distance (*Fig 477*). For sailing the boat sideways, not only wind power, but also current and manpower can be used. In this it is possible, even without using the two protruding beams, to keep the opening of the towed unframed net bag horizontally spread as far as the length of the vessel or the distance of the protruding poles will allow.[475] This method has been widely used in both European and Asiatic fisheries. The sailing boats of the fisheries in the Far East, as in Japan and Korea, generally employ this method. Sometimes other gear can be towed by a broadside or slantwise sailing vessel: in addition to a large unframed net bag, small beamtrawls or framed dredges may be towed. On the other hand, the method is disadvantageous in that when sailing broadside, vessels can achieve only a low speed. Moreover, this method can really only be used by sailing boats. Therefore, for powered vessels, another system has to be used to increase the opening of the trawl horizontally. The single trawl can be towed behind the vessel by towing booms or outriggers, as is done, even today, with otter board trawls (*Fig 478*). But outriggers alone can only provide a limited horizontal opening of the

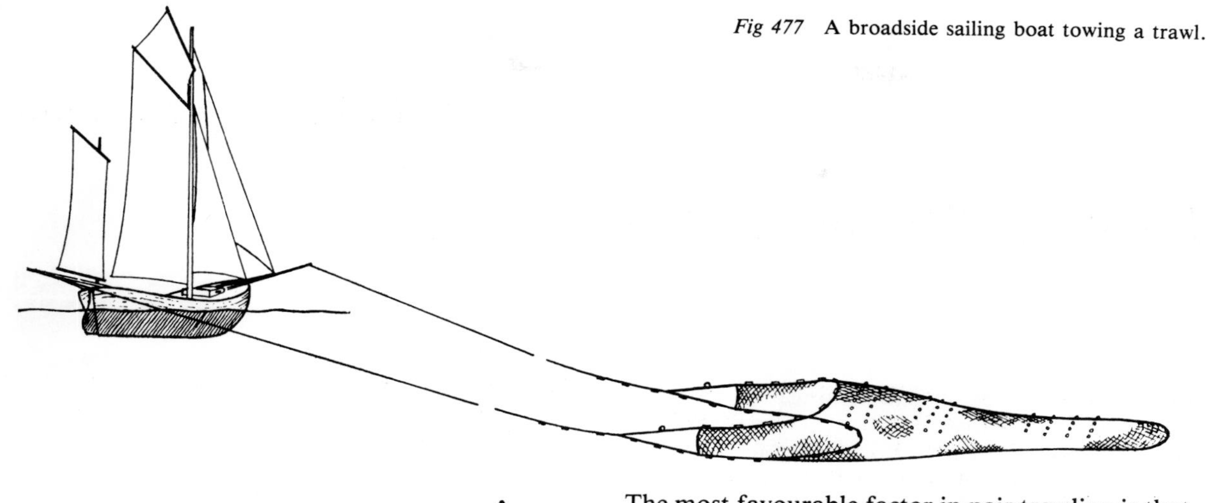

Fig 477 A broadside sailing boat towing a trawl.

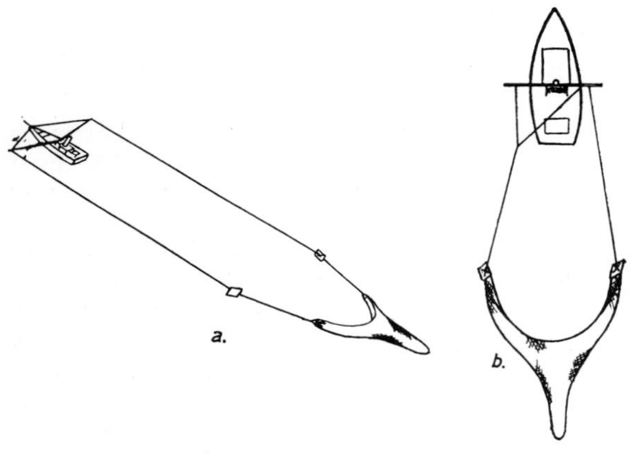

Fig 478 A horizontal opening of the trawl effected by means of sticks together with otter boards in: (*a*) Japan (*NN, 1959*); (*b*) Mexico (*Sanchez, 1959*).

trawl, which then decreases with the length of the warps. Therefore, better methods are required to spread the opening of the trawl wider to increase the fishing area.

21.2 Pair trawling

A much better way of keeping a towed net open horizontally (despite the missing frames or beams) is to tow it not by a single ship but by two equal vessels. This so-called pair trawling, with both sailing and power-driven vessels, is widely known, as it also meets other desirable points in fishing. For instance, double towing power is available when two vessels operate. The net can thus be made substantially larger so that the area of operation is increased and the yields can be expected to be larger. In fact, the yields must be at least double the single quantity in order to cover the costs of two vessels with their double crews, and also earn some profit.

The most favourable factor in pair trawling is that, in contrast to normal trawl fishing methods, the vessels would neither travel across the fish shoals sought to be caught nor tow their warps through them. In that way, the frightening effect of their passage could be avoided – at any rate in shallow waters.

There have been some experiments with methods to increase the efficiency of the gear by three boats towing together two trawls. In contrast to pair trawling with two boats this idea was not successful for nautical reasons and also because of higher vulnerability during bad weather, which may also hamper pair trawling with two vessels. One idea to overcome the difficulty of keeping two or three vessels at a constant distance, is to connect their bows with a wire line of sufficient length.

In Europe, pair fishing with bottom trawls, as carried out by the Spanish pareja fishery, is well known, but towing trawls with two vessels is also popular in many other areas, particularly in the Far East. It is a form of trawling typically used by low-powered vessels since olden times. Primitive forms of pair fishing were in fact practised by the Indian tribes on the Pacific coast of North America before the time of Columbus.[413, 632] Two rowing boats towed net bags through the water, especially for catching salmon. There are also old sketches of South American life, dated 1565, showing Indians towing a type of drag net with two balsa rafts. Much older are the models of pair trawling with papyrus vessels which were deposited in Egyptian graves 3,000 years ago. A disadvantage of fishing with two vessels is, however, that not only have the vessels to be more or less twin vessels – of similar size and power – but the masters of the vessels must also co-operate most accurately. That is frequently possible only in daylight and in relatively good weather. The need to keep uniform distance during towing, and then come close for hauling the catch or for shooting the net, compels these fishermen to discontinue operations under certain weather conditions, even though single vessels could still operate under those same conditions. In addition, difficulties are likely to arise of a human nature; it is not always possible to find skippers who are able to co-operate; to subordinate themselves and to work together amicably for a long period. It is, in fact, a standing joke in the fishing industry that two skippers who are normally on friendly terms may become estranged when they are required to operate their vessels in pair fishing.

21.3 Otter boards for bottom trawling

The most developed method for keeping towed trawls open horizontally is the use of otter boards (*Fig 479*). These boards are, as described in a previous chapter, not an invention of the trawl fishery, but have been known in the hook and line fishery for a long time. As in line fishing, these otter boards are set obliquely against the current. They are thus pressed to one side and so tow the gear in that direction. Such boards in different forms, rectangular or even oval (*Figs 480* and *481*), and of several square metres in size, when attached to either side of the opening of the trawl net suffice to keep it open horizontally. In this way, a net opening is achieved without using beams, without sailing broadside and without using two vessels for towing.

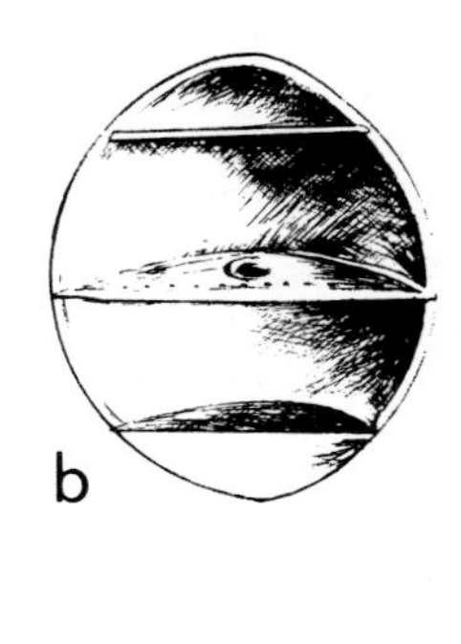

Fig 481 Hydrodynamic otter boards: (*a*) Süberkrüb board; (*b*) spherical board.

The otter board for the trawl appeared first in its present form in Ireland around 1885. First experiments were made by an Irishman named Musgrave between 1860 and 1870.[42] The English trawler, *Irrawaddy* made the first attempts to use such otter boards in 1885 but achieved little success. It required several years' experience before the experiments succeeded and lateral otter boards could be generally adopted. It was in 1892 that the first successful otter board trial was made from South Shields on the English North Sea coast. At

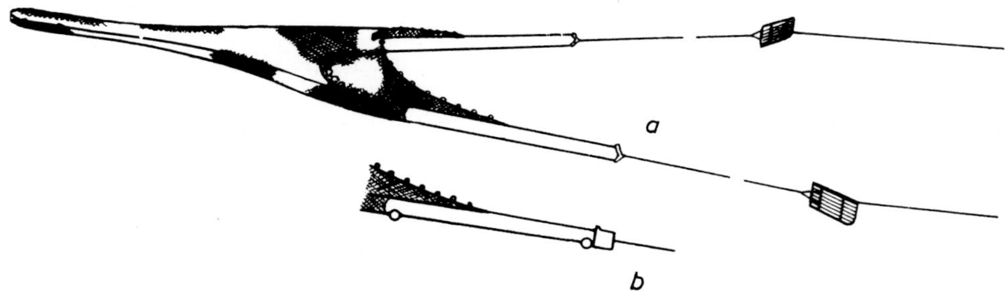

Fig 479 Bottom trawl used for fishing on rough grounds: (*a*) with danlenos as 'butterflies'; (*b*) with pony boards replacing danlenos.

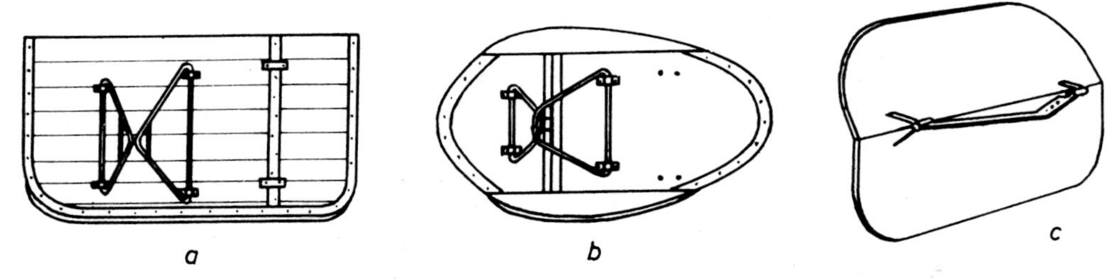

Fig 480 Different types of otter boards: (*a*) conventional flat type; (*b*) oval board; (*c*) V-type.

the same time, gallows for heaving the boards onto the vessel were introduced and the otter trawl was no longer towed by one line, as was done with the primitive trawls, but by two lines. Rapid progress was now made. In 1894, Scott from Grantham applied for the first patent, and this was followed later by a great number of other patents. In 1895 the otter board reached Germany by way of Holland. The owners, Witt and Bartels of Cranz on the Elbe, were the first to equip a German trawler with such boards for a fishing voyage. In the same year (1895) in France the first experiments had been made with the 'chalut à panneaux'. The experiments were so successful that the 'otter trawl' became popular in many countries in the following years. Nevertheless, it was some time before trawling with otter boards spread over the whole world. How slow this development was can be seen from the fact that otter boards were not introduced into Japanese trawling before 1905, and did not appear in other countries until much later (*eg* Malaysia in 1936).

Since the introduction of these shearing devices a number of suggestions have been made for improving the otter boards. The basic idea is to shape the board in such a way that its shearing power (side force) becomes as great as possible while its resistance to towing is as little as possible. Moreover, the boards should have less wear on trawl gear and should be easy to store and handle. Finally, effective otter boards should save power and fuel, a problem which has often been forgotten, but which may become decisive for trawling due to the current oil crisis. Very often, engineering investigations were made without knowledge of the practical needs of fisheries and without knowledge of their influence on fish behaviour. For this reason, only a few types of otter boards have had real success in fisheries.[162]

Originally the otter boards, or trawl doors, were simple rectangular flat wooden plates, strengthened by a steel frame and iron struts (*Fig 480a*). They were not only inexpensive but also simple to handle and easy to store. On the other hand, these flat doors are, in their construction, completely uninfluenced by all hydrodynamic and hydrokinetic rules designed to obtain optimal shearing effect. Many proposals have been made to increase the efficiency of the boards, but most of the new proposed boards were not only too complicated to build and repair, but also too difficult to handle and to store on a small fishing vessel. Others were vulnerable under bad weather conditions. So these ideas only increased the number of patent rights, without obtaining practical success. This should change with the development of mid-water trawls (Chapter 22). Nevertheless, beside rectangular flat doors, a few other forms came into bottom trawling before the middle of this century. The Russians' oval flat otter boards, sometimes slotted, were introduced, their oval outline gliding much better over rough bottoms than did the rectangular flat trawl doors (*Fig 480b*). Moreover, the single vertical slot at mid length improves the efficiency of these oval boards slightly. V-shaped trawl doors (butterfly otter boards) became very popular in small-scale inshore trawling and were designed by the Chinese Capt. Loo-Chi Hu in 1956/57 (*Fig 480c*). A good performance on rough ground is claimed for these boards. Although physical investigations demonstrated that the V-boards had a low shearing power in comparison with other types of boards, these boards are often preferred by successful fishermen. Recently, Scottish investigations showed very strong sand clouds produced by these boards during fishing. It may be that these clouds play an important part in leading fish into the path of the net.[465, 466]

As mentioned before, flat boards have been constructed without regard to aero- or hydrodynamic rules. Concerning the relation between water resistance and towed boards, there is no doubt that like the wings of an aeroplane, bent, moulded or curved boards designed on hydrodynamic principles must give a much greater efficiency than the conventional flat boards. But it was some time before the experiences of the construction of aeroplanes inspired the construction of otter boards with curved surfaces. As far as is known, the first experiments with a curved board were made in fisheries at the beginning of the 1920s (Oertz board) but, like others, without success. It seems that the German engineer F Süberkrüb was the first to succeed with curved boards (*Fig 481a*). These boards are at least twice as high as they are broad. When used with a small angle of attack, an excellent shearing power is created with low towing resistance.[155, 603, 604] These boards are especially made for mid-water trawling (Chapter 22) but in Japan, boards similar, but only one a half times as high as broad, have been developed for bottom trawling. There is no doubt that flat otter boards can be stored on the deck of a vessel much more easily than curved ones. This is especially true for very large boards of twelve and more square metres area, used by powerful stern trawlers in mid-water fishing. Recently this problem could be solved, to some extent, by replacing the large Süberkrüb boards by two smaller ones which together have the same shearing area as the large ones. These two boards are connected together like the wings of a biplane. The so-called tandem boards have the same shearing effect as a single board with the same surface and are much easier to handle.[184, 185] Recently, the Russians made another proposal to replace large Süberkrüb boards used in mid-water trawling by spherical otter boards, so-called saucer-shaped boards, or 'O-boards' (*Fig 481b*). With spherical boards, some difficulties in handling very large Süberkrüb boards could be avoided because boards of this type, with smaller dimensions, can be used with the same effect.[257, 339] In general, two boards are used in trawling, one for port and one for starboard. These boards are not interchangeable. Efforts have been made to construct the boards in such a manner that they can be used on either side of the vessel. However, some interchangeability is possible with flat doors and V-doors, but especially with the spherical boards. Originally the otter boards were made of wood and could be readily repaired, often on the vessel. Later, trawl doors were made of steel. Other materials, such as fibreglass-reinforced plastic or aluminium have been tried, but none of them came into common use. Cambered boards with increased spreading efficiency have been developed in France and have been combined with oval boards suitable, especially, for rough fishing grounds. They are well known as polyvalent boards, which can be used for bottom and pelagic trawling. The problem of multi-purpose boards will be mentioned again with mid-water trawling in the next chapter. When more shearing arrangements are used with trawls, *eg* with mid-water trawls, they are not considered as otter boards, apart from the so-called 'pony boards' (*Figs 479b* and *482*) replacing the danlenos at the end of the wings of the trawl operated on rough grounds. They are so named from the fact that this second pair of otter boards, much smaller than the first, are running behind the large boards, like a pony behind its mother. Otter boards with a great horizontal spreading effect and with a small towing resistance are essential for economic trawling with low energy costs. Of course, the resistance of a trawl gear is not only caused by the otter boards moving against the water and the frictional resistance of the boards on the bottom, but also by the resistance caused by the water flowing through the meshes of the net and against the warps. These factors have been neglected for a long time but are now being recognized more as it becomes necessary to achieve greater speeds with the same propulsive power. On a soft bottom, the boards can be provided with broad mud skids to prevent them from digging into the seabed. Gliding of the gear is also achieved by mud rollers or bobbins of different weight fixed to the ground-wires. They also protect the netting against damage on rough ground.

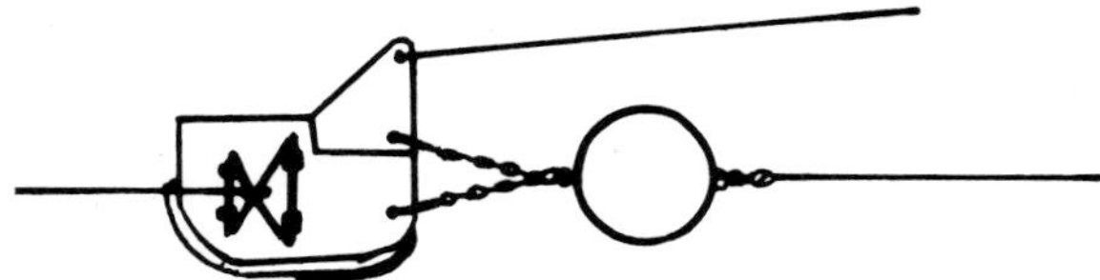

Fig 482 Pony boards for replacing danlenos. (*Nédélec and Libert, 1962*).

21.4 Increasing the vertical trawl opening

In the last section, the horizontal spreading of the trawl opening with different techniques has been described. As long as mainly flatfish, shrimps and other near-bottom animals were fished, a wide horizontal opening of the gear was more important than the vertical opening. The height of such dragged gear, influenced only by the size of the guiding shoes with beamtrawls, or the height of the otter boards with other appropriate trawls, was sufficient. But it was found that sometimes fish stay at a certain distance above the bottom and so high-opening bottom trawls were wanted.

A simple method exists for keeping the opening high vertically as will be discussed with seine nets. This is by fixing upright sticks between the upper and lower edges of the net opening, at varying and graded distances. These serve to keep the net aperture open vertically, without regard to the height of the lateral parts of the net. *Figure 483* shows an old Japanese trawl that is kept open horizontally by a beam, and vertically by just four spreading sticks. It will be understood that the vertical opening decreases with any increase of the horizontal opening, and vice versa. On the other hand, the use of spreading sticks is a simple method of achieving a considerable opening height. It may, however, be suspected that such sticks in the opening of the net might have the effect of frightening fish away from entering the trawl. It is, therefore, now customary to keep the aperture of the net open by attaching floats to the upper line and sinkers, in various forms, to the ground-rope. There has to be a balance between the buoyancy of the floats and the weight of the sinkers in the water. Simple forms of dragged gear may have more weights to keep them in contact with the bottom, and the floats can have more buoyancy, as necessary, to keep the opening of the gear as high as possible. Sometimes, to prevent damage to gear, lines are set at short distances between the groundrope and the floatline. But the same objections which can be made for the sticks set in

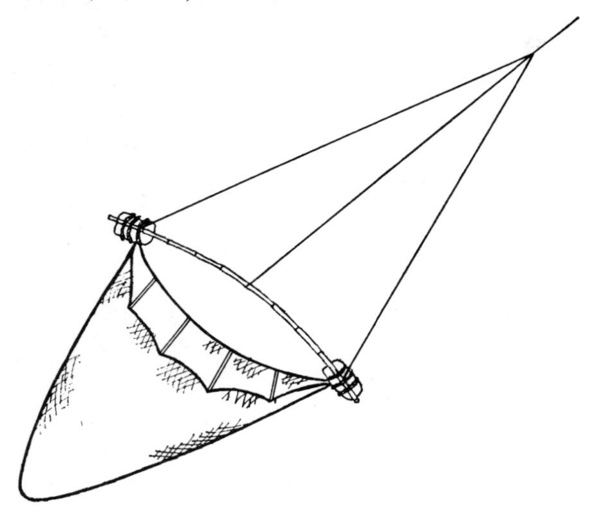

Fig 483 Vertical opening of a beamtrawl by means of vertical sticks. (*NN, 1959*).

the net opening, can be made also against such connecting lines frightening the prey away by their swinging from the entrance of the gear. Therefore, an appropriate relation between floats and weights is necessary.

Floats on towed gear, however, have disadvantages in that they may be pressed back, even downwards, by the resistance of the water. In that case they would no longer fulfil their function. Further, their buoyancy decreases with the increase of towing speed unless the floats are given a shearing shape which would increase their buoyancy with any increase of towing speed. Remarkable progress in this field was made when, in 1920, Captain Johann von Eitzen of Hamburg had the idea of putting a third otter board at the headline of his trawl, adopting the construction of some pelagic nets used by the biological station at Heligoland since 1903 for catching fry and eggs. This trawl, used for pelagic fishing, had two boards on the headline and a single one in the middle of the ground-line (*Fig 505*). Captain von Eitzen changed this by adding a single board on the headline to extend the opening of the gear upwards. Under the influence of the towing speed the upper board acted like a kite above the net opening, counteracting the horizontal spreading effect of the lateral boards and keeping the headline of the net high.[154] Nevertheless, the shape of a trawl opening must be based on the construction of the gear and the type of netting used, so that floats, shearing boards and sinkers do not distort and damage the net through unequal loading. The addition of the extra shearing board helped keep the gear opening at an optimal size and shape while maintaining a greater vertical opening than had been possible before. The net opening became higher and the fish which kept station well above the bottom, in particular herring, could be caught. The result was so remakable that yields increased tenfold, or even more, and this led to the development of the outstanding trawl fishery for herring in northwest Europe.

Very soon it was found that one kite was not sufficient. Second[466] and even third kites were attached, so extending the opening height considerably, as the area encircled by the lines of the kites is also considered to be the fishing area in relation to the net opening. *Figure 484* demonstrates the development of the herring bottom trawl. It will be seen that the aperture of the net was continually being enlarged over the years; in the horizontal direction by enlarged wings pulling the lateral otter boards forward, and in a vertical direction by adding floats and one or more kites. It must be mentioned that for stern trawlers kites are often replaced by torpedo-shaped buoys. This is to guard more effectively against the wake of the propeller.

Recently a new idea arose to increase the opening of a trawl with the help of a so-called 'sail kite' (*Fig 485*). This is a piece of strong canvas or similar strong webbing slightly less wide than or as wide as, the length of the headline bosom, sewn with its longer edge to the trawl net bosom. During fishing, this webbing will be pushed by the flow of water into the trawl, pressing its opening upwards like wooden kites, floats and other lifting devices.[33] By this means the fishing height of the trawl is increased and the drag is diminished. In comparison with the usual lifting devices, the sail kite simplifies the construction and handling of the trawl and the cost of each trawl is reduced. It will be understood that this arrangement can be effective with trawls in which the forepart of the roof (the square) does not stay in a horizontal position during fishing and does not have too acute an angle of attack. With the so-called rope trawls (Chapter 22) a sailkite in the form of a canvas, fixed on the inside of the net opening cannot be used. Wooden kites or floats fitted to the headline of the rope trawls have the disadvantage that these devices can entangle with the ropes when shooting or hauling the trawl. Wooden kites also cannot be used when operating the gear with a net drum. In such cases sailkites of canvas mounted at the headline should replace wooden kites. PE canvas has been used for this purpose (*Fig 486*) and has proved successful when mounted in a suitable manner.[256]

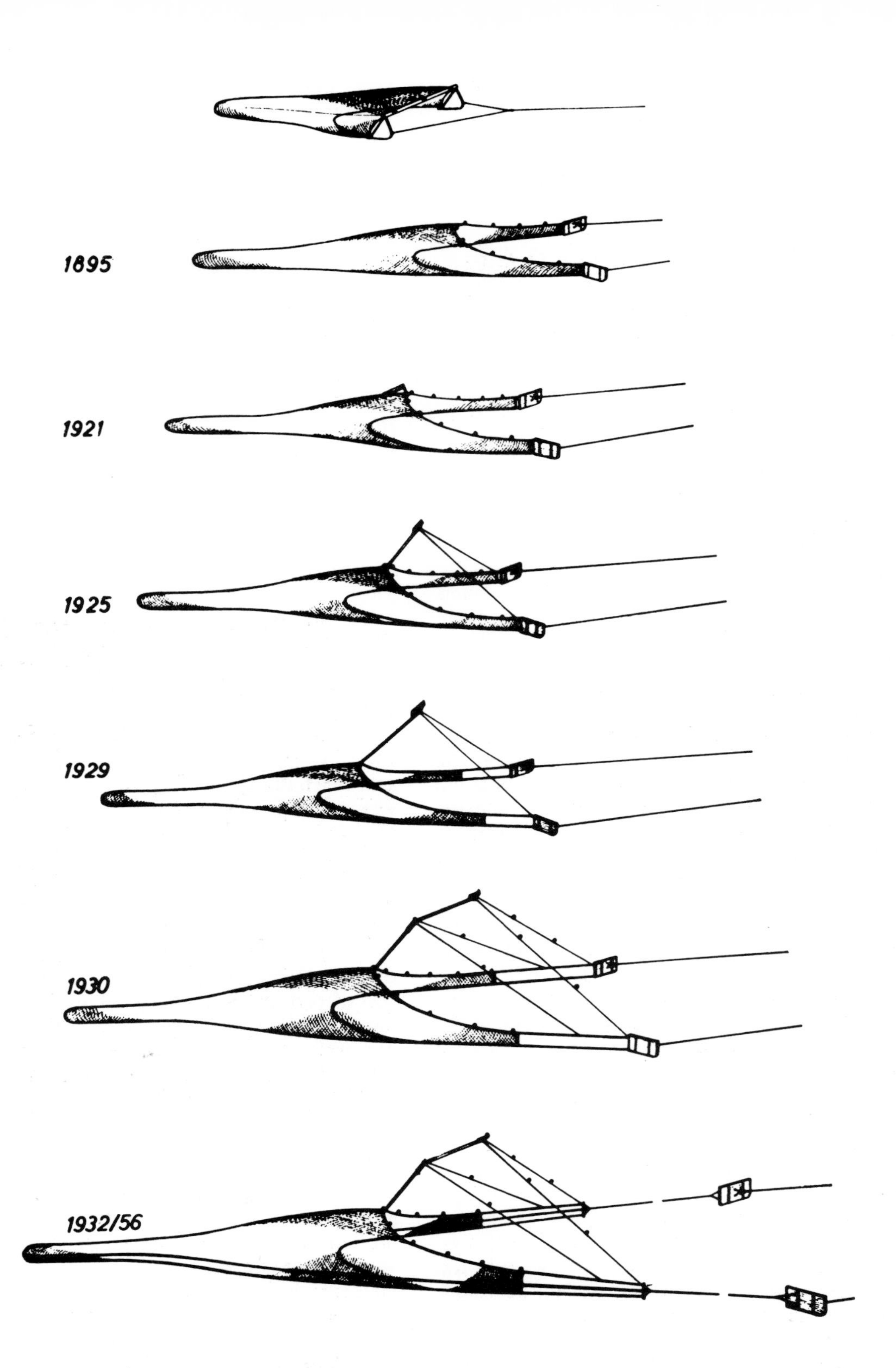

Fig 484 Development of the German bottom trawl used for herring.

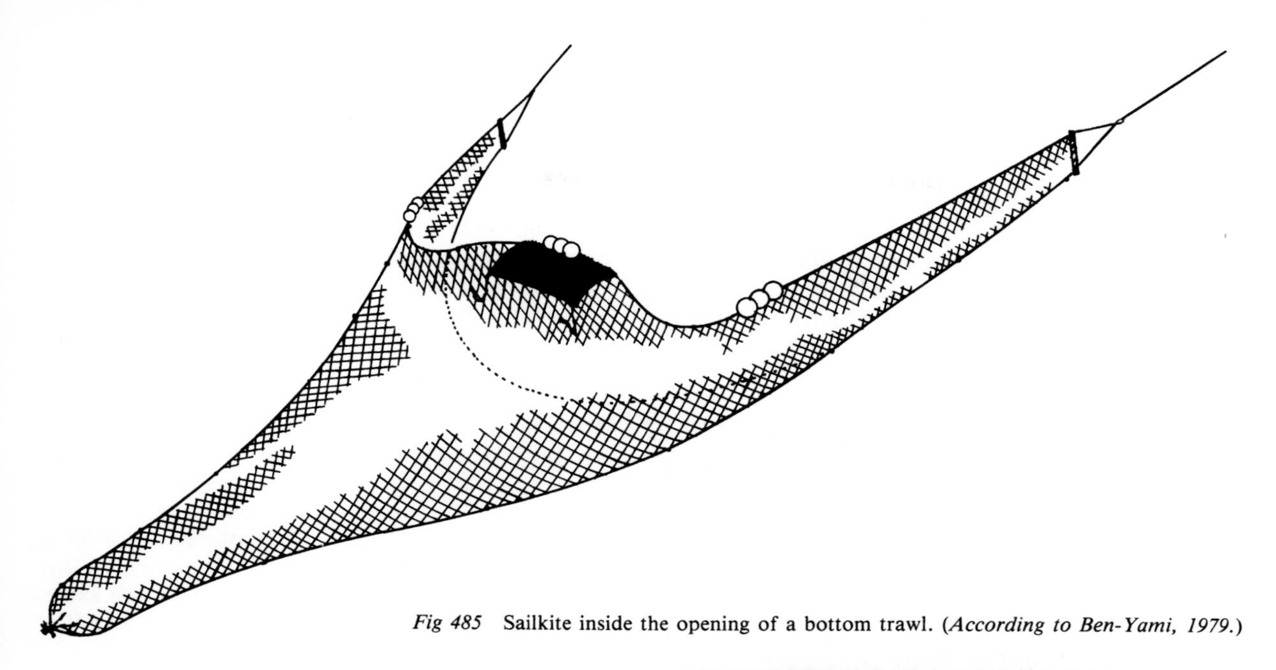

Fig 485 Sailkite inside the opening of a bottom trawl. (*According to Ben-Yami, 1979.*)

21.5 Bottom trawls for sea fisheries

Originally the trawls operated as beamtrawls had a round conical net bag only, as can be seen from drawings published in the last century.[227] This did not change when otter boards were introduced. The net bag of the beamtrawls was retained and the boards were attached to either side of the opening, in place of the runners.[670] To retain the fish, pockets with openings facing backwards were fixed into the bagnet. Then a funnel was introduced into the bag and the afterpart of the bag was made of stronger and smaller-meshed netting. Later, the bag of the trawl was made of two more or less equal panels of netting, the upper and the lower part, which were sewn together as a two-seam trawl. Each part was divided into more than two sections. The end of the bag for the catch was made much stronger, and the so-called codend was separated from the main part of the gear. This meant that the shape of the net became more complicated, and this was reflected in various ways. The trawl used in northern Europe was composed of transverse sections;[191] that of the Mediterranean, like the common Italian type, of longitudinal strips of netting incorporating a large-meshed triangular 'sky piece' (scaghetto) to enlarge the opening. The European shape was adopted by other trawl fishing interests throughout the world. But the net no longer consisted only of a bag, like that used on the dredges and on the beamtrawls. It had been given a slender shape and was equipped with wings. These were lengthened and so extended the net opening in a horizontal direction. Greater width is obtained if legs are fitted between the wings and the boards, and the boards are not directly attached to the wings.

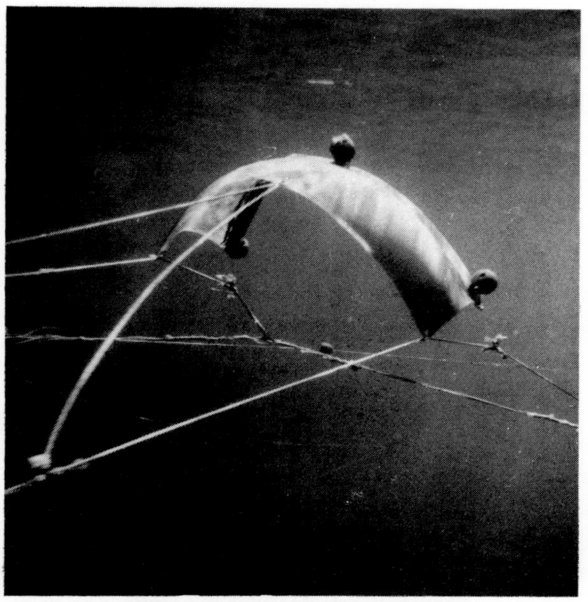

Fig 486 Sailkite for a rope trawl. (*Photo: W Horn, 1980*).

A further important step was taken in the 1920s by the V D trawl (named after the Frenchmen Vigneron and Dahl) in which the legs terminated with danlenos, and so-called butterflies and bridles were fitted between the danlenos and the boards

(*Fig 484*). At that point it was found that with the heavy bottom trawls used in the fisheries of the northern seas, it was helpful if the danleno or butterfly was replaced by another smaller lateral otter board; the so-called pony board sometimes also called danleno board. This supported the horizontal spreading of the net opening (*Figs 479b* and *482*). Many trials have been made, seeking to increase the efficiency of trawls by better construction, as with bigger or higher openings, larger meshes in the forepart of the trawl, and even better materials. By the use of larger meshes in the trawl opening, the water resistance of the trawl could be decreased very much (*Fig 514a*). Sometimes the large-meshed netting in the forepart of the trawl has been replaced by parallel ropes in the so-called 'rope trawl' (*Fig 514b*). The large-meshed trawls, as well as the rope trawls, became not only of interest in bottom trawling, but also much more in mid-water trawling; therefore they will be discussed again in Chapter 22.

The trawl quickly became the fishing gear mainly used in large-scale fisheries. One should not forget, however, that an adequate development of fishing vessels had to occur simultaneously. Sufficient power had to be available for towing these large nets; also adequate auxiliary equipment for handling them. That could not be done without powerful winches. So it will be seen that a constant relationship exists between the development of a trawl net and that of a fishing vessel, the propulsion power and the deck equipment.

In connection with the problem of the towing power of a vessel, it has to be mentioned that in fishing with large trawls, usually one gear only will be operated by a single vessel. This will be, in most cases, an otter trawl. In twin-trawling one vessel tows two beamtrawls or two otter trawls, one on each side (*Fig 487*). In experimental work it has been found that a single stern trawler can tow two trawls simultaneously (*Fig 488*).[161] Also in pair trawling two trawls, connected at their inside wings, can be operated according to a Russian proposal.[468] Moreover, single Asiatic broadside sailing boats can tow more than one gear – multi-net trawling or multi-rig trawling.[475] Multi-rig trawling with modern vessels is recommended especially in shrimp fishing where a large trawl is replaced by several smaller ones. Smaller trawls will have less towing resistance, which means, too, that with the same power needed for a large gear, two shorter (and also cheaper) gears can be operated, and these will together have the same, or even a larger, horizontal net opening than may be possible with a single larger net.[536]

The need for increased towing power became greater with the development of trawls. Manpower may be sufficient for small trawls; they can be towed directly by the fisherman wading in the shallow water (*Figs 424* and *426*), or they are towed

Fig 487 Double-rigged shrimp trawler, for twin trawling, in the Arabian Gulf. (*Photo: H Kristjonsson.*)

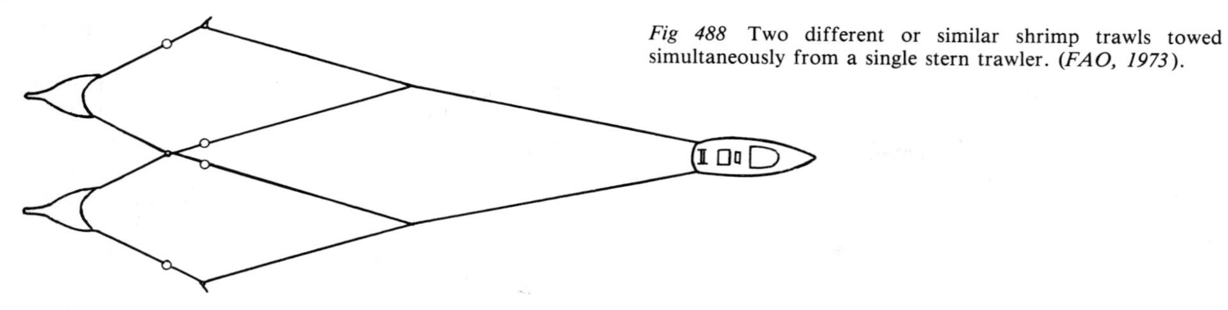

Fig 488 Two different or similar shrimp trawls towed simultaneously from a single stern trawler. (*FAO, 1973*).

like dredges with the help of a hand-operated winch from an anchored vessel, or with a movable vessel towed by hand along a line anchored to the shore (*Fig 489*). In some places horses have to do some towing, even with the smaller otter trawls which have replaced small types of beamtrawls or dredges (*Fig 490*). As is known, sailing boats have more power than those propelled by man with oars. Underwater sails (*Figs 461, 491* and *492*) – now better known as parachute-like drift anchors – not only give better stability to a fishing vessel but also help to drag gear over the seabed.[73] Underwater sails

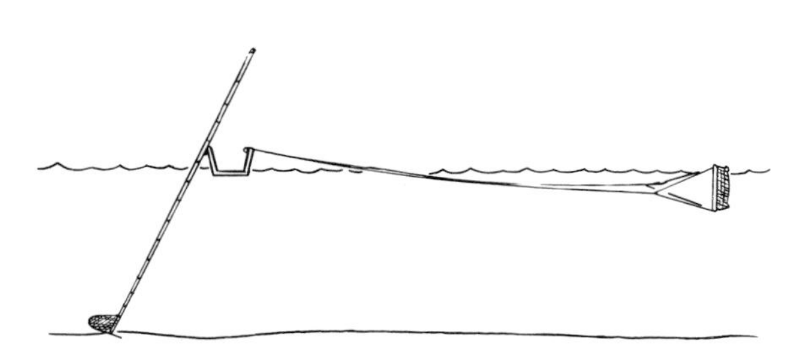

Fig 491 Flat baskets, moved along by the current, tow a Chinese boat dredging for mussels.

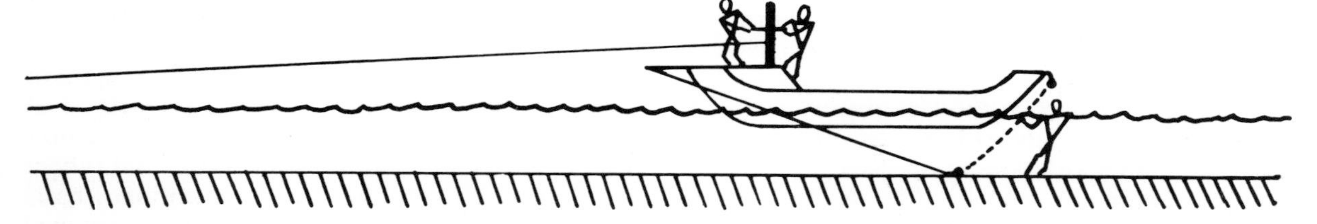

Fig 489 A net fixed behind a vessel and held by a man wading in the water is towed forward by winding the boat along a cable anchored on shore, Kampuchea. (*Fily and d'Aubenton, 1965*).

Fig 490 Horses tow small otterboard nets in shrimp fishing in Oustduinkerke, Belgium. (*Photo: J H Klausing, Ostend, 1968.*)

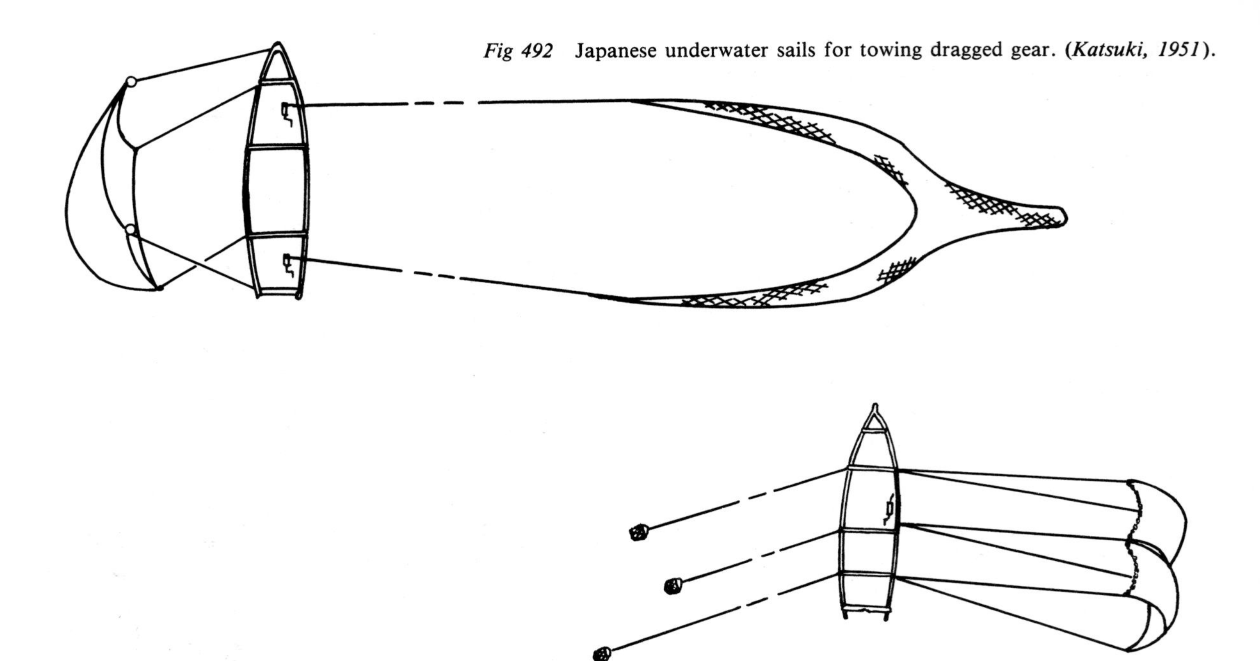

Fig 492 Japanese underwater sails for towing dragged gear. (*Katsuki, 1951*).

are still used in Japan, Korea and Taiwan. Formerly they have been also known in the European inshore fishery.[133]

In the second part of the last century, sails of fishing vessels were replaced by steam engines, and the first steam trawlers were operated in fisheries from Boulogne (France) in 1865, in 1872 from Trieste (at that time part of Austria), and in 1877 from North Shields (UK). In the 1950s coal was superseded by fuel oil. The towing power of trawlers increased from some hundreds of horsepower to thousands, making the efficiency of trawling greater and greater. There are some inter-relations between the vessel, power and deck arrangements on the one side, and the size of the gear and the towing speed on the other. There are many variations in size, construction, rigging and mode of operation for trawls. The development of the German herring trawl, as an example of a light trawl of large size, has been mentioned before (*Fig 484*). In contrast to this type, the heavy bottom trawls operated from Europe in northern waters had quite another development. Designed for demersal fish – but not for flatfish – it was discovered that for this heavy bottom trawl a kite on the headline could also be helpful. But in this case the horizontal opening of the net is more important than the height. The use of pony boards in supporting the lateral shearing instead of danlenos or butterflies has already been mentioned (*Fig 479b*). The bottom trawls which are frequently used on very rough bottoms require special protection from mechanical damage. Efforts were made to provide protection by means of bobbins made of wood, plastics, steel, or rubber on the groundrope in place of the simple, more or less protected groundrope itself. This method of protecting groundropes against any damage is now also used in the form of discs made of old rubber tyres. In addition to the two aforementioned basic types of bottom trawls a lighter one was developed with a high opening to catch fish staying near the bottom, like herring, and a heavier and better-protected one was also developed for fish living nearer to the bottom – the so-called round fish or white fish trawl. In Europe many other types have been operated, especially smaller types for low-powered vessels, particularly in coastal fisheries.[154, 188, 191, 417, 546, 554] Nevertheless, there is a tendency for some unification of the types of trawls. The development of the bottom trawl in northwest Europe has been mentioned first because nowhere else in the world has the trawl fishery established such a degree of importance. Many countries in northwest Europe depended mainly on their landings of sea fish caught by trawls. This is why, in Europe, many experiments have been undertaken by fishermen, fishing companies, naval architects and shipyards and specialized gear technologists, to improve trawling as a large-scale and far distant fishing method. Since the 1950s new synthetic fibres have been introduced for trawl nets, and hand-knitted nets have been replaced by machine-made ones.

The behaviour of trawls was studied during

fishing operations, which produced the first impressive underwater films about trawls and fish behaviour during fishing operations.[367] One of the most important developments took place in the 1950s when stern trawlers were used instead of side trawlers. In many parts of the world the trawl was hauled over the side when the catch was not too heavy, and large-scale side trawlers needed not only special navigation, taking up much time, but also a great amount of manpower (*Fig 493*). The new stern trawlers were equipped with a chute in the stern, similar to the ramp which the whaling vessels had used since 1924. The whole catch could now be hauled in with the help of a winch with less manpower (*Fig 494*). The shooting and hauling of the net, which required so much bodily strength when done manually on side trawlers, was thus achieved mainly by winches alone and in so doing saved both labour and valuable time. The most important advantage of stern trawling over side trawling may be that the net may be shot in any weather conditions. This development stimulated further attempts to improve trawling techniques. Gear designs, tested during fishing operations or as models in flume tanks, greatly helped in understanding trawl behaviour during fishing. The conventional two-seam trawl was replaced by trawls

Fig 493 Hauling the trawl by hand on a small side trawler (lugger).

Fig 494 Modern stern trawler showing the chute up which the net is drawn. (*Photo: T Mengi.*)

with four or even eight panels. Stern trawling made it possible to operate much bigger trawls provided the propulsion power of the vessel was sufficient. In order to operate large trawls, especially on smaller vessels with limited space, and to facilitate net handling, drums or net reels were introduced.[664] Net drums were a North American invention, used with purse seines (Chapter 25) and gillnets (Chapter 29) and later for longlines (Chapter 9) and seine nets (Chapter 24). The drums were developed by the British to the stage where they became capable of handling heavy bottom trawls and also large mid-water trawls (Chapter 22).[148] Net drums became successful not only on small vessels (*Figs 495* and *496*)[183] where deck space is restricted, but also on large stern trawlers with stern ramps where trawls often have to be changed quickly. There are vessels which have more than one drum to store different types of trawls. Where drums could not be used to eliminate the physical effort required of the crew in hauling the trawl, power blocks were used, as they were for operating purse seines (Chapter 25). For easier handling, these blocks are mounted on folding compact cranes (*Fig 497*).

Until recently, trawling was considered the most important fishing method beside that of purse seining (Chapter 25). This was true, and may be to some extent also true today for inshore coastal and far-distant fisheries, for small sailing boats as well as for large self-catching and self-processing vessels. Naval architects and shipyards, fishing companies and research institutes all competed to improve the efficiency of large-scale trawling by increasing the trawl size, towing and winch power, and mechanization to economize on manpower. Trawling should have become one of the first fully automated fishing methods. Such development needs a lot of money but it seemed worthwhile for

Fig 495 Net drum with trawl on a small vessel in Esbjerg, Denmark.

Fig 496 Hauling in the trawl with a net drum on a cutter of thirty metres in length. (*Photo: W Karger, 1970.*)

the future of this and other fishing methods. However, this situation has been changed completely by the extension of Exclusive Economic Zones (EEZs) to 200 miles from the shore, which has led to a lack of suitable fishing grounds for some nations specializing in far-distant fisheries. But there are other factors affecting the modernization of trawling. These include over-fishing of well-known stocks of marketable fish; difficulties in introducing new species of fish and other products of the sea, to fill the gaps in the markets; and the increasing cost of fuel. Small-scale fisheries are beginning to consider how to return to sailing, using modern techniques which are being devised for cargo vessels. Many are also considering whether coal may have now become more economic than oil as a fuel for trawling. It may be that this problem cannot be solved and that trawling in the modern highly-mechanized form will no longer be economic in the future and will have to be replaced by other fishing methods with lower energy requirements.

21.6 Shrimp trawling

Although there are some apprehensions about the future of bottom trawling, especially in large-scale fisheries, this applies less to trawling for high-priced

Fig 497 Swedish trawler with folding deck-crane, power block and net drum. (*Courtesy of HIAB-FOCO AB, Hudiksvall, Sweden*).

products, not only of fish but especially shrimps and other crustaceans. For those, mostly small trawls with less power requirements are used such as the beamtrawls mentioned before (Chapter 20) and small otter trawls. Twin trawling for those species is carried out in the Gulf of Mexico and in the Arabian Sea (*Fig 487*). Fishing is done with two outriggers, on each of which a single net with otter boards is towed with one warp only.[311] As already mentioned sometimes a trynet (*Fig 455a*) is towed on a small davit on the stern of the vessel. Double-rig otter trawling (*Fig 498*) with a trawl system of four trawls does give some advantages and was therefore adopted for shrimping in many countries in Central America, the Arabian Sea and the Gulf of Guinea.[325, 466] Because small-meshed trawls are used in shrimping there is a problem of how to prevent juvenile or undersized fish being caught by shrimp trawls. Even if only the sorting operation could be reduced, a considerable amount of labour on deck could be saved.[161] Two basic ideas have been proposed to separate fish and shrimps. Both are based on the fact that shrimps jump when stirred up, but fish do not – at least not to the same extent. The European proposal for a selective shrimp trawl (beamtrawl or otter trawl) uses a trawl

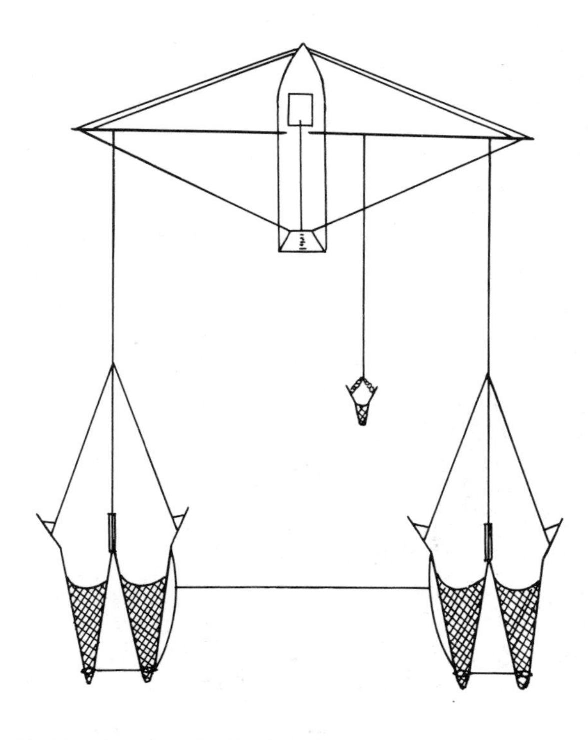

Fig 498 American double-rig shrimp trawl system. (*NN, 1979*).

with a double codend, with a nearly flat horizontal large-meshed netting fixed in the middle of the trawl to separate fish and shrimp. The stirred up shrimps can jump through the meshes of the separator netting, and will be caught in a small-meshed upper codend, whereas the by-catch of fish is supposed to swim under the horizontal netting into the bigger-meshed lower codend (*Fig 499*).[161] The lower codend can also be replaced by chutes through which the by-catch can escape.

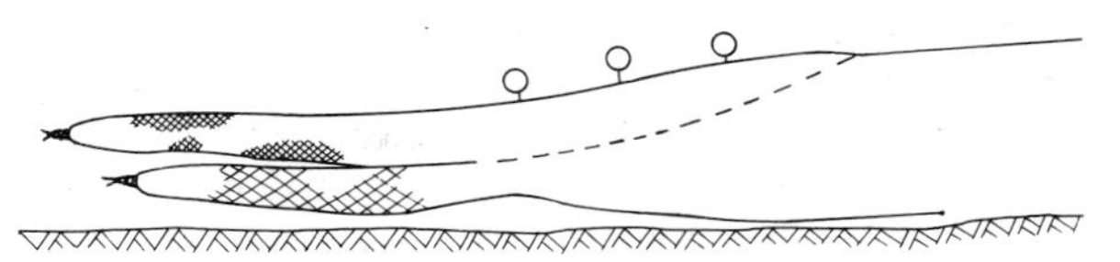

Fig 499 Shrimp trawl with separator. (*Schärfe, 1978*).

The American proposal for the solution of the problem uses a vertical netting, which covers the inner sides of the wings of the net opening, allowing the shrimp to swim through to the single codend of the trawl. The fish are guided by this vertical separator net to a fish escape chute under the codend.[648] It has been found that this method not only allows some shrimps to escape with the by-catch through the chute, but that also the escape chute can become clogged when many fish are caught, and that some smaller fish can be gilled in the vertical guiding nets. To avoid these disadvantages, a new proposal was made recently, based not only on the behaviour of shrimps when disturbed but also on the different behaviour of shrimp and fish opposite an electrical field. The electrification of beamtrawls and otter trawls was proposed a long time ago, in spite of all difficulties involved in using electrical currents to attract and to stun fish and other animals in sea water (Chapter 5). Some experiments with electrified trawls were successful. It was found that in a regular trawl, towed at the usual speed, larger and stronger fish can escape from the opening of the gear at the last moment. This, it was thought, could be prevented by stupefying or killing the fish by electrical pulses at the trawl opening (*Fig 500*).[156, 377, 392, 545] This has been done experimentally and it is claimed that with this technique not only could bigger catches be obtained, but also that the fish was of better quality. The electrification of trawls has been proved in seawater and freshwater.[180, 230] However, the predicted revolution of trawling by electrification has not come true up to the present.

Returning to the problem of separating shrimp and fish in shrimp trawls, it is well known that electrical current can be used in shrimping on rough fishing grounds.[392] With the help of electricity, the shrimp can be brought out of its hiding place. Shrimps dug into the bottom jump out immediately when the electrical current is switched on. The shrimp can jump some centimetres in height, so that the animals come within reach of the trawl towed some distance off the bottom. Shrimps can be caught in this was during daytime as well as night-time hours.[635] Electrified otter or beamtrawls are used in America (Florida), the Netherlands and in Belgium. This knowledge is used for a new proposal to separate fish and shrimp in the trawls. In this case the opening of the trawl is completely closed with a piece of netting which allows water to flow through the trawl but prevents fish from entering. The bottom of the trawl which is made of large-meshed netting, is electrified. By this arrangement, the shrimp is stirred up and jumps through the large meshes of the bottom netting in the trawl, while the fish are driven away by the netting closing the entrance of the gear and by the electrified area under the trawl.[568] This is achieved by using low pulse rates – sufficient to induce a jumping reaction in the shrimp, not enough to induce electrotaxis in the fish, but enough to frighten them away. By this means, the capture of bottom fish and other marine organisms should be eliminated when trawling shrimp.

21.7 Inland water bottom trawls (by Dr E Dahm)
After the sharp rise in the importance of trawls in sea fisheries after the end of the Second World War, trials were started at different places seeking to apply this efficient method of catching to inland waters. Fishing gears related to beamtrawls or drag nets have been traditionally used in inland waters

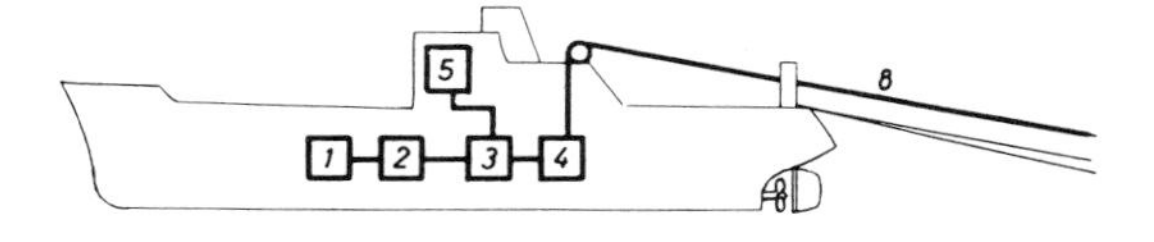

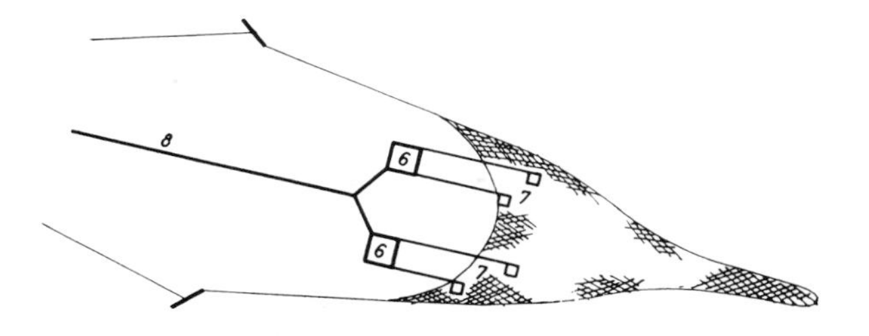

Fig 500 Sketch of electrical trawling method, according to C O Kreutzer (*Scharfe, 1965*) 1. Diesel engine 2. Generator 3. Electrical impulse transmitter 4. Transformer 5. Control apparatus for impulse transmitter 6. Impulse transformer 7. Electrodes 8. Warps.

in the past.[30, 569] Nevertheless, modern trawling can be considered a new fishing technique in most freshwater fisheries. A transfer of the technology of trawl fishing gained in deep sea and inshore fishing to inland waters was only possible where an area of water yielded sufficiently large catches to warrant the necessary investment in towing power, fishing gear and deck machinery.[36, 166, 525] In general, the conditions of inland waters required special constructions and operational techniques.[419, 599] This applies particularly to inland water bottom trawls. If adequate deck machinery is lacking, the size of inland water bottom trawls has to be such that these nets can be shot and hauled by manpower. Insufficient towing power limits the size of the trawl and towing speed. Therefore, inland water bottom trawls are comparatively small and light.[417] To some extent, low towing power can be overcome by using the pair trawling technique by which the power of two boats is concentrated on one net, and a decrease of up to 40% of the towing resistance of a given trawl may be gained if no otter boards are used (*Fig 501*). In this way, relatively small engines may tow a big net.[514] If the weight of the trawl in water is to be suitable for handling by manpower, experience has shown that the possible depth range should be restricted to the first 20 metres below the surface. In lakes with a steep slope, as in Norway, southern Germany or Austria, bottom trawling is therefore only possible to a limited extent. A reduction of the towing speed to increase the depth range only proves efficient at certain times of the day or year, *eg* at night, during the cold season when some fish tend to gather in aggregations, or during the spawning season. The economic use of inland water bottom trawling could only be reached where human interference impeded the use of other efficient fishing gear, *eg* traps, longlines, gillnets and entangling nets. An increase in catching efficiency was gained by electrification of the gear.[180, 230]

Bottom trawling is not possible everywhere, even in shallow waters. Whereas the soft and muddy bottoms of eutrophied lakes in middle Europe offer no severe unexpected obstruction to bottom trawling, this is not so in some Scandinavian lakes seeded with boulders, or on the usually rough grounds of large reservoirs, or on the beds of large rivers where excavation and navigation has left many snags.

Some importance has been gained by inland water bottom trawls in recent years as a useful tool in the administrative task of restoring the disturbed balance of species in water which has been selectively exploited. In many cases this has led to uneven coarse fish populations, because their predators have been decimated by a disproportionate selection of fish. Inland water bottom trawls yielded catches of several tons in a few days and proved an efficient means of restoring the balance with comparatively little expenditure of time and personnel.[124]

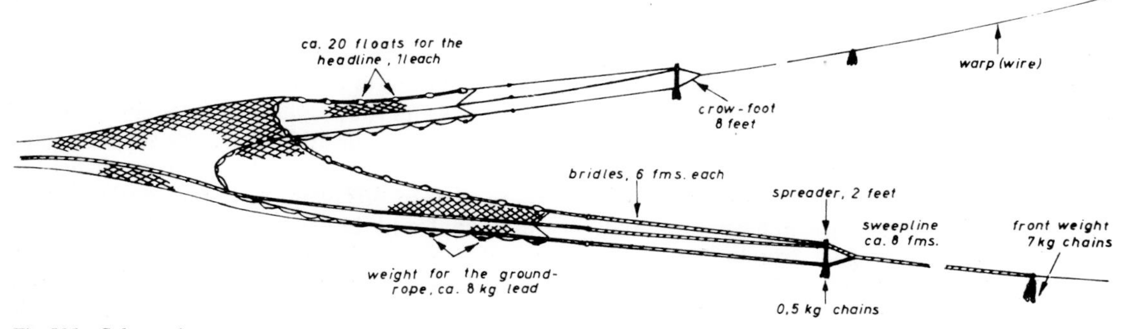

Fig 501 Schematic representation of the rigging for freshwater two-boat bottom trawls. (*Steinberg and Dahm, 1975*).

Chapter twenty-two

Trawl fishery in three dimensions

Dredges and trawls, described in the previous chapter, are used for catching fish or other aquatic animals which live directly on the bottom, or which usually stay near the bottom. Therefore such gears must be as wide as possible in order to fish the largest possible area. The remarkable progress achieved by the herring fisheries industry of northwest Europe when it succeeded in increasing the opening height of its trawl nets has already been described. Herring do sometimes only hug the bottom, but are mostly located several metres above it. Previously, it was not possible to catch them in sufficient bulk with the small trawl nets working along the bottom, as they had but little opening height. Experience gained in line fishing and driftnet fishing has shown that many keenly sought fish, like herring, do not live only near the bottom, but also range in the upper waters, even near the surface. Many fishing gears have been developed for fishing the surface waters and these are described in the appropriate sections of this book.

We now face the old problem of catching fish in mid-waters. Fish detecting instruments have confirmed that many species of fish do undertake regular daily migrations, and that they can be found, temporarily, at considerable distances above the bottom. They could, therefore, never be caught (or only occasionally) by gear trawling over the bottom. Equally, it is also impossible to be sure of catching them with gear designed for operating on the surface of the water because the range of such gear is not deep enough. The unfished area between the fishing range of gear trawling on the bottom and that operating near the surface became greater as the fishery extended out into deeper waters.

Theoretically, there is only one fishing method by which it is possible to catch fish at any depth, and that is with hooks and lines. As has been shown in Chapter 9, some line fisheries operate at depths of some hundreds of metres. But in the great depths of the sea it is difficult to secure large quantities of fish with hooks and lines, as they swim at varying depths. But the echograph, penetrating to 1,500 or more metres below the water surface, reveals fish shoals although they may still be some thousand metres or so above the bottom.

22.1 Predecessors of mid-water trawls and semi-pelagic trawls

For a long time, thought has ranged over the possibility of designing a trawl in such a way that it could not only be used on the bottom, but could also be used for working freely in all depths of water. This was wanted not only in sea fisheries but also in the great lakes, and many attempts had been made to develop such a gear. Whereas, previously, the intention was to keep the trawl in close contact with the bottom, the desire was now to lift it from the bottom. If the depth to be fished is not too great, that problem can easily be resolved. The trawl, and also a seine net, can be suspended by means of floats on the water's surface (*Figs 502* and *516*). The desired depth can be obtained simply by adjusting the length of the connecting lines between the floats and the net. This is a widely used method for keeping trawls and other gear suspended in the water. Asiatic fishermen catch surface fishes by this method (*Fig 503*) and German cutter fishermen have employed the same method to catch sprats and small herrings off Heligoland. In the beginning of such experiments they used trawls and also stow nets suspended from floating iron barrels and rubber floats, even though water resistance reduced the towing speed. Such suspended nets are often shaped in a special way. The upper net of the bottom trawl protrudes like a roof, but the floating trawl is sometimes designed in the opposite way. A bottom trawl was used in an upside down position, or constructed in such a manner that it is not the upper net that protrudes but the lower net, so that the net takes on a shovel-like form. The idea was to prevent fish, which usually dive downwards when confronted with a net opening, from escaping into deep water.

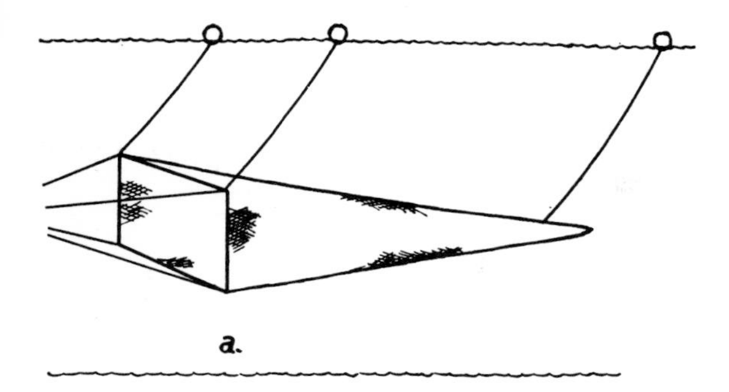

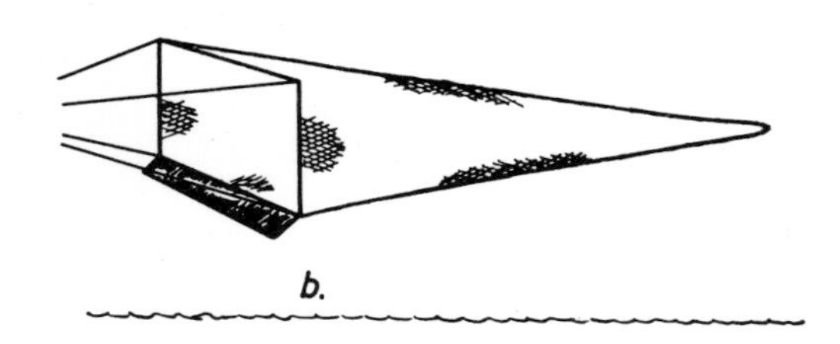

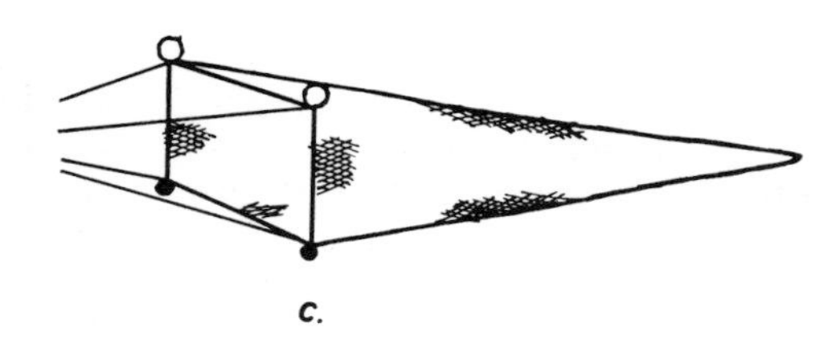

Fig 502 Possibilities for the construction of midwater trawls: (*a*) hanging on floats; (*b*) with depressor; (*c*) balanced by weights and floats.

Fig 503 Japanese midwater trawl used on Kasumi-ga-ura Lake. The gear is hanging on the floats shown on the water in front of the broadside sailing boat.

However, such nets, suspended from floats on the surface, are not the ideal type of gear for fishing the middle waters. The length of the connecting lines between floats and nets is limited and no fishing is possible by such means in any great depths of water. A greater disadvantage is that the depth of the nets cannot be changed during fishing, although the fish may be ascending or descending. Any change in depth can only be made by interrupting the fishing operation and altering the length of the connecting lines. As will be shown later, in modern mid-water trawling, the towing depth of the trawl is regulated by the towing speed without interrupting the fishing operation. Nevertheless, the 'hanging up' method has to be used in mid-water trawling in inland waters where, very often, only a slow towing speed is possible which is insufficient for any depth regulation (*Fig 516*).[599]

A similar disadvantage exists with another patented suggestion which may not have been realized in practical fishing. This was to tow a sledge over the bottom, to which was attached a net with great buoyancy, like that of a mobile kite balloon. By such means, it was thought the trawl could be kept at some distance from the bottom. However, its height above the bottom would be limited by the length of the connecting lines and, therefore, no depth control during fishing would be possible. On the other hand there is no doubt that trawls fishing at a greater distance from the bottom are very successful under suitable conditions. The method of fishing with a trawl with high buoyancy, but nevertheless in contact with the bottom, has been put into practice not with a sledge towed over the ground, but with otter boards gliding over the ground and towing a floating trawl behind (*Fig 504b*) This is the so-called 'semi-pelagic trawl' developed by the French for 'near bottom trawling'. The genuine mid-water trawl, which operates in any depth of water, could not be fulfilled by either of the two proposals described.

Another idea is to provide the net with depressors or diving boards (*Fig 502b*). When not towed, the relatively small net would sink to the bottom, but during towing it would ascend by reason of the resistance of the water acting in the same way as it does on a bucket towed on a line by a sailing boat. Accordingly, depressors were designed to counteract the ascent of the net. The faster the tow, the stronger would be the pressure of ascent, but the depth shearing effect of the depressors would also be increasing. Both forces could be held in balance so that the net would remain floating. By adjusting the length of the warps, the trawl, it was

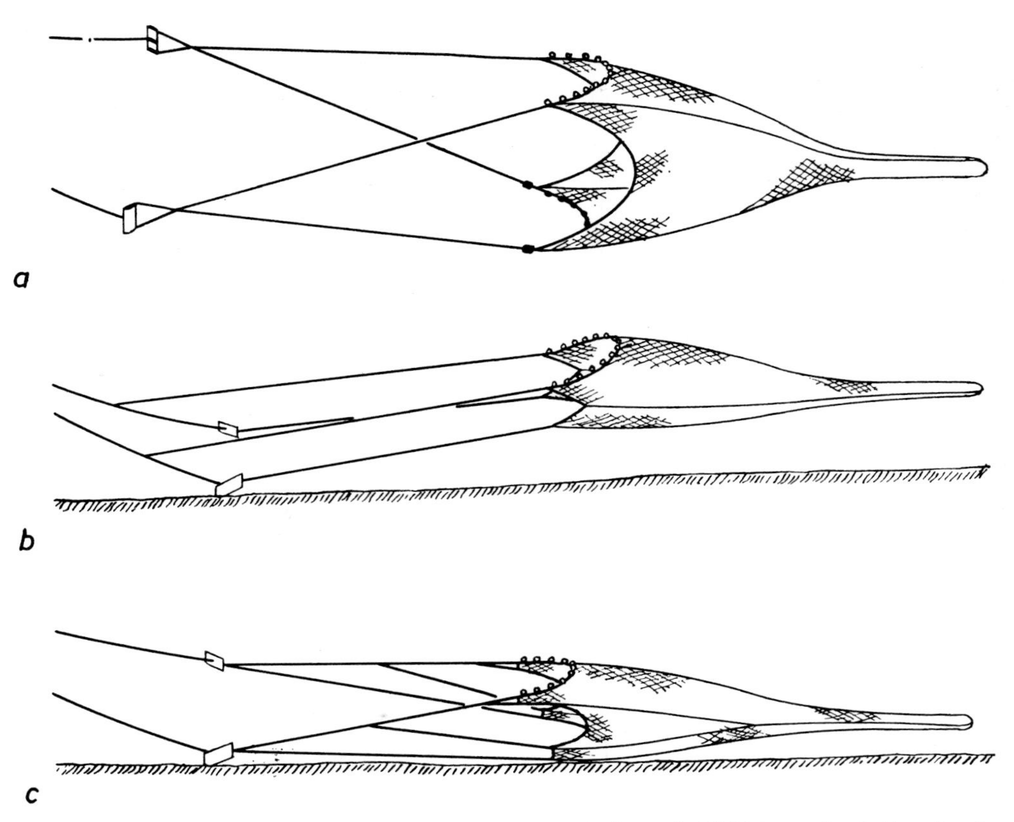

Fig 504 Types of trawls: (*a*) midwater trawl; (*b*) semi-pelagic trawl; (*c*) high-opening bottom trawl.

thought, could be operated at any depth desired. This method has actually been used with several gears employed for catching plankton or young small fish for scientific purposes (*Figs 505* and *506*). By this means it is possible to fish the pelagic area and so one is justified in describing it as pelagic trawling, because the gear can be operated at any depth. The concept has been further pursued on behalf of commercial fishing. With larger gear it is found that a special depressor is no longer necessary (*Fig 502c*). The trawl can be balanced in such a manner that it slowly rises with an increase in towing speed and descends with decreasing speed. Equally it can be towed at a certain depth by an even speed in towing. The necessary depth is roughly secured by adjusting the length of the warps. The longer they are, the deeper the trawl will float and the shorter they are, the higher it will rise. By regulating the length of the warps as well as the speed of towing, real pelagic, mid-water trawling became possible. The range of this fishery is limited only by the length of the warps and the power of the engines for ship and winch. But generally speaking, by this method fishing can be carried out in three dimensions. Mid-water trawling, also known as 'aimed trawling' has been successfully developed; and could become very important in the future.

22.2 Aimed trawling

The prerequisite for the development of a fishery with pelagic or mid-water trawls was the development of fish detecting devices such as echo-sounders and, in particular, of the echograph. As long as these did not exist, it could never be ascertained if there were fish about and, if so, at what depth. Moreover, there was the difficulty of knowing at what depth the net was floating. Fishermen tried to calculate the length of the warps in relation to the towing speed and, correspondingly, at each depth at which fishes were recorded. But there were many errors and, at the beginning of the development of mid-water trawls in the 1950s, it was never clear if there was a failure due to wrong design of the gear or to the fact that there was too great a difference between the depth of the fish and the depth of the floating trawl. Depth recorders fixed to the trawl could not solve

Fig 505 Pelagic trawl held open by two upper kites (not in the drawing) and one diving board, used for catching fish eggs and fry by the Biological Station, Heligoland in 1911. (*Photo: Archives*).

the problem. They were helpful in finding out where the trawl had been during towing, but they could not show the depth in relation to the fish and gear during fishing. This problem was solved at the end of the 1950s by the invention of the 'net sounder'

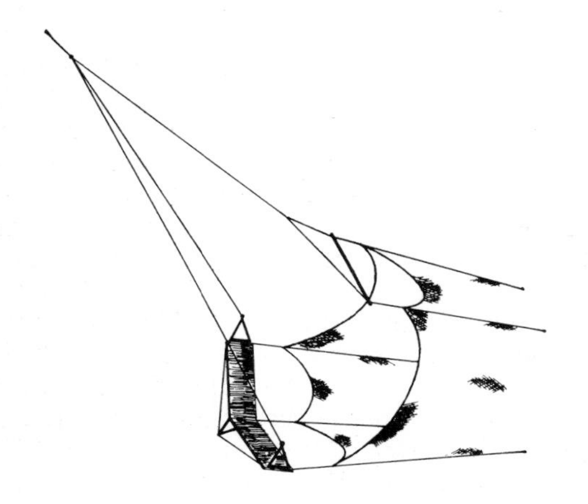

Fig 506 Midwater trawl with depressor: the Isaacs-Kidd midwater trawl.

(netsonde). With the help of a headline transducer, not only the distance of the trawl from the bottom, or from the surface of the water, but also the vertical opening height of the gear can be shown by the recorder on the bridge of the vessel (*Fig 507*). Any disarrangement of the net can immediately be detected.[543] But more decisive is the fact that the position of the trawl in relation to the fish can be controlled constantly during fishing. From observation of fish behaviour towards the midwater trawl, it appears that sometimes fish change their position, mostly swimming deeper, when the vessel is passing over the shoal. As long as the relationship of the swimming depth of the fish and the depth in which the floating gear was operated could not be recorded with the help of the net sounder, many failures were experienced, even when the net was placed exactly at the depth where the fish had been located before fishing began. Now, according to the information received from the netsonde, the trawl can follow the fish until they can be seen between the headline and foot-rope, *ie* until they can be seen to be entering the gear. But

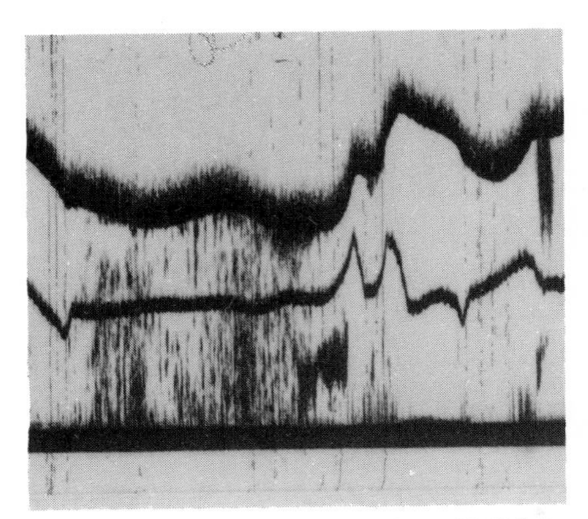

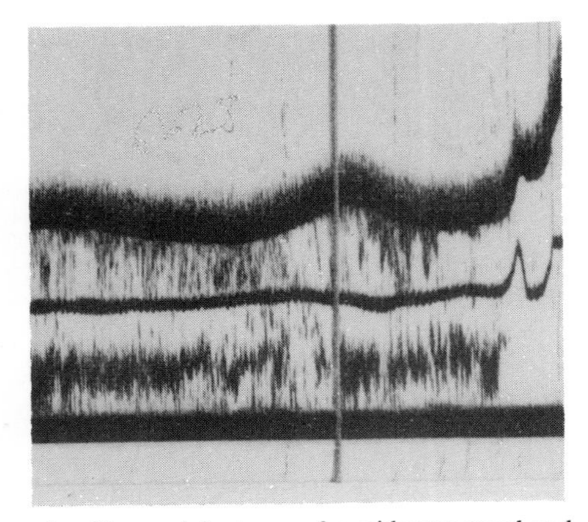

Fig 507 Echograms of net sounders with fish between headline and footrope of a midwater trawl and also between footrope and bottom. (*Courtesy of Honeywell Elac, Kiel*).

it was a long time before the variations of fish behaviour, especially the variations in the behaviour of herring, in relation to mid-water trawls was understood.[402] Today, the netsonde is considered a prerequisite for successful mid-water trawling. Only with the help of this gear is 'aimed trawling' possible. This term was introduced to indicate that, with the help of the ship's sonar and echo-sounder, and with the netsonde on the headline of the trawl, more efficient operation of the net was possible. During experimental work the net sounder became a 'multi-net-sounder', which provided the feasibility of control of the area before the net opening or of measuring the horizontal width of the gear. The net sounder provides many opportunities for controlling the operation of the gear and the quantity of the catch. The fish between headline and ground-rope can be monitored when entering the gear. With an additional receiver, the fish passing under or over the gear can also be monitored. Some apparatus can give a total view of the situation and, at the same time, an enlarged section of the most interesting depth. There are also combinations of equipment providing fish recording and measurement of temperature at the depth of the mid-water trawl.

The signals from the netsonde can be transmitted by wire to the recorder on the bridge of the vessel. This can be by a long cable reaching from the net sounder on the headline of the gear to the vessel. For storing and operating this cable a special winch is needed. Transfer of the signals can also be achieved by radio. In this case the signals are transmitted from the headline to a floating transmitter which sends the signals to the vessel. Both methods have their advantages and disadvantages. Radio transmission can be disturbed by turbulence in the water or by scattering layers.

22.3 Two-boat and one-boat mid-water trawling

It was the Danes who developed mid-water trawling with two boats, and it was not the first time that the fisheries of the world were indebted to this country for an important new fishing method. In 1948 Robert Larsen of Skagen designed the first mid-water trawl when the first echo-sounders were being experimented with in fisheries. The 'Larsen mid-water trawl' (*Fig 508*) became very successful and has been introduced into many fisheries throughout the world.[195] In northwestern Europe, mid-water trawling by two boats became very important in the herring fisheries (*Fig 509*). Not only cutters of 20 to 30 metres in length, but also larger vessels of more than 40 metres in length and 600hp and more, had been successful in two-boat mid-water trawling.[595] Fishing with two vessels, however, involves nautical problems and is especially dependent on the weather. Operations must be stopped at Beaufort Force 5 or 6, depending on the power of the vessels. In addition, the seamen, in particular the skippers, are not always of the kind that are able to work together, not only in co-operating but also in being able to subordinate the wishes of the one to the needs of the other. Many efforts have therefore been made to make it possible to tow pelagic trawls with a single vessel, because that would avoid some human and technical difficulties. Single craft can still operate in wind strengths up to 7 or 8 Beaufort. Two-boat trawling is restricted to small and medium size vessels. The one-boat system can be carried out by larger vessels with more than 1,000hp which can also fish at greater depths and on more distant grounds for species like cod, hake and redfish which, at certain seasons, are to be found (like herring) off the bottom. By using a single vessel, however, it becomes necessary to use otter boards

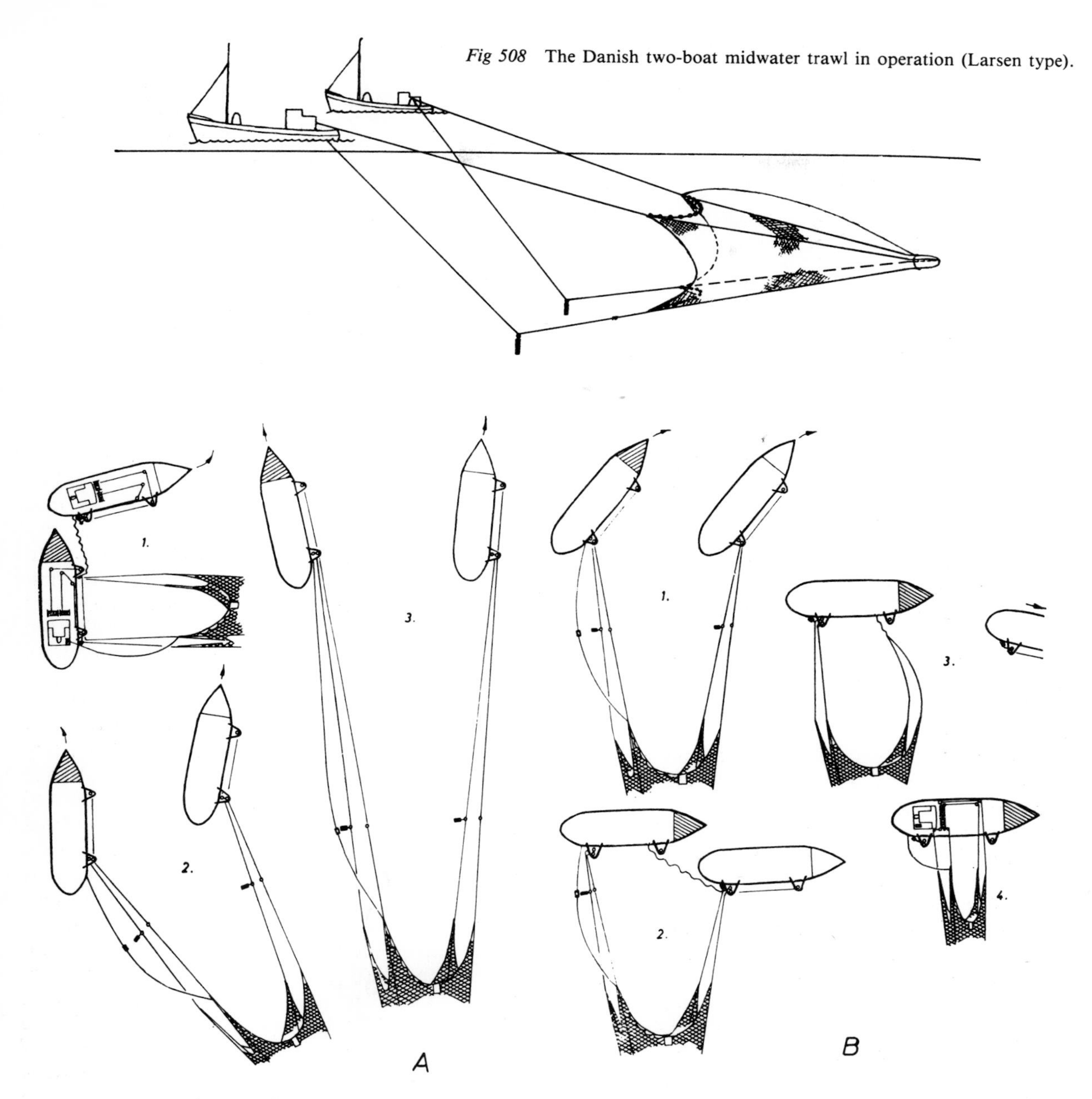

Fig 508 The Danish two-boat midwater trawl in operation (Larsen type).

Fig 509 Operation of a two-boat midwater trawl; (*a*) shooting; (*b*) hauling. (*R Steinberg, 1967*).

for spreading the nets horizontally (*Fig 510*). It was speedily ascertained that boards designed on hydrodynamic principles (higher than broad) were specially suited for achieving that spread. The most common boards for mid-water trawling became the Süberkrüb otter boards already mentioned (*Fig 481a*). These high aspect-ratio cambered boards have not only a very good spreading efficiency, but by increasing speed the boards climb up immediately. This quick response to speed changes gives the basis for the technique already introduced as 'aimed trawling'. There are also other boards operated in mid-water trawling like the aforementioned French polyvalent boards with an oval form. In the beginning of mid-water trawling, regular flat and rectangular boards were used, but they had a high degree of instability which increased with the length of the lines between the trawl and the boards. Usually one pair of boards was used but there have been designs with more than one pair of

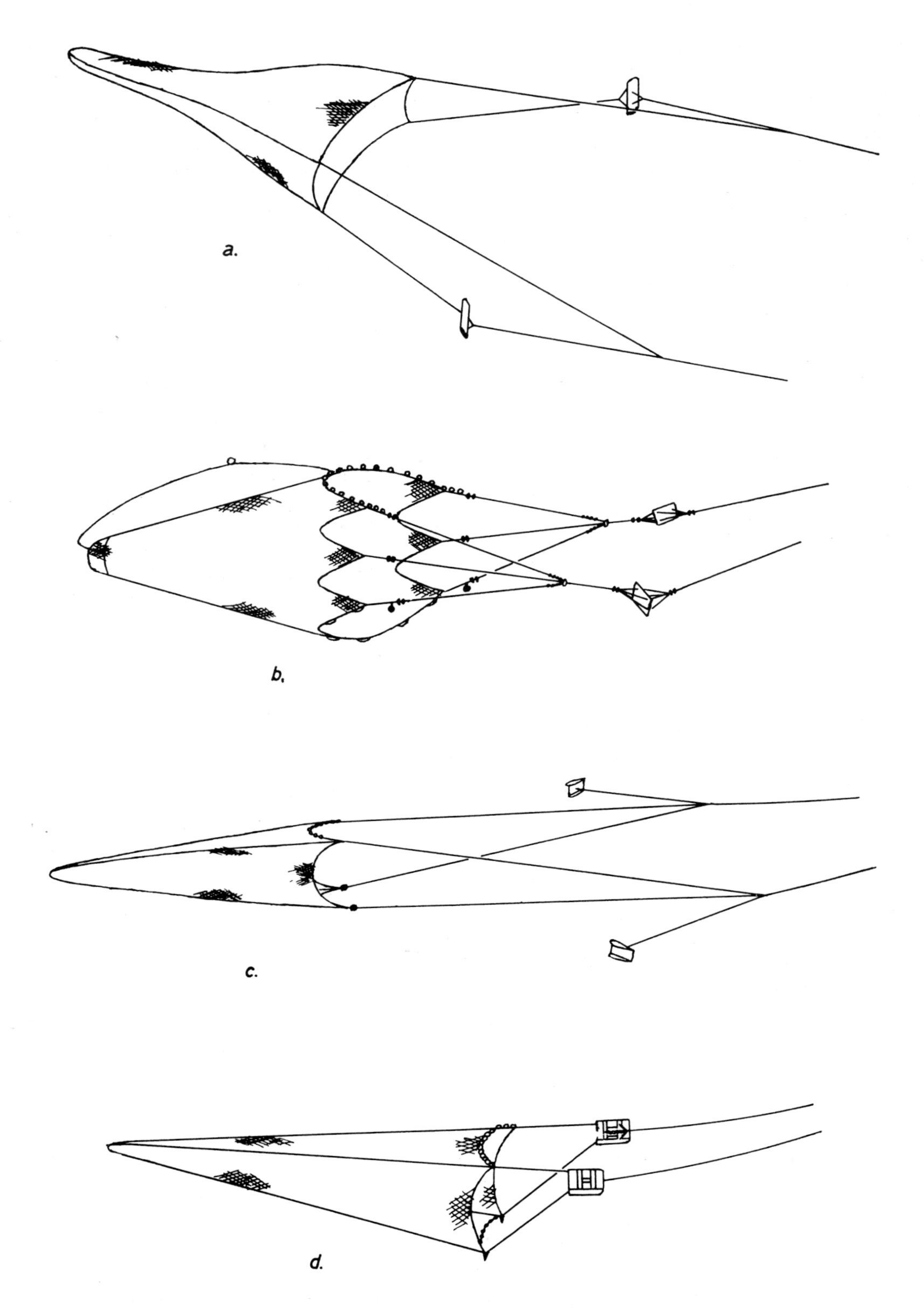

Fig 510 Various one-boat midwater trawls: (*a*) Icelandic Breidfjord trawl; (*b*) Steinar Persson's six-wing net; (*c*) Canadian trawl (*Barraclough and Johnson, 1955*); (*d*) Japanese one-boat midwater trawl.

otter boards (*Fig 511*). There are also French semi-pelagic trawls which have two small pelagic otter boards on the upper wings and larger bottom trawl doors on the two lower wings of a four-seam trawl.[469] Other designs can have different shearing devices, like elevators or depressors on headline and footrope respectively. Not only did alterations in the form of the otter boards become necessary when used in one-boat mid-water trawling but also the trawl itself had to be changed when used in one-boat or two-boat mid-water trawling.

First of all, investigations of fish behaviour made it clear that mid-water trawls must have a wide opening to be successful. Some fish keep a distance of five metres or more off the netting. That means that the opening must extend more than ten metres in both directions. The theoretical net mouth area thus increased from about 250 to about 2,000m², that means even more than 50 metres wide and nearly 40 metres high.[546] This could be realized only by changing the design of the trawl. In the beginning, mid-water trawls were constructed, like large bottom trawls, of two panels – an upper and a lower one. But now mid-water trawls are made as four-seam nets with two equal top and bottom panels and two equal, usually smaller, side panels (*Figs 510* and *512*) to get an optimal size of trawl opening. Moreover mid-water trawls, much more than bottom trawls, must have a low resistance when towed or, in other words, the water flow through the trawl must be good. This means that very large meshes have to be used in the forepart of the trawl and that the diameter of the netting yarn must be small. This could be achieved only with the netting yarns made of polyamide fibres which not only have a high breaking strength with a small diameter but also high elasticity to overcome sudden jerks when a fish shoal enters the trawl. Fishermen sometimes called the mid-water trawls 'fly catchers' because they are very light in contrast to some heavy bottom trawls.

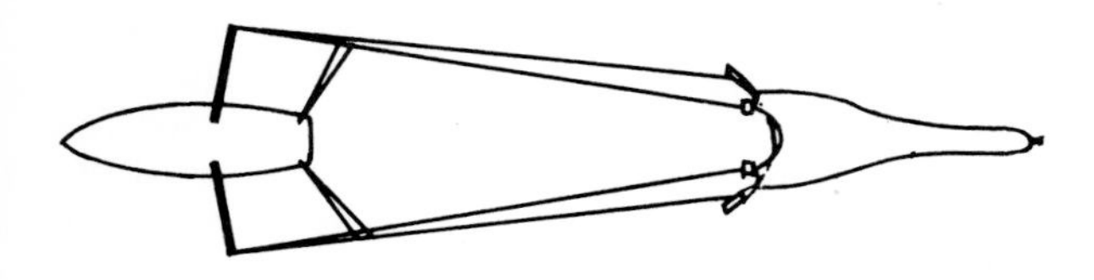

Fig 511 One-boat midwater trawl with four otter boards, used in the Belgian and Dutch fishery.

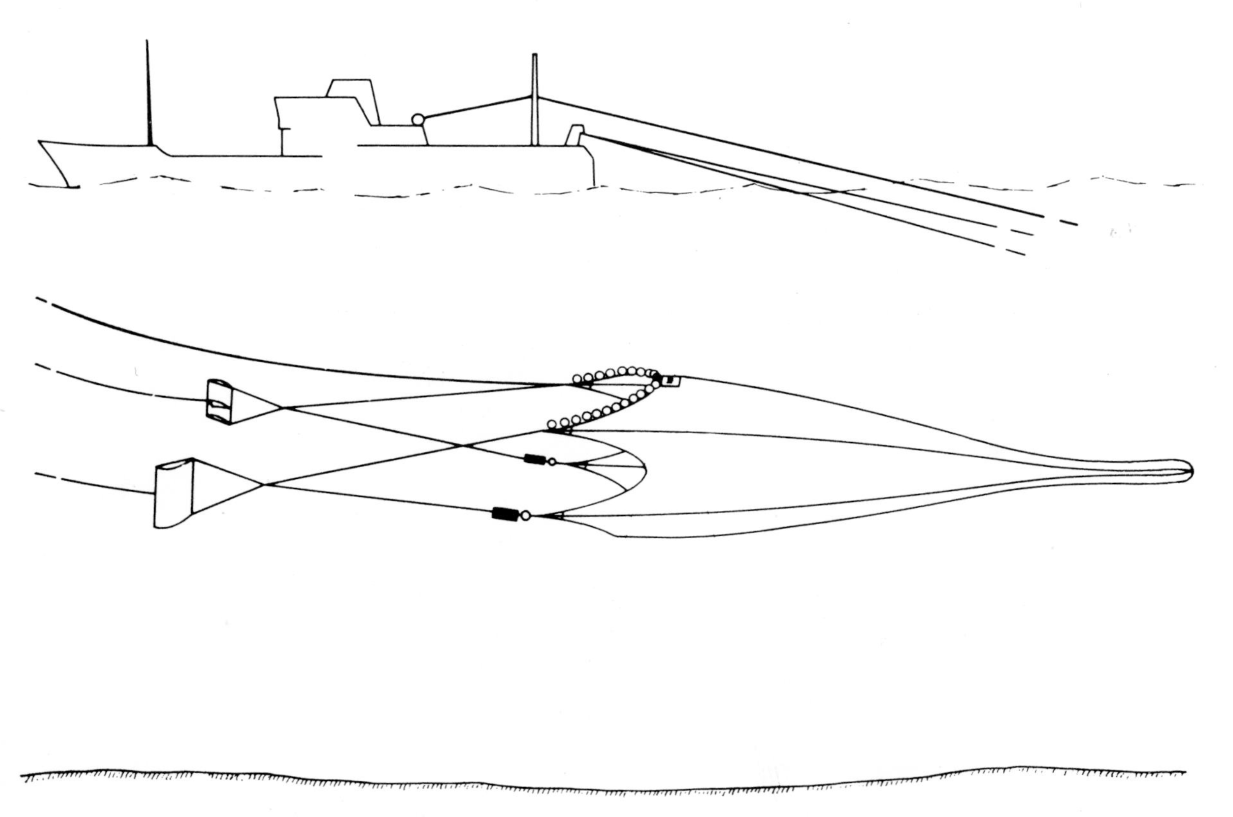

Fig 512 German one-boat midwater trawl with headline recorder (Netzsonde), up/down-type. (*J Schärfe, 1969.*)

Fine netting material is necessary in mid-water trawling to avoid frightening pelagic fish away from the opening of the trawl, which has some water swell which will increase with the diameter of the net material and smaller size of mesh. A new idea for decreasing the water resistance of the trawl arose in the 1970s. This was to replace the netting of the front part of the trawl by a very large meshed one. Until recently it was thought that the forepart meshes should not be larger than 80 to 120cm. Recently the size of these meshes has been increased substantially without losing their effectiveness in guiding the fish into the centre of the trawl. The so-called Biscay trawl of the French fishery has meshes with a length of ten metres in the wings and belly (*Fig 513*), and in the Faeroes and Norway meshes of sixteen metres have been used, especially for fishing for blue whiting in depths of 120 down to 400 metres. With the ten metre wing meshes, a net opening of 1,000 to 1,500m² has to be towed, needing at least 1,200 to 1,500hp. With such large meshes a very good water flow and low resistance of the gear when fishing for very sensitive fish is possible but also, when it is used with bottom trawls, the unwanted catch like crabs, stones and sea trash, will fall between the large meshes out of the gear.[596]

The connecting points of such large meshes, mostly made of plaited lines, are sometimes not knotted in the usual manner, but the four shanks of each mesh side are connected with each other by eye splices (*Figs 513* and *514a*).[58] To prevent floats or headline transducer entangling in the large meshes of the forepart of the gear during shooting, the trawl opening should begin with a strip of small meshed netting.

Another idea, with the object of saving energy required for towing by decreasing the resistance of the gear, came from Poland. This is the so-called rope trawl, also named 'rope wing trawl' or 'spaghetti trawl' by fishermen. In this case, the netting of the front part of the four-seam trawl consists of plaited warps running parallel for a few metres.[596, 597] This design was successful, although the long ropes and their calculation caused some troubles at the beginning (*Fig 514b*). But the water resistance of the gear was decreased very much, as was the undesirable catch such as jellyfish.

Originally, mid-water trawls were designed for small boats in pair trawling. The advantages of the one-boat mid-water trawl and the need for trawls with larger openings resulted in this gear being designed for use by larger and stronger trawlers such as factory stern trawlers only. Mid-water trawls have been operated by stern trawlers of more than 3,000 tons and up to 5,000hp (*Figs 494* and *515*). One-boat mid-water trawls became the gear for use in distant fisheries for herring, and also for pelagic

Fig 513 Large-meshed forepart of a midwater trawl stored on a netdrum in the harbour of St. Jean de Luz, France, (1978).

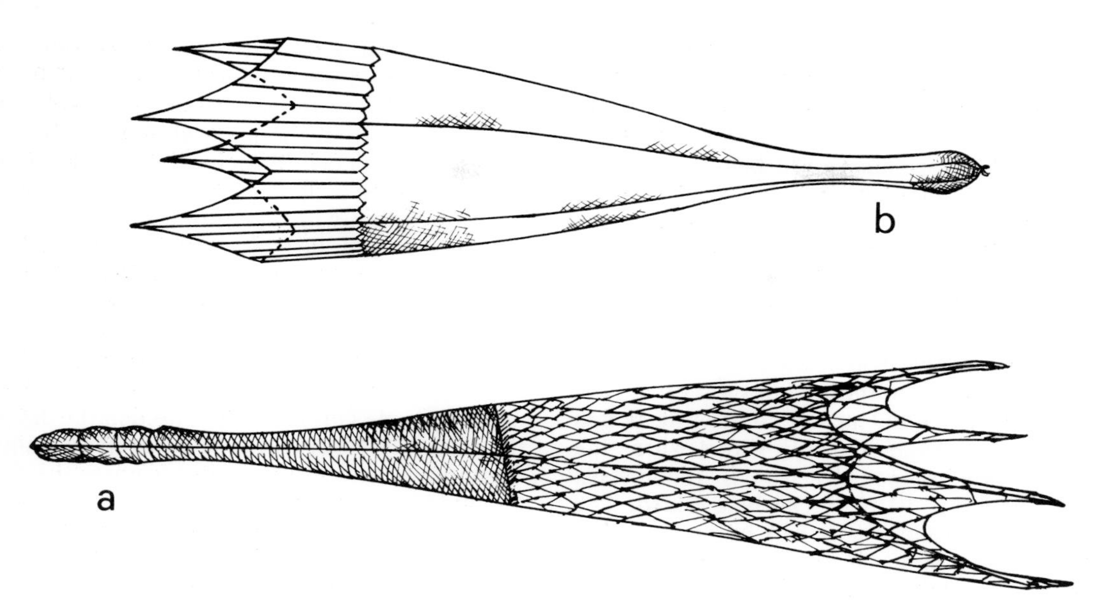

Fig 514 Four-seam midwater trawls with forepart of (*a*) large mesh size or (*b*) ropes, to decrease water resistance.

cod, redfish, pollock, saithe, blue whiting, mackerel-like fish and krill. Nevertheless, there have been some skilled skippers who have succeeded in one-boat mid-water trawling with smaller vessels of less than 300hp. A good knowledge of fish behaviour made it possible to find situations where they could succeed with smaller gear and slower speed. With the increasing size of vessels, and stronger engines, one-boat mid-water trawling became more profitable. Therefore, even today it is possible that mid-water trawling is not used to its full extent.

22.4 Mid-water trawls in fresh water

(by Dr E Dahm)

Mid-water, or pelagic, fishing is also found in lake fisheries. Until recently these fisheries were mostly exploited by efficient, inexpensive gillnets but these are, however, time and labour consuming in operation. Trials to catch pelagic fish in inland

Fig 515 Successful catch in midwater trawling: 80 tons of herring in 20 minutes. (*Photo: J Schärfe.*)

waters by the very efficient purse seines have been undertaken, but have brought no remarkable results.[146, 268, 281] Generally, this applies also to inland water mid-water trawls, but there are a few exceptions which are mentioned below.

A net towed in mid-water requires special towing power because it has not only to be towed forward, as in bottom trawling, but has also to be kept at the required fishing depth. As shown by the development of the inshore mid-water trawls, this can be achieved by buoys towed on the water surface carrying the weight of the net. It has proved advantageous to fasten those buoys not directly at the upper wing tips but at the connecting points between the bridles and towing warps where the front weights are fastened (*Fig 516*). By that means, distortion of the trawl body can be avoided. The required fishing depth can then be arranged by adjusting the length of the connecting line between buoy and front weight. However, this means that the depth cannot be changed during the tow. Careful observation by an echo-sounder before the tow must reveal the depth layer where most of the fish aggregate. In bottom trawling in fresh water, an echograph is a useful additional piece of equipment: in mid-water trawling it is not possible to operate without one.[599]

There are examples of mid-water trawling in inland waters with boats which could carry out the same task in coastal and inshore waters.[166, 263] Generally, on smaller lakes, fishing boats with an engine of more than 20 to 30hp are seldom found because the smaller boats are quite suitable for their main purpose of transporting personnel, fishing gear and catch. However, if such boats attempt to tow a small mid-water trawl of about 20m headline length, they very soon come to the limit of their power. Therefore, the method of pair trawling is to be recommended. Besides which, on such boats there is often a lack of deck machinery, *eg* motor-driven winches, which could facilitate the work of hauling the trawl. For this reason many inland water mid-water trawls are small and suitable for handling by manpower.[417] Such a small size of inland water mid-water trawl should be a handicap to successful fishing. As described in the preceding section, many fish try to keep a safe distance from a moving netting panel. This reaction is used in the design of the giant mid-water trawls of the deep sea fisheries. These huge trawls seek to concentrate the fish in the middle of the net opening, where they swim in the direction of the trawl for a while and then drop back into the codend from exhaustion. Trawls of this size cannot be used in inland waters. Some fishermen nevertheless obtain good catches with small mid-water trawls towed during the night. Fish which respond mainly to optical stimuli apparently at that time have a substantially reduced judgement of distance.[123]

Obviously, in European inland waters, mid-water trawls are, at the moment, only used on a commercial basis for the catch of a relatively few related species (*Coregonus albula, Coregonus artedii* and *Osmerus eperlanus*) where its application has proved successful in saving time and manpower. This fishing method may be inhibited by the fact that with the trawl suspended on buoys it is practically impossible to fish for traces deeper

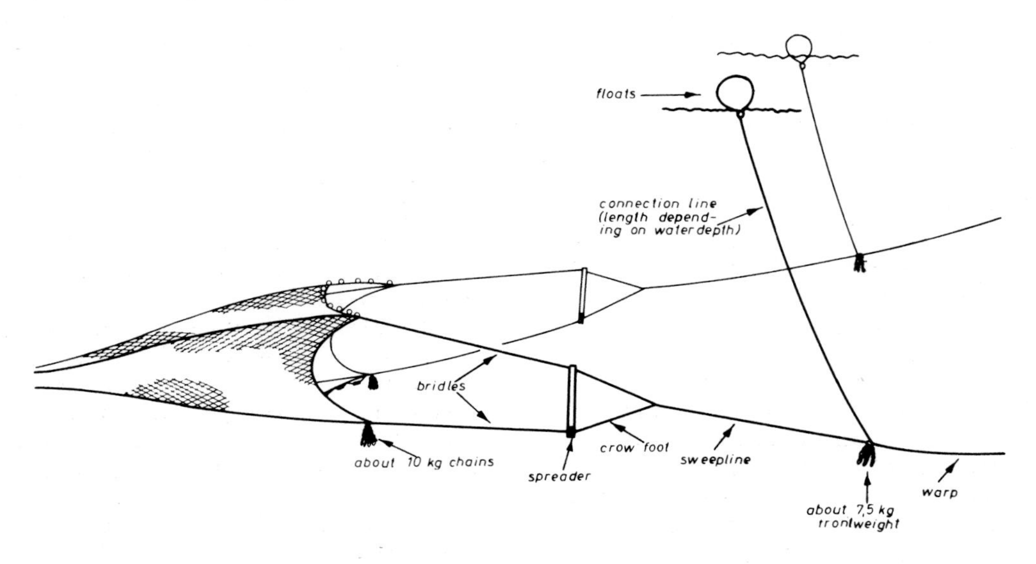

Fig 516 Schematic representation of the rigging for a freshwater two-boat midwater trawl.

than 18 metres. This is because the weight of the trawl is limited by the fact that it has to be handled by manpower, which prevents a descent below that depth at a towing speed of about three knots. By leaving out the carrier buoys, by appropriate distribution of the weights on the bridles, and by reduction of the towing resistance of the towing warps, the depth range may be extended to approximately 40 metres. Without buoys, the depth has to be adjusted by the speed of the boat because the length of the warps cannot be changed during the tow. Accurate instrumentation for measuring speed at this low range is scarce and expensive. An engine revolution counter, found on most larger boat engines, fulfills the same purpose but the relation between depth and engine revolutions at a given warp length has to be determined, at least once, in a calibration table. This can be done by using a third boat with an independent echo sounder over the towed net, but this method is difficult and full of possible errors. The direct measurement of the distance between headline and surface by means of a second sounder fastened at the middle of the headline and connected by cable to a second echo-sounder in one of the towing boats, gives far more reliable results.

In the view of present experience, it is still questionable whether mid-water trawling in inland waters will ever reach more than local importance in commercial fishing. Nevertheless, there are good prospects for scientific application. At many places in the world, scientists are working on methods of ascertaining fish stocks by the use of echo-sounder signals. It was demonstrated by a Working Group of EIFAC, during the evaluation of such a method in a big lake in Finland in 1980, that no other fishing gear is suited to sample pelagic fish concentrations.

22.5 Problems of mid-water trawling

Bottom trawling and, more so, mid-water trawling, have been considered the essential methods for bulk fishing by large self-fishing vessels, especially stern trawlers and large factory processing vessels. For reasons mentioned earlier (Chapter 21) smaller vessels with smaller power requirements, in the form of multi-purpose vessels, are now considered as the fishing vessels of the future.[582] However, there remain some problems which have not yet been resolved adequately. There is the question of a multi-purpose trawl, that is, a trawl which can be used as a bottom trawl or a mid-water trawl. This includes suitable otter boards when operated in one-boat fishing. The question is, therefore, if a trawl suitable for bottom fishing can also be suitable for mid-water fishing. The so-called 'delagic trawl' (this word is a combination of pelagic and demersal), developed in Scotland, is considered the most appropriate gear. It may be used either in mid-water as a floating gear, or in contact with the seabed during the same haul, without changing the rigging. As has been explained earlier, a large net opening is necessary for mid-water trawls but there is no doubt that, in an earlier period, smaller vessels fished with two-seam trawls only, and these could be used for demersal as well as for pelagic trawling, in contrast with the high-opening four-seam trawls which have been very vulnerable to damage when touching the bottom. For mid-water trawling a high opening and light trawl is necessary. For bottom trawling, the high opening is often not so important, but the gear must be sufficiently heavy to have a good bottom contact and a strong resistance to wear and tear. Therefore, it seems as if a combination of a bottom and mid-water trawl, as one-boat or two-boat gear, is a 'contradiction in terms' even today. A hybrid trawl, such as a four-seam 'delagic trawl', can not be as efficient at taking bottom fish or mid-water fish as special trawls for bottom trawling or for mid-water fishing.[176] It seems that there has been more success with otter boards which can be operated in both forms of trawling. Nevertheless, the best mid-water boards are considered to be the Süberkrüb boards: they have a quick lifting power in mid-water fishing, but they do not have sufficient stability for bottom trawling.

A special problem of mid-water and sometimes also bottom trawling is that often large catches of fish can be made within the space of a few minutes. To avoid overloading the trawl for quality reasons is one thing, but to haul big quantities along the chute of a stern trawler is quite another. The problem is not so much the winch power or the breaking strength of the net material as the pressure in the trawl which may damage the soft fish. Therefore some means of determining to what extent a codend is filled has been needed for a long time. There have been a number of ideas for measuring the quantity of fish in the codend, mostly based on some measurable variations of the water resistance of an empty or a filled codend. But there were some surprising results, including the fact that a full codend could sometimes have less water resistance than an empty one. A later idea for measuring the quantity of fish in a codend was developed in Norway (1977) and Germany. It is based on the fact that the shape of the mesh in the different parts of the codend will alter according to the amount of fish it contains. In an empty codend all meshes are nearly closed and in a rhombic form. When fish fill the end of the codend the meshes in this area become more or less opened, nearly to a quadratic form. Along the backside of the codend some sensors are fitted measuring each change of the stretching of the mesh from closed to open according to the increasing quantity of caught fish first in the end of the codend, then in its middle and forepart. Appropriate signals are given from the sensors by wire to the headline transducer and from there, via the cable of the net sounder, to the indicator aboard the vessel. By this means it is possible to see how full the trawl is at any point of time. Overloading the codend and losing the gear and catch by rupture, as happened on former occasions in pelagic fishing for herring and blue whiting, can now be prevented. It is an advantage for the sensors to be small enough to pass through the power block, triplex and similar hauling gear. The sensors can also remain on the trawl when the gear is hauled by a net drum. In this respect, cables are much more vulnerable. This is why partial wireless transmitting became necessary.

Another idea for avoiding rupturing a trawl when hauling it in with a large catch is to remove some of the catch with the help of suction pumps whilst the net is still in the water. The pumping of fish out of the net on board a vessel was of great interest during the time of large catches of herring, and became of interest again with the growth of fishing for krill and blue whiting. This is 'fish pumping' and not 'pump fishing', as will be discussed later (Chapter 31). To combine fish pumping with trawling is an old idea. Most inventions required the towing vessel to be followed by another one pumping the fish continuously from the codend during fishing. This could never be achieved. However, we have to learn that, in the future, smaller fish and animals lower in the web of life in the sea may become important. It has been said that estimates of potential catches from the sea must include the smaller but exceedingly abundant animals such as the krill (Euphausiids) of the Antarctic and the lantern fish (Myctophides) in tropical seas. Methods of krill fishing have been discussed and there are some ideas that in many circumstances a combination of mid-water trawl and pump may prove best.[409] In this case, the catch could be pumped from the codend into a specialized collector vessel astern, which would act as a carrier to and from a shore base or mother ship. Another idea to ensure effective operations in the krill fishery was to use mid-water trawls as pair trawls towed on short warps at low speeds, and to pump the krill out of the codend continuously, or at intervals, through flexible pipes from the after end of the codend, along the towing warps to each vessel.

These ideas of using pumps during fishing proved impractical, with the exception of fishing with a one-boat mid-water trawl towed at low speed, and when the pumps were used only when fishing was finished and the gear hauled to the ramp of the vessel. It is not so difficult for a catch such as krill to be pumped out of the codend during fishing. This can be done by fixing an hydraulic underwater pump, with the suction head outside but on the codend, and leading the tube for pumping, as well as the hydraulic lines, outside the trawl to the separator on the deck of the vessel. From here the catch can be guided directly by tubes to the storeroom of the vessel. In krill fishing, the main problem is to keep the percentage of krill damaged during transportation from the net to the vessel as low as possible.[255] Damage to the catch is always a problem in fish pumping, as well as in pump fishing, which will be discussed later (Chapter 31).

22.6 Progress of trawling in the future?

Some ideas and problems for the future of trawling have been mentioned but it must be said that there are doubts as to whether there will be much further progress with this method of fishing. But though the time of large stern trawlers appears to be numbered, there will be a future for some of the large vessels for economic trawling in special conditions such as in Antarctic waters, and some areas with a known high productivity. Even though the number of large vessels will become smaller, the problems of trawling will remain and new ones will arise, but the efforts made to solve these problems will become slower. Leaving aside the energy problems, trawling in any form is a labour-intensive fishery. It was due to this that the first mechanized methods of fishing were developed, to minimize the hard labour and to reduce the number of people required to operate the gear. It was in trawling that the first ideas arose to create what has been called 'an integrated fishing system' (*Fig 517*). This was to be achieved with some large sophisticated stern trawlers which were not only highly mechanized but also had computer-controlled operation of the whole trawling process. The system could begin with a decision on which area to fish. This can be arrived at from data obtained from satellites on factors favourable for the presence of fish. It is well known that fish cannot be directly detected by satellite, but satellites can give some hints by indicating indirect parameters such as upwellings, surface temperature, water colour (*eg* by chlorophyll) and water transparency. The absence of favourable parameters can indicate where fish are not likely to be found. If an area where fishing may be successful is indicated, the computer can give the data for navigation, taking into account weather and other conditions. After arriving at the fishing place, the search for promising fish schools begins with the help of fish-locating instruments like horizontal echo-sounders, or sonars, or automatic sector scanners. The computer can indicate which school may be the most promising one according to fish species, size, quantity or density of fish concentration. The computer can then provide data for navigating the ship so as to bring the gear to a correct position at the right time for an effective catch. The computer can indicate when to begin shooting the gear and the warps, how long the lines have to be in relation to the depth of the fish, and the optimum speed of the fishing vessel. Moreover, the computer can, with a forward looking multi-net sounder, monitor the position of the fish, which may change for any reason, and can keep the mid-water trawl at the right depth by increasing or decreasing the speed of the vessel. The computer can indicate when the towing direction should be changed or the towing ended because the trawl has the predetermined quantity of catch or because there are no more fish in the direction of towing. The computer can give warning when the temperature in the towing area around the trawl is changing or something is happening to the fishing gear. The computer can give the correct instructions to the engine of the vessel when fishing should stop and when the winches should haul the gear. In each case the computer can only make proposals: the actual decision will be made by the skipper. However, the computer can make calculations not only more quickly, but also with a greater degree of security and accuracy, than is possible by man.[78]

These are ideas which could be introduced in the near future or after some period of experimentation. These ideas have reached a stage of practical solution[222, 549] and the possibility of 'push a button and let the machine do the fishing' is now within reach. However, even under the best conditions, such developments cannot be achieved speedily but only step by step. On the other hand, there are already some developments of this kind, as in the Norwegian 'synchro-automatic trawling system' which includes automatic synchronising of shooting and hauling by the winch, with hydraulic braking to a pre-set warp length, and automatic tension control with alarm to give warning of the trawl being snagged. The main problem is not to make a fully automated trawling system, but to achieve the further development of trawling with less energy and better working conditions for human labour.

INTEGRATED FISHING SYSTEM

A CENTRAL SHIPBOARD PROCESS SYSTEM THAT COMPUTES ALL AVAILABLE INFORMATION AND DATA AND SIMULTANEOUSLY STEERS THE VESSEL DURING FISHING OPERATIONS

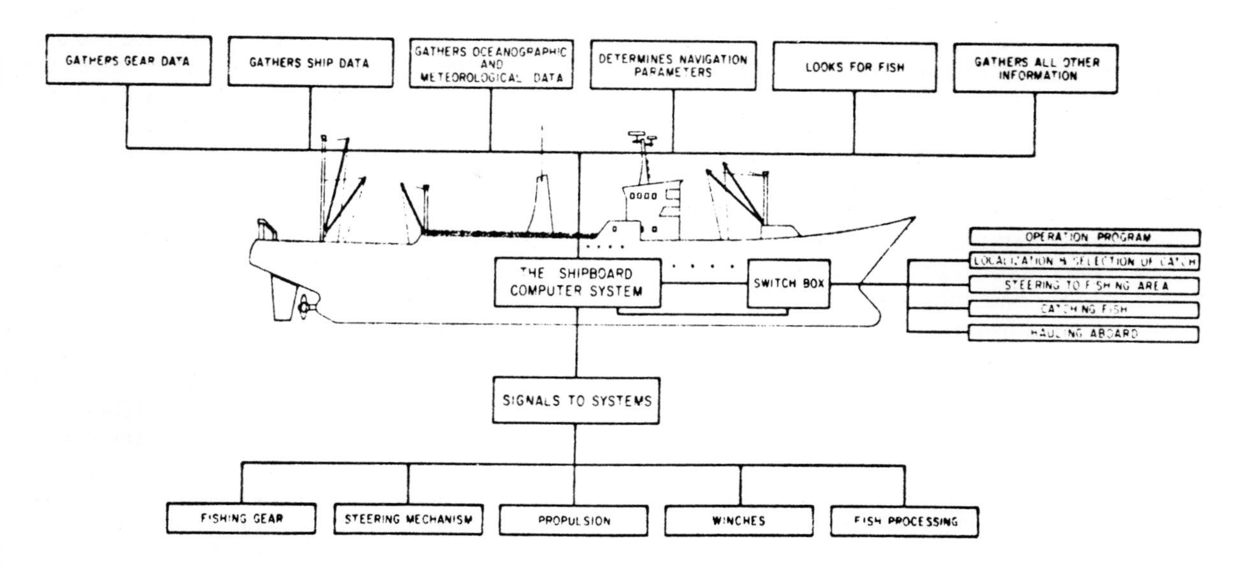

Fig 517 An automated trawling system, similar to those being developed in several large industrial fisheries. The system integrates data from a number of sources, allowing for automatic decisions in the fishing process, including control of the vessel. (J Schärfe, 1979).

Chapter twenty-three

Gods, fishing and the captain's nose

For a fishery to be successful, gear alone and the knowledge of how to make it is not enough. It is necessary to know when and where a successful fishery may be expected, and which tactics should be used. The method of how best to handle that gear to advantage must also be known and practised. The old fisherman who sets his baskets in the lake does this very carefully: he examines the glades in the reeds and studies the depth of water; he searches the bottom growths and notes the direction of the wind to assess how and when it will drive the water towards the bank or beach in a direction most favourable to his purposes. Spring, he may think has come late this year, so perhaps it would be wise to defer starting the basket fishery for a week or two. But soon the time comes to act, for he knows the fish will appear, as they have done regularly for years past. So he considers whether a certain basket should be put at some particularly favourable spot. From it, he recalls, he always secures a better catch than from any others. He does not know why – but it does! It might be that an experienced maker of baskets would recognize that the non-return device of that particular basket was especially well set; perhaps its odour was alluring and attractive to the fish. But most probably there was really no reason at all for its superior catching – save pure chance!

The sport fisherman, too, has sometimes among his many angling rods, one which is his favourite, for with it he has been most successful; so also many a huntsman has a favoured and more successful gun among all those he proudly views in his rack. Certainly there are some things which apparently carry with them more luck than do others. That is a familiar factor in many fields of daily life and is accepted without special thought. But the real or supposedly greater success of any one gear may well have a natural cause. Today people are reluctant to believe that any particular gear may be either blessed or cursed, as was supposedly the case in the more credulous days of their forefathers. Moreover, there are some people in fisheries who have more success than others. Also, today, people are reluctant to admit that a colleague has more skill and experience than themselves. In olden times, and even today in developed fisheries, it is believed that good fortune, or misfortune, comes from powers beyond man and could be influenced by the strict observance of some rules. In prehistoric times the knowledge of these rules and special ritual techniques was a part of fishing technology, as with other techniques too. The ritual techniques had to be respected in order to become successful in fishing. Some remains of this belief survive today, even in highly developed, sophisticated fisheries.

23.1 Benevolent gods and ghosts

The dependence of the fisherman on chance, and the impossibility, in most cases, of predicting the result of a fishing effort, together with the dire necessity of his being lucky enough to secure good catches, are factors that tempt him to seek the favour of those gods or powers that are deemed able to govern that luck. Thus the fisherman shares the desire for the benefit of luck in common with the huntsman, the farmer and the seaman.[41] He feels himself to be confronted with powers stronger than himself when he seeks to win a catch from the waters of river, lake or sea. That feeling of dependence has been expressed in various ways – and among peoples of all nations. No phase of primary production, including that of fishing, exists without a belief that there are powers beyond those of man himself which may favour or hinder the success of hunting, fishing or harvesting. The great festivities of the Christian fisherman are connected with divine services and processions to the sea or to his port, where the boats and their fishing gear are blessed by the priest. The Blessed Virgin is worshipped as the Star of the Sea, just as Holy Peter, as well as Saints Anselm, Nicholas, Anna and Helena are worshipped as the protectors of the fisherman and asked for their help. Their images are placed in harbours or on mountains – often looking out to sea with a gesture of blessing. Other figures are placed under water like the famous figure of 'Christ of the Abyss' in the John Pennekamp Coral Reef State Park off the coast of Florida,[561] or the Holy Family placed by Italian fishermen in an underwater cave of Conca dei Marini near Amalfi in the Gulf of Salerno. All this is done with the hope of reward of successful fishing.

Such feelings of dependence on powers outside man can be found with all fishermen of the world, wherever there is something like a religious feeling. The Lord, or gods, are asked for help, as in the 'Grand Pardon' of the Breton fishermen. Fishery knows many benevolent gods specializing in fisheries in different countries. For the Japanese, Ebisu, one of the seven Gods of Happiness (*Fig 518*), is the protector of fishermen. His symbols are an angling rod and a large fish which he holds in his hand. With the Chinese fisherman, it is his ancestors who protect the house, the fields and the fishery. Food and beverages are offered to the ancestral spirits in the hope that they will enjoy the favour of those gifts and in return will protect their children and grandchildren and ensure their making a good catch. It is thought they would take revenge if they were not so honoured. In Black Africa also, fishermen practise this invocation of ancestral spirits to aid fishing. On the other hand, not only benevolent but also hostile powers are believed to exist, which fishermen try to frighten away, like the Koreans do with some smoke ceremonies, or the Chinese do with the noise of fireworks. Sometimes the frightening of evil ghosts by noise, *eg* by hand clapping, can have the practical effect of frightening away crocodiles, piranhas or water snakes before a man enters a river, and this is done by the Xingu Indians.[225]

Fig 518 Ebisu, one of the Japanese gods of luck, is the patron of fishermen. Copies of this woodprint are sold to the pilgrims and visitors at a temple in Mito.

Dread of danger, anxiety of being unlucky, and fear of punishment for disregarding the divine laws are the fundamental ideas that dominate the minds of all fishermen, whether Christians or non-Christians. The idea that man governs nature and moulds it for his purposes has not been developed or accepted by the primary producers of the sea, the fields or the woods, but only by those behind office desks in the towns. The successful breeder of efficient types of cattle or of high quality commercial plants, even if he quite consciously masters the laws of heredity and economics, also feels himself to be confronted with powers from whom he needs favourable patronage. He is well aware that all his activity, all his efficiency, are not in themselves sufficient (or, he says, perhaps they are 'not yet' sufficient) to gather the harvest, to make the hunt successful or to haul the net from the water neither empty nor damaged. Just as seamen do, so many fishermen, farmers and huntsmen maintain belief in the old gods; they respect their demonic powers and animistic conceptions and believe that all things, even fishing gear, are inhabited by good or evil ghosts and that the fish, as animals to be caught, are nothing but brothers hidden in different bodies.[280] Because of these ideas, the fishing gear – the net, the trap, the angling rod – all become partners possessed of individual powers and to manufacture them is a creative act. It has already been recorded that many peoples in the past held the idea that the art of net-making was first taught to men by gods or heroes.[62] The traditions of fishermen in fact are full of legends of how mighty gods and saviours graciously unbent to teach men the use of fishing gear. Nowadays, these legends are used to prove that non-terrestrial intelligences may have brought such, and other, knowledge from other stars!

Thus in all continents – even when nowadays it seems strange or anachronistic – fishing or, to be exact, fishing technology is still related to ideas which may be considered by some as religious imagination and by others as superstition. This may disappear with increasing education and training but the fact remains that, in many areas of the world, some belief remains that the efficiency of fishing gear is connected with the knowledge of special ritual techniques which have to be carried out during its construction or operation.

23.2 Ritual techniques

As mentioned in the last section, there was – and is still today – the belief that to be successful in fishing it may not be sufficient just to know how to construct fishing gear. Nor is it sufficient to know when and where fish can be caught. It is not even sufficient to know which tactic of fishing to employ, if certain rituals are not observed and obeyed prior to and after the catch. In the minds of some fishermen the knowledge of, and obedience to, such rules is as important as the knowledge of the fishing technique itself. Only by the strict observance of certain ritual techniques sanctified by tradition do they believe that the fishery can be successful. A modern report from Polynesia mentions that non-participation in the ritual is frowned upon and is regarded as a guarantee of poor catches.[673] These beliefs, prevalent in a fishery, may have various consequences. God, or the gods and ghosts, may be implored to bless the fishing. Strictly speaking, that means that the stronger powers are being asked to guide the fish so that the fisherman may capture them. The so-called masters of the animals in lakes, rivers and in the seas have to be asked, persuaded or even corrupted, so that some of their 'people' can be taken. There are many such rites, rules or customs well known today, often respected but not mentioned for fear of being considered primitive. They refer to the making of fishing gear, sometimes even to the gear itself and to the boats, to the operation of the gear, to the behaviour of fishermen and sometimes also of his relatives before, during and after fishing. They refer also to the handling of the catch, especially to the first fish caught. Only a few of these rules may be mentioned in the following.

That fishing gear is sometimes blessed by priests, women priests, medicine men or magicians and sorceresses is well known. It may be of interest that in some African fisheries not only are different rites necessary for different types of gear, but also for passive and actively operated fishing gear. With passive gear – so it has been told from the former Rhodesian area[82] – only magic and medicine and not the skill of fishermen could increase the catch of the gear. The same is said of the use of fish poisoning, which needs important ritual observances to be successful.[666] Another point of interest is that very often the rituals are exclusive to men only. Women are not allowed to see the ceremonies and in some places they are not even allowed to touch fishing gear or boats. With some people, especially in Black Africa, the males are forbidden to have any intercourse with women while the manufacture of fishing gear is proceeding, or during the time of fishing. Sexual behaviour is very often linked with success in fishery as one of the commonest forms of ensuring luck in undertakings.[82] In former times, in Oceania, even the girl-friends, wives and daughters of bonito fishermen were enjoined to strict chastity during the absence of canoes at sea. Breaking this rule was believed to bring bad luck and even disaster to the fishermen.[476]

But man has tried not only to exchange offerings for a good catch of fish, or to persuade and corrupt gods and ghosts; there are also some references to his obtaining success by kidnapping! There are legends of fish kings having been caught and set free on their urgent pleas of freedom and, in return, the legends tell of their thankfully guiding other fish into the fisherman's net! If the fishermen should disregard the desire of a fish king they will, they feel, be ruined. English people have their traditional 'Herring King' and the Bretons their 'Sardine King'. Success, it has also been believed, can be ensured if the king can be caught and chained, so that he is unable to migrate with his own folk as the Masurians did with the 'Stinthengst', a larger species of smelt in Mikolajki (*Fig 519*). That captivity, it was felt, would ensure a constant and successful bulk fishing.[676] This king of smelt has been said to have a golden crown, which is explained by biologists by the fact that, with older fish, the yellow brain can be seen through the transparent bones!

Fig 519 'Fish king' chained up on a bridge over a lake near Mikolajki in Masuria to guarantee good catches. (*Photo: Dr Tesch, 1959.*)

23.3 Offerings for preparing the catch

By tradition, sacrifices are made to the gods of the sea in order that they may grant rich catches of fish. The first and the last fish are thrown into the sea in return. The first drink on board is dedicated to them or some drops of the fishermen's own blood are cast into the sea.[422] Temples are dedicated in East Asia to the Dragon King of the Sea, who answers the prayers of fishermen in distress and is believed to be able to keep them from harm – though he could not protect the crew of that unfortunate Japanese fishing vessel, Lucky Dragon, from the devastation of the atom bomb. At dusk, Indian fishermen on the Malabar coast put little candles on the paths leading to their huts. At that hour, the Goddess of Happiness, Lakshmi, is believed to be searching for lodgings for the night. Maybe, it was hoped, she would find the way, remain in the hut during the night, and reward her host with a rich catch the next day.

If, according to the animistic conception, fish also have a soul, the fisherman becomes guilty when he kills one.[615] This point was mentioned in connection with the cormorant fishery. The ritual techniques connected with fishing may, therefore, also be intended as an apology either to the fish that has been killed or to the protecting ghosts who may have been defied or offended. In fear of their revenge, a reconciliation with the victim is sought through the ritual performed. In the forecourt of a temple in the vicinity of the Tokyo fish market there is a stone dedicated by the owners of fish restaurants to the crayfish that are killed for their guests. There are more for fish and turtles near a shrine for an Indian goddess of good fortune in Ueno Park in the neighbourhood of Tokyo University (*Fig 520*). On a small island called Saikai-to, off the coast of western Japan, in the small town of Kayooiura, a requiem is still held for the repose of the souls of whales killed by the whalers who formerly fished by catching the whale in entangling netting. This service has been held over five days beginning April 29, every year since 1679.[374] In August of each year the priests still travel along the Sumida river, which runs through Tokyo, to ask, with their prayers and drums, for forgiveness from the fish. In that river, however, fish are scarcely ever caught by fishermen for they have been mostly killed by the city's foul waste water!

Fig 520 Monument in honour of fishes killed for gourmets in fish restaurants; in Ueno park, Tokyo.

With prayers for reconciliation, another desire is often associated, namely that the fishing resources shall be maintained in spite of the catch that has been taken. So the Gods of Fertility are implored to increase the stock and to prevent suffering from overfishing. According to ancient ideas, the benevolence of the powers is often associated with rules for the regulation of fishing. The return of the fish first caught has already been mentioned. The fish and turtles caught first are, in the minds of the South American Indians, the mothers and grandmothers of all those caught later. Frequently such rules contain the germ of modern legislation for the conservation of fishing resources. According to the rules of the South American Indians, for instance, fish must be allowed to remain undisturbed during the spawning period, young fish must be spared, and the quantity caught must be restricted to the quantity required for food, as it is considered an insult to the water spirits if fish are caught and left to deteriorate.[686] All of which are very sound principles.

Special rituals are also intended to frighten evil ghosts from hindering successful fishing. These can have very practical reasons. From Black Africa, ceremonies are described to prevent interruption of fishing by snakes and lions![82] Evil ghosts have also to be persuaded not to destroy the nets or to damage the boats. As already mentioned, women are often forbidden to touch gear or boats. Seamen and fishermen still do not like women on board vessels for fear of misfortune. Frequently this taboo refers to women during times of physiological indisposition and this taboo is also current in hunting traditions. This restriction may also include priests, advocates and disbelieving foreigners! (It seems that salmon fishermen in the rivers of England and Wales especially considered parsons and preachers as an omen of ill-luck.[279]) If a prescribed person did board a fishing boat, ceremonies and offerings were thought necessary to clean the vessel from the bad influence these persons may have caused. With the modernization of fisheries, however, the old rituals are disappearing. Yet, during the First International Fishing Gear Congress arranged by FAO in Hamburg in 1957, a paper from Viet Nam was submitted which dealt with the profitability of nylon fishing nets as compared with those made of the local ramie.[627] It was therein mentioned that the price of ramie nets always included an amount for the sacrifices to be offered to the Goddesses of the Sea. For nylon nets no such sum was mentioned, the inference being that modern fishing gears no longer needed the help of the gods, such as that of the tradition that sailing boats should be launched with ceremonies (including the sacrifice of a fowl) involving the help of the God of Fortune. So much have these ceremonies disappeared in relation to modern creations, that no function was considered necessary in connection with the launching of powered boats supplied by various nations under the programme of assisted development.

23.4 Surviving amulets and customs

Today, only sad relics of the old rituals are still to be found in the modern rational world. Sometimes they are mixed up with Christian symbols. For instance, there are the Irish and Portuguese fishermen who tie a small bottle of holy water to each boat; and, in the wheelhouse of Italian or Iberian fishermen, images of saints are to be found. Further, the Italians often attach a red or white painted cow horn to the wheelhouse of their boat as a lucky symbol (*Fig 521*). Those same horns were earlier attached to the medieval caravels of the Mediterranean to protect them from the hostile powers of ghosts. The horns are said to have originated from the time of Apis, the Holy Bull that the Egyptians worshipped at Memphis. Italian

Fig 521 Auspicious (for good luck) red-painted cow horn (arrowed) on the wheelhouse of an Italian sardine vessel in Fiumicino. (*Photo: J Schärfe.*)

fishermen who settled on the California Pacific coast took with them that same custom from their homeland; but instead of the cow horn large antlers are nailed to the so-called crow's nests of the very modern tuna vessels (*Fig 522*). Horns of all types of animals are considered as receivers of magic power all over the world. Conspicuous are the amulets of the fishermen of Senegal, called 'grigri', made of the horns of sheep and goats filled with different auspicious herbs (*Fig 523*). Up to twenty horns can be found in a canoe, mostly on its bow. In other areas there are little bottles containing liquids; little packets of plastic with sentences of the

Fig 522 Auspicious deer horn (circled) on the look-out of a modern Californian purse seiner for tuna in San Pedro, 1962.

Fig 523 Collection of magic goats' horns, called 'gri-gri', in a fisherman's canoe in M'bour, Senegal, (1977).

Koran; small bones or parts of bones, together with some things which are considered more as curiosities. This custom is found scattered along the coast of western Africa, including Madeira.

Well known as a means of help and protection are the famous eyes on both sides of the bow of the vessel; sometimes also on the stern (*Fig 524*). These eyes are sometimes carved from wood, more often painted on the hull of the vessel.[258, 259, 260]

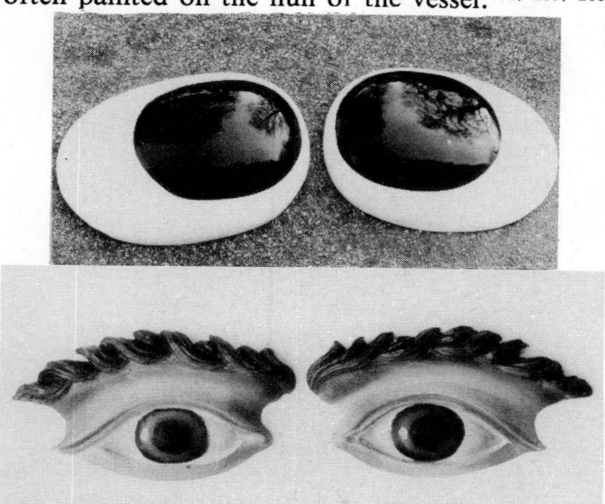

Fig 524 So-called 'oculi': (above) stylized ones of a Chinese junk and (below) more realistic ones from Malta. (1966).

They are called 'oculi' and are generally considered helpful for observation, inspection, turning aside, protecting, guarding or blinding the look of another eye, especially an evil one.[317] The need for protection against an evil eye is especially believed in the Mediterranean, where vessels of Portugal (*Fig 525*), Spain, Italy, Malta (*Fig 524*), Yugoslavia and Greece, even today have more or less realistic eyes to prevent the evil eyes of a jealous contemporary frightening away the fish from the gear, or attracting a strong wind. With the exception of the Turks, such eyes cannot be seen on the vessels of Islamic fishermen in the Mediterranean. The eyes were also known in early times on the vessels of the Egyptians, Greeks and Romans. This oculus was the eye of the Egyptian god Horus, who guided the deceased to the land of shadows. These symbols survive today. Sometimes the eyes are replaced by rhombic ornaments, by stars, or even by fishes. It has been noticed that the oculi in the drawings of old Greek sailing vessels on vases or bowls have been exchanged for drawings of dolphins. Also many transitions of the old eyes can be seen on modern smaller vessels.[317] During the Middle Ages ships could have on their bows, for protection, the heads of bulls, with eyes and horns, and Portuguese

Fig 525 Portuguese fishing vessel with oculus for protection in the harbour of Sesimbra, 1964.

fishing boats of the Algarve, called 'calao', had such heads until the end of the last century.[24] But there is also another area where such eyes can be seen today – on Chinese vessels of East and South Asia (*Fig 526*). Here some people think that these eyes are endowed with magical powers which enable the vessel to find the safest way across the sea.[499] Moreover, the eyes are thought of as something that is today considered as a fishfinder!

There are many other relics of old customs, even on modern fishing vessels. One of them is that some fishermen like to nail the tail fin of large fish to the top of the mast, as did their forefathers, in order that they may have good luck. On herring drifters in the North Sea, it was the tail fin of large tunny when this fish was found in northern waters. In olden times, sailing vessels had the tail fin of a freshly caught shark at the end of the jib to encourage a good wind. The number of surviving rituals cannot be counted: nor can the number of amulets still used in fisheries. They can be woven into the netting, fixed on the fishing gear or in the vessel, worn on the body of the fisherman or tattooed into his skin. Some customs are distributed worldwide, even today, although their meaning is forgotten. So that they may have good luck, herring fishermen spit into the mouth of a fish and throw it overboard. Strangely enough, on the other side of the Atlantic in the Guyanas, Indian fishermen have a similar custom. They blow into the mouths of small fish, put them back into the water and ask them to send larger specimens of their kind.[662, 686] When launching a boat, Turkish fishermen used to slaughter a ram, and to demonstrate that they had done so, the skin of the offering was fixed on the bow of the vessel. Today, this skin is replaced by

Fig 526 Chinese fishing boats with oculi in the harbour of Keelung (Taiwan).

a red towel, as is done in other Islamic countries. Sometimes parts of the vessels were painted with the blood of the offering. In many countries a cock is offered as a sacrifice but it has to be black and its blood must be spread over the boat. This was done up until 1900, even in Brittany. The red blood of the cock was then replaced by a bottle of red wine broken over the vessel. This may be the origin of the tradition of a bottle of champagne being broken on a vessel today during a launching ceremony.[423]

23.5 Computer against the captain's nose

There are still many other things considered to be either lucky or unlucky, especially on the coasts. But these examples may suffice. Nevertheless, there are fishing captains who are supposed always to be lucky. They have the same type of vessels, the same nets and equipment as others, but their vessels are said always to return with full holds. These skippers have the 'right nose' for finding favourable fishing grounds and it is often said, as a joke, that their nose is the most important part of their body. Huntsmen know from their practice and experience how important sudden intuitions are to their luck in hunting; and many a captain has had the experience of rising in the middle of the night, after an unsuccessful day, and taking a sudden decision to change course, only to arrive almost immediately at a rich fishing ground.

Despite all electronic detecting instruments, and despite all efforts to design the most efficient fishing gear based on technical calculations, 'luck' still influences success in fishing – and in that field some people have a foreboding, an intuition, or a hunch, and others simply have not. Instinct has to be trained too. In a modern publication about whaling in Antarctic waters[677] it was stated that a captain, although gifted with instinct, needs years of experience to become a good hunter in whaling, but when this instinct was missing he remained always a poor hunter. Huntsmen have the same experience. There is obviously something suppressed by civilization, which attracts the huntsman to reconquer it. Maybe it is an ability to conceive secret connections, a 'holy gift' to recognize supernatural things[41] or perhaps a saying of the sport fishermen is right: 'You cannot catch a trout, if you do not think like a trout!'

But people are still looking for an explanation of why one fisherman has greater success than another. Why he has a better nose to 'smell' where the fish are. One answer is that modern man has lost his instinct – now suppressed by his intellect.[235] He has lost the ability to register facts subconsciously. Under similar conditions, this stored knowledge can cause the right decision. It may be that this is the basis of luck in fisheries even today. If this is the secret of the captain's nose, a computer could do the same, and much better, by storing more facts and arriving at better conclusions. Some people think that it is possible not only to mechanize fishing methods to save manpower, but also that the system of fishing may be automated by using seaborne computers to support the decisions of the skipper. If this proves right, then the benevolent gods and the captain's nose will be replaced by well-fed computers. In years to come, we shall see!

Chapter twenty-four

Seining in fresh and sea water

In their fishing activities the Romans employed a large gear which they called 'sagena', and as they occupied very large areas of Europe this net was introduced by them to many countries. The terms 'segi', 'saege', 'zege' and similar ones are still used in Switzerland, southern Germany and the Netherlands. In France the gear is known as 'seine' or 'senne' and, in the British Isles, as 'seine net'. The gear is now known all over the world. The Romans did not invent this fishing gear. The early Greeks knew of seine nets (sagene), as did the Phoenicians and Egyptians, at least since the third millenium BC (*Fig 527*).

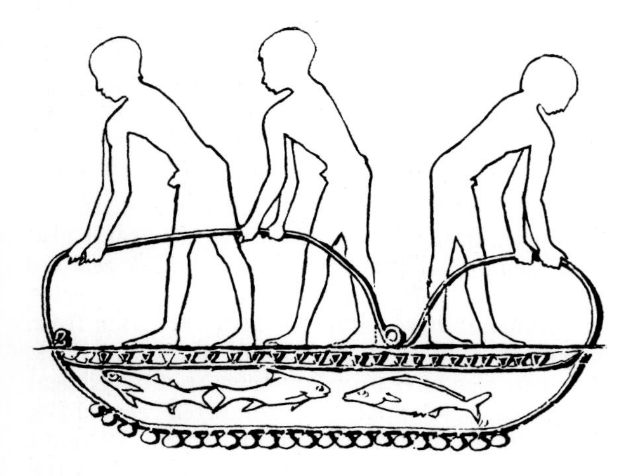

Fig 527 Egyptian seine net fishery according to a wall painting in the grave of the Prince Rahotep in Medum, 4th dynasty, about 2575BC.

In its simplest form the seine net is a net wall consisting of two wings and a section to hold the catch (the bunt or bag) more or less in the middle (*Fig 528*). The wings are long and each is lengthened by a long towing line or warp. For the bunt it is sufficient that the net is allowed to hang loosely. For this reason, this section of the net is deeper than the net forming the wings. For large catches it is better for the section between the wings to incorporate a bagnet of appropriate size. This bag may also incorporate a retarding device to prevent the escape of the fish, especially when towing has to be interrupted for any reason. The two constructions show that there are two basic types of gear: seine nets without a bag (*Fig 528a*) and seine nets with a bag (*Fig 528b*). It is thought that seine nets without a bag were evolved from a net wall, while the seines with a bag may have developed from a bagnet like the stow nets mentioned earlier. It is not necessary for the bag to be exactly in the centre and in this case the wings are not of equal length (*Fig 528c*). As will be described later there are, in early and modern

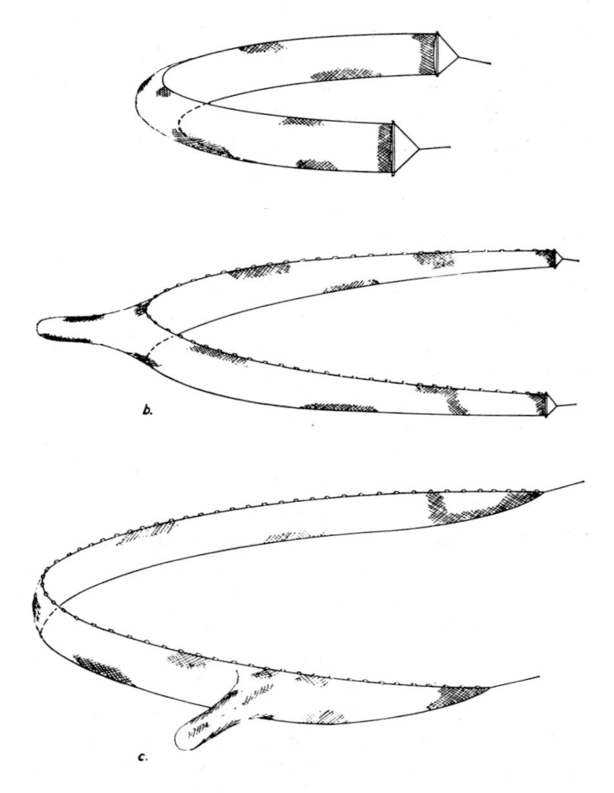

Fig 528 Seine nets: (*a*) without bag; (*b*) with bag in the centre; (*c*) with bag in the side.

fisheries, seine nets with more than one bag. But generally speaking the net is composed of a central bunt (bagnet or loose netting) for securing the catch, and wings attached to either side of it. The wings are connected with the towing or hauling lines, also called drag lines, which may be operated in such a manner that they work like a lengthening of the wings. Also the hauling lines may be of unequal length.

There is also a third form of seine net. In the Indian freshwater fishery, a beach seine is known which is like a seine net without a bag but with a pocket along the lower edge of the gear (*Fig 529*).[192]

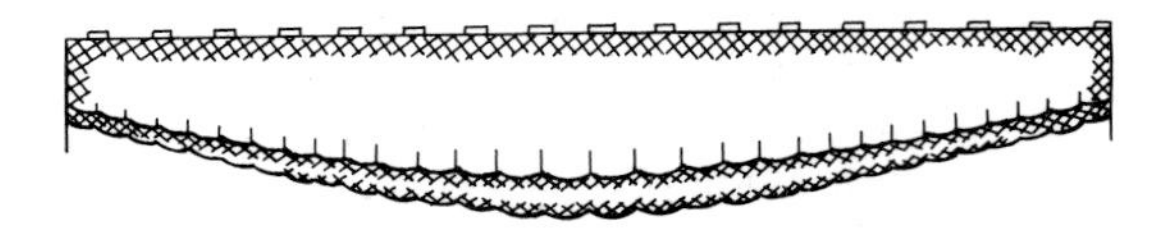

Fig 529 Indian seine net with pockets along the leadline. (*George, 1971*).

There can be one or two rows of such pockets, made by folding the lower margin of the netting along with the footrope and the sinkers. The folded netting can be laced to the netting at regular intervals, thus sectioning the entire long pocket into a series of smaller ones. All three types of seine nets are operated in such a manner that the gear is set in a circle around an area considered to contain fish. They are caught by hauling both towing lines simultaneously to a place determined in advance. This place can be on the shore, or at one or two anchored boats. By towing, the wings come closer and closer, sweeping, frightening and concentrating the fish towards the catching part of the gear until the catch can be lifted out at the hauling place. Not only the wings but also the towing lines attached to the wings help to drive the fish. To increase the herding effect of the towing lines, they can have attached to them twigs (*eg* branches of coniferous trees), leaves, straw and nowadays also strips of plastic and other material.

Although there are very small seine nets, generally this gear is typical of large-scale bulk fisheries in fresh waters, especially in lakes and on the seashore (in the form of beach seines), and also in sea fisheries where they are operated in the open sea as boat seines. The possibility of larger catches is increased with the size of the gear. It is therefore not surprising that there are seine nets with wings some hundreds of metres or even kilometres in length. Not only the wings, but also the towing warps supporting the herding effect, can be of considerable length. This means that the operation of large seine nets is very labour intensive – and also expensive, at least until recently.

Setting and hauling of seine nets can be done in two different ways. The simplest form is to set and haul the gear from the same place, as is generally done in beach seining and also in some freshwater fisheries. In this case the gear can be operated by a single boat (or by a fisherman wading in shallow water or swimming) towing the warp in a loop shape from the shore and setting first a wing and then the bag, then turning back towards the shore and setting the other wing and the other warp on the return to the starting point. Hauling begins by simultaneously drawing in the towing lines by hand or by winches until both wings and the catching part of the gear have reached the shore. Another form of setting and hauling a seine is to work with two boats. In this case setting begins as it would with a trawl; the bunt first, farthest away from the beach and about opposite the hauling place. The two boats then sail away from the setting place of the bunt, each setting (shooting) first a wing and then a towing line. In most cases the boats do not sail immediately towards the hauling place but begin hauling the lines some distance from each other to keep the gear widely spread for as long as possible. Before reaching the hauling place the vessels come nearer to each other until they can haul the last part of the wing and the bunt with the catch between them, or the gear is towed ashore where the catch can be brailed out.

Seine nets have nothing to do with purse seines (Chapter 25) which have quite another principle of catching, although the operation of the gear is also called 'seining' and the boats operating this gear are called 'seiners'. In contrast to purse seines, seine nets discussed here cannot enclose the catch from beneath, which is characteristic of purse seines. Seine nets also have no relationship to dragged gear such as trawls (Chapter 21), from which they differ very much in construction and operation. To make their differences quite clear the following comparison is given:

Details of seine nets

construction	long wings, no (or small) bag
bag placing	different (*Fig 528*)
bag number	no bag, or one, or more
mode of setting	one wing first
catching area	limited by the length of the wings and hauling lines
catching depth	limited up to 50m in lake fishing; 400m or so in sea fishing

hauling place	fixed in advance
catching unit	haul or set

Details of trawl nets

construction	no, or small, wings; large bag for the catch
bag placing	in the middle only
bag number	one only in general; sometimes two
mode of setting	codend first
catching area	unlimited, so long as dragging is possible
catching depth	more than 1,000m; nearly unlimited
hauling place	at any time, not fixed in advance
catching unit	towing hour

By the contrasts shown above, it may be clear that the seine nets are restricted to working at a specific place and operate quite differently to the much more mobile trawls. But it has to be confessed, too, that there are examples where circumstances create different situations so that opinions and practices may differ.

24.1 Simple seining gear, and 'baby' seine nets

The method of catching fish or other prey by herding them between two movable barriers of any material may be a very old one. In the African fisheries, long rolls of grass are known which are used in the shallows for herding fry.[361] Also, the long papyrus walls (used in Africa) or walls made of palm leaves (Tahiti), can be operated like seine nets when they are used in the shallows to catch small fish. Lines, screens, mats, clothes or other webbing can be used for seining.[655] Of course, sometimes it may be questioned whether this form of fishing is more akin to dragging or drive-in fishing (Chapter 26) or to seining.

As mentioned before, in the very beginning of manufactured nets it was possible to make only very small pieces of netting because of the difficulty, in the first place, of providing suitable net material and in the second place because of the time taken in knitting by hand. The earlier modern seines may, therefore, have been of much smaller size. They may have been small sheets or winged bags of netting held between two sticks (*Fig 531*). Such 'double-stick-nets' of small type can also be used

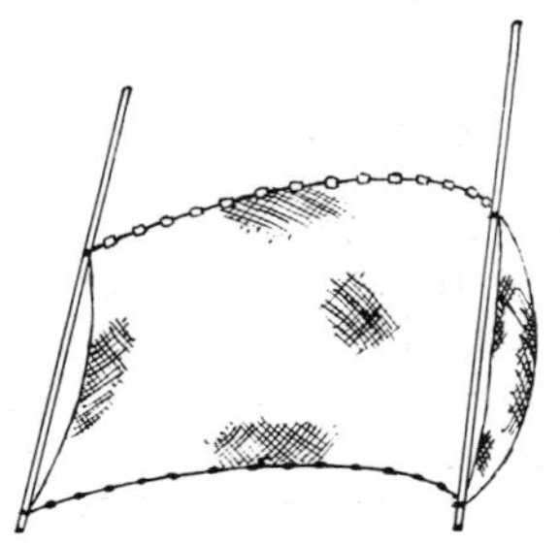

Fig 531 A double stick net.

Fig 530 Turkish fishermen hauling a seine net. The fish are driven into the bagnet by beating the water. (*Photo: T Mengi.*)

for scooping up the catch. If they are of a larger size (so-called 'pole seines') it becomes possible to encircle an area and thus to narrow the space and so secure the entrapped fish in the way described for typical seine nets. Double-stick-nets of varying sizes are to be found all over the world. They are especially popular with river fishermen (*Fig 532*).

Fig 532 Small Korean double-stick-net with bag (1960).

Small, seine-like double-stick-nets are held in the river current and they attempt to encircle their victims and lift them with the net from the water. But there are also typical miniature editions of seine nets known in east and south Asia (*Fig 533*). This gear is operated by a single boat or by two fishing boats as is done with the 'sardine hand operated trawl'.[445] This gear is by no means a trawl but a typical seine net. Therefore, it would be better called a 'baby seine net' and not 'baby trawl'. That this is not a trawl can be also seen by the long wings in comparison to the short bag which is typical of seine nets.

24.2 Seine nets in freshwater fisheries

Seine nets without bags and with bags are both widely used in freshwater fishing. Seines without bags are frequently used in pond farms for taking samples. They are also used in river fishing. More popular in fresh waters, especially in lakes, are seine nets with bag. In lake fisheries, seines of considerable size, with heavy bags are often employed. They are used the whole year round in Europe, especially in the winter-time when the fish are concentrated in schools near the bottom of the lake. The fishing areas of the European lakes and the hauling places on them are well known; in fact, they have been named from olden times and have been duly recorded on fishing charts. As long as the seine-like gears are of small size only they can be spread and maintained in the correct vertical position by two lateral rods like the double-stick-nets. With larger gear, however, the edges of the wings and the opening of the net bag must be kept high and open by special arrangements. That can be done by a great number of spreading rods, sometimes called stick stretchers, fitted to the net at regular distances (*Fig 534*).

In Africa (Lake Tanganyika), seine nets were used with spreading rods and not only one bag, but sometimes with several bags. The 'sennes à poche multiple' from this lake have three, four, or even more bags for securing the catch.[361, 503] In Lake Chad the seine nets are composed of many single bagnets, each 10 metres wide. The total row can be 200 metres long and the different parts are owned by different fishermen. Each fisherman gets only the catch from his own part of the net. The seine

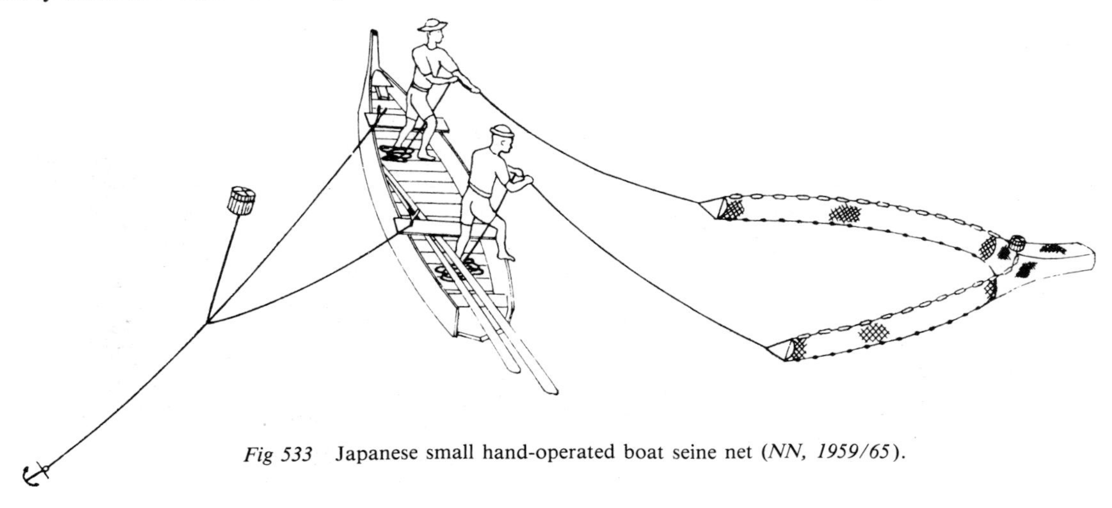

Fig 533 Japanese small hand-operated boat seine net (*NN, 1959/65*).

nets with many bags from Lake Malawi are kept open by rods attached to either side of a bag. Those of the gear on Lake Chad are one metre high. In general, to keep the seine net in a vertical position, another much more important method is used. This is done by attaching weights at the lower edge (the lead line), and by arranging floats along the upper edge (the cork line) and on the upper side of the bag of the net. With many passive and active fishing gears, floats and weights are accurately balanced so the net is held in a vertical position almost as though suspended. With seine nets, floats can be mounted in such numbers that the gear hangs on the water surface. But mostly the weights are heavier, so that the gear sinks to the bottom of the water, but is held wide open by the floats.

Fig 534 A seine net with spreading rods in South India.

In fresh waters the gear is set on a suitable place with two boats, with the bag or net set centre first, then the two wings, and lastly the towing lines, each laid in a large arc and encircling the area to be fished. Both ends of the towing lines are brought to a fixed place on the shore or to an anchored boat. With the help of a winch (usually hand powered), the warps, with the gear and its bag, are hauled. When the bagless seine net is operated, the foot-rope is hauled faster to make a more pronounced bag at the centre of the gear. To prevent the fish escaping from the slowly towed net opening, they are frightened into the gear by beating the water before the net opening (*Figs 530* and *535*).

In freshwater fisheries, the places for hauling the seines are often sited on specially prepared spots on the bank. In larger waters, they must be sometimes situated in one or two boats anchored in shallow water. As mentioned before, the gear is drawn over the bottom by the two lines from the beach or from anchored vessels. There may be an exception, that the middle part of the gear can be held by a boat or, with smaller gear, by a swimming fisherman, all drawn with the help of a winch to an anchor on the beach.

Seine nets are generally towed over the bottom. If the ground is soft, arrangements are made to prevent the nets from cutting into the bottom. But in freshwater fishing, seines can also be used over considerable depths of water; that is, for fishing pelagically, such as with the 'Klusgarn', a seine net used formerly on Lake Constance since 1534. This pelagic fishing net was pulled up from the depths almost vertically (*Fig 536*). When this was done at high speed, the meshes came up nearly closed and therefore unwanted small fish were also caught. To

Fig 535 Seine netting in the lake of Plön in northern Germany. The wings of the gear are towed together and the fish are frightened into the bag of the gear by the boat in the middle.

Fig 536 Hauling of the 'Klusgarn' in Lake Constance.

avoid this, efforts were made to fix the time during which the net was hauled from the water, so that the small fish should have time to escape through the open meshes of the non-towed netting. This was difficult to control and because large quantities of fish fry were wasted, this pelagic seine was forbidden in 1967 and, even though in 1975 its reintroduction was proposed to overcome some overpopulation of bream (*Abramis brama*) it was not allowed.

Similar pelagic seine nets are known in the African lakes. Such a net is shot by two canoes, which may drag the net for a short distance. The men splash the water vigorously to scare the fish towards the bag and, while hauling the net, they work in such a way that the foot-rope comes up faster than the headrope. In fresh water, seine nets are used in ponds and lakes, and, as far as the current will allow, also in rivers. Mostly they are used with at least two boats, or without boats but brought into the right position by men entering the water and maybe swimming. This is done very often in tropical waters but was also known in temperate areas.[279] Seine nets can also be operated by fishermen wading into the shallow water, or in the form of beach seines, with one man on a raft or boat rowing along the beach and another man walking along on shore at the same time. They can also be operated by horses, as practised in South America, in Rio Uruguay and Rio de la Plata, as well as in the Columbia River of North America.

A very serious objection can be raised against the use of some types of seines in fresh waters and this is that they have only a small degree of selectivity. Fishes of all sizes are taken and it is often impossible to spare young fish, even with wider meshes. Freshwater seines, as used in some areas, are said to damage the fish stocks, therefore, very often other fishing methods are advocated which work more selectively.

24.3 Seining below ice

One very special method of seine fishing is that used below ice in northern countries. By means of a clever system of holes the large winter seine is pushed beneath the ice until it can be hauled again from the water (*Fig 537*). In this case the operating system differs from that with one or two boats

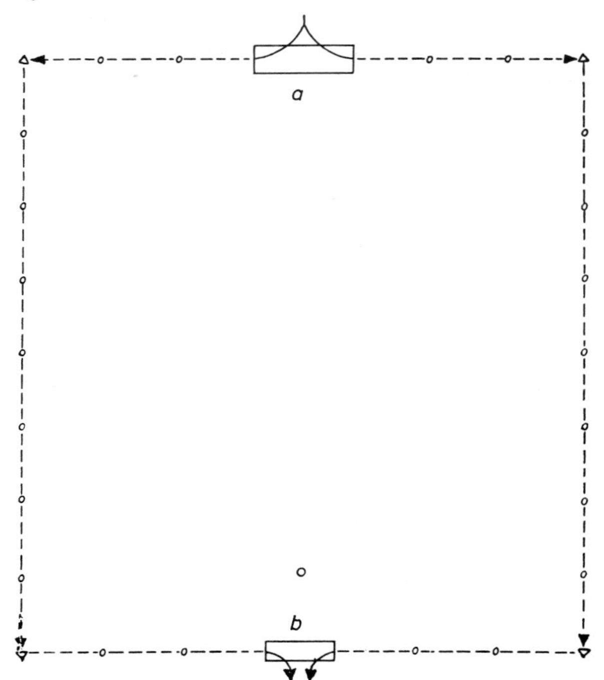

Fig 537 This plan shows how a seine net is operated under ice: (*a*) the hole for shooting the net; (*b*) the hole for hauling the net. In front, a small hole for frightening the fish into the bag of the seine net. On the sides are small holes for pushing the net forward below the ice.

mentioned earlier. The seine used for this ice fishing is also composed of a large bag with very long wings. For shooting, a hole, sometimes a triangular one, is made in the ice and first the drag lines are pushed under the ice simultaneously; the two wings follow, the bagnet follows last. Usually the drag lines are attached to long wooden rods. These rods floating beneath the ice are pushed forward by means of special forks from one ice hole along to another, towing the lines behind. Reaching the first hole, some part of the line is taken out of the water and is towed by a small hand-operated winch placed on a sled. In this way the lines and wings, with the net bag, are horizontally widely spread out below the ice on both sides. Then the rods are pushed along with the gear from one ice hole to the other to the hauling place, in form of a much larger hole in the ice. Here the rods and lines are pulled from the hauling hole until the wings and the net bag can be brought out. To prevent the escape of the fish before hauling the bagnet, the fish are frightened with special sticks acting as scarers. Sometimes frightening lines (*Fig 588*) are used for the same purpose.

The main problem of seining below ice is to make the holes in the ice, which is sometimes more than one metre thick, and to transport the hauling lines with the gear under the ice from one hole to the next. The long wooden sticks provide one method: another method is to push the lines forward with so-called 'jiggers' or 'jigging machines'. These are implements that creep along the underside of the ice with the help of a lever pulled by a rope operated by the fisherman (*Fig 538*). This is the same implement used to set gillnets in Canadian lakes under ice during winter-time (Chapter 29). Another sophisticated proposal is to replace the long wooden sticks by small floating tubes of steel, which are guided by electromagnets similar to those used for lifting and moving scrap iron. The magnets should be towed on the surface of the ice, moving the steel tubes forward with the hauling lines and net below.[558]

There is no doubt that seining below ice is a very successful fishing method for large-scale fisheries in northern countries with large lakes. But it also is a labour-intensive fishery, especially when the wintering places of concentrations of fish are not known, or vary from one year to the other. The making of large numbers of holes in the ice can be an exhausting job. But with the use of jiggers or electromagnets the number of holes can be reduced. The most labour-saving method of making holes in the ice is with the help of electrically driven ice axes wherever electrical current is available. This equipment is very like the rock-drilling machines used by the ice fisheries of the USSR.

24.4 Beach seining

Beach seining, or fishing with beach hauling nets, is a very old fishing method in coastal fisheries. It may even be the oldest method for bulk fishing in the seas. The setting of the gear from the beach, maybe by means of a single boat, is mostly done in such a way that the drag line of one wing remains fastened to the beach, while one wing, the net bag

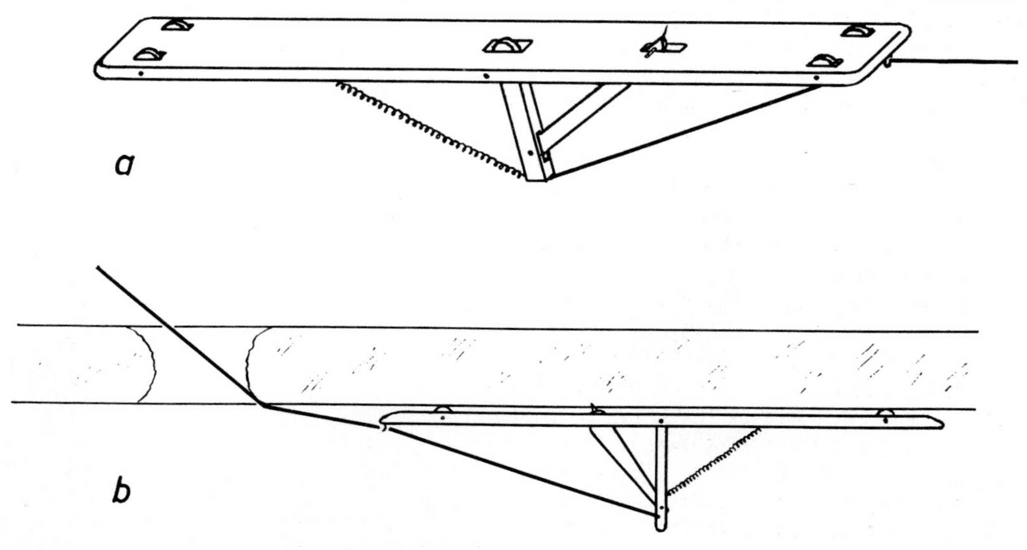

Fig 538 'Jigger' for towing lines under ice: (*a*) the spring is stretched by pulling the line. When the line is let go the board is pushed in the opposite direction by the thorn; (*b*) the jigger in operation.

and then the other wing with its drag line are taken out in a wide arc and then brought back to the beach (*Fig 539*). Sometimes the second line is longer than the first one in order to encircle a wider area. Then the hauling lines are towed simultaneously from the beach, herding the fish opposite the bag or bunt of the gear. Also the ground-rope is sometimes made shorter, to make the bagnet more voluminous. The ground-rope has to be always in touch with the bottom (*Fig 540*) and should reach the shore before the headline.

Setting can also be done without boats, as on the west coast of Africa where swimming fishermen set the net in the sea before it is towed onto the beach, accompanied by the swimming men (*Fig 541*). In Peru, two fishermen wade with the net into the surf until the water reaches their breasts, then they set the seine net and tow it with much strength on to the beach.[413] On the Turkish coast of the Black Sea, the fisherman sometimes rows his boat, accompanied by two boys along the shore looking for fish. If a shoal is found, the net bag is set, held in its middle by the fisherman remaining in the boat. The boys jump into the water with the towing lines and swim to the shore on each side of the shoal. On the shore, the boys haul the net, smacking the water with the towing lines to prevent the fish escaping, until they are completely encircled by the wings of the seine net. The fisherman follows with the boat, watching the bag of the net and the fish shoal. To be successful, all manipulations have to be done very quickly.

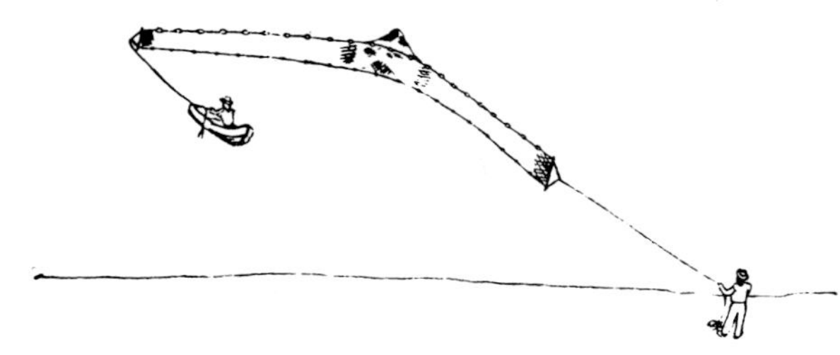

Fig 539 Plan for operating a beach seine.

Beach seines differ very much in size and construction. There are small ones like some 'sweep nets' for catching salmon,[190] but there are also very large ones. In any case, to use beach seines successfully it is necessary to have a fairly smooth bottom and not too much surf. They cannot work effectively in the estuaries of rivers when there are floods.[657] On the other hand, small and large quantities of fish are caught, particularly the herring-like species, as long as they come sufficiently close to the beach. If the stocks of these species of fish migrating near the shore are really decreasing then the beach seine fishery will probably decline more and more.[408] As mentioned before, beach seining is a form of early large-scale fishing, operated on the sea coasts and in some large lakes (*Fig 540*). Extremely large beach seines are used and have been used from early times. It has been said that the Maoris of New Zealand had beach seines

Fig 540 Beach seining in Lake Van in eastern Anatolia, Turkey, 1974. The groundrope is already ashore.

a mile or more in length, requiring 500 people to handle them.[499] As a modern example, it can be mentioned that in Sri Lanka the very important beach seine, with wings each of 400 metres in length and towing lines up to even more than 2,000 metres, requires 20 to 70 people to operate it.[621] Beach seines need many helping hands. This is not only true in fresh waters, but is much more so with the larger gear used on the sea shore (*Figs 541* and *542*). Seining is hard work for a collective of men. Nevertheless, until recently not much had been done to mechanize this fishery, with the exception of the introduction of some manually-operated winches, but there are some new ideas for mechanization.

24.5 Boat seining in sea fisheries

With the ever-growing tendency of fishermen to operate further out from the beach to secure bigger

Fig 541 Beach seining on the coast of Togo. The hauled gear is accompanied by swimming fishermen. (*Photo: R Steinberg, 1955*).

Fig 542 Chinese beach seining with floats keeping the netting above the water surface to avoid the escape of jumping fish. (*Kasuga, 1975*).

catches, it is not surprising that the sea fishery – more than the freshwater fishery – is now operating seines from vessels as boat seines. In northwest Europe the 'snurrevaad' of the Danes, also called the 'Danish seine', is well known as a boat seine.[471, 536, 616] Seining as discussed in this chapter, is a fishing method in which the seine net with long wings, and long towing lines which have a high influence on the catch, is set around a certain area with a fixed place from which the gear is set and hauled. In sea fisheries this fixed place can be an anchored boat or a set buoy. The importance of the long towing lines is that they come nearer and nearer during hauling, frightening the fish between them along the wings and into the bag of the gear. This action can be enhanced by towing the gear for a short distance, like a dragged gear (usually not done with seine nets). Towing for a longer distance has no purpose, because the gear with closed lines will catch no more fish, but where two boats are operating one gear, as in pair trawling, so also in pair seining towing could be operated for some time.[617] This means that, from the point of the catching method, seining is something like pair trawling. In Canadian pair seining two vessels operate the gear with the aim of spreading it around the fishing area as widely as possible: towing is limited to the stage of bringing together the two draglines as usual also in single boat fishing. In the following, only typical seining, with one vessel and without long towing time, is described.

It has been said that Danish seining was introduced by the Danish fisherman Jens Laursen Vaever in 1848. The net is set out from an anchored dhan (marker) buoy in the same manner as is done with a beach seine. The operation is carried out by a larger vessel or by an additional smaller one launched for this purpose. First, one drag line is put into the water, then one net wing follows and, while the cutter swings round in an arc or circle back to the buoy, the bagnet and the other wing with its drag line are set. Thus a big area is encircled by the time the boat comes back to the anchored buoy or the cutter from which it started out (*Fig 543*). Now the net is hauled in by the anchored boat, which is done by hauling the two drag lines simultaneously with the help of a rope-coiling machine (*Fig 544*) until the bag with the catch can be taken on board the vessel. Decisive for the success of the operation is the fact that the two draglines must contact the bottom near the opening of the gear as far as possible to frighten the fish together between the two lines and guide them into the netbag. This assumes clear water and good sighting conditions

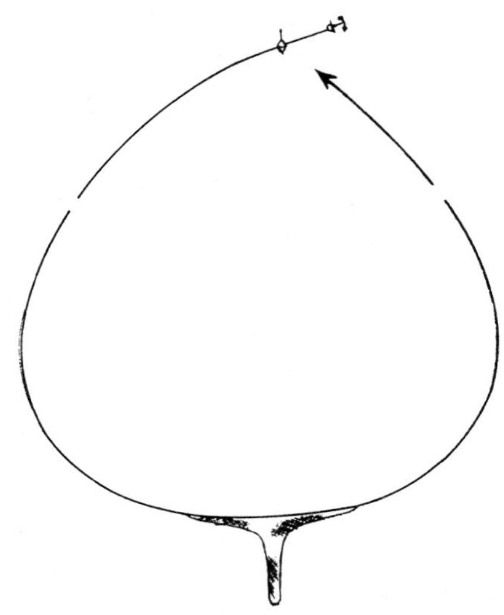

Fig 543 Danish seine net called the 'snurrevaad'.

otherwise the frightening effect does not work. If the catch is sufficiently large the vessel will remain on this place making one set after the other but always following the tide so that the current is flowing into the net opening when the gear is hauled. By this means the area to be fished is changed with each setting. The coiling machine for the draglines, as well as many coils of rope and a brightly coloured buoy, were considered typical of Danish seiners.

Danish seining is a daytime fishery for the reason mentioned before: four to ten sets can be made in a day in summertime. It can also be carried out in wind forces Beaufort 7 to 8. Other variations of this type of Danish seining (also called 'anchor seining') have been developed – like 'Scottish seining' or 'fly dragging'. In this case the seine net is set from a free-floating marker buoy as described before. When the vessel has reached the buoy again, it is lifted aboard, the two ends of the hauling lines are connected to the winch and dragging and hauling begins from the forward-moving vessel. It is claimed that fly dragging brings in larger catches than the original operation with an anchored buoy. On the other hand, fly dragging needs more energy than anchor dragging, and increasing prices of fuel may make the latter more successful economically.

Many coils of ropes are carried by the vessels engaged in this form of fishing. The original ropes made of natural fibres are nowadays replaced by synthetic ropes with a lead core to ensure that they sink immediately when set. The coils were stacked on both sides of the vessel in such a manner that the line was ready to run out for the next set. Each coil had a length of about 120 fathoms, over 200

Fig 544 Rope coiling machine for Danish seining in Killybegs (NW coast of Ireland, 1956).

metres.[617] The number of coils depends on the depth to be fished. It may be five or six with a small vessel fishing at about 70 metres, and ten to fifteen for a larger one fishing down to 180 metres or so in depth.[471] The stacked coils of lines have always been dangerous, and their handling became more difficult when heavier and larger-diameter ropes became necessary. Therefore reels, set on the deck of the vessel, were developed to handle the lines (*Fig 545*). These reels, with up to 4,000 metres of heavy dragline, take up deck space and their weight may influence the stability of the vessel in spite of their relatively broad beam. To overcome this problem for smaller vessels, the lines are stowed in special tanks placed below deck, underneath the coilers.[665] This has the advantage of providing a clear area for the lines to be set or hauled and less deck space is required. But it has the disadvantage of the loss of some fish-room space. It appears that the earlier idea of rope storage on two or three reels on deck is more popular. The number of reels depends on the method used to turn the ropes, after hauling, for a new set. The size of the reels is determined by the number of coils they can hold. For hauling the seine net, a power block can be placed at the stern of the vessel.[616] This can be similar to a block used for purse seining, or a three-part reel more typical for seining (*Fig 546*). With this hauling device, the net can be hauled in such a manner that it can be laid ready for shooting again.

24.6 Modernization of seine net fishing

Compared with trawling, seining needs less towing time and uses less fuel. On the other hand, especially with beach seining and seining under ice, it is a labour-intensive fishing method and some capital is required to acquire the larger gear. Such capital can sometimes only be raised by a group of fishermen. Nevertheless, seining remains an artisanal fishing method and large-scale company operations are rare, although there are some exceptions. Such an exception is the Korean Kwan-Hyon-Mang fishery, originally established in Hiroshima in Japan (*Fig 547*). This method is used in fishing for sardine-like fishes with a type of 'mid-water seine net' hanging on floats and operated by two towing boats. Besides those, two net boats, three smaller boats, one cooking boat and one motor boat are required, with a total crew of forty five – a regular fleet. The two motorized towing boats draw the netting together in a similar way to the Danish seine nets. Real towing, as with the two-boat system, was forbidden up until the beginning of the 1960s. Since that time, the towing boats have worked as in pair trawling and the typical seining with this gear became known as low speed mid-

Fig 545 Modern seining with drums for the draglines Esbjerg, (1979).

Fig 546 Powered reels for hauling the seine net. Esberg, (1979).

water trawling but, of course, now with more modern boats.

A very modern form of nearly large-scale boat or beach seining has been developed in Tasmania for catching the so-called Australian salmon (*Arripis trutta*). In this case the seine net is not set until the fish are plotted by airplane. When this is successful the vessel launches a smaller boat for the setting of the seine net. This may be a rowing boat because the fish are very sensitive to noise and will easily be frightened away. The seine net has a detachable bag in the case of hauling from the vessel, or it is used as a bagless gear when hauling is done from the beach. Hauling on the beach can also be done with tractors and other four-wheel-drive vehicles in this Australian fishery.[168, 506] The Soviet Union may be the first to introduce, for beach seining, motor winches which may be mobile, on the beach, or installed on boats. In the Caspian Sea, a number of machines have been designed to facilitate major beach seining operations for herring fishing.[440, 461, 608] Generally, two motor cars are needed to operate the beach seine, although there are some Russian proposals to work with one car only. An Israeli method is to fit each vehicle with a hauling wheel. For towing the ropes of the beach seine, a gipsy head is mounted on this wheel. Two such vehicles are placed near the water line, as close as possible. The rope of one wing of the gear is

Fig 547 Korean surface seine net (Kwan-hyon-mang). The net is hanging on the floats to be seen between the two boats.

attached to one of the vehicles, the net is set as usual, maybe with the help of a boat, and the second line is brought back to the second vehicle. Both vehicles haul the ropes over the gipsy head and coil them inside the vehicle. When the net reaches the beach, hauling of the lines is stopped and the net passes over the hauling wheels until the bag appears and can be towed onto the beach with the help of the vehicles. It must be emphasized that, during hauling, the vehicles have to be firmly braked, otherwise they can tow themselves into the sea![463]

Nevertheless, generally speaking mechanization came late to seining especially in freshwater fishing. Here the first attempts to mechanize the operation of seine nets were made during the last World War to overcome the lack of manpower during that time. Different methods have been developed, especially in the German inland fishery.[79, 243] In one of the oldest methods, the two towing lines were hauled by a small powered winch. Each hauling line was lengthened with an additional line reaching to the bag of the gear. On this additional line the wings were fastened with small lines which could be freed very easily. By means of this additional line the wings, when hauled, fall into the vessel when freed (*Fig 548*). Another method was developed some years ago by which the gear was hauled by a small winch from an anchored boat, as can be seen in *Figure 549*. By this method, the seine net is hauled in stages, which has the disadvantage that some fish may escape when the gear is stopped before beginning a new stage. A more satisfactory method was introduced some years ago in the Masurian lakes of Poland and recently also in Germany with good results. Two motorized net drums are used with two special boats with inboard motors. Each

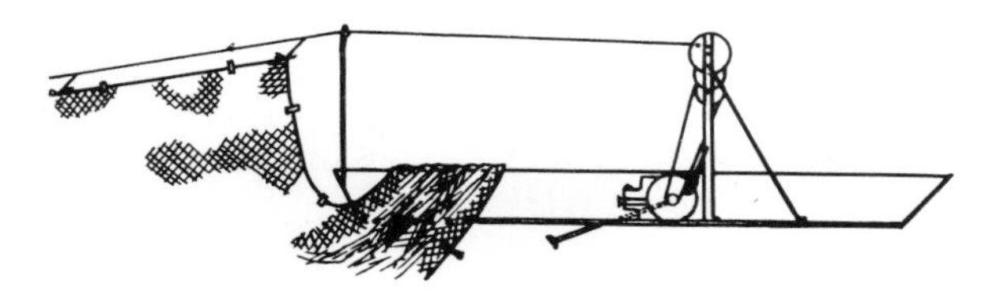

Fig 548 Motorized hauling of the wing of a seine net with an additional line as operated in Germany (1939).

drum holds one dragline and one wing of the gear (*Fig 550*). The two boats operate as in seining with two boats. The gear is hauled in one draw without interruption.

There is no doubt that of all types of seines, the boat seines in sea fisheries are the most interesting ones. Recently many attempts have been made to improve the gear because it is a fishing method needing low energy. In order to keep the net and the wings wide open for as long as possible, floating otter boards like the 'Hong Kong diverter' (*Fig 551*) were attached to the ends of the wings, some distance before the towing lines. It is true that by this means the fished area remained a large one for a longer period (*Fig 552*), but there is some doubt whether more fish are caught. Moreover, the towing resistance is increased, which means more energy is needed and this detracts from one of the advantages of boat seining – its low energy needs. Other proposals include electrification of the seine net with copper wires along the headline and foot-rope as electrodes.[129, 220] The current comes from a generator placed in one of the towing boats. As with trawls, the use of electrified seine nets has not been very successful up till now.

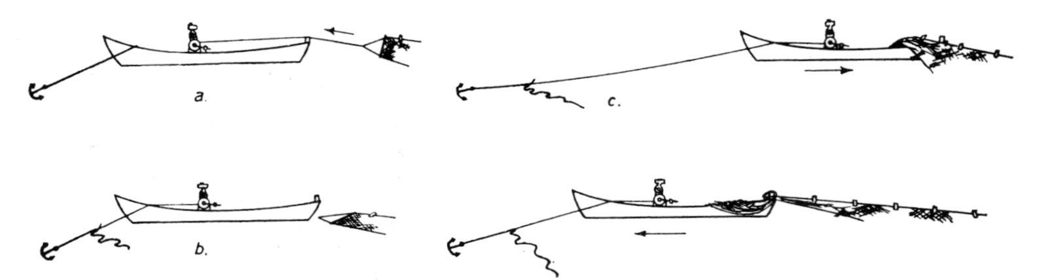

Fig 549 Mechanization of seine net hauling in a German lake fishery. (*v Brandt and Kaulin, 1966*).

Fig 550 Mechanized seining by hauling each wing of a seine net with a special anchored pontoon with net drum on a lake in northern Germany. (1980).

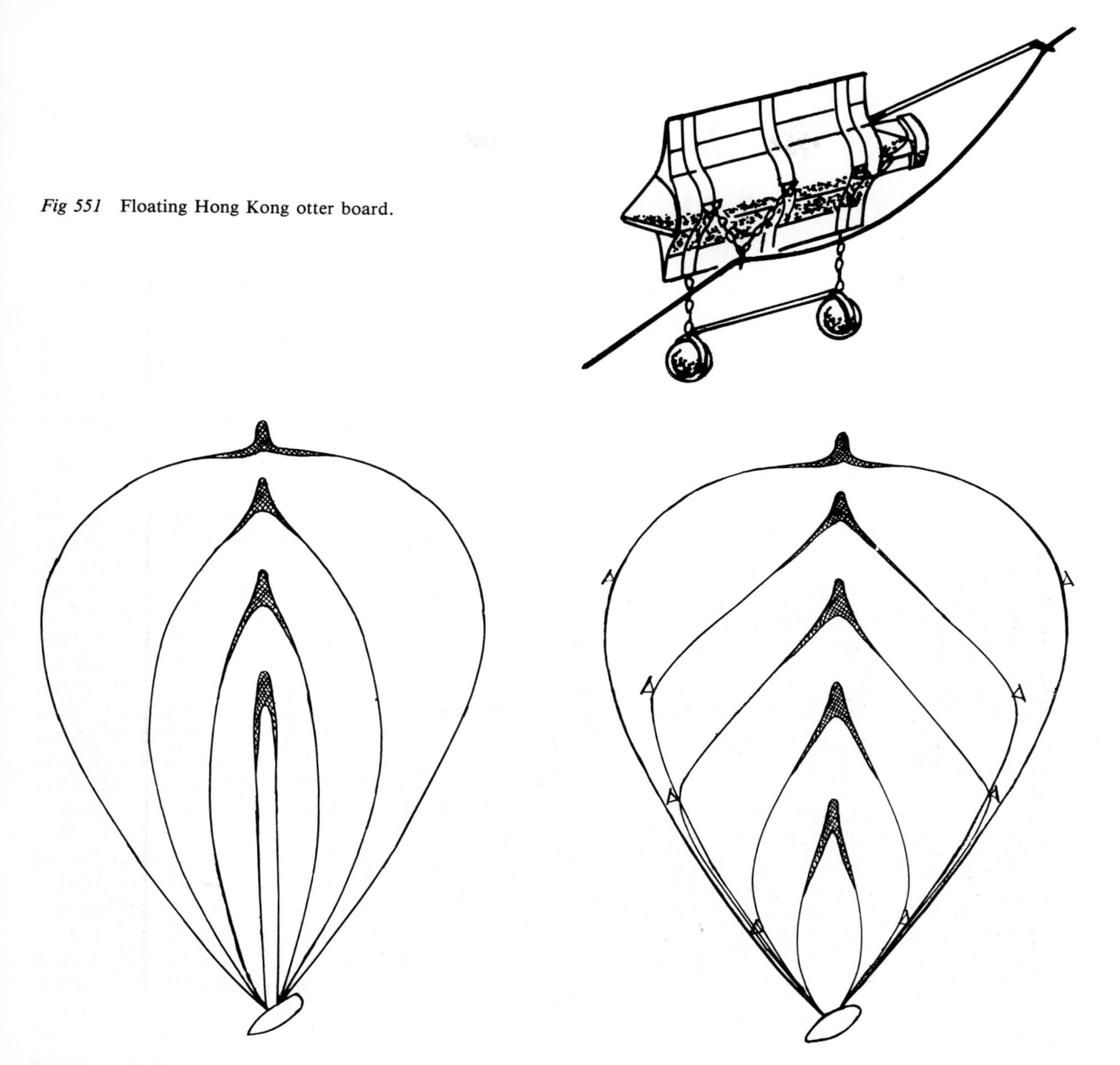

Fig 551 Floating Hong Kong otter board.

Fig 552 Expected shape of a Danish seine during hauling, without, and with, floating otter boards. (*According to Buckingham, 1975*).

Chapter twenty-five

Fish shoals and surrounding nets

Some species of fish appear in large shoals, not staying near the bottom but ranging pelagically in the water as detailed in Chapter 22 on mid-water trawling. Whilst fishing in 'three dimensions' with the mid-water trawl was unknown, such shoals could be fished only if they sometimes came near to the surface in large quantities, or if they migrated in shallow water nearer to the shore at regular intervals. When these shoals entered shallow water or penetrated into bays, firths or estuaries, vigorous large-scale fisheries could develop with simple fishing techniques. This shoaling of fish at certain seasons in coastal waters influenced the lives of the local people. Instances of this are the fishing of the salmon and herring shoals off the American north and northwest coasts, the cod shoals off the Lofoten Isles and the Pacific coast of Canada, and the herring shoals, formerly common off the Swedish west coast, and still occurring off the south and central Norwegian coast and to some extent around Iceland. The coalfish and capelin off the Norwegian and Icelandic coasts, and the herring shoals of the Georges Bank, are also examples, as well as the shoals of mackerel, squid and sardine-like fishes and some types of tuna in many parts of the world. Formerly, even porpoises were caught when shoaling off the coasts of the Black Sea. There are many other examples of seasonal fish shoaling near the shore and on banks influencing coastal life by causing large migrations of fishermen eager to catch them. Even in fresh-water areas, large shoals of pelagic fish are often found concentrated in shallow waters where they can be caught with simple methods. It is relatively simple to close a bight once a shoal has entered it. A dam can be built, a plaited fence or wall of nets may be set to close the bight, and the fish can then be caught as the enclosed area is gradually reduced. The Norwegians employ this principle for herring fishing in the spring when the fish enter their fjords in millions. With the aid of one or two walls of netting reaching from the surface of the water to the bottom, the fjords are effectively blocked. The so-called 'stengenot' used for that purpose is but a simple wall of netting with floats on the upper line and sinkers on the lower line. The catch, very frequently, is simply scooped out of the water.

Just as a fish shoal can be enclosed in a bight, so can it also be encircled in shallow water by means of fences and nets. The prerequisite is that the shoals be encircled quickly before they can escape, and also that the water is not too deep and the bottom not too uneven, so that the encircling can be done properly. In Yugoslavia, on the Dojran Lake – that interesting water which has already been mentioned in a previous chapter – fish shoals are caught, even today, by being encircled with wickerwork fencing and then concentrated in a narrow chamber.[14] What can be done with fences can be done much more easily with netting. Gillnets (Chapter 29) and entangling nets (Chapter 30) can be used to encircle fish. Sometimes also a gear is used which is operated like a seine net with a high opening (Chapter 24). Such a method was known for encircling sardines in the early English fishery. The shoal would be surrounded by a special type of net (a Cornish pilchard seine) reaching from the surface to the bottom, and the net with the shoal in it was then slowly worked nearer to the coast. There the fish were removed with small seines or by means of scoop nets.[127] Strictly speaking, this is a variation of seining. The main area for catching large pelagic or surface shoal fish is, however, the high seas and men have always endeavoured, by every possible means, to take advantage of such shoaling of oceanic fish. Moreover, some people think that stocks of pelagic fish, squid, crustaceans, and some smaller prey such as krill and sardines, will form the basis of larger yields of sea fisheries in the future, and predict that there will be a trend to catch smaller pelagic sea animals, not currently harvested for feeding men and animals.

In deeper water, where the nets hang on surface floats and do not reach the bottom, such a method cannot be entirely successful. Under such circumstances, the encircled prey will dive under the net and no catch will be made unless predatory fish below the net ring prevent the fish from diving into deeper waters.[64] In the examples described so far, the shoal has only been encircled from the side. In some waters the fishing area would be enclosed below by the natural bottom or by thermoclines, or, in rarer cases, by predatory fish waiting below. But in deep water where the nets do not reach to the bottom, fishing gears have to be designed to surround the fish shoal from below as well as from the sides in order to prevent them escaping in any direction – especially into the depths. This can be achieved with shovel-shaped gear, which surround the fish completely when the ground-rope is lifted. Similar, and better known, are lampara nets, which work on the same principles of surrounding the shoal both horizontally and vertically. Quite different in construction and operation, but with the same effect, are purse seines. These are now the most important gear for catching pelagic fish and, according to the statisticians, purse seines may produce the highest percentage of the total catch of the world. Purse seining for pelagic fish near the water surface, and trawling for bottom and mid-water fish or other prey, are therefore considered by some people the most important fishing methods in commercial bulk fishing.

25.1 Lampara-like surrounding nets

To catch pelagic fish near the water surface, the fisheries of East and South Asia have invented a number of gears which are shaped like a dust pan (*Fig 553*). Once the shoal has been surrounded, then the fourth side – the open front side of the net 'shovel' – is closed by the anterior edge of the net being lifted. These gears are used like pelagic seines, but they have a protruding bottom and can only be used on the surface of the water. There are various types of these nets and we will meet some of them again in the next chapter, on drive-in fisheries. One type of net which can be pushed beneath the shoal of fish or squid to encircle it from each side has become familiar all over the world; this is the lampara net originating in the Mediterranean (*Fig 554*). It is also shaped like a dust-pan, but is provided with wings. While the net bag, or bunt, is made of small-meshed netting, the wings are made of coarse material with wider meshes. The dust-pan shape is attained because the weighted ground-rope is much shorter than the upper line which carries the floats. This construction causes the middle part of the gear to be formed like a bag, as has been seen with the so-called 'seine nets without bag' (Chapter 24). In contrast to the seine nets, the lampara nets are sometimes called 'purse seines with bag'. This name should be avoided because, in contrast to genuine purse seines, this gear has no arrangement for pursing (see next section).

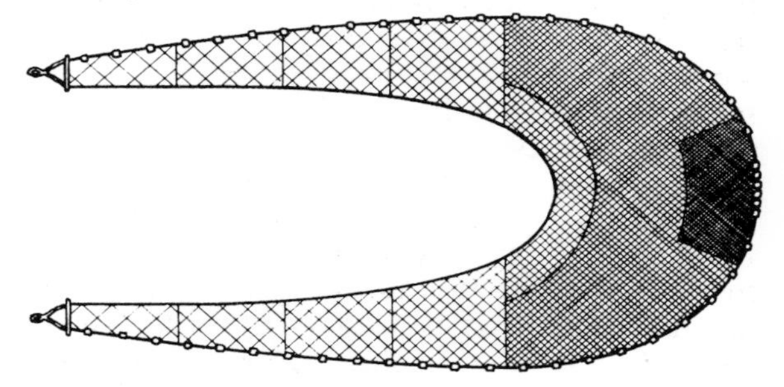

Fig 554 Design of the lampara net. (*Dieuzeide and Novalla, 1953*).

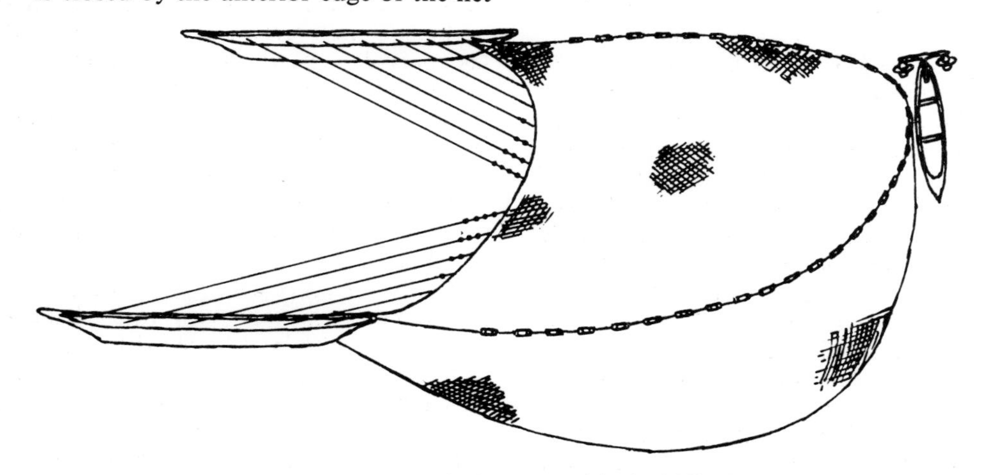

Fig 553 'Sapyaw', a dustpan-like encircling net used in the Philippines. (*Umali, 1950*).

The net itself is now mostly used with a single vessel, like a boat seine operated by a single vessel. The end of one wing is fastened to a buoy and from that buoy the remaining net can be carried by a boat around the fish shoal. The buoy can also be replaced by a boat, or skiff, which remains at the spot, or drifts slowly while the main boat encircles the fish shoal. That boat then returns to the initial spot and begins, uniformly, to haul the two wings. The leadlines come together closing, downwards, the area surrounded by the gear before the wings are drawn together. To prevent fish or squid escaping before the gear between the two wings is closed completely, a submerged fishing light is often hung from the vessel into the water or a line with white boards is submerged and moved up and down. Splashing, or 'cherry bombs', or loud hammering on the deck, or the gunwhale, can serve the same purpose.[293] The last step of this technique of operating the lampara net is shown in *Figure 555a*. This pulling together of the wings is typical of lampara netting or lampara-like surrounding nets. When this is finished and the catch in the net is concentrated at one side of the vessel, with or without the help of an additional smaller boat, hauling can begin. As mentioned before, the typical lampara net originated in the Mediterranean area. The name is said to originate from the Italian word 'lampo', as the nets are usually employed with lights. This gear is now known in many parts of the world. The Italians took the Mediterranean lampara net to the California coast for fishing sardine and mackerel (1905).

Beside the typical form of the lampara net, many other variations are known (*Figs 556* and *558*). All these nets have the typical shape of a winged dust-pan with upper and lower lines of various lengths and varying meshes for the individual net sections. Small meshes are used in the net bunt for the catch, and very large ones in the wings. Lampara or lampara-like nets are operated by smaller vessels to catch small bulk fishes – as in the Mediterranean and South Africa especially for sardines, in Argentina for anchoveta and mackerels[117, 547, 564] or in Japan, not only for sardines, but also for sea bream, dolphins and flying fish.[475] Lampara-like nets are also used for catching live bait for pole-and-line fishery (Chapter 9).[417] The Indians of the

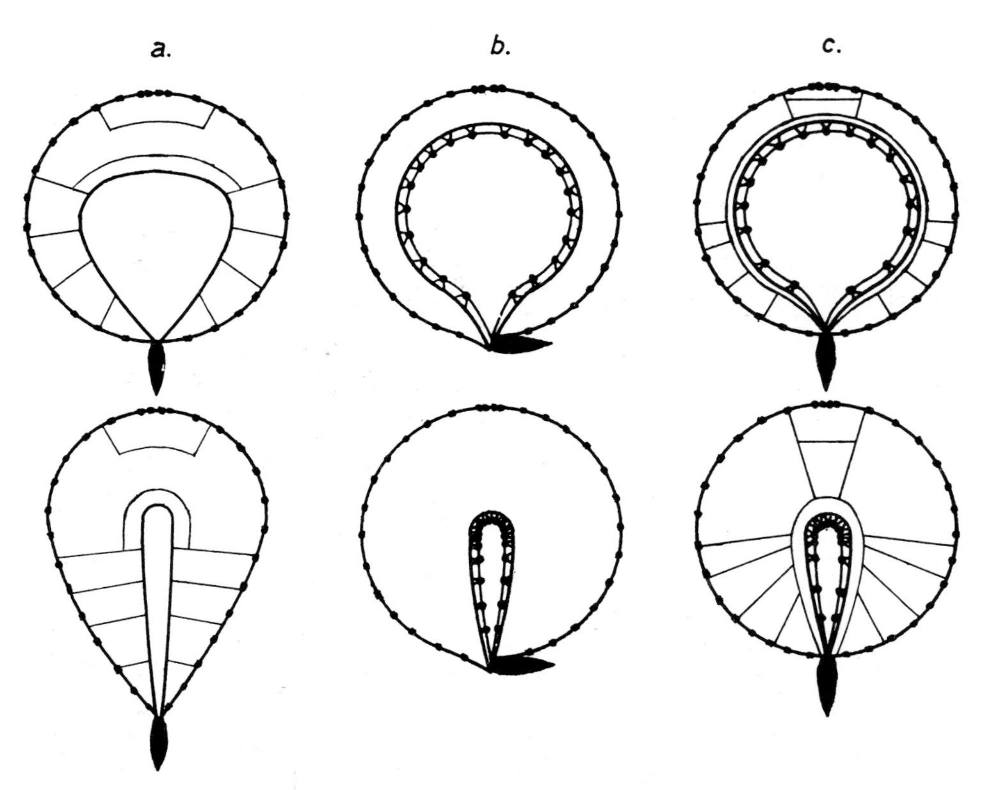

Fig 555 Main types of encircling nets illustrated with their method of operation: upper row when encircling the fish shoal; lower row when the gear is closed. (*a*) Lampara net; (*b*) purse seine; (*c*) ring net. (*Dieuzeide and Novalla, 1953*).

Malabar coast use their lampara-like 'kolli net' (*Fig 557*) in the same manner, also with two boats, especially for sardine-like fishes. They are also operated during the night with lights. The Japanese 'nuikiri ami' (*Fig 556*), and many other types of full or semi-surrounding nets, are used with two boats in the Japanese fishery (*Fig 558*) for sardines, flying fish and dolphins. They resemble the lampara net.

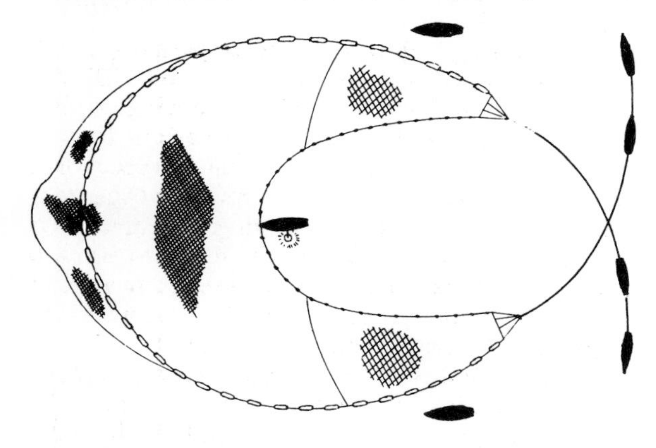

Fig 556 'Nuikiri Ami', a lampara-like Japanese encircling net. (*NN, 1959*).

Lampara nets are not restricted to sea fisheries. This gear has also been introduced in the Great Lakes of America for commercial fishing.[244] They are very effective when operated over rough ground where seine nets and trawls cannot be used. A suitable lampara net for inland waters is about 200 metres long, 20 metres deep at its middle and four metres deep at its end.[336] Another reason for operating lampara nets in the lakes may be that sometimes the beaches are unsuitable for hauling a gear like a seine net, as is the case in some of the larger African lakes.[244]

Fig 557 Indian 'kolli' net. At the back is the shovel-like net and in the forefront are the two large meshed wings.

25.2 Purse seines

For catching pelagic fish near the water surface, another type of gear is now used which is not only more effective but more recent than the lampara nets. These are the purse seines. Like lampara nets they work on the same principle by surrounding the fish both vertically and horizontally. But in contrast to the lampara nets, closing of the bottom of the

Fig 558 Japanese surrounding net in operation. (*Modern Fishing Gear of the World, 1959*).

Fig 559 Lampara nets being dried on the shore in Nazaré, Portugal.

net to prevent the escape of the fish is done in quite another and more complicated manner. Purse seines are made of long walls of netting, sometimes several kilometres in length, with a leadline of equal length or longer than the floatline. With this form of construction, no permanent bag can be incorporated in the netting, in contrast to lampara nets. However, some form of bag shape is necessary to retain the catch. This is achieved by incorporating a suitable loose form of hanging (see later). Characteristic of the purse seines are the rings hanging at the lower edge of the gear (*Figs 566, 568* and *569*). They can be made simply of wood, lead or iron, and be more or less heavy implements. Today, they are often made of non-rusting metal alloys in a more oval form, and with a mechanism to open the ring. The purse line runs through the rings. The net is set round a detected school of fish. This has to be done very quickly; therefore, the sinking speed of the net is an important feature of the gear. Especially fast sinking purse seines have been developed for tuna fishing. After setting, the gear is closed by hauling the purse line running through the rings at its lower edge (*Fig 560*). By this operation the purse seine is pulled together and almost closed, thus hampering the escape of the trapped fish. The fish are now concentrated within the towed netting and can no longer escape. As can be seen in *Figure 560b*, one part of the netting,

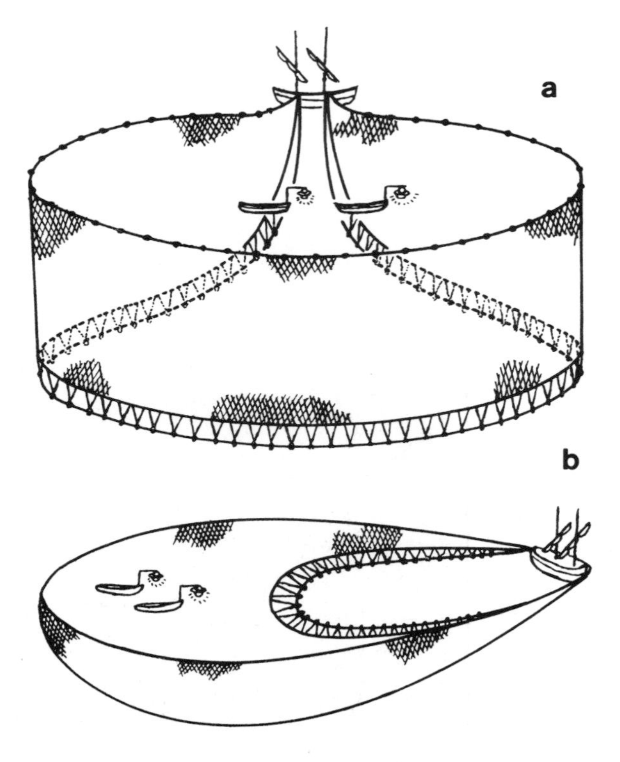

Fig 560 Sketch of purse seine operation with two boats. (*Bertuccioli, 1955.*)

formerly hanging vertically for encircling the fish, is now towed more or less horizontally under the fish to prevent their escape downwards. This part of the netting keeping the catch, the bunt, need not always be in the middle of the gear as will be shown later on. In any case this part must be made of one of the strongest materials used for the gear. When purse line and rings are taken on board, the netting is dragged tighter. This was done originally by hand (*Fig 561*). This procedure has the object of concentrating the fish closer together so that they can be bailed out or sucked up by fish pumps into the hold of the purse seiner. Very often, fishing with surrounding nets is a nocturnal activity for sardines or squid. The fish are lured, concentrated, and kept in a certain place by means of so-called 'light boats'. These can be one-man rowing boats (*Figs 175* and *176*) or unmanned floats in Greece (*Fig 177*) and Israel.[31]

Today, strong surface lamps (and sometimes also underwater lamps) are used as the source of light (Chapter 11). Light fishing can be carried out during dark nights without bright moonlight or when the sky is cloudy and (this is true for all surrounding nets) when there are no high waves. During daytime, in the Malayan fisheries, instead of fish-gathering lamps, lure lines are used (Chapter 11). To find out if enough fish have concentrated at the required place, fish searching implements are now used. In the early traditional tropical fishery in South Asia, and even now, the assessment of the concentration of fish will be made by underwater listening. To do this, the swimming fisherman hangs with one hand on the railing of a sampan and puts his head under water from time to time. Experienced fishermen can not only make estimations about the species of fish: experts, particularly the Thais, can distinguish up to six different species and they can also determine whether there are many fish or a few only, whether they stay near the bottom or nearer to the water surface and, of course, in which direction the fish can be found.

Purse seines are considered to be one of the most recently developed gears in large-scale fisheries for pelagic fishing, and can be used on the high seas far from the coastline. Generally it is supposed that the typical purse seine, with rings and purse line, is of American origin. In one version the purse seine, as described, is said to have been developed from the beach seine used in the American menhaden fishery off the Atlantic coast of the United States, as well as on the west coast from Alaska to California. It has also been said that the first purse seine was developed in the fjords of Rhode Island in 1826. Others think that a fisherman of Maine invented the purse seine for catching menhaden in 1837. Chinese fishermen have used

Fig 561 Hauling a purse seine by hand from a Japanese purse seiner (two-boat system) before introduction of the power block. (*Photo: M. Nomura*).

purse seines on the American west coast at least since 1863. In any case, most people agree that the general use of purse seines for menhaden began after the American Civil War (1861-65).[541]

On the other hand it is known that lampara nets were introduced into California by the Italians at the beginning of this century. Purse seines may also have been introduced to the North American Indians by European immigrants from the Mediterranean and Aegean Sea areas.[680] In this connection it is of interest that in an early edition of Duhamel du Monceau's *History of Fisheries and Fishes* (Vol. 2, Section 3, Chapter 11 of the 1772 edition) a sardine gear used by the Basques and operated 'comme une bourse' (like a purse) is described. After mentioning the dimensions of the gear it is stated that on the lead-line, at distances of four feet, are placed rings of horn similar to those used for curtains. Through these rings is passed another line (a purse line) by which the net is closed when full of fish. Such a description suggests that the gear was a genuine purse seine. Unfortunately, the author obtained this description second-hand, and is therefore unable to provide a drawing — though he does claim to have seen the gear himself at some earlier date. The fact remains that this gear can be considered a true purse seine, operated (even if only occasionally) off the coast of France in the late eighteenth century.

Later on, the purse seines, like other surrounding gear, were distributed from America to many other parts of the world. As far as is known, in Europe, Sweden was the first to adopt purse seining from the USA. This was in the early 1880s in the Bohuslän herring fishery off the Swedish west coast. The Norwegians introduced purse seining a little later, about 1890. Scandinavian fishermen took the purse seine to Iceland at the end of the last century (1899-1904). In 1906 the Swedes made the first attempts to use purse seines in the Baltic; the Danes followed suit, and in 1913 the German Baltic fishery also adopted this new gear for the herring fishery. Here it was in use until 1956, but after that no more – because of the lack of herring, and manpower!

In 1882, Japan adopted the new fishing method, and started purse seining for tuna and bonito in 1913. The Californian fishery for tuna followed suit in 1914, and Norway ten years later. Purse seines have been used to catch salmon (since 1886), also many clupeids, mackerels, cod, capelin and other fish, not only in sea waters but also in the large fresh-water lakes of Africa, Israel and Turkey. Purse seining became popular around the world, slowly in some areas but rapidly in others due to new inventions and improvements. The purse seine was considered important because, until it was evolved, pelagic surface fish could only be caught with drifting gillnets or in shallow water near the shore. Now it was possible to catch them in deep water, further away from the coast.

25.3 One-boat and two-boat seining

There are two different methods of purse seining: the one-boat system and the two-boat system. Both have their advantages and disadvantages, but purse seining with a single boat is now considered more economical, even though shooting a purse seine with the two-boat system may be quicker and a larger gear can also be operated than with the one-boat system. In two-boat purse seining, two boats, each carrying about half the gear, operate together – setting each part simultaneously, beginning with the middle of the seine net. In one-boat purse seining the gear is set, beginning with one end, around the located fish shoal. This method of operation has some influence on the construction of the gear. Generally speaking, the main part of the net of a purse seine is made of the same material with constant mesh size. Only that part of the gear where the catch will be concentrated, the so-called bunt, will be strengthened, and its position in the gear varies according to the method of operation in the two-boat or one-boat system.

Purse seines vary greatly as regards length, depth, hanging ratio* and size of mesh, depending on the fish to be caught and the personal experience of the skipper. The relationship between length and depth is about ten to one.[529] Examples of the differences in extent can be seen in *Figure 562*. The longest purse seines are those used for tuna and bonito fishing and these are often about 1,000 metres in length. In 1972 a Norwegian tuna purse seine was recorded as being 1,500 metres long and 200 metres deep, and weighed 25 tons. In 1973 a Spanish tuna purse seine was 1,690 metres long and 135 metres deep, and weighed 23·7 tons without accessories. In other types of fishing, large purse seines are used, as in the Faeroes (1975) for herring and mackerel, 630 metres long by 162 metres deep; and for capelin and sprats, 540 metres long by 135 metres deep.

The operation of the purse seine seems to be simpler in the two-boat system. This can be done even by rowing boats. In this case the two boats are towed by a motor boat to the fishing ground. The setting and hauling of the nets is done there by those two rowing boats (*Fig 563*). It may be that one

*Hanging ratio means the relationship between the length of the rope on which the net is mounted, and the length of the stretched netting.[275]

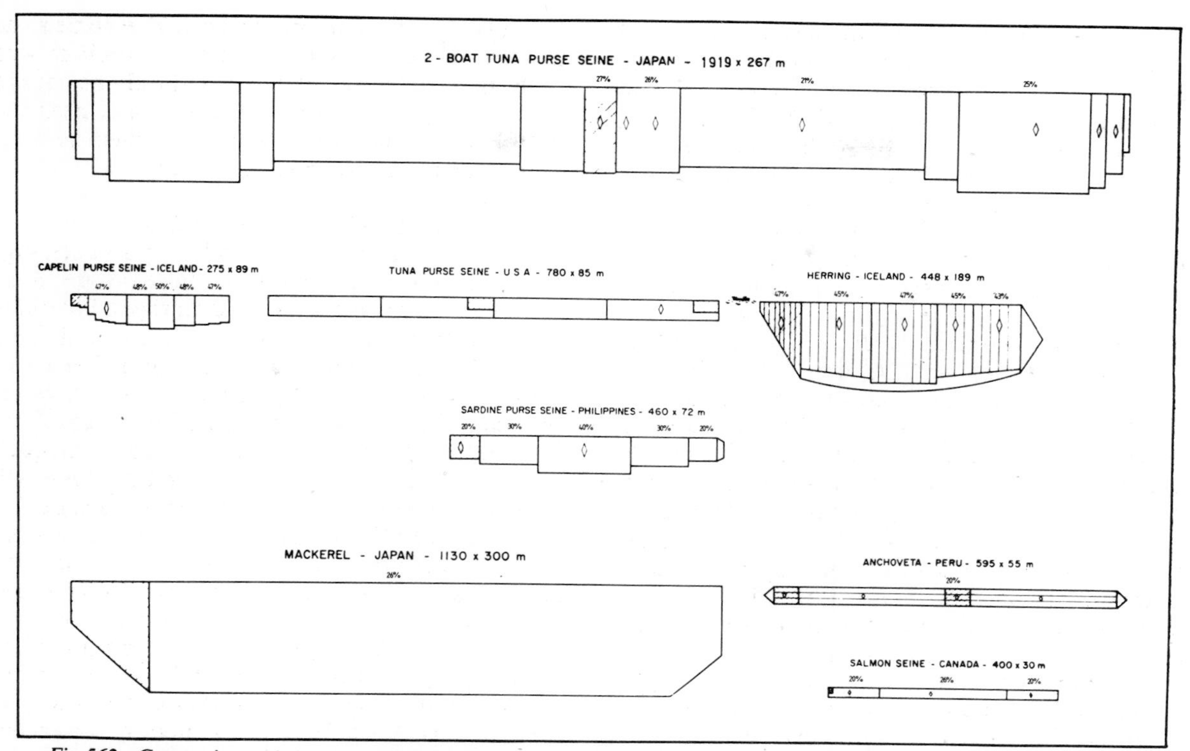

Fig 562 Comparison of the size of different types of one-boat and two-boat purse seines. (*H Kristjonsson, 1971*).

vessel is powered (*eg* about 80hp) for towing an unpowered vessel with the fishing gear and the small boats with the lamps for attracting fish (*Fig 176*). So it was in Greece about 1960. Twenty years later the towing boat had about 400hp and the five manned lamp-boats were replaced by four unmanned floats with lamps (*Fig 177*). Also, in this case, the net is shot and hauled by the two vessels (one powered, the other unpowered) and these purse seines can be very large (*Fig 564*). Another example, with slightly larger vessels for the same two-boat system as used by the Japanese is seen in *Figure 565*. If the fish shoal has been encircled by the net, and the purse line is pulled together to purse the net so that none can escape towards the bottom, then the net is hauled in the manner described. First the lower part of the net with the ring and purse line is lifted. By hauling the net uniformly from both boats, the fish shoal is concentrated in the middle of the net, that means in the strengthened bunt (*Fig 566*). Finally, the fish are packed in the central strengthened part of the net, which bulges like a bag

Fig 563 Setting a two-boat Thai purse seine with rowing boats.

Fig 564 Showing the mending of two-boat purse seines on the Island of Mytilini, Greece.

Fig 565 The hauling of a Japanese purse seine, two-boat type.

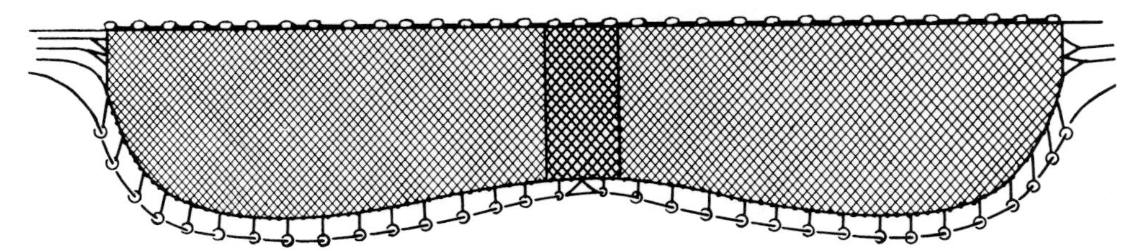

Fig 566 Diagram of a Japanese two-boat purse seine with the 'bunt' in the middle.

between the two boats. In calm conditions the fish are then lifted out by hand-operated scoop nets.

All surrounding nets have a large number of closely spaced floats, to avoid sinking of the gear when large quantities are caught (*Figs 566* and *567*). Nevertheless, the sinking of a full gear can happen, when frightened fish press each other downwards in their attempt to escape into the depths. In most cases when the fish are concentrated before hauling

Fig 567 Shooting a Peruvian purse seine with one boat and a skiff. (*Photo: Brandhorst*)

them on board, a second vessel is necessary to help to keep the floatline over the water surface. In two-boat seining this will be done by the second boat. In place of the two-boat system, in some areas it is now more and more general for only one boat to be used. Strictly speaking, one vessel with an auxiliary boat, the so-called skiff, is considered best for handling this type of fishery. The size of these large powered boats is directly related to the size of the net and the size of the seiner. One end of the purse seine is fixed to the skiff and set first with the net from the stern of the vessel. For this, many modern purse seiners have a ramp at the stern (*Fig 575*) similar to, but shallower than, that of a whaler or stern trawler. The end of the purse seine is held by the skiff until the vessel encircles the shoal with the net (*Figs 567* and *568*). When the encirclement is complete, the skiff is released and the lower part of the net is closed by pursing. The purse line is hauled first, together with the rings (*Fig 568d*). Then the hauling of the net begins, to concentrate the catch. As the hauling of the net (in contrast to the two-boat system) is only handled from one net end, the strengthened part of the net, which finally takes up the catch, must not be located in the middle of the purse seine, but placed towards one end. (*Fig 569*). When pursing and hauling a large gear by a single vessel, it could lead to the hauling vessel towing itself into the ring of the net. This is not so bad if it happens at the beginning of hauling. It could create a situation similar to that shown in *Figure 290.* The fish circling in the net will be guided away from the opening of the incompletely closed gear. If this towing effect into the gear is not wanted, the hauling boat should be towed by the motorized skiff to keep the boat away from the surrounded fish. After the drying up, *ie* concentrating the fish in a small part of the net, brailing begins by hand or semi-mechanically (*Figs 418* and *584*). If very heavy catches are obtained, a purse seine can also be divided into several strengthened parts with one bunt each, or strengthening can even be incorporated throughout the whole net. That means the purse seine can have a bunt reaching from one end to the other.

It has to be remembered that these types of gear are for catching pelagic fish on the surface only. The Norwegians have developed a special purse seine for fish that stay in deeper waters. The so-called 'synkesnurpenot' hangs on floats on the surface of the water, like some early types of pelagic fresh-water trawls (*Fig 570*). A similar type of 'mid-water purse seine' has been introduced in Japan.[222]

25.4 Variations of lampara nets and purse seines

As mentioned before, purse seines and lampara nets are used for the same purpose. Pelagic surface shoals of fish are caught by surrounding them completely, and preventing them from escaping downwards. Where the fish shoals to be caught are small, lampara nets are more economical because they require less time for shooting and hauling. Therefore, in some fisheries, both types of surrounding nets are operated. The gears have characteristic differences in construction, as can be seen from the following table:

	Lampara nets	*Purse seine nets*
Ground-rope and headline	ground-rope shorter	equal length or ground-rope longer
mesh size in the main part	different sizes	same size
rings for purse line	no rings	rings of different types
strengthened bunt	in the middle	in the middle or at one end
hauling with	both wings simultaneously	both wings or from one end.

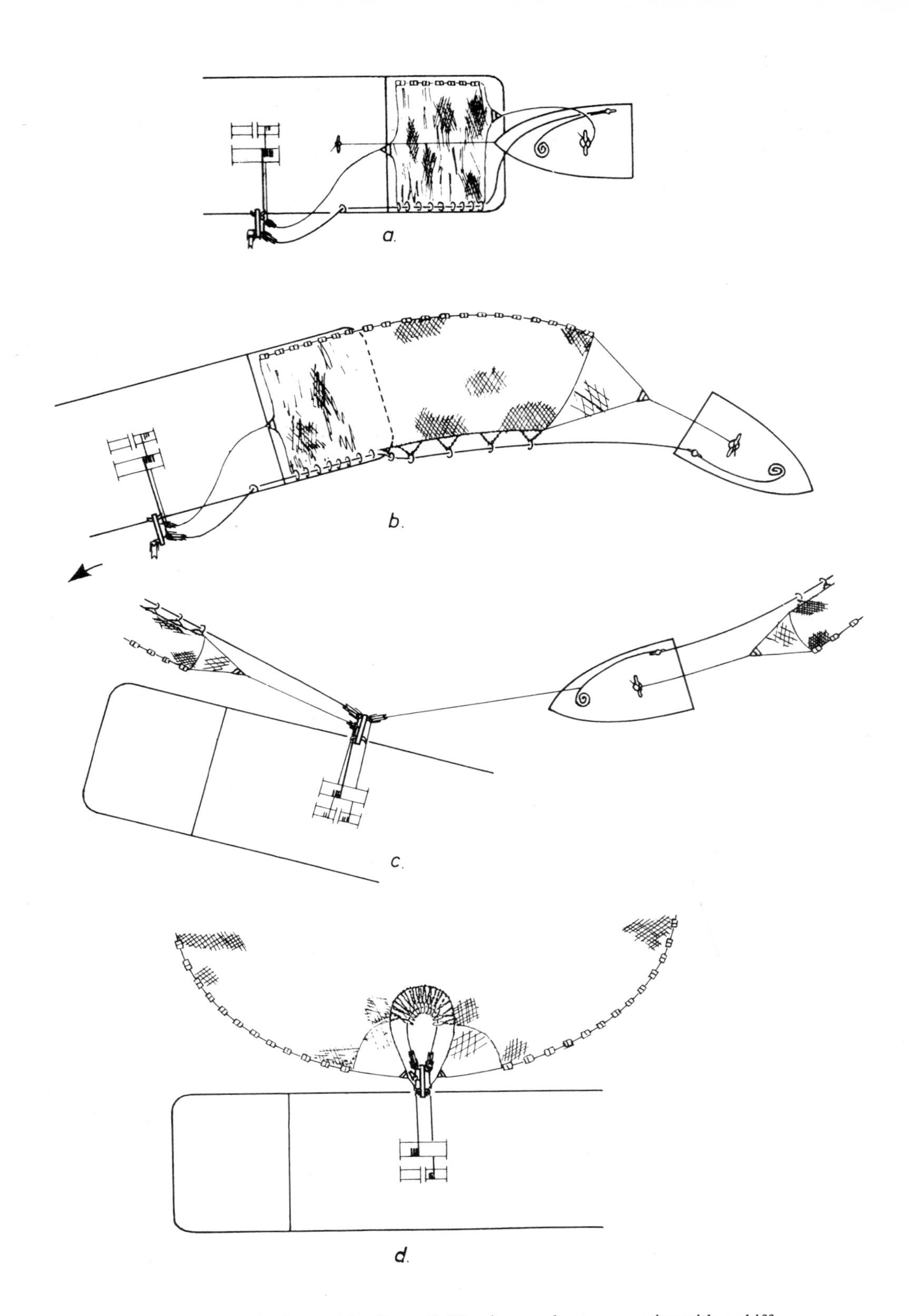

Fig 568 Setting and hauling a Californian one-boat purse seine with a skiff.

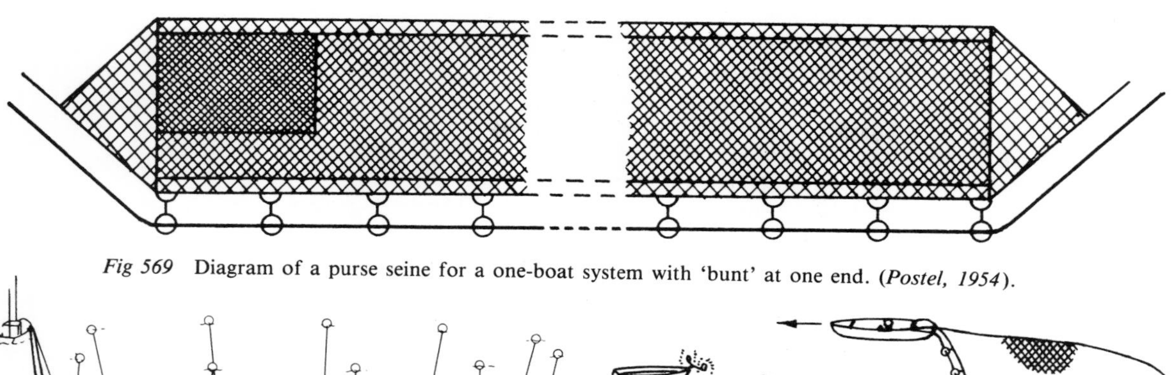

Fig 569 Diagram of a purse seine for a one-boat system with 'bunt' at one end. (*Postel, 1954*).

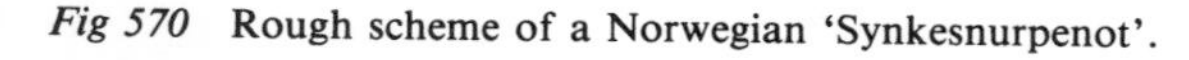

Fig 570 Rough scheme of a Norwegian 'Synkesnurpenot'.

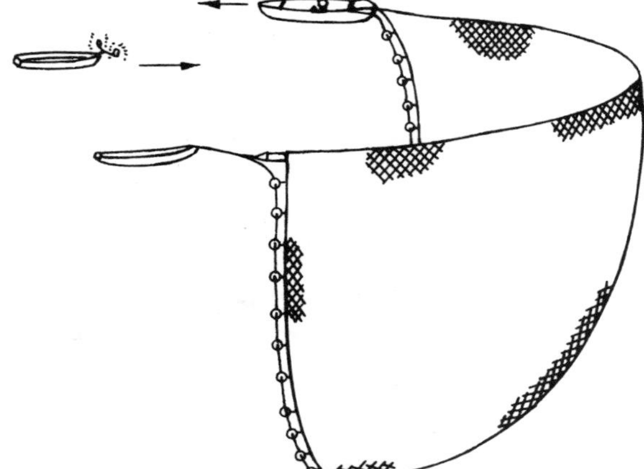

Fig 571 So-called 'chiromila' purse net of Lake Tanganyika, Zambia. (*Nédélec, 1975*).

Between the purse seines and the lampara nets there exist many transitional types. They may be designed as typical purse seines, but the various net sections are made with varying mesh sizes just as the lampara nets are. But they can also be typical lampara nets – that is, with the ground-rope shorter than the headline, but in this case they are provided with additional rings and a purse line so that they can be pursed like a real purse seine. For all these intermediate hybrid forms the term 'ring net' should be used[501] (*Fig 555c*).

There is another interesting gear for catching fish by surrounding them, also from beneath, but not by closing the bottom but by closing one side of the surrounding gear according to the pursing system. This is a special gear operated in different forms on Lake Tanganyika, called 'chiromila'[32, 417] or, as used in Lake Nyassa, 'chilimila'.[244] This gear is used to catch pelagic fish in open water. It may be of Arabian origin, brought from the sea fisheries of Aden in the Arab slave trading days.[244] The gear hangs down from the water surface in the form of an open calotte (*Fig 571*). It seems that such nets are most effective in catching small pelagic fish when the water is not deep, so that the gear can almost touch the bottom, or when the fish are concentrated during the night with the help of light at a suitable place. The gear is towed by two boats, which come together for closing the opening of the net as soon as the lightboat is inside the netting. Then hauling begins by pursing the line from both boats simultaneously.

25.5 Mechanization and improvement of purse seining

The fishery with surrounding nets requires many helping hands. This is especially true for hauling netting some hundreds of metres in length. *Figures 558, 561* and *565* give only an impression of how many people were formerly needed to operate a gear like a purse seine. In modern industrial countries, a fishery needing many labourers can no longer be maintained because this labour is too expensive. This is the reason why not only pursing winches but also various kinds of net hauling systems were introduced into this fishery. Mechanization was initially directed mainly at the hauling of lines with the help of capstans or winches. The gear itself had to be hauled in by hand and therefore needed many hands. This applied to both methods of bulk fishing – with trawls as well as surrounding nets. There could be some mechanical help by hauling the netting over a long roller – maybe power driven – mounted on the rail like that for hauling gillnets used in the herring driftnet fishery. There may have been, also, some non-powered or even powered pulleys to facilitate the hauling of purse seines. There are some in use today (*Figs 572* and *573*), but they are not effective enough to do the hauling of the heavy gear without some additional manpower. Therefore a spectacular development appeared when the Yugoslavian-born fisherman, Mario Puretic, introduced in 1953 the so-called 'power block'. This, and the introduction of synthetic fibres for purse seine netting, was considered a revolution – especially for tuna fishing.[376, 553] The power block is a mechanized V-shaped pulley, originally driven by an endless rope from the winch of the vessel but later driven hydraulically. By hanging the block on the end of a beam (derrick), nowadays also on a crane at some height over the water surface (*Figs 574* and *575*), the narrow angle of the net creates sufficient friction in the rubber-lined 'V' sheave to apply a strong tractive effort on the netting. By means of these powered blocks, the net is hauled much more quickly and with less manual work – manual tasks being confined to controlling the mechanical operation of the gear (*Fig 576*). When hauling, the net comes from the power block onto the deck of

Fig 573 Greek power block for two-boat purse seines for pilchard; in the harbour of Molivos, Lesbos, Greece (1968).

Fig 572 Japanese net hauler for the handling of purse seine nets.

Fig 574 Californian tuna purse seiner with power block operating from San Pedro. (1962)

Fig 575 Modern French purse seiner with ramp in Concarneau. (1977)

Fig 576 Hauling the net over the power block avoids much manual work. (California, 1962).

the fishing vessel where it can be stacked in folds for immediate use in the next set. Before this, the net was often hitched onto a so-called turntable which was turned to the right position for the next set, so enabling the net to run out in the best manner. In two-boat seining the nets can be hauled simultaneously from both ends by means of two power blocks. Therefore, off the coast of southwest Africa, some vessels are fitted with two power blocks in order to haul in a shorter time (*Fig 577*).

Salmon purse seiners of the Pacific were the first to use power blocks, then followed the fisheries for tuna and herring. Today, all species of pelagic fish like menhaden, pilchard, sardines, anchovy, mackerel, capelin and others are caught with purse seines operated with power blocks. Even the small boats of the French pole-and-line fishermen now have a characteristic small power block to haul their small surrounding gear for bait fishing (*Fig 578*). With the introduction of the power block, purse seining made an important step forward in adapting this formerly labour-intensive fishery to modern needs. This was done long before such methods were introduced into modern trawling (Chapter 22).

Not only are purse seines now operated with power blocks but so too are some other types of gear. Power blocks are used for transporting the nets on board the vessel, or back onto the wharf (*Figs 579* and *580*). The different uses caused many variations to appear in the construction and dimensions of the power block. And it is not only power blocks that can be used for net handling in purse seining. One hauling device is known under the name 'Triplex' (*Figs 581* and *582*). This net winch hauls the gear by means of three rubber-coated rollers rotating simultaneously in the opposite direction to each other. The net is threaded between the rollers to create friction. By this system the net is prevented from slipping when it is heavy with a large catch, or under rough weather conditions. With this system the net can be hauled from a lower height than that necessary for hauling with the usual power blocks. On the other hand, a second transporter block is needed to take the purse seine to its stocking position on the vessel, often on a higher place. As explained earlier, the power block requires the net to run over the block at a narrow approach angle and this is achieved by hanging the block as high as possible. But the high position of a heavy block can itself cause problems. This is avoided by the Triplex net hauling device which was specially made for fishing in rough waters where heavy catches are expected.

There is also another device for handling and storing the smaller purse seines and other fishing gear, and that is the net drum. When this is used, the purse seine is hauled over a large roller at the stern of the vessel and wound up together with the

Fig 577 Southwest African pilchard vessel with two power blocks and fish pump for transferring fish from the net into the hold. (1965)

Fig 578 French pole-and-line fisher with power block for bait fishing with a small surrounding gear. St. Luz, (1978).

Fig 579 Power block for gear transportation in the French harbour of St. Luz. (1978).

Above. Fig 580 Icelandic purse seiner with power block and drum for transportation (1970).

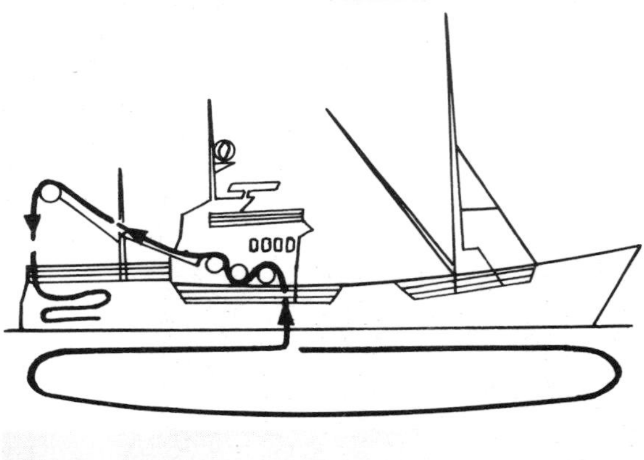

Left. Fig 581 Working diagram for hauling and transportation of a purse seine with Triplex.

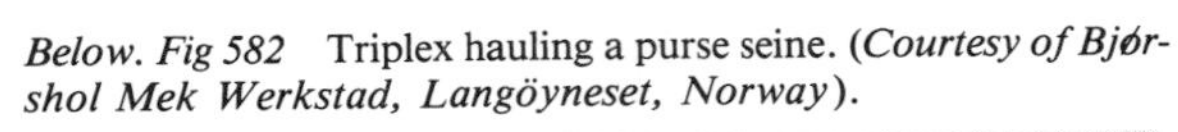

Below. Fig 582 Triplex hauling a purse seine. (*Courtesy of Bjørshol Mek Werkstad, Langöyneset, Norway*).

purse line on a large drum.[113, 241, 245] This reel is used in purse seining for setting, rewinding, and carrying the gear. Drum seining originated in Canada for salmon fishing with purse seines. It has been said that this reel was constructed in 1935 but forgotten again until 1953, when drum seining became successful in the American salmon fishery and that for herring. Nevertheless, hydraulically powered drum seining was temporarily eclipsed when power blocks became available. Since then, the advantages and disadvantages of the two methods have been the subject of debate. Sometimes drum seining, sometimes block seining, is considered as the most effective method. Both have advantages and disadvantages.[245, 456, 680] The main advantage of drum seining may be the fact that the number of crewmen can be reduced to four including the skipper, in contrast to the six or seven men needed for block seining. A disadvantage is that the purse seine needs a special construction. The floatline and the leadline must be nearly the same length, otherwise the gear would not come in evenly. In contrast, any purse seine can be operated by a power block as long as the floats can pass the block. Drum seining has the advantage that, when setting the gear, the operation can be stopped at any stage when it seems suitable. This is not possible in block seining, where the whole gear has to be set before retrieving can begin. Another advantage of drum seining is that the gear can be hauled in twice as fast as in block seining. This means that more sets can be made per day, maybe 17 instead of 10. This is an advantage when fishing in areas with small shoals of fish. The drum has more power, which means that the vessel can be pulled more strongly into the ring of the set gear than with a power block. Therefore, a more powerful skiff is needed in drum seining, to keep the seiner out of the circle of the purse seine. Finally, when a purse seine with a power block high over the vessel is being hauled, fish and jelly fish can drop out of the netting, and may fall into the faces and eyes of the fishermen watching below (*Fig 576*). Such problems do not arise with drum seining. These differences demonstrate why there are various opinions on the value of each method. The possibility of reducing manpower costs makes drum seining attractive – but this method is prohibited in some countries, such as Alaska.

Just as hauling the lines and the gear had to be done by hand originally, so too did brailing the concentrated catch with hand-operated scoop nets, called 'brails'. For brailing small fish, mostly simple, but very deep scoop nets with long wooden handles are used (*Fig 583*). With the help of a winch and four people, the catch can be brailed from the gear directly into the fish hold of the vessel. In the California fishery these scoop nets can lift out several tons of fish at a time. For brailing larger fish like tuna, a special type of scoop net is used,

Fig 583 Brailing mackerel with a long-handled scoopnet with a very deep netbag. California, 1962.

which is less deep and which has a bottom that can be opened and closed with a purse line and rings, and works in a similar way to the purse net itself. (Chapter 19, *Fig 418*). *Figure 584* shows how this brail is operated. Brailing purse seines with scoop nets is a labour-intensive and time-consuming

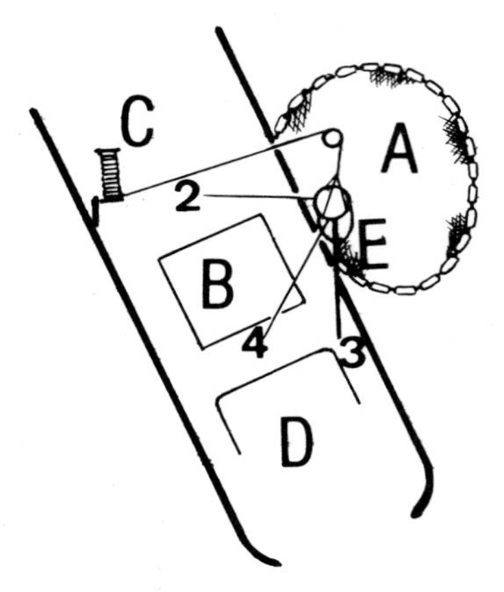

Fig 584 Plan of the operation of a pursed scoop-net for brailing. (*a*) purse seine; (*b*) fish hold; (*c*) winch; (*d*) bridge; and (*e*) brail with handle. (*1*) operator of the winch for lowering and lifting the brail; (*2*) operator of the line for towing the brail in the right position before emptying; (*3*) operator of the handle of the brail; (*4*) operator of the line to close and open the brail.

process. To improve purse seining, pumps were introduced to empty the gear.[99] In this way the fish may be removed even more rapidly, not only from the net to the fish hold but also from the hold to shore (*Figs 577* and *585*). In the anchovy fishery of South Africa and in western South America, the labour-saving pumping method could originally be employed only for small fish or those that would not be damaged, or where damage was not important, such as industrial fish for producing fish-meal. This has changed since the 1950s. Now improved pumps are available which can pump fish undamaged for human consumption.[462] In the menhaden fishery, a successful method was developed of combining a purse seine with a fish pump with a suction head which is also an anode. With such an electrified pump the fish can be transferred not only much more quickly, but also in better condition.[220]

It has been mentioned in the first chapter, that the excitement caused by the introduction of synthetic fibres for netting materials (with unexpectedly successful properties) is over. This does not mean that no further improvements in the employment of these materials is possible. In Chapter 18 knotless netting, made according to the

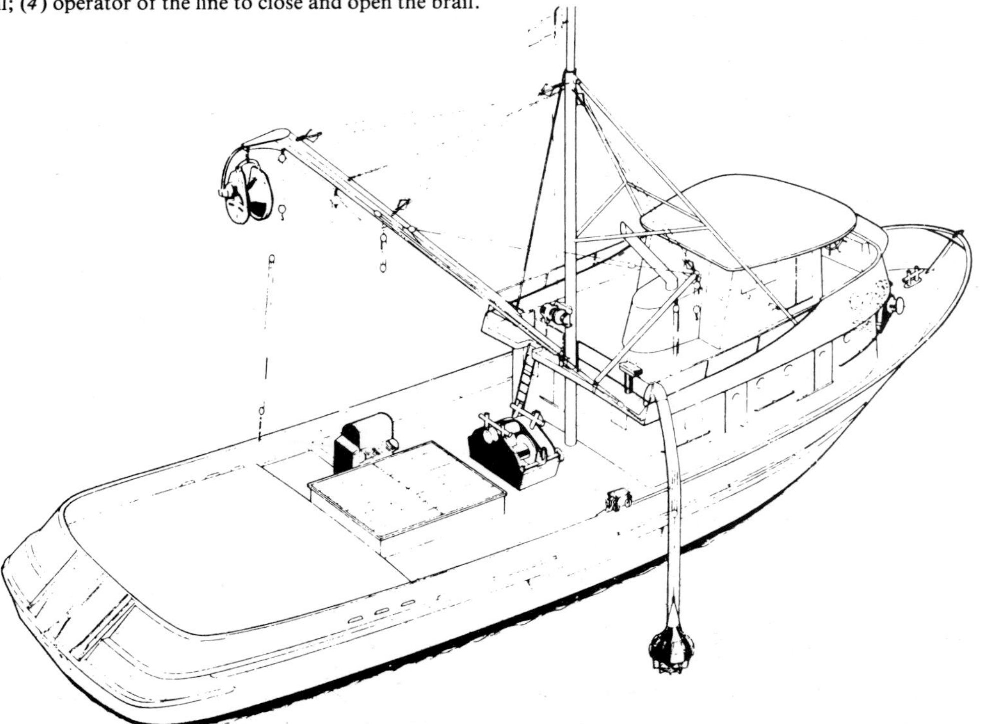

Fig 585 Sketch of a typical purse seiner with power block and fish pump. (*Courtesy of MARCO, Seattle, Washington.*)

Raschel system, has been mentioned, and also the fact that these meshes can, instead of the usual quadratic or rhombic form, also have a hexagonal one (*Fig 397*). Norwegian investigations revealed that purse seines with hexagonal meshes have some advantages over netting with rhombic meshes. The reason may be that the meshes with the hexagonal form stay open much better, and therefore have a lower water resistance. This can mean not only a better sinking speed of the purse seine but also that it is lighter and easier to handle. This may also apply to other gear made until now of knotless netting according to the Raschel system.[481]

As can be seen, many efforts have been made to improve purse seining. This demonstrates too how efficient this method of fishing is considered to be. Of all these efforts the invention of the Puretic power block may be the most important one, even though some think that the drum seine/fish pump method will be the one of the future. By mechanization of the hauling devices, the purse seine fishery has achieved the same status as the modern trawl fishery by stern trawling. By such mechanization, the growing running costs due to rising wages could be countered to some extent. In that way the purse seine fishery meets modern requirements and will, in future, together with the trawl fishery, remain the leading method for bulk fishing of pelagic shoals. But there need to be greater efforts made to decrease the time of searching, by the introduction of better fish finding methods, not only with the help of spotter aircraft (aeroplanes and helicopters) but also by satellites which can survey large fishing areas.

25.6 Porpoises and tuna purse seining

It is well known that very often porpoises travel for unknown reasons in tight association with yellowfin tuna. While the air-breathing dolphins hunt near the water surface the yellowfin tuna habitually swim beneath them. That is why, to catch tuna with purse seines, the so-callled 'porpoise fishing' or fishing 'on porpoise' method is operated. The practice started in the late 1950s. A search is made for a shoal of porpoises and, when found, the purse seine is set around the shoal of mammals above and the tuna below. This brings some trouble in separating tuna and dolphins when hauling the gear.

Even though porpoises are capable of leaping easily over the cork line of the purse seine, they show little tendency to escape in this manner. By trying to escape through the meshes, some hundreds of thousands of dolphins are estimated to become entangled in the nets and drowned every year. The problem was to find a means of retaining the tuna and, at the same time, freeing the trapped porpoises. Both animals are about the same size, therefore no regulation of the mesh size can help to separate them. Many experiments have been made to frighten the dolphins out of the gear by acoustic methods. Playing back the alarm call of the dolphins, or other acoustic signals including that of killer whales hunting porpoises, have not succeeded. In most cases fisheries are not interested in catching dolphins. Moreover, by the US Marine Mammals Protection Act of 1972 the porpoise has become a protected species and the number of porpoises allowed to be killed has been restricted. Practical fishermen found how to decrease the high mortality of porpoises in purse seining for yellowfin tuna off the American west coast. Two different procedures to release porpoises have proved effective – one by some alterations to the method of purse seining, and the other by gear construction. To release the trapped dolphins, the so-called 'backing down' or 'backdown' method was developed by Captain Anton Maizetich, in San Pedro, California, in 1959/60 (*Fig 586*). The principle of this method is that when two-thirds of the purse seine is hauled, the vessel moves in reverse in a wide arc. By this movement the gear forms a long channel instead of a round circle. The porpoise tend to congregate at the extreme end, far away

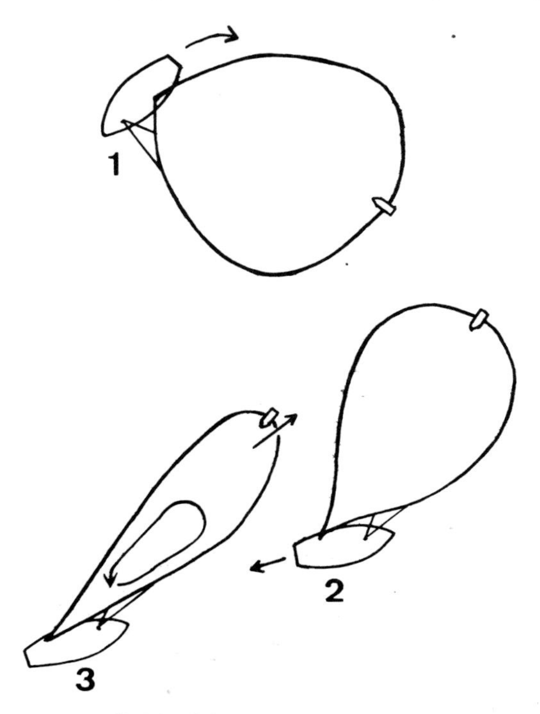

Fig 586 So-called 'backdown method' for releasing porpoises from a closed purse seine. (*Bahram et al, 1977*).

from the vessel, while the tuna generally range back and forth in the channel between the dolphins and the vessel. At a time when the tuna are near the vessel, the ship is backed rapidly, causing the cork line at the end of the channel to become submerged. At that moment the porpoises concentrated there may escape. Normally, three or four such rapid backdown surges are necessary to get the dolphins out of the purse seine.

Porpoises may become entangled in the meshes by their closed or open jaws as well as their pectoral fins. To avoid this, another experienced captain of California, Harold Medina, in about 1971 replaced some parts of the netting in the backdown area of the gear by small-meshed netting. This reduced porpoise entanglements very much. Of course, by this alteration the buoyancy of the gear can be lessened to such a point that the corks sink so deeply that they are squeezed by increasing water pressure and the gear can no longer rise to the water surface. When this method became successful in avoiding killing porpoises, an apron of small-meshed netting was fixed at the end of the channel formed by the backdown. This apron forms a ramp that makes it easier for the dolphins to swim over the cork line during backdown.[22, 348]

Chapter twenty-six

The drive-in fishery

We are accustomed to talk of active and passive fishing gears in literature as well as in legislation. It has already been mentioned (Chapter 1) that it is a mistake to think that all active fishing gear are moved or towed and that all passive gear are stationary. Whether the gear is moved or not does not determine an active or passive gear. What is important is whether the fish takes the gear involuntarily or voluntarily. Angling lines, also movable gears like drifting or pulled lines, are passive gears as the fish accept the bait voluntarily. Rip lines, however, are active gears because the fish is taken more or less involuntarily. But there is yet a third possibility, where both the fish and the fishing gear may be called passive, that is in cases where the fish to be caught are driven into the gear. That can become necessary if the bottom is so rough that towed gear cannot be employed. This may be the case with coral reefs or around volcanic islands. Here the bottom may be so rugged that even passive gear like pots or longlines are lost when being hauled, through being caught on the rocks. Another reason to drive the prey into a gear may be that the quantity of fish actively entering a passive gear is so small in relation to the time involved that the gear has to remain set for a very long time before a profitable catch has developed. But that is impossible in tropical waters and can scarcely be done even in the Mediterranean. The fish first caught would very quickly die in the warm water, or would soon be eaten by crayfish or other predators. In such cases the so-called 'drive-in' fishery would be useful. To achieve that, both normal and specially constructed fishing gears are set up into which the fish are driven.

As discussed in Chapter 11, many methods are known of frightening fish. In shallow waters they can be driven into a gear by rows of wading and splashing people. This is a specific fishery for large families, hordes of villagers or whole tribes. The participation of many people driving the game sought to be captured is an old principle in both hunting and fishing practices. Not only fish can be driven into a gear; in a few cases it is known that crayfish have also been driven into small gear.[345] To catch fish by the drive-in or driving-in method, many small gears can be operated or a single large one. In both cases it is a collective fishery, with sometimes up to a hundred or more people co-operating. Driving the fish is not only done by wading men but can also be done by horses and cows as mentioned before in Chapter 11. In deeper water, fish can be driven by swimming and diving fishermen, as the Japanese are doing in the coastal waters of the Ryukyu Islands and in other places where the bottom is too rough for towed and dragged gear.[242] Fish are mostly driven by noise created by striking the water with branches, poles and paddles, or by beating the gunwales or garboards of a fishing boat as mentioned for frightening jumping fish with the 'white board method' (Chapter 17). Sometimes fish are driven into a fishing gear by casting stones into the water. Such stones can be used many times over by tying them on a line and dragging them back for recasting. The Japanese use this system, just as do the Greeks and the Turks. Through using marble, the Greeks speak of a 'fishery with white stones' (*Figs 587* and *598*).

Fig 587 Fishery with 'white stones' in Greece to drive fishes into gillnets. (1958).

Occasionally special noise-making implements are known for operation outside the water, like those formerly used in the Philippines to drive fish into a large trap.[640] Generally, however, implements are used to make the noise under the surface of the water. Such an instrument can be a wooden stick with a steel pipe or a hemispherical device fixed at the end of the stick, which is pushed into the water in special rhythms. Such 'pulse sticks' are also used to prevent the escape of fish before a fishing gear like a seine net or a surrounding net is closed (*Fig 530*). Such scaring implements are even used to frighten eels into trammel nets.[181] During the night, fish can also be frightened by light used under some conditions. Indians of North America have driven salmon by swimming with torches.[625] A new idea is to use electricity for this purpose. In this way a modern form of drive-in fishery was developed for driving the fish in small rivers into gillnets or specially constructed bagnets using electrical currents.[220, 232]

26.1 Scare lines

In Chapter 11 the so-called lure line has been mentioned for attracting fish and other water animals. Similar lines can be used also for frightening fish. These so-called 'scare lines' are made in a boa-like manner by twisting ropes together with some leaves, or using twisted leaves alone (*Fig 588*), or by twisting old netting together.[192] In not so deep water the scare lines are used horizontally, like a seine net, to drive the prey together and to concentrate them in shallow waters. This is done, *eg* on fishing grounds with rough corals in the South Seas. For a fish drive on the Tonga Islands a community of about 30 people may be involved. For the scare line, coconut fronds are wound round a rope which is set around a large area to be fished. The scare lines are then pulled towards the shore. As the lines come closer, the fish are concentrated and are finally caught with some other gear.[315, 673]

The fishery with scare lines is known not only in south and southeast Asia[200] but also in Africa.[244] Native fishermen on Lake Victoria in Kenya put broad floating garlands of papyrus in a circle on the water near the shore, and the suspended stalks from these bundles surround the fish like a net or fence. To concentrate the fish further, the circle is gradually diminished by towing it to the beach, when the small fish that have been unable to escape are scooped up with a bagnet.[244, 663] In this case the scare lines are used like a fishing gear and do not drive the prey into any other gear, but they can also be used for driving the fish forward into a fishing gear set beforehand on a suitable spot. This is done especially in the reef fishery, where bottom-dragged gear cannot be operated.

In deeper water, the lines for fish chasing are not used in a horizontal direction, but in a vertical one when transported by swimming fishermen or by boats (*Fig 589*). Such long vertical lines, reaching nearly to the bottom and provided with palm leaves, are moved towards the drive-in net at the Ryukyu Islands by swimming fishermen or by boats. Up to 100 fishermen can participate effectively with vertical frightening lines in such a fishery.[445] Frequently, too, some divers are engaged in this hunt to kill larger fish with spears[28].

The idea of operating scare lines in fishing may be a very old one, based on the possibility of driving fish together by towing branches of trees with leaves along a watercourse, a method which not only may have been known in prehistoric times in northern Europe but was also reported in 1794 as having been used by American Indians. This is why some people think that such towed brushes are the earliest forerunner of dredging fishing gear.

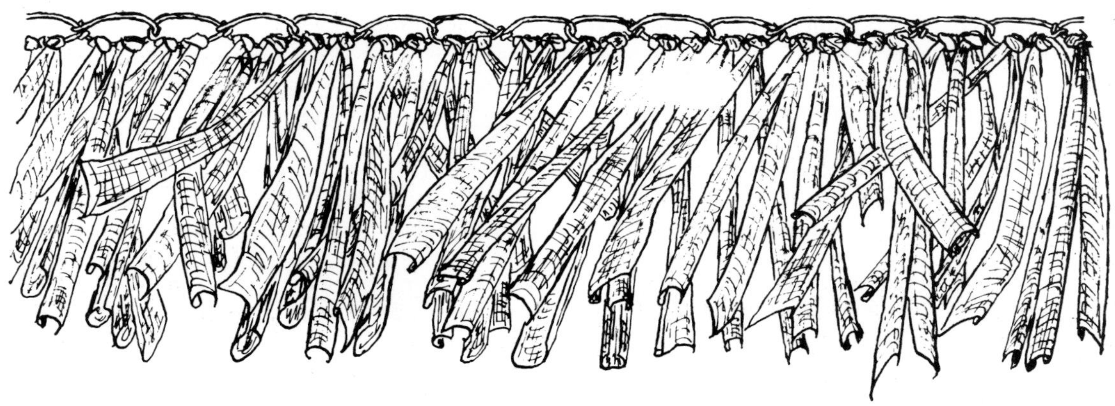

Fig 588 Part of a frightening line used in Laguna de Bay, Philippines.

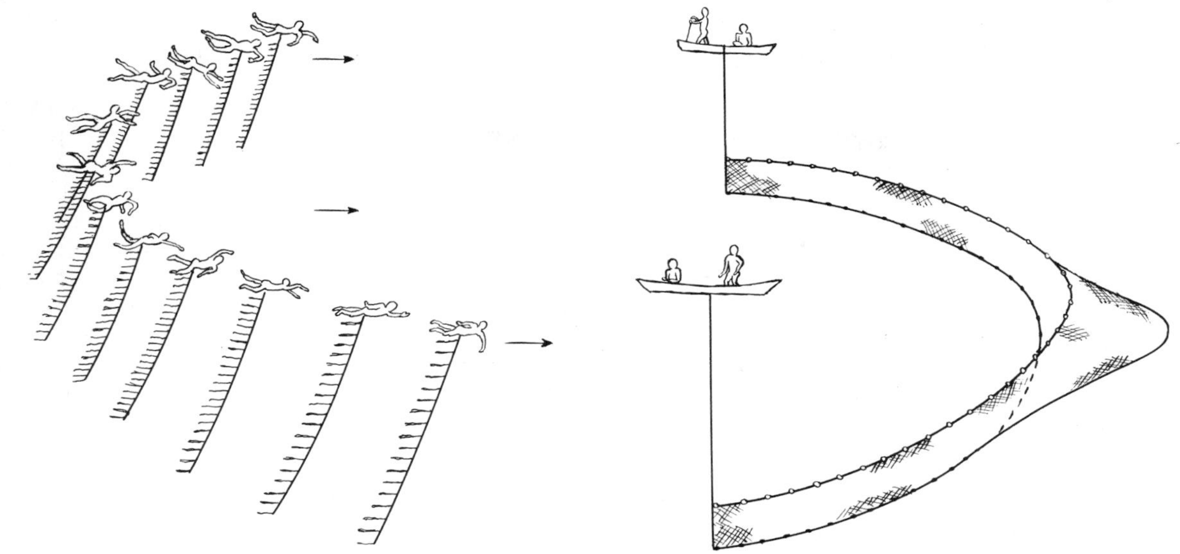

Fig 589 Drive-in fishery with divers over rough ground near Ryukyu Islands. (*NN, 1959*).

26.2 Genuine drive-in nets

Almost all fishing gears can be used for drive-in fishing, but there are some types that are not effective unless they are combined with drive-in tactics. There are movable as well as stationary specialized gears for this fishery. The simplest form is to fish in very shallow water using old clothes, no longer of use, such as the lamba of the women of Madagascar or the sarong of Indonesian women. Two women hold the cloth at a shallow angle in the water while other women and children drive the fish onto the cloth[65] (*Fig 590*). In Oceania, women use a mat for the same purpose and sometimes also in Europe boys can be seen using their shirts in their enthusiasm for catching minnows.

Fig 590 Young girls fishing with a 'lamba'. The fish are driven from the left into the cloth held open like a bagnet. Madagascar, 1964.

But there are more specialized gears for drive-in fishing. *Figure 591* gives a characteristic example of such a gear from the Japanese fishery. In design, it could be a seine net or a long-winged trawl that has been fixed by anchoring. Generally speaking, nets specialized for drive-in fisheries usually have a dust-pan shape similar to that used by some of the older types of surrounding nets. *Figure 592* gives an example of a stationary dustpan shaped drive-in fishing gear with a frightening line, operated from a canoe behind the gear. Once the fish have been driven into the net or on to the net shovel, the gear must be closed by lifting the front edge of the bottom of the net so that the fish cannot escape again. Usually these are nets of considerable size and have been known and used from south Japan to as far as Burma. *Figure 593* is another example of a large Japanese stationary gear used in the drive-in fishery. Sometimes fishermen wait for the fish to swim into the gear at random, during their migrations, before beginning to haul the catch; sometimes fish are driven by noise into this gear. The fish are caught by gradually lifting the bottom of the net which concentrates the fish in the farthest corner of this gear. A well-known net for the drive-in fishery with lights is the 'torch net' (sometimes called the Chinese torch net) used especially in the southeast Asia sardine fishery.[64] The net is kept stationary in the current by two boats, while a third boat at first concentrates the fish by means of lights and then guides them into the net (*Fig 594*). The method used in the Chinese fishery at Taiwan and Hong Kong has been carried out successfully, quite recently, by one motor vessel only. This keeps the

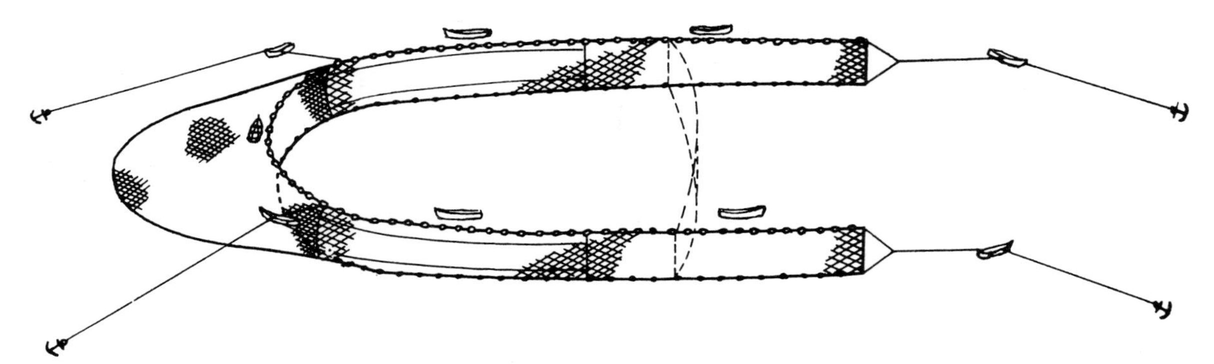

Fig 591 Japanese drive-in net (Iwashi nakabiki ami) for catching sardine-like fish. (*NN, 1959*).

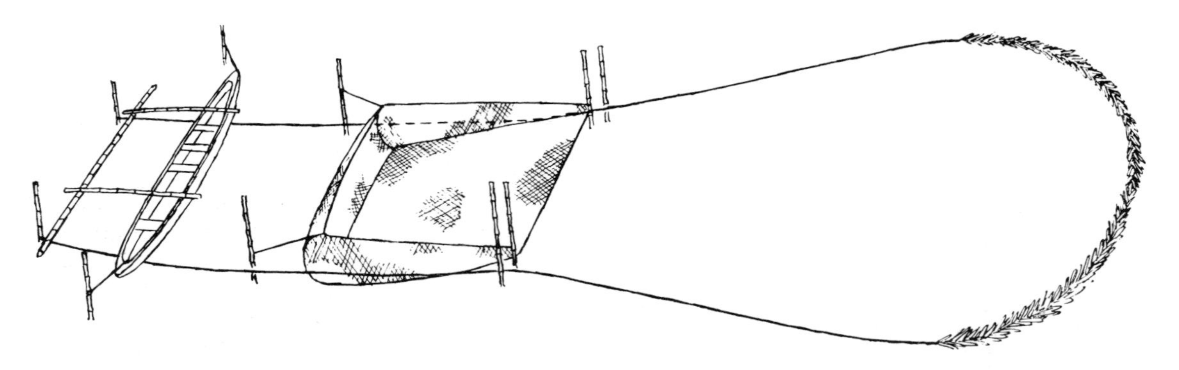

Fig 592 This drive-in net used in the Philippines is rather like a dustpan in design. The fish are driven into the net by a frightening line seen on the right-hand side. (*Capco and Manacop, 1955*).

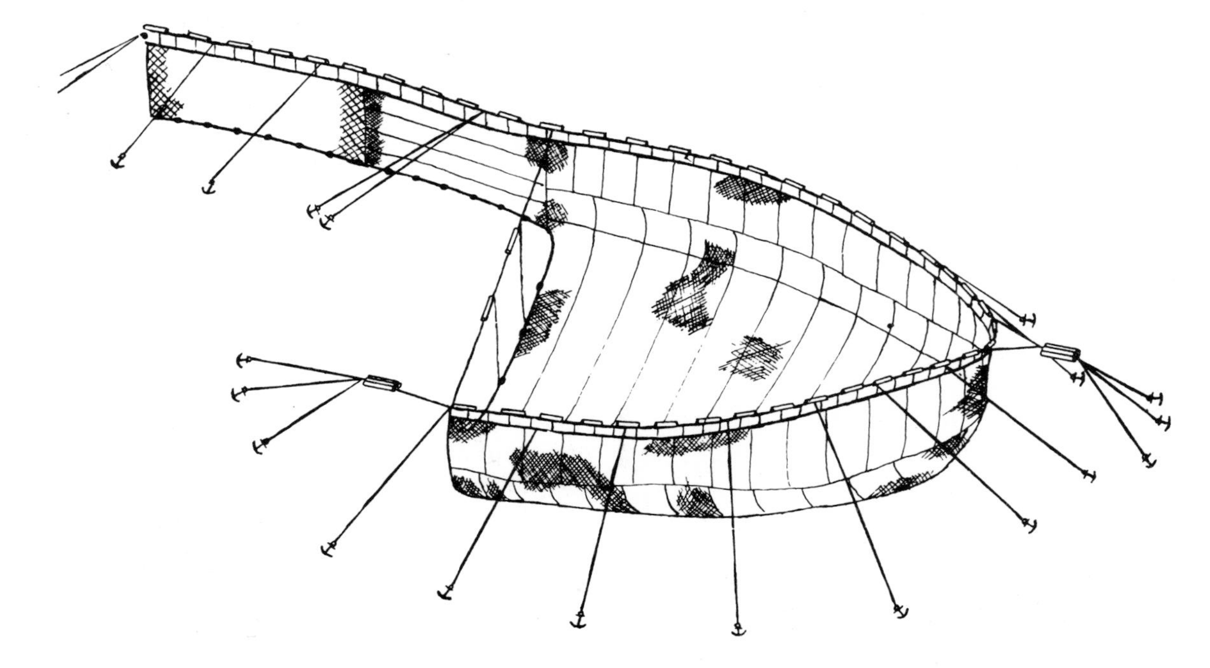

Fig 593 Japanese triangular barriers for sardines (*NN, 1959*). This is called the 'Oshiki ami' and when the fish enter the catching room the bottom net is drawn up.

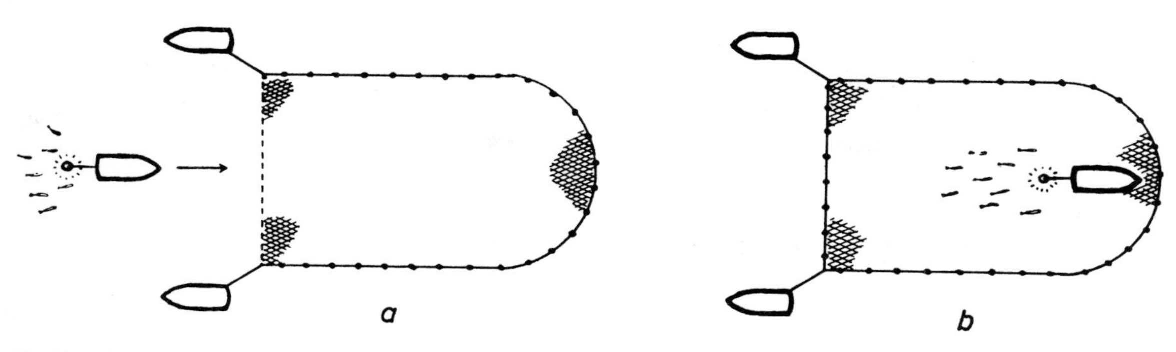

Fig 594 Chinese torch net operated by two boats: (*a*) a boat with a lamp attracts fish in front of the opening of a torch net; (*b*) the fish are guided into the net. (*Li Kwan-ming*).

net stretched in the current by bamboo rods over the side or over the stern, and the fish are guided into the net by means of an underwater lamp held on a long pole (*Fig 595*).

Fig 595 This shows the operation of a Chinese torch net fishery with one boat: the fish are attracted by an underwater lamp (to be seen in the middle of the picture). At this moment the groundrope has been hauled, to close the gear. (Taiwan, 1960).

26.3 Encircling gillnets

Fishing gears designed especially for the drive-in method are not very common. Usually, well-known fishing gears, especially gillnets, are used for this fishing method. In this case a shoal of fish found in not so deep water can be encircled completely with gillnets (Chapter 29) and, when frightened by any method, they will gill and entangle themselves in the surrounding netting. For frightening, a boat is usually placed in the middle of a shoal encircled by gillnets and then the fish are frightened by noises. In Florida, fishermen operating such 'run around' gillnets regularly use 'cherry bombs' to drive fish into the nets.

Sometimes the net is set around a shoal not in the form of a circle, but more in the form of a spiral. The fish are then frightened by striking the water with sticks or oars and by this means are driven into the gillnet, just as Turkish fishermen do to catch kefal (grey mullet) even when a great number are jumping over the floatline (*Fig 596*). The use of stones tied to a retrieving line to frighten

Fig 596 Turkish fishermen driving mullet into a gillnet set like a spiral in the Black Sea harbour of Samsun. (1967).

fish into encircling gillnets has been already mentioned at the beginning of the chapter (*Fig 587*). This technique of drive-in fishing with gillnets is so wide-spread and important that some people consider 'encircling gillnets' to be a special type of fishing gear like stow nets or trawls. This method is especially known off the Mediterranean coasts and also off those of West Africa and south Asia. Sometimes not only are gillnets used for this purpose but also three-walled trammelnets and two-walled nets (see Chapter 30). In European fresh-water fisheries, trammelnets are used in this manner. In this case a certain area of reed is surrounded with the nets and the fish are driven into the net by thrusting a long stake in a special manner into the reed bed as demonstrated in *Figure 597*.

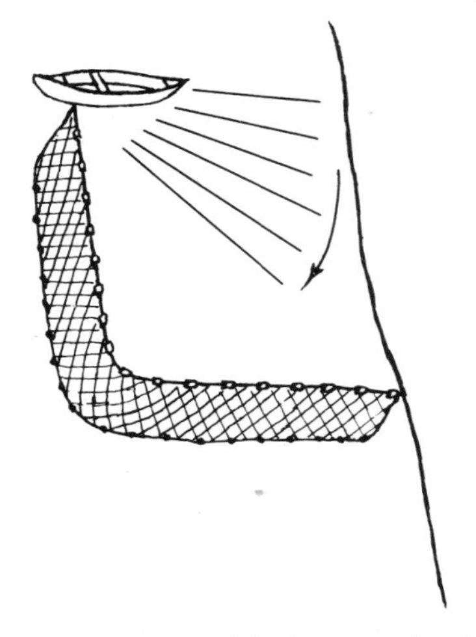

Fig 597 Operating a German drive-in trammelnet in freshwater fishery.

Fig 598 Turkish fisherman in the Bosphorus driving fish with the help of a white stone into a scoop net (above). The white stone is fixed on a line and a stick like an angling rod (below). (*Photo: T Mengi, Istanbul, 1977.*)

26.4 Other gear for drive-in fishery

There are many other types of fishing gear which can be used for a drive-in fishery. It seems that scoop nets are especially preferred for this fishing tactic. These can be scoop nets in the usual round form or, better still, like push nets. A round scoop net is used by Turkish fishermen in the strong current of the Bosphorus where, close to the shore, fish migrate against the current. The net is placed behind the fish which are scared back into the gear by throwing stones. To use the stones more than once, they are fixed to rods with short lines as in pole-and-line fishing (*Fig 598*).

A scoop net with quite another shape, nearly like that shown in *Figure 409b*, is used in a drive-in fishery of the Santa Cruz Islands in Oceania.[315] In this case a collective of maybe ten men, each with two nets, encircles fishes seen during daytime or at night in order to catch the frightened fish with their scoop nets. During ebb tide the men may also stay in a line waiting to catch the fishes swimming with the outgoing tide. The form of the scoop nets used in this manner can differ, but in principle it is always the same method – known in Oceania, Asia, Africa and Europe. A few examples follow.

The gear in the form of a push net is known as a 'glib' in northwestern Europe (*Fig 599*) and other variations of this gear are widely distributed (*Fig 600*).[30, 569, 644, 690] The method of operation can be seen in *Figures 599* and *601*. The last figure shows young Turkish men operating this method in a small river flowing into Lake Van in eastern Anatolia. One of them stays in the river, pressing a large scoop net with a half-round opening and a very long bag, against the bottom. Two others try to frighten fish with sticks into the gear. In principle this is always

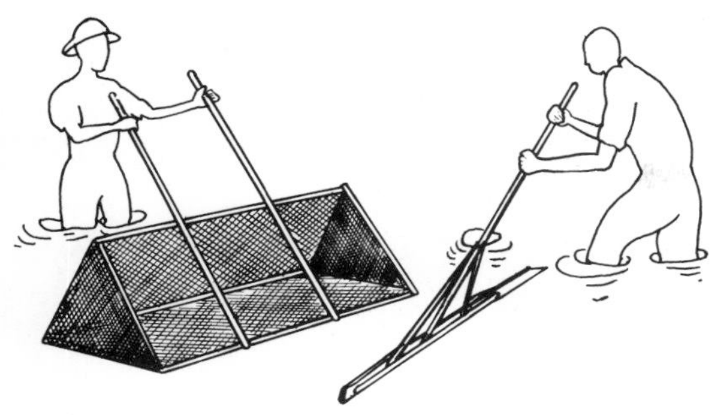

Fig 599 So-called 'glib' for catching eels off the European North Sea coast.

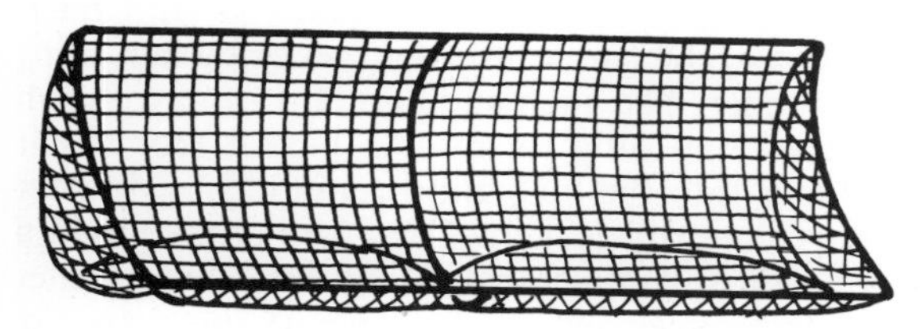

Fig 600 Chasing gear from eastern Europe. (Seligo, 1925).

the same method of operation. In eastern Europe it was known that two gears fishing opposite each other could be very effective.[569] In this manner crayfish also are caught in Latvia.[345] But there are other examples known in other parts of the world. Nearly the same description can be given to the method used in Oceania where two fishermen work together: one keeps the scoop net in the shallow water, the other drives the fishes into this net by wading and splashing the water.

There are still more types of fishing gears for the drive-in fishery. Traps like baskets and fyke nets are also used for this purpose. Even tubular traps are used, placed on the bed of a shallow stream with the mouth directed upstream. The fishermen or fisherwomen proceed upstream for some distance and then return downstream, splashing and shouting in order to frighten any fish which may be about and so drive them ahead into the open mouth of the traps.[261]

Possibly there is no gear which cannot be used to harvest fish by frightening. Even liftnets (Chapter 27) are used by Turkish fishermen in the Bosphorus. They use stones to frighten small fish like sprats, anchovies or horse mackerel over the gear, and then lift the nets. It may be surprising to learn that some types of cast nets are used in the drive-in fishery. In the so-called 'dhor' fishery in Indian fresh-waters, two or three cast nets are tied together in such a manner that they form something like a stow net. The fish are driven into the gear with scare lines. As soon as the fish have entered the gear, the upper part of the mouth of the gear is dropped, confining the prey in the gear.[192] It may be that gear which can also be operated without drive-in tactics should not be mentioned here. Nevertheless, we should understand that besides a few genuine drive-in fishery gear there are also many others which can be operated with the same tactics. The most important may be the gillnets operated as encircling nets.

Fig 601 Young Turkish men driving fish into a pushnet in a small river flowing into Lake Van, East Anatolia. (1975).

Chapter twenty-seven

Liftnets and fish wheels

A description has already been given of how small scoop nets can be pushed beneath any prey sought – either fish or crustaceans – and lifted with them from the water. On the same principle, another group of fishing gears – but a very different one – is used in almost the same way. These are called liftnets or dipnets. Whereas the scoop nets are bags pushed beneath a fish that is seen or suspected to be present, the dipnets are sheets of netting lowered into the water in the hope that the fish will later swim over them, or that crayfish or shrimp will creep on to them. Strictly speaking, the term 'dipnet' is not quite correct. The catch is not made by dipping the nets, but by lifting them again from the water at the right moment when the fish sought to be caught have gathered over them. The term 'liftnet' is therefore much more correct. The reference here to 'nets' is due to the fact that in modern fishing only liftnets made of netting are known. It must, however, be supposed that like many others these gears made of netting had predecessors that were made of twigs and bast. Herodotus, the Greek historian, reported that some lake dwellers had such an abundant supply of fish that they had only to lower a basket from their dwellings into the lake and they could lift it after a short time full of fish. They would have used a wooden lifting implement. Many fish would gather beneath those dwellings because of the domestic offal thrown into the water. It may be of interest to note that the descendants in this area, Rumanian fishermen, did operate the same technique with baskets used as liftnets.[13]

Modern liftnets are made of netting set horizontally on the bottom or kept suspended in the water. For small and middle-sized types, as used for hand liftnets and for some stationary ones, the netting is kept spread by a stretching device. For small types the netting is fastened in a round frame without a handle (*Fig 602*), but some may have square or triangular frames (*Fig 603*). They are also kept spread by transverse rods, especially if the

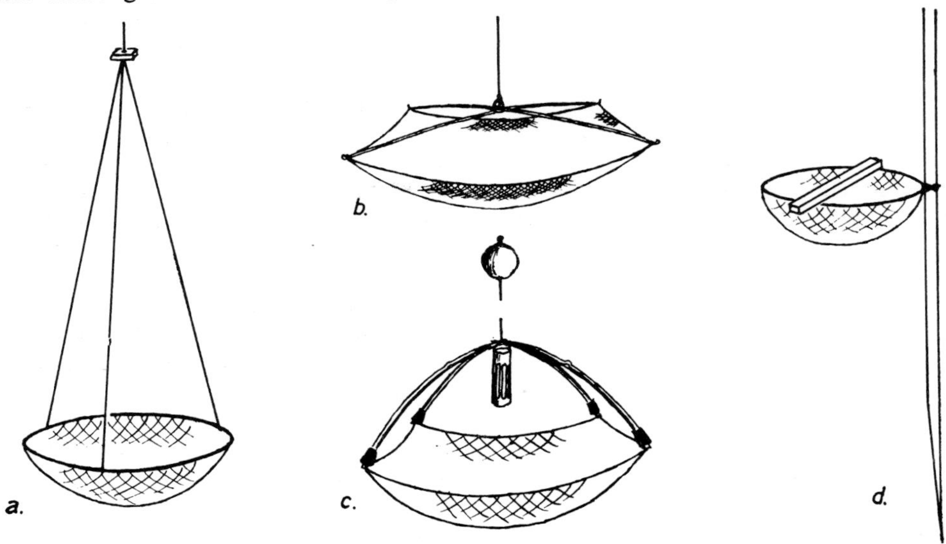

Fig 602 Various small hand liftnets: (*a*) crayfish ring; (*b*) bait net; (*c*) Philippine liftnet with bait box; (*d*) fixed crayfish net.

Fig 603 Square-framed liftnet of the river Danube near Passau. (*Photo: Graf v Mandelsloh.*)

stretched nets are large (*Fig 614*). These rods have the advantage that when folded, with the netting wrapped around the rods, they can be easily transported. The flat liftnets used by sport fishermen for catching bait fish can be handled in this way, but many other nets used by commercial fishermen can also be similarly transported. With the very large liftnets, however, frames or crossing rods cannot be used – and that problem, with the so-called blanket nets, will be discussed later.

In order to attract fish, crustaceans and other aquatic animals over the liftnets, bait is often put on the nets or suspended over them. Over large liftnets, lamps are also installed to attract both fish and crustaceans. In general liftnets are flat, especially the smaller types. By quick lifting, the prey is pressed onto the netting and so prevented from escaping. Sometimes deeper bags of netting are used, especially when large quantities are expected, because the bigger types of liftnets can be hauled only slowly. To give the net a deeper form the middle of the netting is sometimes weighted with stones. Such weights also help to accelerate the sinking of the net. On occasions the centre is strengthened, or a second, loose, wide-meshed netting layer is sewn onto it to hinder the fish by entangling them when the net is hauled. For better operation of the middle-sized and large liftnets, especially to overcome the adhesion effect when the netting has to break free from the water surface during lifting, gallows with rollers or levers have been used since ancient times. It may be that some liftnets were the first mechanized fishing gear in this respect.

27.1 Portable hand liftnets

Small liftnets can be used as hand nets, and large numbers of this gear are often operated by a single fisherman, mostly for catching crabs. Round framed liftnets can hang by three lines fastened to a ring (*Fig 602a*). Those with transverse rods hang on a single line. *Figure 602c* shows a hand liftnet with bait box. The gear is set on the bottom of a river, marked by a red ball floating on the water surface. Small liftnets can be fixed also on a rod, like the crayfish rings in European freshwaters, and by this means they can be set on the bottom (*Fig 602d*). In the shape of ski sticks they are used in the Malayan fishery[93, 107, 487] (*Fig 604*), and also in the fisheries of Finland and Baltic countries[342, 345]. The end of the pole is sharpened and is pushed into the mud until the hoop lies on the bottom. The bait is held about 10cm above the level of the hoop, sometimes in a wire bait holder, or is fixed directly on the hoop. The gear has to be monitored at regular intervals.

Liftnets are usually set separately, even when used in large numbers. The reason is that they have to

Fig 604 Ski-stick-like lobster rings of Thailand.

Fig 605 Baited liftnet for the lobster fishery off the coast of South West Africa.

be lifted carefully without losing the prey. The lobster rings belong to the hand liftnet type of gear and are widely distributed in commercial fisheries. As an example, the rock lobster fishery off the coast of southwest Africa can be mentioned. These baited lobster rings have a diameter of 70cm, are rather deep, and are fixed on floated lines of 20 fathoms length (*Fig 605*). This may also be an example of a very small gear not only being operated as a traditional fishery but also becoming an implement of highly developed industrial fisheries – the important South African lobster fishery.

It is understandable that in commercial fisheries the small hand liftnets are mostly used to catch crabs, which do not escape as quickly as fish do. But many variations in gear construction are known in fisheries to prevent the escape of crabs and fish from the bag of a liftnet. *Figure 606* gives two examples of crayfish liftnets used in Finland. The construction of the gear, made of wood or wire, reduces the possibility of escape of the crustaceans. Modern forms of small and large liftnets are made with wooden frames and netting. Moreover, the entrance can have a tube as a non-return device so that this gear can be considered as a basket with an opening at the top (see Chapter 16). Such a similarity to traps with non-return devices is shown in an old Danish liftnet with a funnel – a feature typical of traps (*Fig 607*).

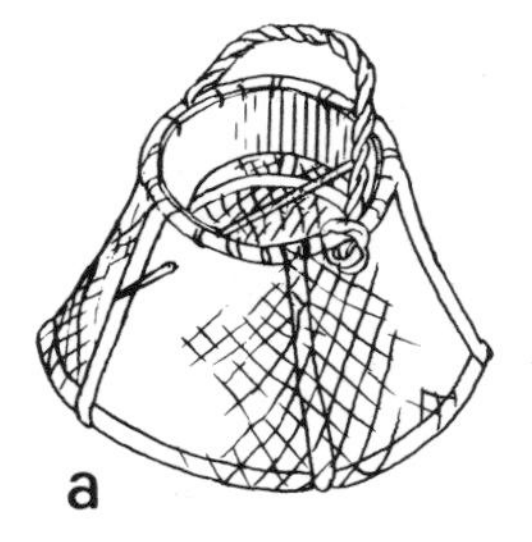

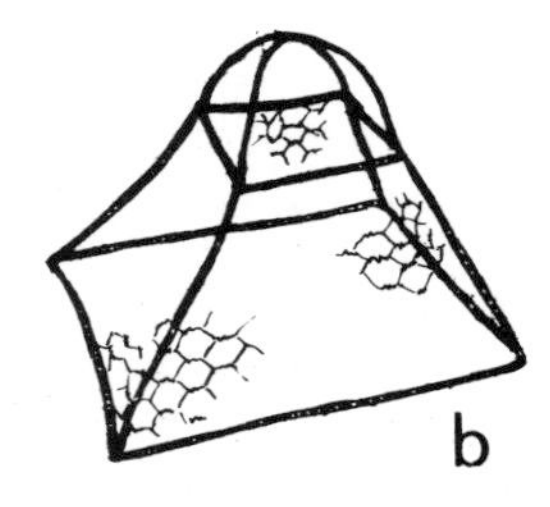

Fig 606 Crayfish liftnets of Finland: (*a*) *Lehtonen, 1975;* (*b*) *Mäki, 1969.*

Not only crustaceans are caught with hand liftnets but also fish, especially middle-sized and larger ones. Nevertheless, sport and commercial fishermen catch bait fish with liftnets (*Fig 602b*) from bridges in rivers, and on the sea coast from harbour walls. As long as the gear is small it can be hand-operated. It has been recommended that such hand-operated liftnets should not be larger than 1·25m square. The resistance of the liftnet by adhesion increases with the size of the netting and with smaller sizes of mesh. For this reason, liftnets for bait are, in general, 0·80m or 1·00m square,

Fig 607 Danish crayfish net with retarding device.

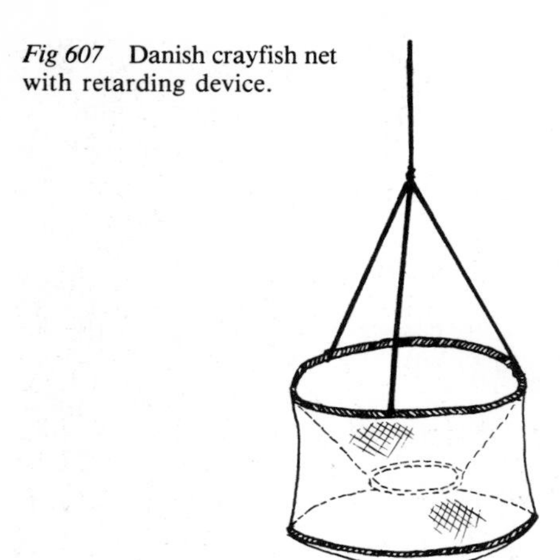

with a mesh width (bar) of 12mm to 15mm. Sport fishermen use small liftnets, sometimes called dropnets (also a wrong name, like dipnets) for landing hooked fish when angling from a pier where the usual landing nets cannot be used. If the hand liftnets are larger, they are dipped into and lifted from the water by means of a long pole (*Fig 608*). The pole is handled like a lever to achieve support in making the lift from the water. A special hole in the ground, or a foot put forward, or a leg well set provides the necessary leverage. By this simple method of mechanization of the handling of liftnets it becomes possible to overcome the resistance of the water and the surface tension mentioned before.

Fig 608 A hand liftnet used in Bangkok (1960).

To avoid the escape of fish in British fishing, a hand liftnet has even been developed which can be closed by shutting the opening hoop by means of a line. This is the so-called 'purse hoop net' of Wales[127] (*Fig 609*). The French know of a similar gear.[577] The Malayan fishery also employs a collapsible hand liftnet,[487] and last but not least, the Japanese fishermen knew 'closing hoop nets'[294] long

Fig 609 The purse hoop net of Wales, which can be closed. (*Davis, 1958*).

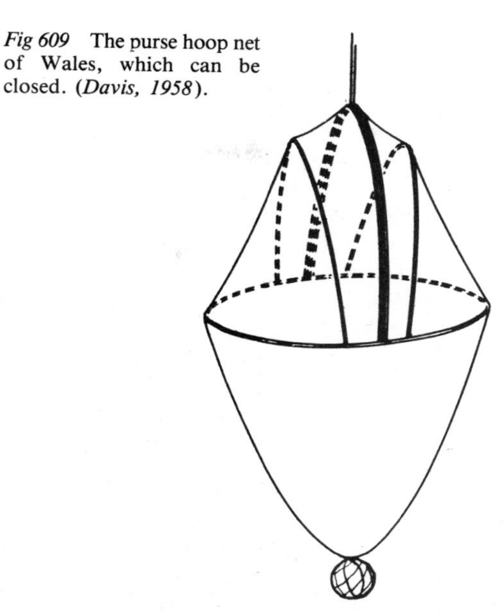

before scientists invented similar gear for scientific purposes. By using this principle of closing the net, there is much greater security in preventing the fish from escaping. Small liftnets can also be used to catch snails, as the Japanese and Koreans do. In this case there is no danger that the prey will escape when hauling. The liftnets are used on the longline system and look like traps, but are without any retarding devices (*Figs 610* and *611*).

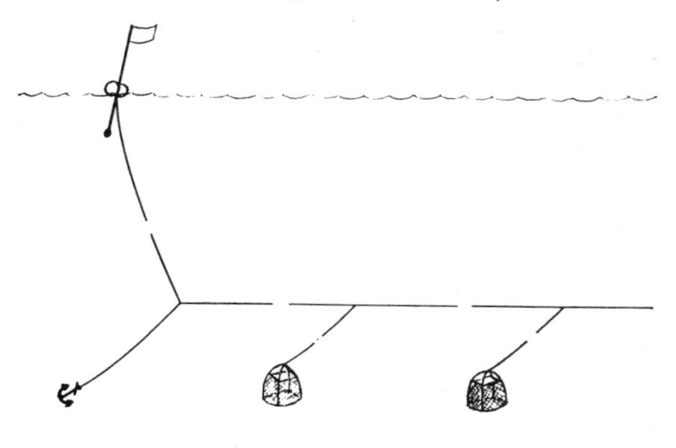

Fig 610 Korean gear for catching snails. (*NN, 1968/70*).

27.2 Stationary liftnets

If the liftnets become larger, some better mechanism is needed to reduce the manpower needed to operate them. This is especially so for very large liftnets which will be mentioned in the following sections of this chapter.

The stationary liftnets used in Asia and usually called 'Chinese liftnets', work on the lever principle as described for the scrape nets (*Fig 427*). The net is balanced by counterweights so that it can be

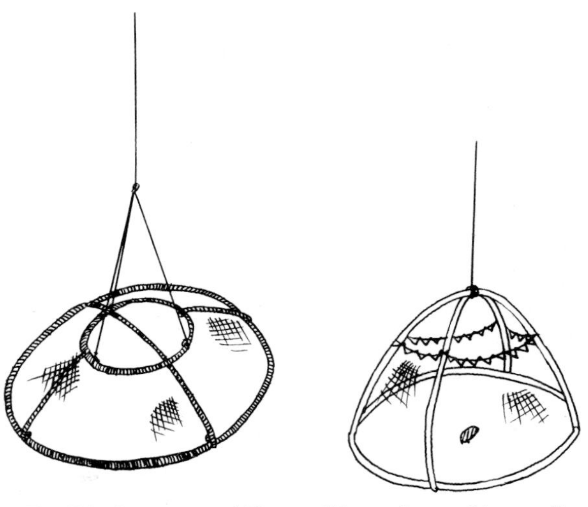

Fig 611 Japanese and Korean liftnets for catching snails.

Fig 612 'Chinese' liftnet operated off the Malabar coast, southern India.

pivoted for dipping and lifting. Such nets set on the beach may be found on the South Indian Malabar coast, where they were apparently brought by the Portuguese (*Fig 612*). During the night, lamps are hung at the crossing point of the rods to attract the fish. Depending on the current, this fishing lasts until noon. After the netting has been skilfully folded, the fish are removed by means of a long-handled scoop net. This has to be done very quickly as otherwise the crows which abound there steal the fish from the net. Installed on bamboo rafts, these types of nets with long levers are very common in the fisheries of east and southeast Asia (*Figs 613* and *614*). It is an impressive spectacle to see how easily (apparently) these giant nets are sunk and lifted. This casual elegance may have induced a Dutch surgeon, who travelled in the Philippines in

Fig 613 Liftnet installed on a bamboo raft in southern Taiwan.

the sixties of the last century, to write the following: 'The people have very little trouble with that fishery and that is what matters, provided they do not know a way to abstain from working at all – which they would prefer at any rate![688] One should not forget,

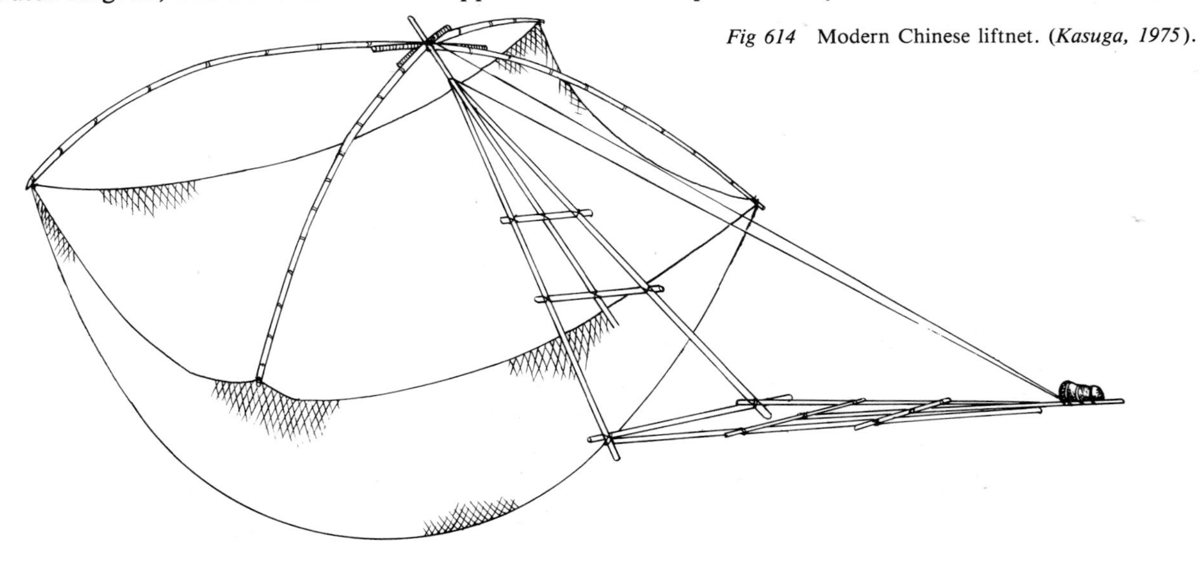

Fig 614 Modern Chinese liftnet. (*Kasuga, 1975*).

however, that the net must be lifted and sunk at short intervals, which requires heavy bodily effort in spite of the balancing equipment. Fishery is not such easy work as it sometimes seems to people who lack full knowledge.

Because of the general shortage of wood, the crossed rods of the large liftnets are often composed of several parts. Jokes have been made about this fact, and comparisons drawn between the construction of the rods with the farcical drawings of Debout, the French cartoonist. It should, however, rather be the subject of admiration that the people of these countries have been able to build such large crossed rods for these big liftnets strongly enough, in spite of this shortage of wood.

The more modern stationary liftnets known in European fisheries are operated with the help of hand- or motor-driven winches. They are operated especially in rivers, in the upper part and down to the estuaries, as far as they are not polluted. The gallows required for this method are preferably installed on bridges, moles or other protruding buildings (*Fig 615*). As with the salmon fishery on the upper Rhine, the so-called 'Stuhlfischerei' or the 'bilancia' of the Italians, solid buildings with waiting rooms and accommodation for the fishermen may even be constructed for this fishery (*Fig 616*). On the Austrian Danube, similar arrangements exist known as 'Krandaubel'. This is a liftnet with a gallows placed on an anchored vessel with a little house for shelter (*Fig 617*). Similar houses with liftnets are also operated today in the Swiss part of the upper River Rhine. These types of liftnet no longer work on the lever system with a two-armed lever on the longer part of which hangs the net and, on the shorter, arm, the counterweight.

Fig 615 Stationary liftnets to be seen on the harbour mole of Ostend. They can be hired by sports fishermen for bait fishing.

Fig 617 Austrian 'Krandaubel' on the River Danube near the Island of Wörth. (*Photo: Dr Bruschek.*)

Fig 616 Liftnets with houses for shelter in Fiumicino, Italy. (1959).

The modern Swiss liftnets are also operated with a gallow. The net is held spread out like the middle-sized liftnets by two crossing arms (*Fig 618*). The gear is operated with two small hand-operated winches. With one of them (1) the liftnet can be moved farther out over the water of the river. With the other winch (2) the gear is let down into the water or lifted when a catch is expected. Moreover, the lifted gear can then be moved again nearer to the working place. This working place, with the two winches, is inside a small hut where the fisherman can sit comfortably on a chair to watch the gear.

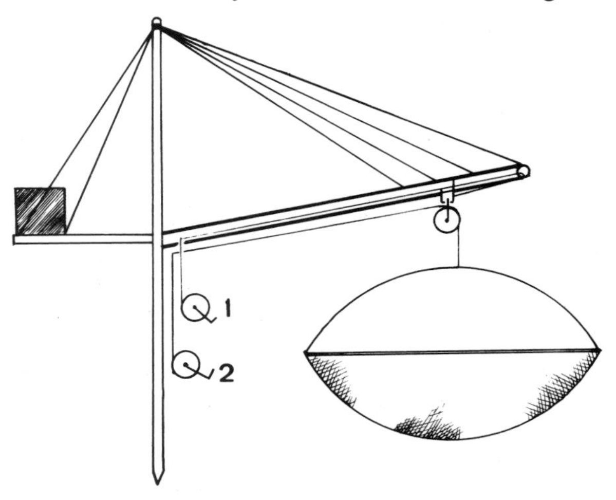

Fig 618 Diagram of a liftnet in the River Rhine near Basel 1974. Winch 1 moves the net closer to, or farther from, the bank: winch 2 raises and lowers the net.

This fishery is, therefore, called 'chair fishing' or in German 'Stuhlfischerei'.[305] It is of interest that the place where the net is dipped and lifted in or out of the water is sheltered behind a small artificial wall, where the fish like to rest. In the River Rhine this fishery originally specialized in salmon. To attract fish, a captured female salmon, tied to a long line, was towed slowly over the liftnet. The 'lure' might then be followed by some male salmon which were then caught, together with the luring female[331] (see also 'sexual lures' in Chapter 11).

27.3 Blanket nets

Obviously the net surface, if enlarged even further, can no longer be stretched by frames or rods. In this case the so-called 'blanket nets' have to be kept stretched by some other means. They can be operated as stationary gear, or on a boat as movable fishing gear. Some of them are placed on the Italian sea shore as a further development of the smaller Italian bilancias mentioned before (*Fig 616*). In general, the construction of a blanket net is less complicated. Non-framed netting, sometimes of impressive size, is hung with the help of some beams over the water at some distance from the shore (*Fig 619*). As stationary gear, the blanket net can be held by rammed-down piles on the shore or in shallow water. The netting is dipped and lifted over blocks at the end of the piles. Sometimes it is sufficient that dipping and lifting is done with one side of the blanket net only. So with another method the blanket net is held on one side by piles and operated

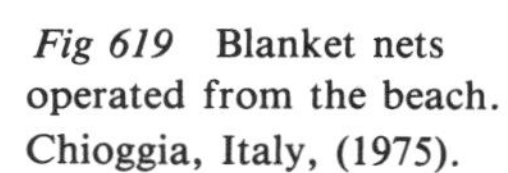

Fig 619 Blanket nets operated from the beach. Chioggia, Italy, (1975).

from the opposite side from a boat. Finally, the blanket net can be worked from a variable number of boats, as will be discussed in the next section of this chapter. Stationary blanket nets held by blocks fixed on four piles, one at each corner of the netting, are even used in river fishing as can be seen in *Figure 620*. They are operated from both banks. This method is known in many different areas of the world, particularly in the modern freshwater fishery of the Chinese mainland.[289]

Fig 620 Italian blanket net in a river near Terracina.

On the sea shore the netting can be operated from one side only. For this fishery a large sheet of netting is fastened on the one side to stakes standing in the water, so that its edge projects over the water. The central section of the net is spread on the bottom, covered by the water. The opposite side lies on the bank which, preferably, should be elevated. When the fish have gathered over the net lying on the bottom of the water, the net is quickly lifted up from the bank or beach, so that the fish fall into the bag which is formed by the netting between the stakes and the bank or beach. Then it is a simple matter to remove the fish from the net using scoop nets. Such nets are used even today off the Turkish Black Sea coast (*Fig 621*). The large rectangular nylon nets are fixed on the shore side by a row of poles in the water. The opposite two corners are fixed on lines leading to two high platforms, with an observer on each. When enough fish are over the netting, the gear is lifted and the fish are taken by scoop nets as usual. The Turkish name of this gear is 'dalyan', but this is misleading because larger pound nets for tuna have the same name. It may be that the blanket net of Sinop, shown in *Figure 621*, is the largest gear of this type. According to old Turkish and Russian drawings,[434] this gear was used in great numbers until the last century (*Fig 622*).

Another method of operating large blanket nets from a stationary or anchored platform in the sea is typical of the Malayan fishery of Hong Kong, Malaysia and Indonesia. Even though the definition is not clear, the gear is called 'kelong' in Malaysia and 'bagan' in Indonesia. In Malaysia these are large stationary platforms, with houses for the shelter and living accommodation for fishermen (*Figs 623* and *624*). From this platform the liftnet is operated with the help of simple hand-driven winches (*Fig 625*). Stow nets are also used from these platforms. Whichever gear is used, these permanent fixed 'fishing stakes' are considered an undesirable fishing method in Malaysia because trawling and gill netting can be hampered by the platforms and especially, by the remains of stakes left under water when the position of the platform has to be changed for any reason. Moreover, the operation of the kelong becomes difficult because of the lack of manpower. For building such arrangements, no rams are available and the long trunks of the nibong palms used to hold the platforms became rare in Malaysia and now have to be imported from Indonesia. It may be of interest to know that some of these liftnets can have leaders

Fig 621 Large Turkish blanket net (dalyan) off the coast of Sinop, Black Sea.

Fig 622 Old Russian drawing of a fishery with blanket net. (*NN, 1871*).

Fig 623 So-called 'Kelong' off the coast of Johor Baharu (Malaysia) opposite Singapore (1978).

Fig 624 Blanket net hanging under the platform of a Malaysian 'kelong' (1978).

Fig 625 Blanket net operated by a 'kelong'. (*Abu Bakar, 1977*).

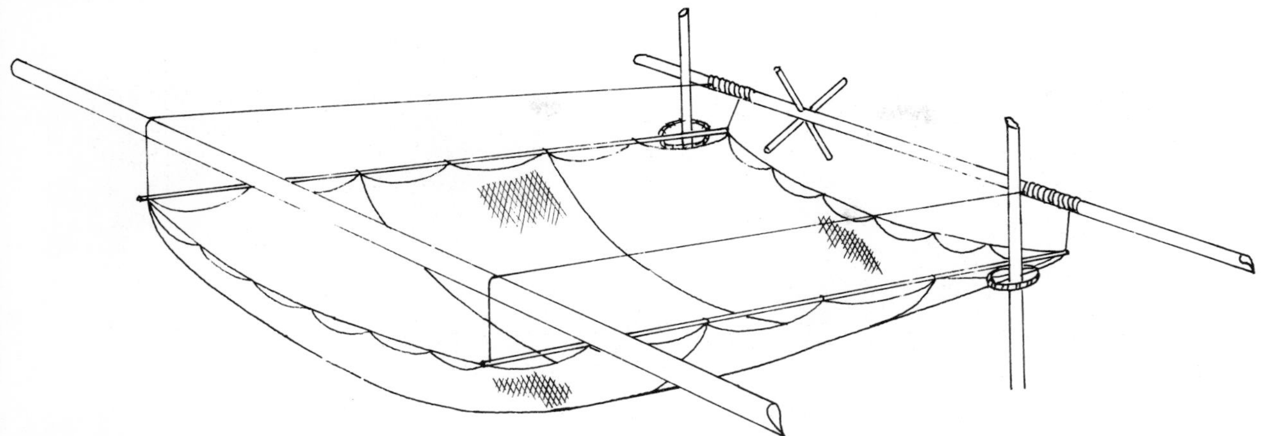

like wings for traps (*Fig 626*) so that sometimes this gear is considered as a large trap, even when the catch is cleared by a liftnet. The Indonesian platforms are also stationary but set on anchored rafts (*Fig 627*), from which the liftnet is operated as usual. This is also a night fishery and the fish are attracted by light. The platform has a building as shelter for the fishermen, and also a room for preparing the catch. The same method can be used if one side of the blanket net is fastened to poles and the other to a boat lying alongside, as with the Philippine 'kabyaw'[630] or the old 'aloli dela' of the Sinhalese of Sri Lanka.[488] That technique has been used in Europe as well as in Asia.

More popular are blanket nets used only from vessels. The simplest way to achieve this is for sheets of square net to be held at each corner by a boat so that they can be lowered and lifted in combination. Such liftnets, worked by four boats, are in fact widely used in freshwater and sea fishing (*Fig 628*). Four-boat liftnets are used in Scandinavian fishing as well as in east and south Asia. In Malaysia, the four-boat liftnets are held and operated by anchored boats, and lure lines are brought over the gear with a fifth boat. During the night a floating lamp is also used. This lamp is connected to each of the four boats with a line of monofilament, so that the light can be positioned in the best possible place over the gear. When enough fish are concentrated, the four vessels begin the hauling of the netting. For this, the boats come nearer to each other and the catch can be hauled by scoop nets.[487] Smaller types of blanket nets, of 15 to 20 metres long each side, can also be operated

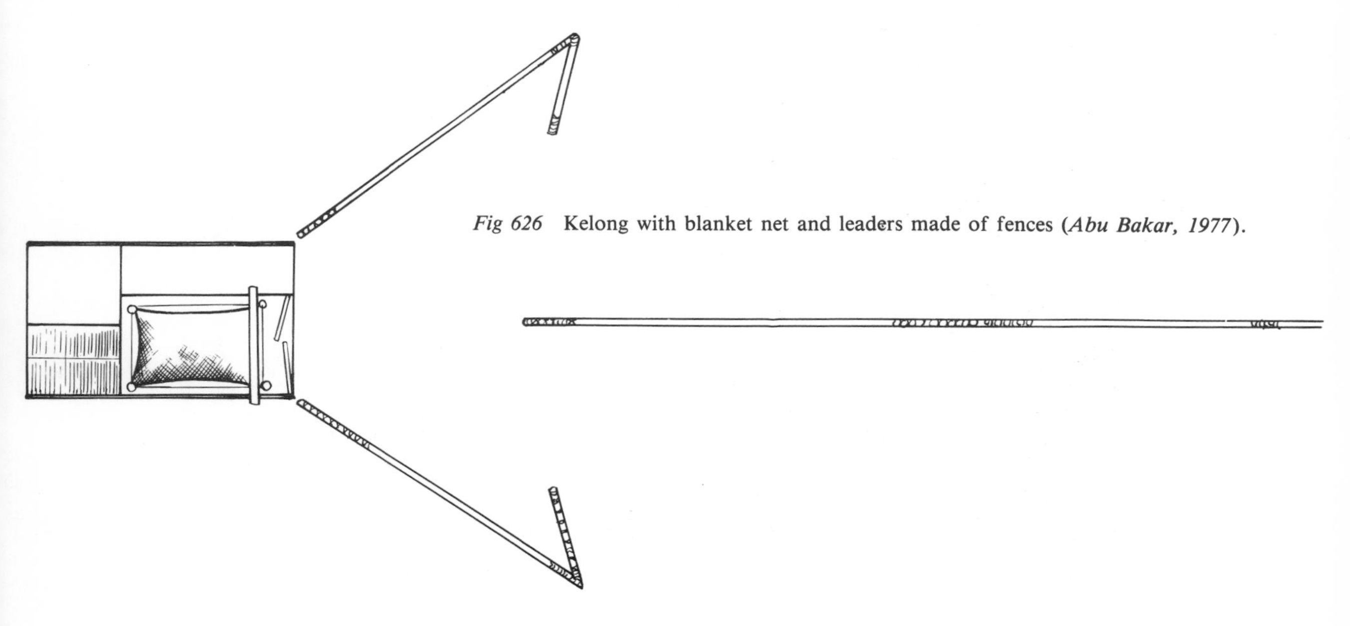

Fig 626 Kelong with blanket net and leaders made of fences (*Abu Bakar, 1977*).

Fig 627 Indonesian 'bagan' in West Flores, Indonesia. (*Photo: Kollmannsperger, 1971.*)

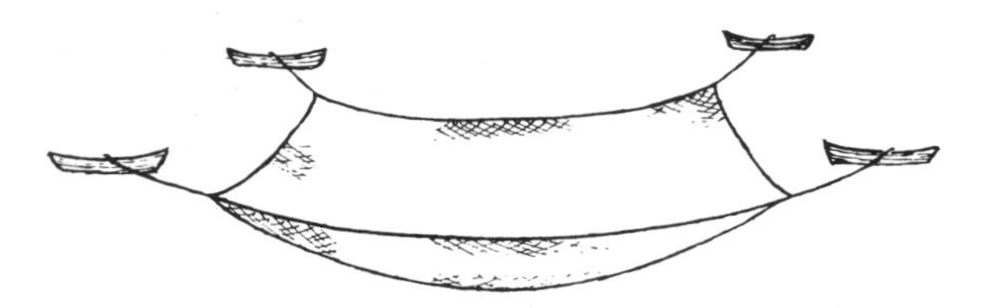

Fig 628 Norwegian liftnet operated by four boats for sea fishing (*Brobak, 1952*).

from two boats only, as fishermen of Lake Nyasa (Mozambique) are doing.[119] Here also light is used for luring the fish over the gear, or some bait is scattered over the net with the help of a small boat. In the Far East not only are four-boat blanket nets with rectangular netting known, but so also are some with an irregular extension, as can be seen from the Korean three-boat lift net (*Fig 629*). There are not only Japanese four-boat lift nets but also five, six and eight-boat types operating blanket nets.[445]

27.4 Modern boat liftnets

As mentioned in the last section but one, smaller liftnets can be operated with gallows. In most cases, these consist of a stationary gear on a promising place in fresh or sea water. If such gallows are installed on rafts or boats in fresh waters (*Figs 603, 614* and *617*), the liftnet becomes mobile. In this form liftnets have also been introduced into the sea fishery (*Fig 630*). There are, for instance, the

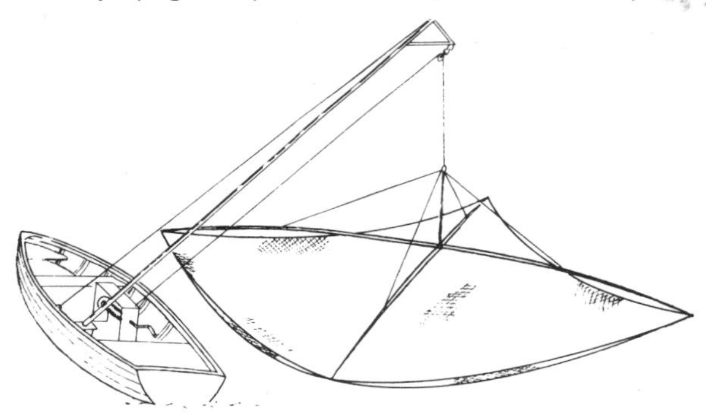

Fig 630 A Lowestoft boat liftnet. (*Davis, 1958*).

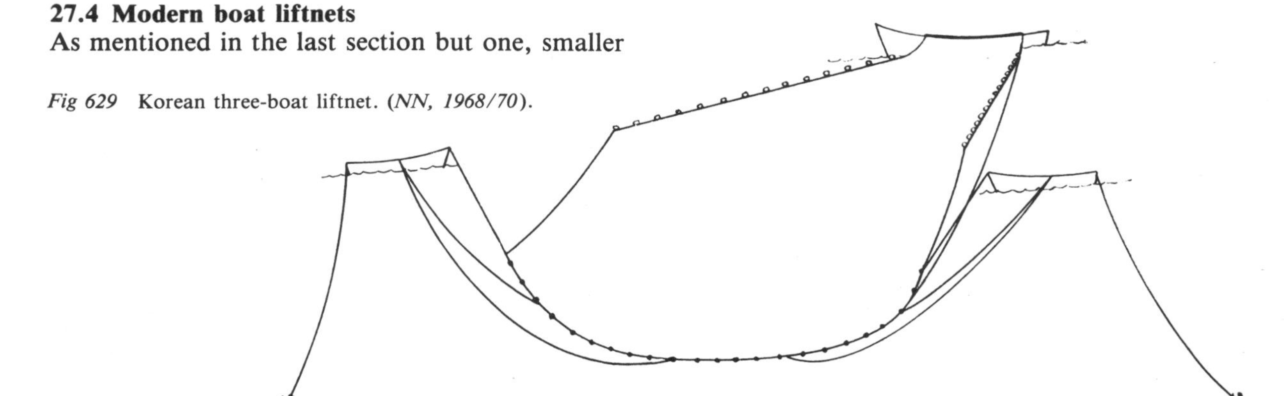

Fig 629 Korean three-boat liftnet. (*NN, 1968/70*).

Russian liftnets in the Caspian Sea for catching sprats from an anchored boat (*Fig 631*). For that purpose, two nets are used alternately from the starboard and port sides for capturing fish attracted by light. In contrast to stationary liftnets, these mounted in vessels have the advantage of being able to change their fishing place when necessary. As seen before, the old Chinese liftnets (*Fig 613*) are also operated mostly from rafts. There is no difficulty in operating smaller framed liftnets from vessels, as can be seen in *Figures 617, 630* and *631*.

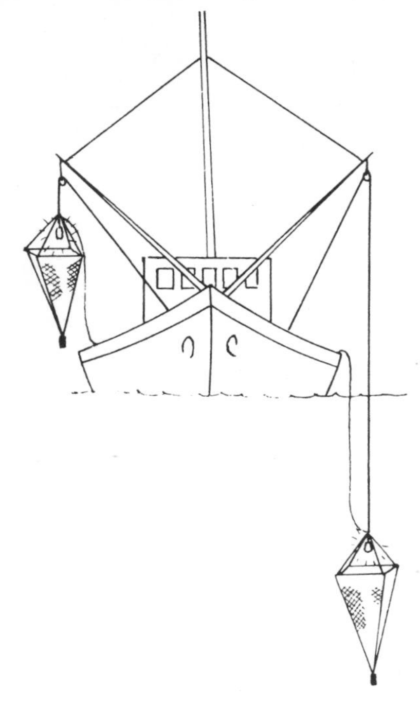

Fig 631 Russian boat liftnet used in the Caspian Sea. (*NN, 1951*).

But there is an example also of a large framed liftnet used in sea fisheries for catching bait. It is used by Portuguese fishermen of the Azores and Madeira. The wooden ring of this liftnet is composed of two pieces which can be folded together like some ladies' purses (*Fig 632*). This liftnet is operated from a vessel with tne help of sticks (*Figs 633* and *634*).

Medium-sized unframed blanket nets can also be operated from boats (*Fig 635*). But in this case the size of the blanket net must be smaller in comparison with the stationary ones operated from the shore (*Fig 619*). Nevertheless, there are some boat liftnets which are not just beach liftnets placed on a vessel but are specially developed for boat fishing. There are two such highly developed fishing gears – one originated in the Philippines, the other in Japan. The Philippines have adopted single-boat

Fig 632 Large liftnets for bait fishing hanging up for drying in Camara de Lobos, Madeira (1964).

liftnets provided with a rim which shapes them like a box on the top.[510, 547, 630] These liftnets, called 'basnigs', have undergone a special development (*Fig 636*). They were originally nothing more than the liftable bottom of a large trap (a), but by about 1920 they developed into a stationary gear mounted between poles (b). That developed further (1924) into a gear worked by two boats (c) and finally into a liftnet spread by poles installed on a single boat. This took place about 1935 (*Figs 636d* and *636e*). When the problem had been solved as to how such nets could be set and hauled from a single boat, the basnig became an efficient large-scale fishing gear by 1950. The fish are attracted by light and guided over the sunken net. The Philippines now take 90% of their sardines by means of this gear. It may be of interest, that a similar construction to that shown in *Figure 632c,* but with a much deeper liftnet, is operated with two or three canoes on Lake Tanganyika, Burundi.

Another type of specialized boat liftnet for a large-scale fishery is the Japanese 'bouke ami' (*Fig 637*). This gear is better known under the English name 'stick-held dipnet'.[473, 475, 547] The blanket net is held by sticks on one side of the vessel. The fish are meanwhile attracted by strong lights on the other side of the vessel. Then, by switching off that light and, when a large shoal has been attracted, switching on a single lamp on the other (port) side above the dipnet, the fish are guided beneath the

Fig 633 Large framed liftnets in use during fishing off Ponta Delgada, Azores (1962).

Fig 634 Middle sized framed liftnet for catching bait fish in the harbour of Horta, Azores (1962). In the foreground is a water-filled permeable container for live bait.

Fig 635 Blanket net operated by boat near Comacchio, Italy. (1975).

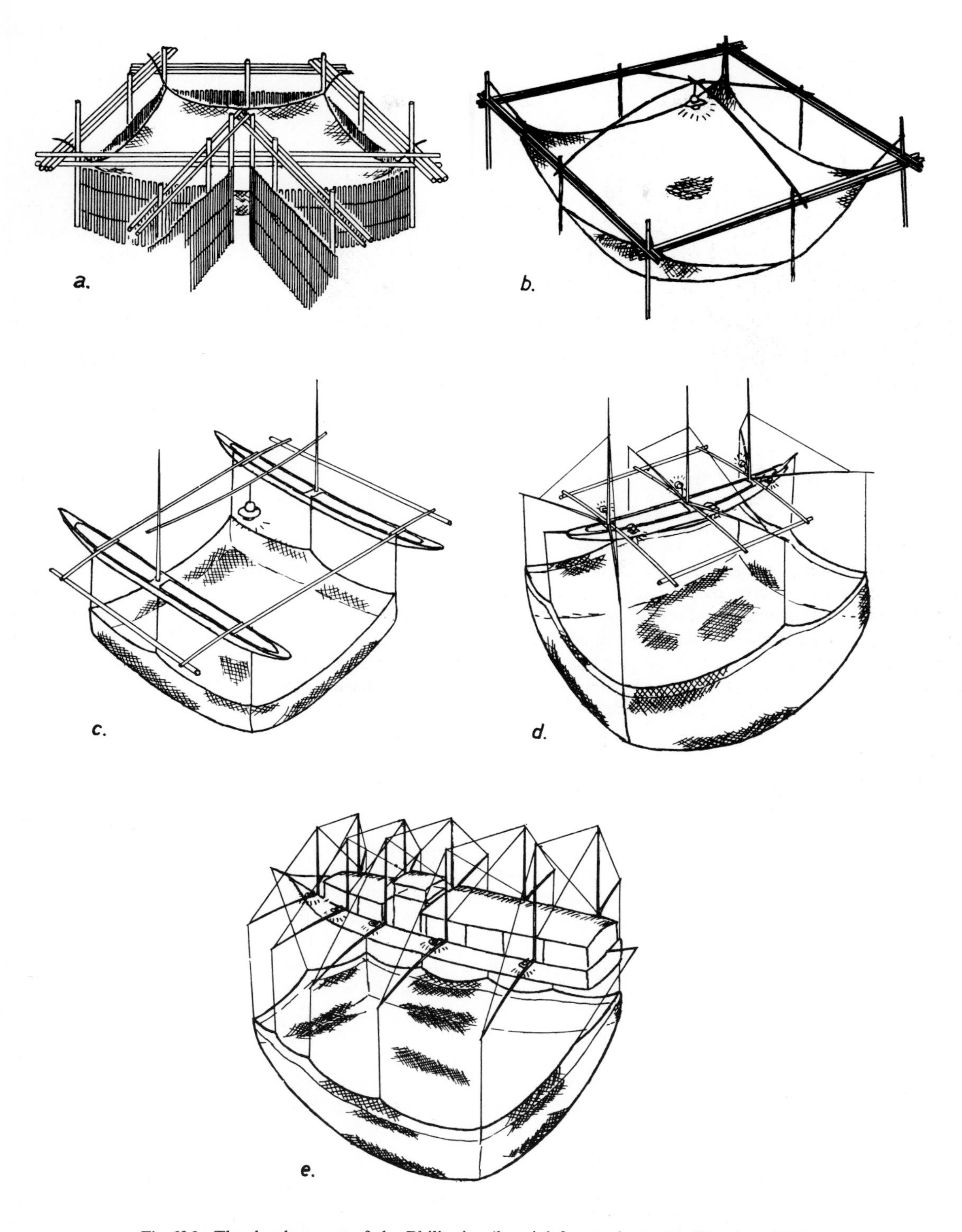

Fig 636 The development of the Philippine 'basnig' for work at sea. (*Rasalan, 1959*).

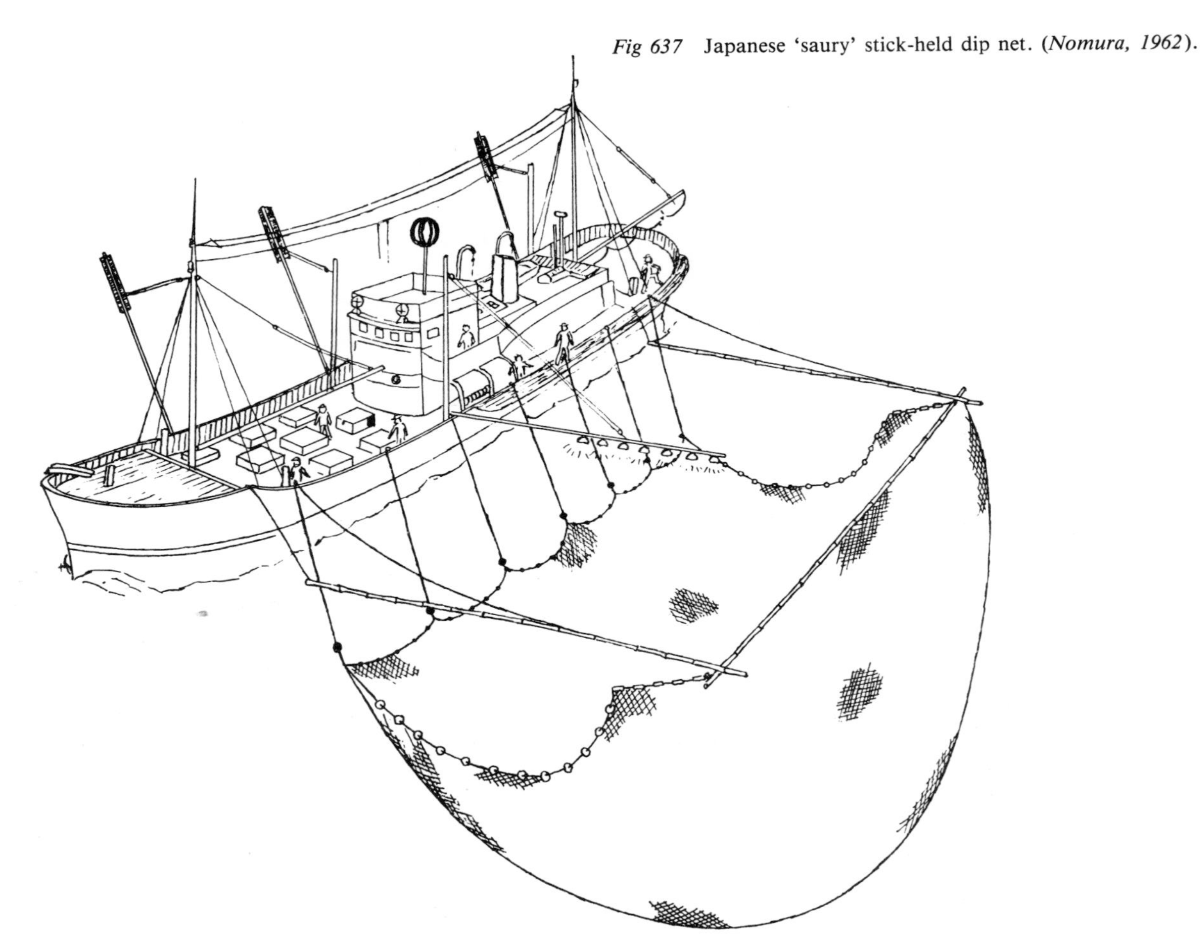

Fig 637 Japanese 'saury' stick-held dip net. (*Nomura, 1962*).

keel or around the vessel into the net over its lowered side. When enough fish are gathered, the lowered side of the gear is hauled and the caught fish are brailed. This net, too, has proved very efficient for catching pelagic fish. The fish are not only attracted by light but also by bait scattered over the netting. Then the fish are caught by suddenly lifting the net. The Pacific saury (*Cololabis saira*) is especially caught by the Japanese with this gear. The method was adopted in 1955. As a large crew is needed to operate this gear there are some doubts if commercial application of the stick-held dipnet in the usual form is ever likely to be economic. Therefore attempts have been made to mechanize this fishing method and to modify it by pivoting the vessel through 90 degrees, thus bringing the net under the shoal instead of attracting the catch over the netting.

27.5 Fish wheels

The fishing gears by which fish are caught by lifting the net placed beneath them include a particularly strange group; the fish wheels. These are large undershot water wheels with two or three shovels, operating like lift nets and lifting from the water fish that are ascending the river.[26, 234] The fish must be taken by scoop nets very quickly before they fall back into the water from the wheels, which are permanently rotating in the current. Generally, however, the shovels are canted in such a way that the fish, when lifted by the wheel from the river, slide automatically into a collecting box (*Fig 638*).

There is some evidence that the original automatically-driven fish wheels were built in France in the River Garonne and in the River Rhône in the area of Avignon. Here this gear was operated to catch shad when they were ascending the river for spawning. Originally, the fish may have been caught by large scoop nets. The first step forward in the development of this gear was the connection of the handles of two scoop nets which turned like a wheel around their connection point in the current of the river. This gear was known as the 'Sarlan double'.[125] With this gear the fish caught by one of

Fig 638 Diagram of Alaskan salmon fish wheel.

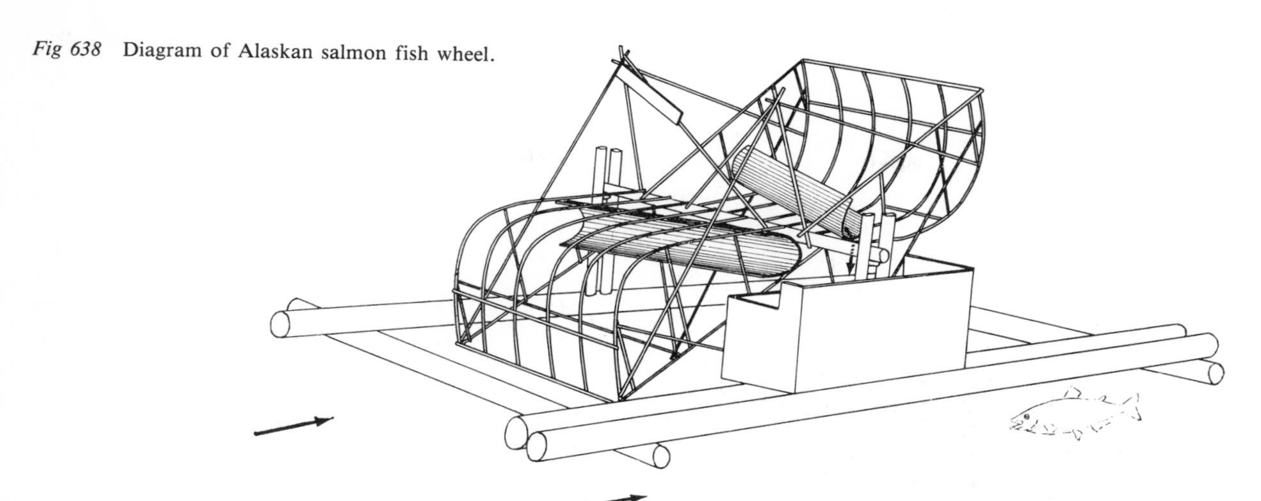

the two rigid wings of the gear had to be taken out quickly by the watching fishermen, otherwise it fell back into the water and escaped. The gear had to be permanently watched because it could happen that, when running too slowly, the shovels could stop turning when both were out of the water. Then the fisherman had to keep the gear turning by pushing forward the shovels. This difficulty was overcome by the introduction of two oar-like boards fixed at 90° to the catching shovels. With this adaptation the gear was always in contact with the running water and therefore constantly driven (*Fig 639*). The problem remained of taking the caught fish out of the shovels before they fell back into the river. This was solved by adding slanting slides made of reed (*Arundo donax*). With these, the fish slid automatically from the shovel into a collection tank on board the vessel with the wheel. Nevertheless, the fish wheel could not work unwatched. This fishery came to an end when the shad, migrating against the current, could no longer do so when the current of the River Rhône was interrupted by damming up the river. Therefore, these fish wheels have not been operated since 1974.

Until the 1950s, fish wheels were also known to be used in the River Tiber in the ancient centre of modern Rome. The Italians named the gear 'giornelli' or 'girarelli'. It is thought that knowledge of fishing wheels came to Rome in the fourteenth century when the Popes returned from their

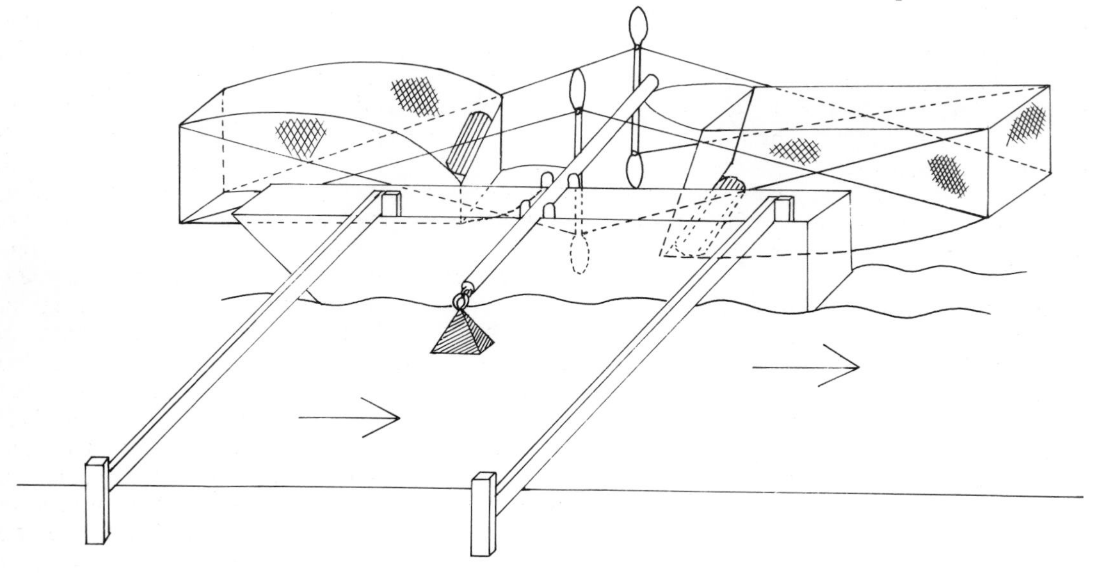

Fig 639 Diagram of fish wheel operated in the River Rhône till 1974. (*Drawn by masterfisherman M L Ramaye. Arles, 1975.*)

captivity in Avignon. The last gear in Rome was near the Ponte Sisto (*Fig 640*). When, one springtime, this wheel was destroyed by floods, it was not rebuilt. As can be seen from paintings of E Roesler Franz (1845-1867), there may have been many fish wheels by the bridges of Rome during the last century. One of his paintings of the Ponte Rotto, formerly Ponte Emilio (Pons Aemilius) even shows two fish wheels. Twaite, shad, and also salmon, have been caught with this gear.

Fig 640 A fish wheel used on the River Tiber, Rome, Italy.

Fish wheels are also used on the west coast of North America for capturing salmon as they ascend the rivers, especially the rivers of British Columbia. From there, their use spread as far as Alaska.[25, 26] The Indians of central Alaska even now use simple water wheels for fishing (*Fig 641*). Nowadays, commercial fishermen are not allowed to use these wheels, but Indians and trappers obtain food for themselves and their sledge dogs with them. But that might be no coincidence. It must rather be supposed that the knowledge of the fish wheels (as with other fishing gear) was taken to the west coast of America by immigrants from the western Mediterranean. Some very highly advanced stationary and movable boat fish wheels are operating today on the Columbia River in Oregon, USA (*Figs 642* and *643*).[460] They are also used for salmon fishing, especially for supplying the breeding stations with spawning fish. The Japanese, too, have introduced and used fish wheels in Hokkaido for the same purpose.

Fig 641 Fish wheel operating on a branch of the Copper River in Alaska. (*Bartz, 1950.*)

Fig 642 A stationary wheel in the Celilo area, Oregon, USA. (*Photo: Donaldson.*)

Fig 643 Moving a 'sow' or boat fish wheel, on the Columbia River, Oregon. (*Photo: Donaldson.*)

Chapter twenty-eight

Cover pots and cast nets

The liftnets described in the preceding chapter secure their catch from below. Completely the opposite in their method of operation are so-called 'falling gears', which are clapped down on the fish or other animals to be caught – which are thus taken from above. This can be done with the help of two types of fishing gear: wooden cover pots and cast nets made of netting. There are many variations of these two types, and also some hybrids. The main thing with the liftnets is that the fish or crayfish appear over the net, and are then lifted with it from the water where the prey can easily be taken. If a falling net is clapped over an aquatic animal it is then well enclosed by the gear, but not yet removed from the water so as to be really in the possession of the fisherman. The situation is simply that of a little boy, who, having cast his cap over a frog, is not yet sure whether he will capture the frog or whether it will escape him when the cap is lifted. Nevertheless, if we agree with Burdon's definition, the prey is caught when it is held in a condition in which its chance of escape is negligible.[92] This is true for the boy's cap, as for all types of falling gear. Nevertheless, the problem remains of securing the prey in the hand, and this is solved in a number of different ways.

Fig 644 Cover pot used at Kerala, southern India.

Fig 645 Indian boy fishing with a cover pot in a paddy field.

28.1 Cover pots

The simplest falling gear is the cover pot or plunge basket, sometimes also called a thrust basket according to the manner of operation. Usually the cover pot is of wicker construction, like a beehive with an opening at the top (*Fig 644*). The basket is clapped over the animal by the fisherman wading in shallow water and the prey inside the pot is taken out through the opening. This catching method will only be successful in turbid, especially muddy, water wherein grow many plants, including floating water hyacinth (*Eichhornia crassipis*) as in tropical areas; otherwise the victim will escape. It is also a method used for fishing in inundated paddy fields (*Fig 645*). This is a fishing method used primarily for capturing single fish and those that have dug themselves into the mud. Operating cover pots is known in Asia as well as in Africa. Single pots are usually used blindly on the supposition that something might be caught, and the method is more effective when a large number of operators, usually women, are working together (*Fig 646*).

The fish that is caught must next be secured with

Fig 646 Thai women fishing by means of cover pots. (*Photo: FAO.*)

the hand through the opening at the top of the plunge basket. Small scoop nets can also be used for this purpose; and in addition, spears can be used if the fish to be caught have poisonous spines, or if aggressive dangerous snakes are expected. Seldom are the fish removed from the cover pots by grasping them with the hand slipped in from below the lower edge, although this may have been the original method for securing the prey. Recently, a new idea for securing the fish under the cover pot has come from Thailand. In this method the cover pot has a netting to close the opening at the bottom. A ring of netting is fixed at the inside of the pot, and this can be drawn together by a line running through the rings fixed on the rim of the netting like a purse seine (*Fig 647*). In this case the fisherman has to reach into the pot to reach the purse line of the bottom netting and to draw it together before hauling the gear with the catch. Purse lines are not used for the gear construction very often. They are well known with purse seines (*Fig 555*) and their brails (*Fig 418*); they are also known with a special type of cast nets (*Fig 653*); but their operation with coverpots may be an exception.

Fig 647 Cover pot from Thailand, closable with a bottom net. (*Photo: Tropenmuseum, Amsterdam*).

Cover pots are a specific gear of the freshwater fishery – especially in inundation areas and in estuaries; less so in shallow coastal waters. While the liftnets do not depend on the depth of water – the fish need only be within the range of the nets – the cover pots, as used in the original form, can only be operated in knee-deep water. That is a disadvantage, as also is the difficulty of removing the fish. How both problems may be solved is a matter still to be discussed.

Cover pots are widely used in east and south Asia, in the Melanesian part of Oceania, in Africa and southeast Europe and even in south Germany.[9] In southeast Europe they are considered to be the fishing gears of the White Russians and the Magyar fisheries.[278] The old fishery of the Indians in America did, however, use cover pots too. The plunge baskets found in South America might be considered to be the same as were built by negro slaves after the original pattern. But there is some evidence that cover pots may have been known in pre-Columbian times in the New World.[301]

A very remarkable adaptation to modern times can be seen in Rumania. Here the old cover pots made of wickerwork have been replaced by steel oil barrels – without the bottom and with netting replacing the top[18] (*Fig 648*). The purpose of the netting is to prevent the fish jumping out again. Clever boys also fish here with other round tube-like implements (*Fig 649*), including bottomless waste baskets. This is striking evidence for the survival of an old fishing method considered useful even today.

Except for the origin of the material, wooden cover pots scarcely differ from each other. All in fact are of much the same pattern. It is, however, possible that the relationship between diameter and height, and their size, may vary. Tiny cover pots of only 15cm in height and 15cm in diameter have been developed for use in the paddy fields of the Philippines. There are others which have a height of more than one metre. In the African fishery of Angola there is a plunge basket which is provided with a handle, and with a lid at the side which can be opened for removing the catch. The same design, with a handle, has been seen on the south coast of New Guinea. By this construction it is possible to fish in waters deeper than the height of the pot.

Fig 648 Rumanian fisherman using an iron barrel as a cover pot. (*Photo: Balcalbaşa.*)

Fig 649 Rumanian boys fishing in a backwater using drums *etc* for cover pots. (1976).

28.2 Lantern nets

Wooden plaited cover pots have, of course, a certain weight and are thus limited in their size, especially when no bamboo or other light wood is available for making them. In some countries, cover pots are fishing gears reserved for women and children. Therefore they must not be too heavy. It is therefore better if they can be made with netting instead of wood, in the same way as has been done with many other fishing gears. Such pots with a wooden frame covered with netting are known as 'lantern nets' (*Fig 650*). *Figure 651* shows the

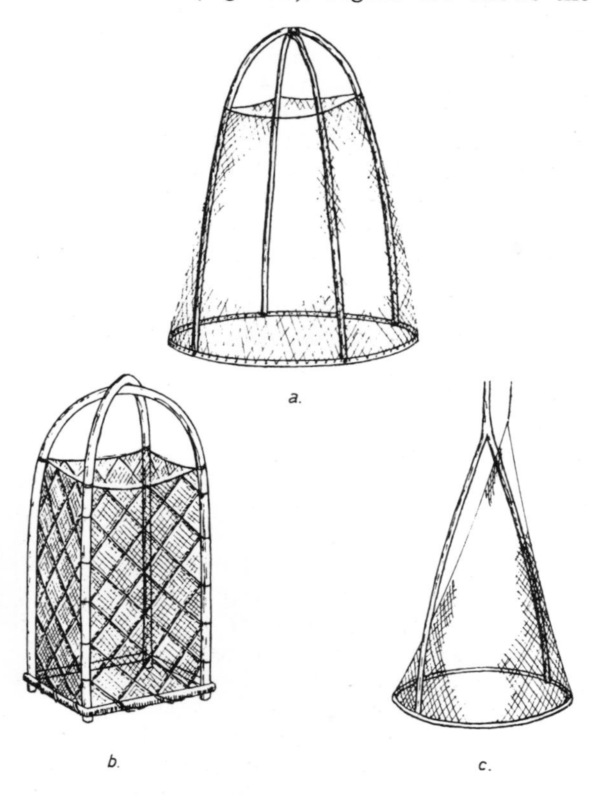

Fig 650 European lantern nets: (*a*) southern Germany; (*b*) Hungarian-type with trammelnet: (*c*) old 'Deckbären' of Switzerland.

operation of a lantern net in the River Danube in Hungary, and *Figure 650a* shows one which is still used in southern Germany for the capture of spawning fish, and of predatory fish in shallow, turbid or overgrown waters. The wickerwork has been replaced by netting held by two crossing rods.

Fig 651 Hungarian fisherman fishing with a lantern net in the River Danube. (*Photo: E Solymos, Baja, 1974.*)

By the use of netting the weight has been diminished and the size increased. The south German basket is 140cm in height (that is about shoulder height) and the opening is about 90cm in diameter. Similar gear is known in the Philippines and is called ‘salakab’ (*Fig 652*)[630]. If the netting should now be replaced by a trammelnet, as is the case with the Hungarian lantern net, the problem of making the actual catch is also solved. While trying to escape, the fish becomes entangled in the meshes of the trammelnet and can be taken out of the water together with the gear (*Fig 650b*). This construction also has the advantage that the gear may be operated in deeper water.[587]

28.3 Cover nets

As mentioned before, most cover pots and lantern nets can be operated in shallow water only, otherwise it becomes difficult to remove the fish covered by the gear. It has been mentioned too, that in some cases, when the water is not much deeper than the height of the gear, cover pots with a handle are used and the catch is taken out of the gear by hand, from an opening at one side. In these conditions it may be much more effective to use lantern nets covered with entangling netting (Chapter 30). But there is another way of solving the problem of how to use the cover technique successfully in deeper water.

In the African and east and south Asiatic fisheries, there is to be found a cone-shaped net which is held open by a hoop and usually stretched by three or sometimes even four or more sticks (*Fig 653*). This variation of the gear is also used like a cover pot, but before the net is clapped over a fish, the top of the conical net is held fast. Once the target fish is covered, the net is allowed to fall: the fish then becomes entangled in the loose netting. In this way the problem has been solved in a simple manner; namely, to actually secure the fish which has been covered by the gear, and to fish in deeper water. The wooden frame may be connected to a long handle, and the covering net bag held with a suitable long line (*Fig 650c*). This idea led to many variations in construction, such as the bag for the catch being inside the frame (*Fig 653*), as well as outside[552, 588] (*Fig 654*). In Switzerland, this long-handled gear is known as ‘Deckbären’ (this means cover trap) and in eastern Germany it is called

Fig 652 Fishing with a lantern net in Laguna de Bay, Manila. (*Photo: FAO.*)

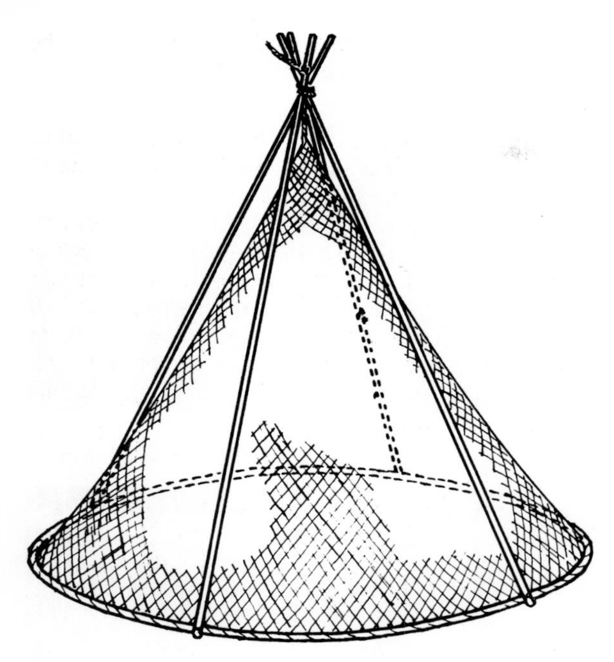

Fig 653 A lantern net from Central Africa. (*Monod, 1928*).

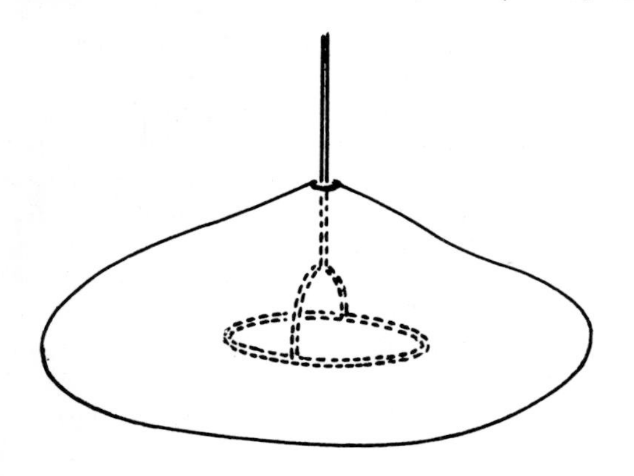

Fig 654 Rumanian hand-operated cover net. (*Antipa according to Bacalbasa, 1965*).

'Stuker' which has something to do with the operation of the gear by a quick pushing action. This gear is lowered carefully from a distance of half a metre of so above the observed single fish, *eg* carp or bream, and then the catch is made by pushing the ring of the bagnet very quickly onto the bottom. The bag is loosened, the fish trying to escape swims into the bag, and the gear is hauled immediately.[552] The handle and the length of the line fixed on the conical end of the net bag can each have a length of about two metres. With such gear an effective fishery can only be carried out in clear water where the prey can be seen. This method of fishing is also done with lights, during the night.

There are many more examples of the same idea. The Rumanians have a similar gear for fishing under ice[13] (*Fig 654*), but there are also many other forms like that in Hungary (*Fig 655*). This form of construction has also been used in Poland and in the Baltic countries including Latvia.[345] There exists another cone-shaped net used as a falling net in the fishery of the lakes of the south German Alps. This, however, is without any stretching sticks (*Fig 656*). That gear is composed of only a net cone and a ring. Held at the end by a line, it is lowered carefully from the boat over a spawning fish when one is seen. As soon as this has been done, the ring of the net can be turned up by a second line. The frightened fish is then entangled in the net. In Finland a similar gear is used – especially to catch perch over hard bottoms where spears cannot be operated.[363] That the fishery using this covering gear is effective is evident by the following. It has been said that formerly, in the River Rhine, fishermen operated

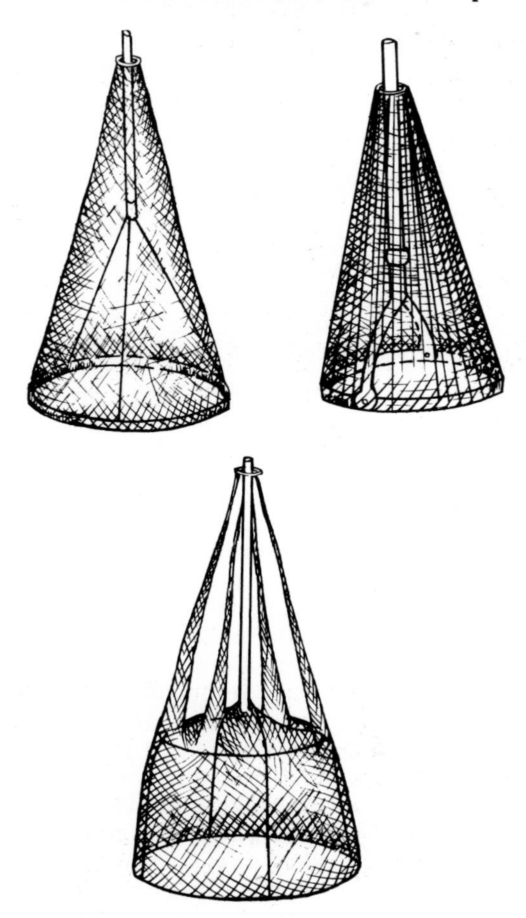

Fig 655 Different types of Hungarian cover nets. (*E Solymos, 1965*).

Fig 656 Falling net developed and used in southern Germany (*Sims-See*).

Fig 657 Turkish fisherman casting a net in an Anatolian lake. The cast net is constructed of triangular sections of netting.

Fig 658 A cast net falling on the water like a circle in Sri Lanka. Great dexterity is developed by fishermen in using this method. (1960).

liftnets like falling nets to catch bream.[51] In this case a liftnet with a deep bagnet is stretched by two sticks and framed by wire. When fish were expected, the gear was let down suddenly to create a bag with the opening downwards. The covered fish tried to escape and swam into the bag hanging over the wire when the net was hauled. So a liftnet became a cover net!

28.4 Hand cast nets

A quite different type of falling net is represented by the cast nets. Generally these are circular nets which, as the name implies, are thrown. They have to be thrown or cast with great skill in order to fall flat upon the water's surface (*Figs 657, 658* and *659*). Then, quickly sinking by reason of their weighted edges, they fall over the fish that has been seen or is supposed to be there. In contrast to the cover pots, the cast nets can only be employed in waters that have no obstacles or plants and, possibly, have a smooth bottom. If the ground is uneven, fish and crayfish cannot be completely covered by the net and will escape sideways. This also explains why it is that cast nets are not used in areas that are fished by cover pots, and vice versa.

Hand cast nets are today widely used all over the world. They have come to Europe, in particular to south Europe, by way of Greece. The Greeks took over the cast nets from the Near East and introduced them into the Mediterranean area, from where they spread over Europe and North Africa. It is suggested that the cast nets were originally developed in India and spread from there over east and south Asia into Oceania, the Near East and Europe. Drawings of cast nets more than one thousand years old are to be seen in the ruins of Angkor in Kampuchea. They were doubtless taken to the east coast of Africa by Arabian merchants and tradesmen. They may also have arrived directly from India. The Europeans, especially the Portuguese, took them to the west African coast. They arrived at the Zaire river during the last two centuries and spread up that river with the earliest travellers and their west African followers around the beginning of this century.[361]

In central Africa they are not known or used. Like hooks and lines, the cast net is not suitable for use in the waters of virgin forests. In contrast to this, cast nets are considered as one of the mainstays of the fisheries in the flood rivers of southern

Fig 659 Cast net fishing on the lagoon of Benin. (*Photo. G. Fortoh/FAO.*)

Africa, especially in the flood plain lakes and in the main streams at low water, when the fish are sufficiently concentrated to give a good chance of capture.[654] Europeans also introduced the cast net into the New World.

The operating of a cast net requires considerable knowledge, and several different variations are known. The correct method of casting the nets can only be acquired by practical experience as it is done by a skilled movement of the whole body. On this point the Japanese say that a fisherman should be so efficient that, depending on the conditions obtaining, he should be able to cast the net in such a manner that it takes on a flat round shape, or that of a temple bell*, or even of an umbrella. These nets are cast from the river bank, the beach, or from a boat. In the latter case, however, either a stable boat or a high degree of skill is required of the man casting the net (*Fig 659*). The fishermen of southern India are said to be especially skilful in operating from a boat. Peruvian fishermen are able to cast their nets while sitting on a raft. In this case the casting point is very near to the water surface and it needs great skill to cast the net under these circumstances.[413] In Columbia, sometimes ten or more boats fish together. The boats encircle a shoal of fish, frightening them together by noise with the oars during the process of narrowing the circle. On a given signal all the fishermen cast their nets, with a diameter of about four metres, so carefully that the nets nearly touch each other.[523] A collective fishing with cast nets is known in many parts of the world, like Africa[654] and Asia. As known from other gear operated in a collective, the catch of many gears cast at the same time is larger than if the cast nets are thrown one after the other.[9]

Casting from a boat is also practised by Turkish fishermen in the Black Sea. Here – most unusually – the cast nets are used in very deep water, of 150 metres and more. Sometimes the net is not cast but is let down in the water and spreads itself while sinking to these great depths. The net is required to cover the fish and, when being hauled, to collapse into folds so that the fish remain in between its folds. To make sure that the net will spread when cast, and will collapse when hauled, its edge is weighted with lead or chains. To attain the right shape, the hand cast nets are constructed very carefully.[80] Their size is designated by the radius or the circumference of the net and is limited by the technique itself. The radius of the gear is identical with the height of the collapsed net. Mostly the hand cast nets have a radius of two to three metres. But cast nets with a radius of more than seven metres are used.[244] The African cast nets are

*The Asiatic temple bells are more barrel-shaped, differing therefore from the conventional European shape of a bell.

known to be extremely large (*Figs 659* and *660*). The operators must be very experienced to cast such a large net in such a manner that it falls flat, like a circle, on the water surface (*Figs 657* and *658*) and sinks, fully spread in that form, to the bottom of the water.

Cast nets usually have a central retaining line (*Fig 661*), which is held in the hand for hauling the net. But there are some cast nets without a central line (*Fig 661a*). Then the fisherman must dive in after casting, in order to haul the net. Even if there is a central line, the fishermen may dive in to arrange the nets in the right position at the bottom of the water to prevent any fish, that are perhaps not quite covered, from escaping during the hauling of the net. That is frequently done in the cast net fishery of south Asia. It has been observed in African fisheries that the gear, with the fish, will not be hauled by a line, but that a diver takes each single fish out of the netting under water before hauling back the gear.[651]

The gear can be a simple circle of netting and the fish are entangled in the net webbing which collapses when carefully hauled. The meshes can be of such a size that the fish are gilled in the meshes as with gillnets. Many of the African cast nets are simple entangling fishing gear or are designed to keep the fish in the meshes (*Figs 661a* and *661b*). Finally, the cast net may have pockets at the edge, in which the fish get caught when the net is being hauled. These pockets can be fixed by turning up the lower edge of the net and fastening it by short

Fig 660 Very large cast nets of the Ivory Coast. (*Photo: Steinberg, 1965.*)

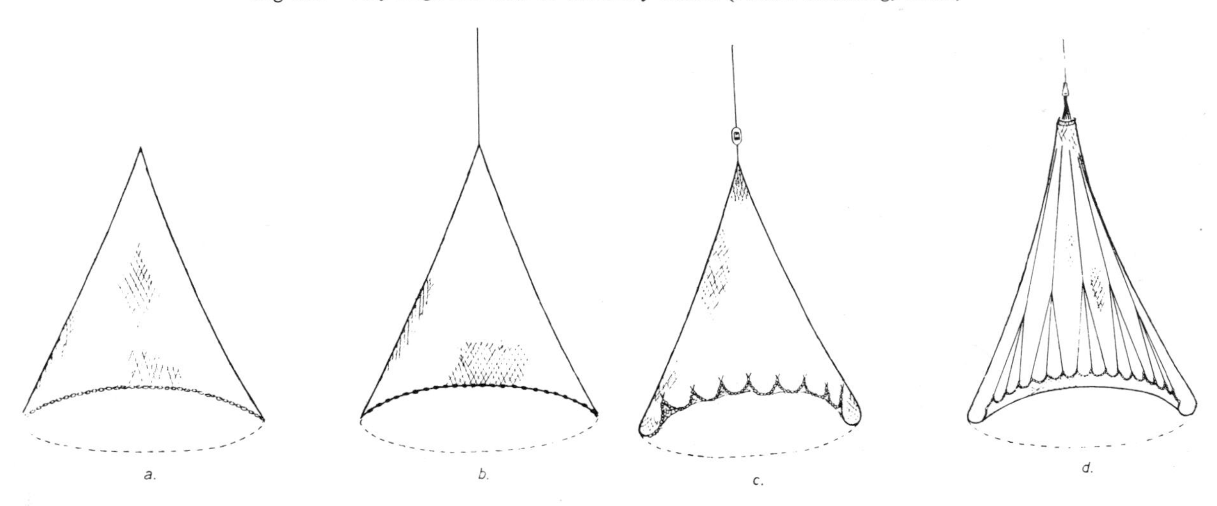

Fig 661 Showing the different construction of cast nets: (*a*) without central line and without pockets; (*b*) with central line and without pockets; (*c*) with central line and fixed pockets; (*d*) with central line connected with pockets.

lengths of twine, forming a cast net with fixed pockets (sometimes erroneously called 'Spanish type', *Fig 661c*). Alternatively, each of these twines can be connected to the central line – forming a 'stringed' cast net (erroneously called 'English type', *Fig 661d*). In the case of the stringed cast net, the strings can be connected individually to the leadline or each string can end with three tie cords (*Fig 661d*). The construction and operation of a stringed cast net is quite different from that of a cast net without pockets (*Fig 661a*) or with fixed pockets (*Fig 661c*). With the stringed cast nets, the pockets are formed during the hauling of the central line. The apex of the gear has an opening held by a short tube of different material, to tow the strings together with the central line. Cast nets without pockets are used in water in which plants or obstacles are expected. Cast nets with fixed pockets are especially made for shallow water, free of obstacles; the other type with pockets is considered to be better for deep waters free of the danger of the different lines entangling themselves around stones and other obstacles.[172]

Besides these well-known cast nets, there is another type of hand cast net which is seldom found and may be known only in south eastern Europe. This is a cast net without pockets, which has no central line, but instead employs a purse line through rings of lead at the edge of the net (*Fig 662*). Russian and Turkish fishermen[278], fishing in the Black Sea[384], know of this sophisticated gear. The gear is cast like a normal cast net, but the fish are caught by a pursing action after the gear has fallen over some fish like a net bag. When the line is pursed, the gear is hauled out of the water with

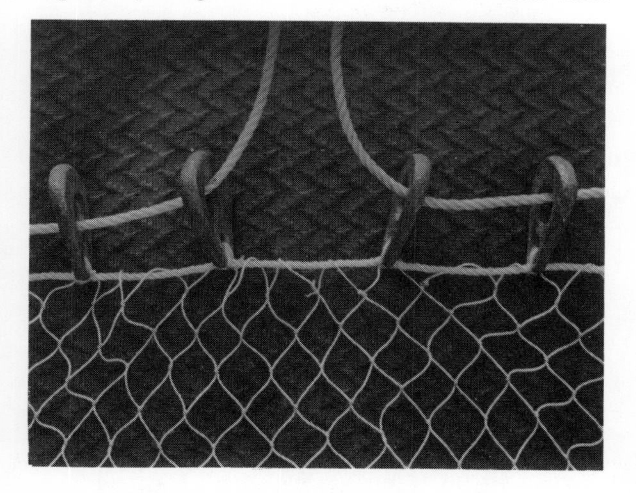

Fig 662 Leadline with rings and purse line for pursing a bag-like cast net. (*Photo: T Mengi, 1977.*)

the pursed leadline first, an operation quite different from that of the usual cast net (*Fig 663*). The advantage of this gear is that when cast it needs no contact with the bottom, as is necessary for the common cast nets. Therefore, it can be operated in deeper water to catch fish in mid-waters.

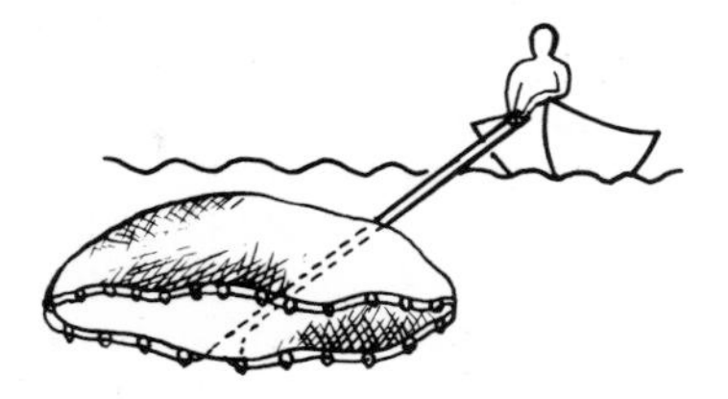

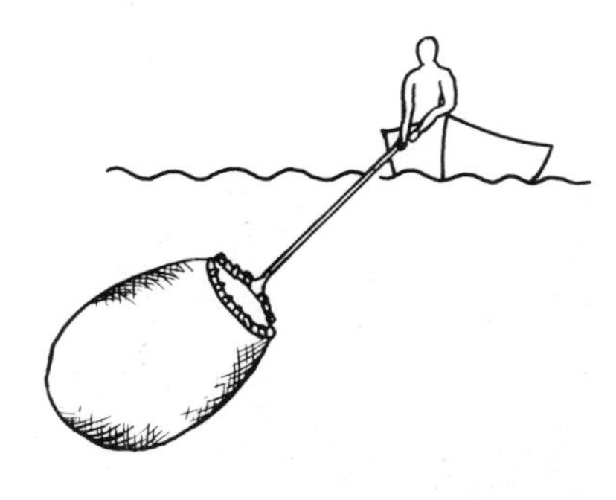

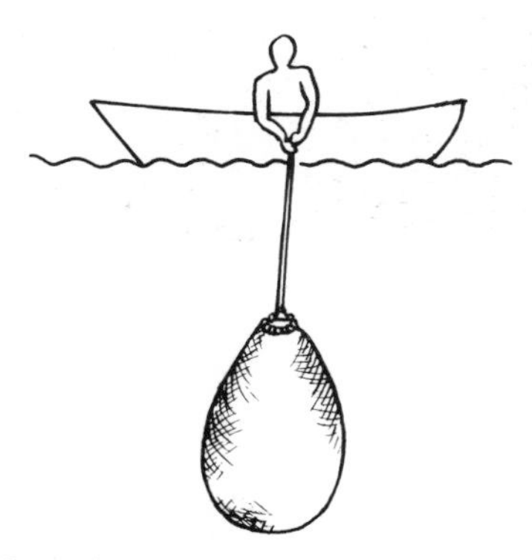

Fig 663 Operation of a cast net with purse line in free water without contact with the bottom. (*Mengi, 1977*).

28.5 Boat cast nets

As with liftnets, it is only possible to enlarge cast nets by hanging them on a gallows – in which case they can no longer be manipulated by hand. By this means it becomes possible to easily lower and haul them, even if they are of considerable size. They can be stationary gear but are usually installed in a boat to make them mobile (*Fig 664*). The spreading of such a gear must be done in a different way from hand casting.[306] To achieve a satisfactory spread, in the example under discussion an iron ring of at least two metres in diameter is used to keep the central nets spread while the free edges, with the leads attached, hang down like a bell. The edge is connected with a central line by means of twine and, thereby, the pockets can be formed, as has been described above for some types of hand cast nets (*Fig 661d*). Prior to casting, the pockets are completely closed so that the lead weights lie quite high. Just before the gear is lowered, the pockets are suddenly opened, the weights fall down and the edge spreads out as in *Figure 664*. Thus the net is let down, spreading widely as it goes and covering a large area. When the gear has fallen right to the bottom of the water, it is lifted a little and the pockets are closed with the help of the twines connecting the leadline with the central line. Now it can be hauled out of the water, hopefully with a catch. Such stationary cast nets were formerly used on the River Havel and, until some years ago, in the estuary of the River Elbe, partly in the port area of Hamburg. If they are colloquially called 'all wedder nix' – this means 'again nothing' – that is not to be taken as a reflection on their efficiency, but rather to demonstrate the shortage of fish owing to the modern pollution of the River Elbe!

The catching area covered by this semi-stationary boat cast net is no greater than that with the usual hand cast nets, but the net is easier to set because, for casting, little manpower is needed. There are still larger cast nets, but they are so big that they cannot be used as set or stationary gear. They have to be cast or set from moving boats. These are large round net webbings provided with weights at the edges, as is typical for cast nets. They can resemble an enlarged hand cast net with fixed pockets. In the river fishery of German speaking countries, these nets are called 'Schleifgarne'. According to their special operation they are also called 'drift cast nets'. Prior to being used, part of the net is hung over the side of a boat which is allowed to drift transversely in the current. Only a narrow edge is held fast along the boat, as well as the central line. In this way the gear is towed for a time with its lower edge sliding over the bottom and driving the fish forward. After a certain time the net is let down completely. It then spreads like a hand cast net on the bottom of the water to cover the fish, and is then carefully hauled by the central line (*Fig 665*), as is usual for cast nets. Such nets were, and are still, used on the large rivers of mid-Europe; the Elbe, the Rhine and the Danube. But they are also known in other European rivers like the River Mosel. Here such a gear with a circumference of 40 metres (that means a radius of about 6.4 metres) has been operated.[322, 343] Even today these drift cast nets are considered helpful for catching small fish in river fisheries.

Fig 664 Cast net on the River Elbe. (*Photo: Klust.*)

Fig 665 Hauling a 'Schleifgarne' on the River Rhine near Bacharach.

In the Far East, Japanese fishermen know a similar gear, but it is in a more rectangular form ('nagashi ami'). In the freshwater fishery of the mainland of modern China, an over-sized cast net is used. As can be seen in *Figure 666* this gear is operated with a winch placed on a net boat with some gallows and is spread over the bottom by four additional rowing boats. The gear has fixed pockets as in *Figure 661c*.[289] Nevertheless, it may be said that these boat nets have not, by any means, the same importance as the hand cast nets, which are used in commercial fishery in all parts of the world, and often also for taking samples in pond farms.

28.6 Polynesian rectangular nets

As has been said, cast nets are round nets with or without pockets and are thrown by experienced fishermen in such a manner that they fall like a circle on the water surface. But the idea of catching fishes by throwing a sheet of netting over them has also been achieved in another manner. Polynesian fishermen are considered as the inventors of rectangular cast nets as 'a special form between cast net and seine net'.[9] These are strips of netting of different sizes, which may have floats on the one side and sinkers on the other and are thrown in such a manner as to either prevent the escape of fish from the bank into the open sea, or to catch fish directly.[9, 128, 486] This type of gear has been adopted also from Micronesian and Melanesian fishermen, and is therefore known from the Solomon Islands to as far as Easter Island. A special type of these nets is the 'manavi', a net used by the inhabitants of Botel Tobago (Lan Yü) in the east of southern Taiwan.[288] This is a rectangular net four to five metres in length and one metre wide, stretched between two bamboo rods of one and a half to three metres in length. The fisherman stays in the shallow water (the ideal depth is about one metre) in a bent position, and keeps the float line in his mouth or (when the teeth are no longer so good!) between chin and breast, and stretches the net between the

Fig 666 Modern Chinese giant-size cast net for freshwater fishery operated from a net boat with winch and four rowing boats. (*Kasuga, 1975*).

two sticks (*Fig 667*). When he lets go the net, the netting whips forward, surrounding or covering the fishes. It is considered necessary that at this moment the fisherman takes one stamping step forward, simultaneously shaking the two sticks to frighten the fish into the netting spread behind them in the water. Then the sticks are brought together and the netting, with the fish, is towed onto the beach like a very small seine net – which encouraged the definition mentioned above. Of course, this is a very individual form of gear. But ideas different from the usual fishing gear are rare in fisheries and therefore are worthy of mention.

Fig 667 Fisherman of Botel Tobago island (Lan Yü) with Polynesian rectangular cast net before whipping forward the netting.

Chapter twenty-nine

Gillnetting

With many fishing gears made of netting it is found that fish sometimes hang in the mesh. In trying to swim through a mesh of netting which is a little smaller than the largest circumference of their body, they get stuck or, in other words, 'meshed'. This can happen at the beginning of the dorsal fin of the fish, but mostly it will be behind the opercula and the gills – *ie* they are 'gilled'. The pressure of the mesh twine on the throat of the fish can cause the opercula to spread, and the net twine then hooks behind them so that the fish can go neither forward nor backward. By struggling to become free from the mesh the fish can further entangle itself. It may happen that small fishes can pass a mesh of a certain netting without difficulty, but bigger ones can be gilled, or gilled and entangled, and others, especially large ones, can be caught by entangling only, all in the same netting.

As a result of these observations, special gear has been constructed to catch fish by gilling. These are the so-called 'gillnets' (*Fig 668*), discussed in this chapter. Other gear has been constructed to catch fish by entangling. These are the so-called 'entangling nets', which will be considered in Chapter 30. Gilling and entangling are two different principles of catching, but both can happen in the same fishing gear. On the other hand, gear used, *eg*, for catching crabs by entangling, should not be called a gillnet, as is sometimes done in literature. Gillnets are net walls kept more or less vertical by floats on the upper line and mostly by weights on the ground-line. It is necessary to distribute floats and sinkers in an even manner. It was, therefore, an advance to replace a large number of floats by 'swimming lines'. These are plaited lines, incorporating floats, which provide a more evenly distributed buoyancy. For the same reason sinkers have sometimes been replaced by small chains and, later, by plaited lines filled with small pieces of lead. To prevent the entangling of larger meshes with single floats, net rings made of plastic can be used as floats, as in the northern European countries.

Fig 668 Gillnet fisherman of southern Germany. (*Photo: Graf v Mandelsloh.*)

For the same reason, galvanized steel rings can be used to replace sinkers (*Fig 681*). Handling the gear is much easier with steel rings instead of sinkers, and they keep the gear some distance off wrecks, which are promising places for gillnetting but are, unfortunately, inclined to damage the net by hooking.

Gillnets are usually set across the direction of the migrating fish, so that they try to make their way through the meshes of the netting. For this reason, gillnets can be operated in a variety of ways. There are bottom nets, set on or near the bottom to catch demersal fish; there are anchored floating gillnets to catch mid-water fish; and there are free-drifting gillnets to catch surface fish as well as mid-water fish. There are further methods of operating gillnets in quite a different way. One is the encircling gillnet already described with the drive-in fishery (Chapter 26); another is the dragged gillnet used in some freshwaters. Further, set gillnets can be operated in such a form that they work like two-dimensional traps.

Generally, gillnetting is a clear-water fishery, used where there is not too strong a current and no floating vegetation (which can make the nets ineffective by filling up and joining the meshes). Other undesirable matter includes mass-produced micro-organisms (water blossom) from natural causes or due to pollution. Gillnetting is not a fishery for deep waters. In too-deep water, the hydrostatic pressure can compress the usual floats of cork or plastic to such an extent that they lose their buoyancy and the gear can no longer function. Nevertheless, with suitable floats, gillnets can be operated at a depth of 150 metres and more.

If dragged and encircling gillnets are excluded, gillnets are passive fishing gear (Chapter 1). That means that the fish has to voluntarily try to swim through the meshes of the unwatched fishing gear. To encourage the fish to do so, even baits have been fixed in the meshes, *eg* by Somalian fishermen on Lake Tanganyika. Coloured pearls woven into the meshes of the set nets by Zaire fishermen may have the same attractive effect. Also with gillnets for mackerel some attempts have been made to lure the fish into the net with glittering artificial bait tied on the netting. As explained earlier, the fish are caught when they try to penetrate the meshes of the netting voluntarily, but they will do this only when the wall of netting seems easy to slip through. For this reason, the gear must have certain properties of construction and of the material from which it has been made. There may be some doubt if these different properties could have been achieved in earlier times, and it is questionable whether effective gillnetting was possible then. When a fish was gilled in an early netting made of thick, stiff, non-elastic material, it was more or less an accident, or special conditions pressed the fish in large shoals into the netting, as in the old north European herring fishery with drift nets made of hemp. The current high efficiency of gillnetting in sea and fresh water was not possible before the introduction of synthetic fibres for net making.

There is a long list of the properties of a gillnet which may influence its efficiency and it may be that not all are known even now.[75] Some of them depend on the gear construction, like mesh size and mesh shape, which is influenced by the hanging of the netting, which also influences the slack of the netting. Of these properties, mesh size may be the most important. By the use of the correct mesh size and a high degree of uniformity in the size of all meshes, the gear becomes highly selective – so important for the management of a fish population. There may be no other gear which is as selective as a gillnet in taking fish of a uniform size. Other properties influencing the efficiency of gillnets depend on the material used for the netting of the gear. The most important are its low visibility, which depends not only on the material used but also on its thickness, its knots (mostly double knots), its colour, and its contrast with the surroundings where the gear is set. Other properties influencing the efficiency of gillnets are that the net should have the greatest possible softness and that it should have the lowest possible swelling from immersion in water. Just as a vessel pushes a bow-wave ahead of it, so does a swimming fish. This wave is reflected by more or less solid objects, and the return swell is recorded by the sensitive lateral line of the fish which operates as a kind of automatic apparatus for recording distances. The stronger the returning swell, the more will the fish endeavour to avoid what is ahead. The net twines of the gillnets therefore have to be made as fine as possible, thus again reducing their visibility. To decrease the swell, the netting should not be held tensely but should be as slack as possible. Slacking may be obtained in the construction of the gear by making the side lines of the gear much shorter than the depth of the netting. But this may increase the entangling effect of the gear more than the gilling effect. On the other hand, the water resistance of the netting will be decreased.

When comparing the visibility of a gillnet with its softness and its water resistance, visibility is the most important. The volume of a catch decreases with increasing visibility. It must be borne in mind that the visual faculty of fish differs not only according to the species but also (by some evidence) according to their age and physiological condition. Therefore it is essential that the gillnet should contrast as little as possible with its surroundings. Efforts have therefore been made to dye these types of nets so that they are as invisible as possible and harmonize closely with their surroundings. A white cotton net, for example, would contrast far too much with what are usually darker surroundings, especially in clear waters (*Fig 669*). In the fresh waters of Europe, the prevailing colours are bluish-green and brownish, and these have therefore become the principal colours used for nets. However, waters change colour within short periods, and certainly within the course of the year. Many fishermen, therefore, have equipped themselves with nets of various colours, so that they may always have available nets suitably dyed, or so camouflaged as to blend with the colour of the water.

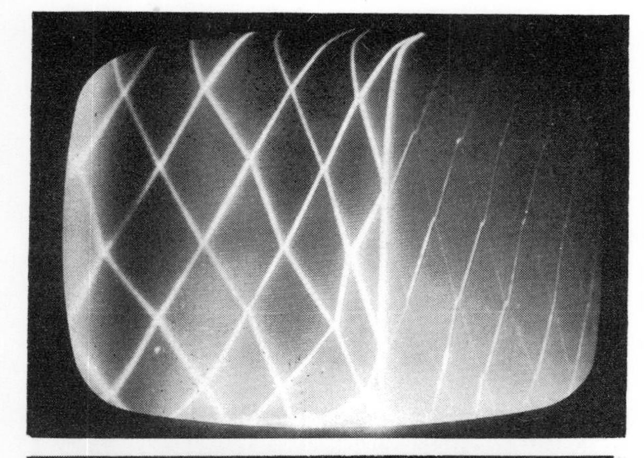

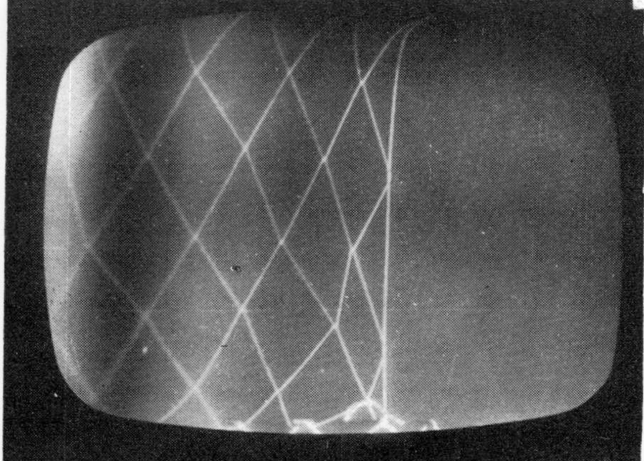

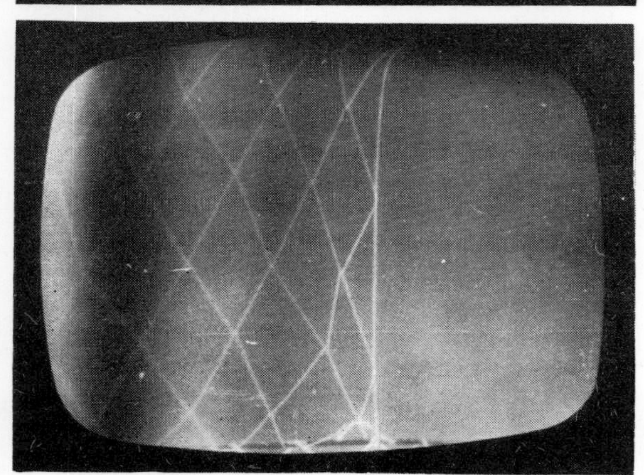

Fig 669 Gillnets made of cotton yarn (*left*) and polyamide monofilament (*right*). Both yarns have the same diameter. The visibility is decreasing with decreasing light intensity in deeper water (from top to bottom). The photographs are taken from the screen of an underwater television system.

The efficiency of these nets has been increased sometimes by several hundred per cent when natural fibres have been replaced by less visible synthetic fibres (PA multifilaments), especially by transparent monofilaments (PA) or monotwines (twines made of monofilaments of PA and also PE).[75, 594] That fact has caused gillnet fishery to expand considerably in recent years, and has decreased effort in some other fishing methods like beach seining, which need more manpower and more money. Gillnets made of monofilaments of surprising transparency, scarcely visible and without any disturbing sparkle in the knots, (*Fig 669*) have been manufactured by machines in Europe since 1953, and even by hand in many parts of the world, so that they meet the condition of contrasting as little as possible with any surroundings, even if the water colour should change (*Fig 670*). With the help of synthetic netting materials of low visibility, it was proved possible to fish in clear water, and during daytime, in the clear brown-water lakes of northern Europe or in the clear oligotrophic lakes of the Alps, where any effective fishery with gillnets made of cotton was formerly only productive during the time of thaw – characterised by turbid waters. Moreover, it was found that catches included species not formerly caught, and that of the known species, larger fish were caught than with netting made of natural fibres, even when the finest cotton, like Mako, was used.

Fig 670 Hauling a transparent gillnet in northern Germany.

The second important property of netting material used for gillnets is the softness of the twine. Visibility is more important, so that a hard net with a low visibility will catch more than a soft one with a high visibility; but from two nets of the same visibility, the softest will catch more. The importance of visibility decreases with the turbidity of the water. So it may happen that the same gillnet with low visibility and high efficiency in clear waters, may catch less than others in muddy waters, because the others have a higher degree of softness. It has been mentioned before that the netting yarns of gillnets should be as fine as possible, to decrease visibility and to increase softness. On the other hand, netting of very fine material is not only difficult to handle but is more prone to damage than thicker material. Moreover, very fine netting material may cut and damage some species (*eg* herring), known as 'soft' fish.

29.1 Bottom set gillnets and anchored floating gillnets

Stationary gillnets set on the bottom between stakes and anchors are used in lakes and coastal fisheries for catching the most common commercial fish (*Fig 671*). To give these nets a good contact with the bottom, which may be more or less rough, the leadline can be about 10 per cent longer than the floatline. These nets can be set in shallow water, but also up to 50 metres in depth in fresh waters, and in sea waters sometimes more than 150 metres (Icelandic cod nets are used down to 100 fathoms).

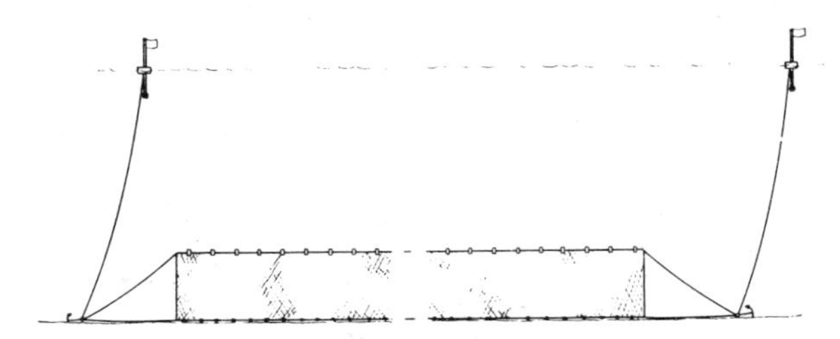

Fig 671 Anchored bottom net for sea fisheries.

In areas that have great differences between ebb and flood tides, set nets can be arranged with very long poles. An example of this can be seen in the set nets of the tidal area of Nova Scotia on the Canadian Atlantic coast. These are very famous, for they are set between such high poles that when ebb time comes the fishermen have to remove the fish from the net by means of ladders or by standing on a horse carriage. The rise and fall of the tide is here over eight metres, so that at ebb tide the gillnets hang with the fish high above the dry ground.

Usually gillnets are not used as single nets: a number are linked together. Bottom set nets can be set as straight walls or in a bow-shaped pattern (*Figs 672b* and *672c*). These pattern arrangements can be taken further so that the layout of the scheme resembles that of a two-dimensional trap with a slit funnel (*Fig 672a*). A special form of this combination between gilling and trapping is known in Israel in Eilat on the Gulf of Aqaba (Ben-Yami, verbal). Here gillnets are set in the form of a hook, with the longer end to the coast, in water of more than ten metres depth. When fish enter the bow of the hook, the part open to the shore is closed by a stop net. The enclosed fish are caught with a beach seine, but the gilled fish are taken out of the meshes by divers.

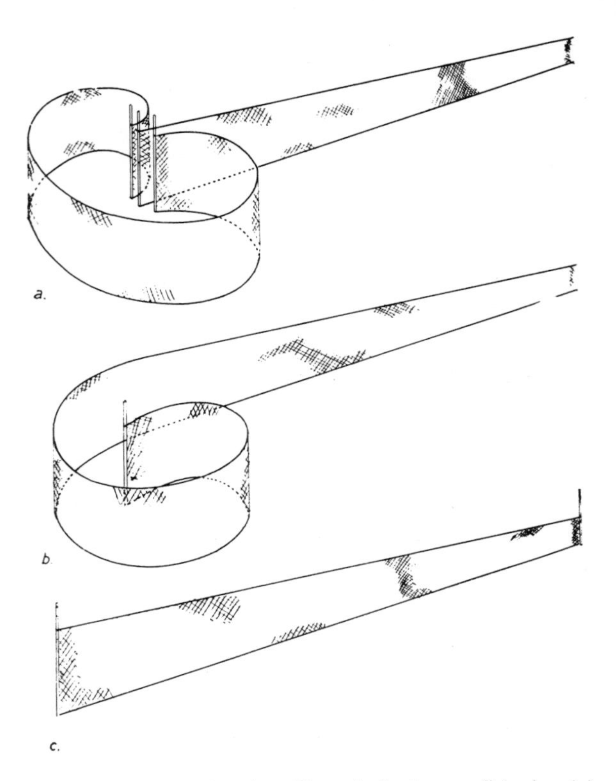

Fig 672 Methods of setting gillnets in freshwater fisheries: (*a*) with a turning made of at least two nets; (*b*) turning at the end of a single net; (*c*) simple setting.

In northern countries stationary gillnets are also used during winter-time under ice. To do this, holes are made and the nets are pushed under the ice with sticks reaching from one hole to another. As is known for ice fishing with the seine net (Chapter 24), also for the setting of gillnets under ice, a 'jigger' (*Fig 538*) can be used, as by the Canadians, to pull a rope from one hole to another. With this line the net can be brought into the right position even under a thick layer of ice.

Stationary gillnets can also be set at some distance from the bottom by long connecting lines between sinkers and net. The fishermen say the nets are staying on 'legs'. These legs can be very long, causing the nets to float some metres over the bottom. They are called 'floating gillnets'. They are suspended between anchors on the bottom and floats on the surface (*Fig 673*). Such specially fine nets are used in the mid-European freshwater fisheries, principally for taking the more valuable pelagic species of fish. The fishermen of the smaller lakes in the Alps, and the north German fishermen, both catch Coregons with anchored floating net walls of this type made of the finest, scarcely visible material (*Figs 668* and *670*).

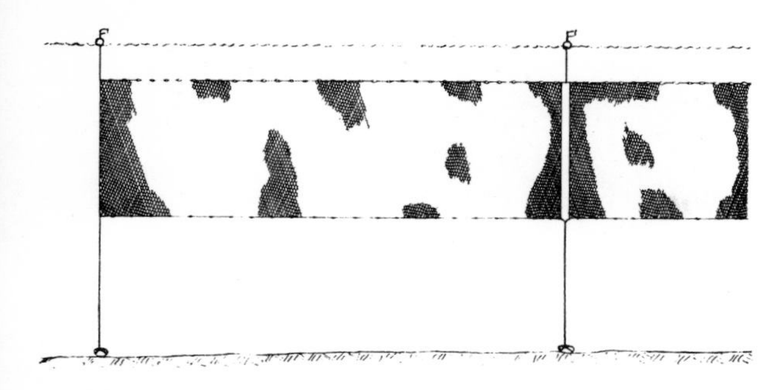

Fig 673 Floating gillnets for catching white fish in a lake in northern Germany.

29.2 Driftnets in sea fisheries and in fresh waters

Driftnets are especially used in sea fishing (*Fig 674*), particularly to catch herring, mackerel and sardines, but also for salmon and tuna and some other schooling fish (*Figs 675* and *676*). In a sea fishery the nets may drift independently, accompanied by a vessel, but generally they are fastened to a boat that drifts with them. In English fishing a whole row of nets is called a 'fleet' or 'gang' and they are closely watched during the night so that they can be controlled and hauled at any time, without searching for them. The method of operating very long rows of driftnets is particularly important because large areas of water can be covered by the drifting net walls, which are sometimes up to four kilometres in length. In this way they are able to filter large volumes of water and so catch even scattered fish or fish schools in sufficient commercial quantities. There are some differences in the rigging of driftnets (*Fig 674*) but in general the netting is 'framed'. That means each net has not only a floatline and leadline but also side lines to give the gear better stability for handling. When the leadline is omitted, the catch will be made primarily by entangling (Chapter 30) and not by gilling. There are many ways of rigging driftnets to avoid the influence of the movement of the vessel on the gear.

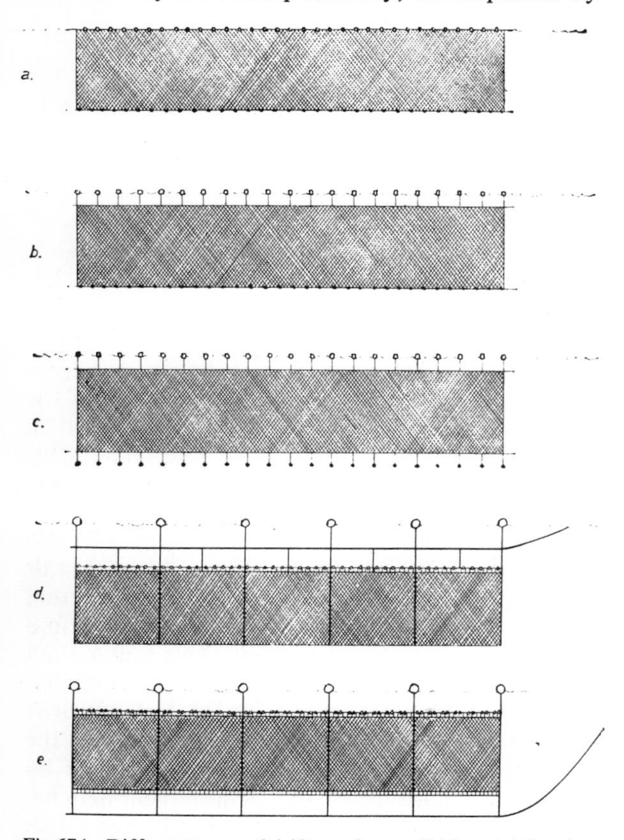

Fig 674 Different types of driftnets for sea fishing: (*a*) floating at the surface; (*b*) floats with special lines keep the net deeper; (*c*) lines between net and floats as well as between sinkers and net; (*d*) European driftnet for herring, German type; (*e*) European driftnet for herring, Scottish type.

Fig 675 Shooting of driftnets from a German herring drifter.

Small drifters operating for herring in the western part of the Baltic hang their driftnets between anchored floats and the drifting vessel (*Fig 677*).

In contrast to sea fisheries, driftnets are not used much in freshwater fishing because the areas are so limited. Only in very large lakes are floating gillnets sometimes allowed to drift freely and unwatched. In rivers, fishermen use only very small driftnets. With one end fixed on a boat and the other on a big float, the whole system drifts downstream with

Fig 676 Hauling a herring driftnet with a good catch.

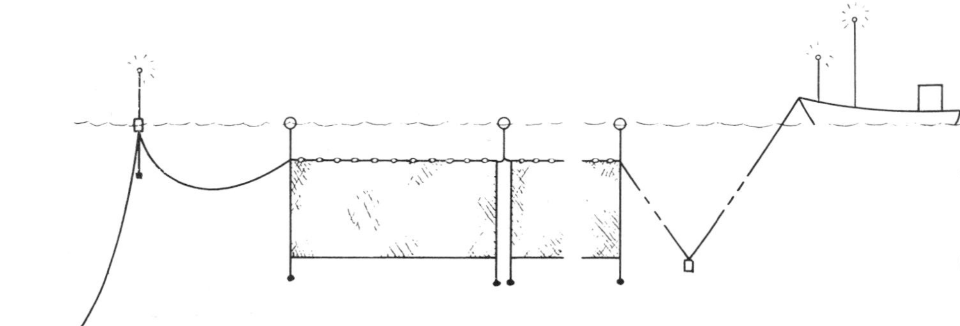

Fig 677 Anchored driftnet for catching herring in the Baltic off the east coast of Schleswig-Holstein.

the water current. Sometimes two boats with driftnets are used in a river fishery as in the Finnish salmon fishery. Because it was found, in Finland, that sometimes the salmon could be frightened by the noise of rowing a boat, one of the two boats could be replaced by a float or by a so-called 'towing board'[639] (*Fig 678*). This board was worked like a shearing board, towing the gear on one side by floating in the middle of the current. It has the same function as the boards used today for trolling in some countries of northern Europe.

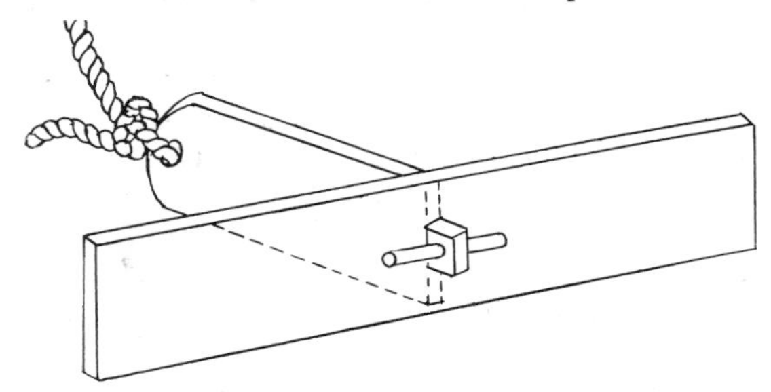

Fig. 678 Finnish towing board for driftnets in salmon fishery. (*Vilkuna, 1975*).

29.3 Dragged gillnets

Gillnets are passive fishing gears when not operated as encircling nets in the drive-in fishery (Chapter 26) or as dragged gillnets in fresh waters. In the latter case the gillnets are towed, like trawls, in shallow waters by two men or by two boats. This method seems to be known in different parts of the world. The technique is described from central and southern Africa,[361] including Madagascar,[65] and also from Argentina.[116] In South America this method seems to be a variation of the driftnet fishery. The gear is operated with the current in a river, with a rowing boat on one side and a float on the other, similar to driftnet fishing in rivers. The difference is only that the gear does not drift completely free in the current but is towed over the bottom, gilling the fish which try to escape by swimming against the current. This Argentinian net of extravagant construction is used to catch a fish called 'surubi' (*Pseudoplatystoma fasciatum* or *P. coruscans*).[117] The meshes of the upper part of the gillnet are knitted of a double twine and those of the lower part of a triple twine (*Fig 679*). The

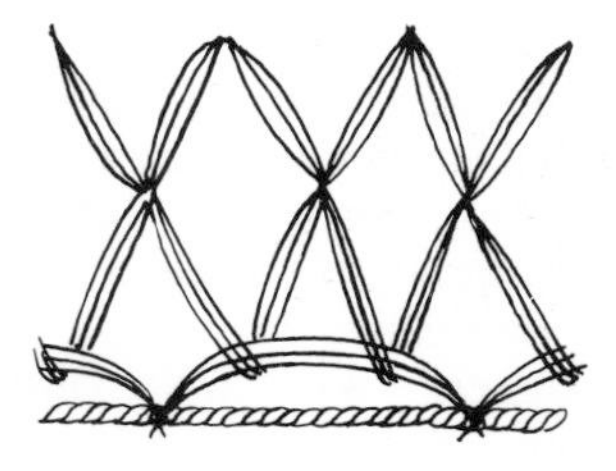

Fig 679 Gillnet, upper part made of two netting yarns, lower part of three, operated as towed gear in the Rio Parana, Argentina, for catching 'surubi'. (*Cordini, 1955*).

explanation of this unusual construction may be the following: a single twine would not be strong enough to catch large fish. Two or three twines twisted together are stronger, but such twine may be too stiff. When two or more twines are only taken together with no, or only little, twisting, the result will be a stronger netting yarn – without increased stiffness. The towing of gillnets is also known in the Far East for catching marketable milkfish in ponds. In this case, some gillnets are joined together and towed along the length of a pond.[110]

29.4 Advantages and disadvantages of gillnets

Gillnets are a fishing gear with a high degree of selectivity, regulated by the mesh size. They contrast with entangling nets (Chapter 30), which have a very low selectivity. It has also been mentioned that this selectivity is very important for the management of a fish population. Because, with the gillnet, fishermen can decide on the size of mesh to be used so that only fish of a certain circumference are caught (smaller ones would be able to swim through the net), the use of the passive gear gives the advantage that fish stocks can be exploited more selectively than by any other gear. In order to spare young fish, or fish that are too small for the market, the authorities administering freshwater fishing sometimes allow only gillnet fishing and will not tolerate or permit fishing with dragged gears to be carried out.

Gillnetting is of special interest for artisanal fisheries because it is a low cost fishery. Not so much has to be invested in nets and their maintenance. Moreover, no specialized vessels are needed, and in tropical areas these nets can be operated without any vessel, by swimming and diving fishermen. As rowing boats or simple motor boats with a low power are adequate for gillnetting, only a small crew is needed when using a relatively small number of nets. Therefore, this method of fishing is widely practised all over the world and can be considered as a typical small-scale fishery method which can be very effective, especially when monofilament nets are used. These advantages decrease when larger numbers of nets are operated. These can make this fishery labour-intensive in gear making and mending, setting and hauling, and especially by the work of removing the gilled and entangled fish from the netting. Therefore, all fisheries that employ large numbers of gillnets are today expensive, but the use of gillnets does permit careful fishing.

The quality of the fish caught is appreciated much more than that of fish taken with other gear, particularly those caught by dragged bottom gear. Better quality may be true for driftnets as caught fish are removed fairly promptly in contrast to set nets, which have to stay longer in the water and may suffer losses by predatory fish or crabs. Sometimes it is mentioned that due to the higher elasticity of some synthetic netting yarns, the gilled fish are pressed much more and die quicker than in gillnets made of natural fibres. This adversely affects the quality of the catch.

At the beginning of this chapter, the advantages afforded by the introduction of synthetic fibres, in particular of transparent monofilaments, were stressed, particularly in relation to the efficiency of the gillnets. Such nets not only catch more but, being non-rotting, can also be used much longer. Experience, however, has revealed one disadvantage which even roused the attention of the Fisheries Division of the Food and Agriculture Organization of the United Nations. This was the problem of the so-called 'ghost nets', similar to the problem with some traps for crustaceans discussed in Chapter 16, but it arose first with gillnets. As is well known, synthetic net twines used in fishing nets do not rot; if such a rigged gillnet is lost during fishing, it can be recovered, even after some years have elapsed, still in useful condition. Proof of that came in this way: some Icelandic fishermen had the bad luck to lose some of their gillnets when fishing for cod in bad weather. After a fairly long time, these nets were found again and it was then revealed that they had continued to catch fish in the meantime. The net showed clearly that fish had been caught, had died and had rotted in the nets, but were steadily replaced by new ones so that the process went on. It was accordingly feared that if a great number of gillnets became lost, or if many nets were fraudulently set, then whole sea areas might be gradually depleted. The problem was, how could the undesired fishing of such 'ghost' nets be prevented? The solution was relatively simple and was this: that the floats for keeping the nets in a vertical position for fishing should only be fastened by twine made of natural fibres. Then, should the nets be lost, the twines holding the floats would soon rot, the floats would separate from the nets and those nets would collapse in a heap on the sea bed and so no longer catch fish.[584, 619] The problem of ghost fishing is not so critical with gillnets as it may be for fish pots. Lost gillnets are usually so heavily entangled that they would be very unlikely to catch fish, and some think that the probability of synthetic gillnets fishing as 'ghost nets' is overestimated.[175, 619]

But there is one advantage of gillnetting not yet mentioned, which has become very important recently. Gillnetting is one of those fishing methods with a low energy consumption calculated on the relationship of fuel/fish (both in kg). According to Norwegian investigations the relationship is similar to that of longlining.[158] It may be that this fact will have a growing influence on the fishery with gillnets in the near future.

29.5 Mechanization of gillnetting

The introduction of synthetic fibres like PA, PE and PP as multi-filaments but especially the transparent monofilaments developed about 1950, gave a strong impetus to gillnetting. Gillnets made of PA monofilaments increased catches many times over. In sea fisheries, gillnets made of PE monotwines are used for catching Spanish mackerel. In this case the catches are not increased so much due to the stiffness of the material, but because of this the entangling of the fish has been reduced and this has avoided the time wasted in taking the fish out of the gear. The proof of the importance of this fishing gear can be seen in two facts: the original natural fibres were very soon replaced by synthetic ones, and all efforts were made to mechanize the operation of the gear. As mentioned before, gillnetting on a small scale can be a low cost fishery, but on a large scale it becomes a labour-intensive fishing method. Due to the increasing catches of gillnets made of synthetic materials, interest in gillnetting increased and, in a relatively short time, gillnets were converted from natural to synthetic fibres and mechanization in gear operation developed quickly and will continue to do so. The desire to convert from natural to synthetic fibres, especially to monofilaments, was so pressing that fishermen, especially in Asiatic countries, undertook the troublesome work of knitting – by hand – stiff monofilaments, long before the mechanized net factories could do so. This is one of the rare cases in which the growing importance of a fishing gear influenced its mechanical production. Not only were netmaking machines adjusted to work up monofilaments in netting; also the mounting of gillnets became mechanized. In Russia, Finland and recently also in Germany, special machines have been developed for mounting the netting automatically on floatline or leadline. Moreover, the joining of two nettings can also now be made automatically.

Some progress was also made in the mechanization of the operation of gillnets. Originally, gillnets were set and hauled by hand only. To keep the nets untangled and to make transportation and handling easier, the nets were strung by one row of meshes on thorn-like sticks made of wood or plastic (*Fig 680*) or on simple wooden clamps (*Fig 681*). When setting, the nets

Fig 680 Wooden spike for storing gillnets.

Fig 681 Danish gillnets, with iron rings as weights, stored on wooden clamps.

can run immediately from the thorn or clamp fixed on to the mast of the vessel. When fishing with long fleets of nets, the first attempts were made to mechanize the handling of the gear in order to decrease manpower requirements. Net-driving rollers were placed on the bulwarks of the vessel and net haulers, with separate vertical gurdies, were introduced.[178] As with other fishing methods in sea fisheries the increasing of the size of a gear, or its operation in deeper water, needs at least an improvement of the deck's machinery for gear handling. For setting and hauling gillnets in deeper water, stronger net haulers are required. Originally, simple reels were used, as in line hauling, but now they are hydraulically powered and specially designed for hauling gillnets (*Figs 682, 683* and *684*). Power blocks mounted on a davit, boom or crane are also used for hauling gillnets, sometimes in a specialized form to facilitate the handling of the gear[536] (*Figs 685* and *686*). Just as in purse

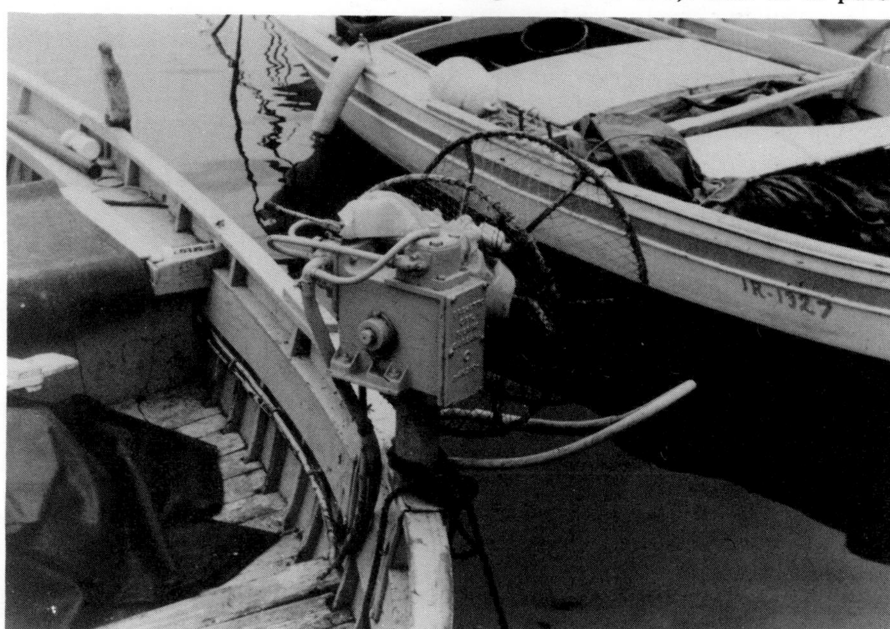

Fig 682 Hauling reel for gillnet in Anzio, Italy. (1976)

Fig 683 Modern hydraulically-powered line hauler near Kiel, Germany.

Fig 684 Danish gillnet hauler in action. (*Courtesy of World Fishing Exhibition 1980, Press Office*).

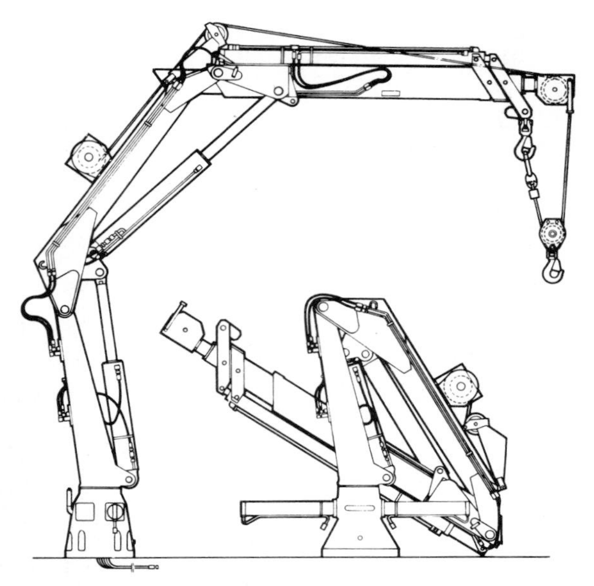

Fig 685 Special crane, with folding boom, for the operation of fishing gear. (*Courtesy of Hiab-Foco, Hudiksvall, Sweden*).

seining and longlining, drums are also used for hauling and storing of gillnets (*Figs 687* and *688*). As in New Zealand, a drum holding a gillnet can be mounted on the vessel in such a manner that it can easily be removed and transported by truck to a net loft for inspection and repair. While this is done, another drum, loaded with net, is fitted into the vessel so that fishing need never be interrupted.

At the end of the 1970s, in Denmark, a new method for operating gillnets was introduced. This was by hauling the netting over an endless rubber belt against which it is pressed by a plastic roller which moves freely up and down. The roller weight is regulated by filling it with water (*Fig 689*). With this construction the roller can go over thicker netting, as well as over the fish which may hang in

Fig 686 Cranes with power blocks for the operation of gillnets or purse seines in Suao, Taiwan. (1978).

Fig 687 Californian fisherman shooting from a drum an anchored gillnet for sea bass. (1967).

Fig 688 Gillnetter with a large shark net on a drum in the harbour of Akaroa in New Zealand (1981).

Fig 689 Danish automatic gillnet hauler. (*Courtesy of Grenaa Smedie og Maskinfabrik, Grenaa, 1979*).

Fig 690 Icelandic net shaker for driftnets. (*Courtesy of Veltak Ltd, Hafnarfjordur, Iceland, 1980*).

the gear. There are different variations of this system especially designed to avoid any damage to the gilled fish. In general, gilled fish are taken out of the netting separately by hand. When large quantities of smaller fish like herring are caught, it is no longer practical to take each single fish out of the mesh, but they can be shaken out by strong up and down movements of the net by the hauling crew. To replace this hard work, especially exhausting with the more elastic synthetic nets, shaking machines were produced by various manufacturers. This was done a long time ago in the USSR, unfortunately without any favourable reaction from the former large driftnet fishery for herring in the North Sea. Since 1975, with the recreation of the herring stocks, such machines in different sizes have been available from Iceland (*Fig 690*). With the help of drums the net with the gilled fish is pulled through the machine, thus shaking the fish out of the meshes. Another larger machine, designed especially for the Alaska herring fishery but also for salmon gillnetting, has been manufactured in the USA. The machine is designed to provide smooth, continuous hauling and simultaneous shaking of the net. These machines could improve working conditions on board drifters. The problem with the shakers is to keep the quantity of fish damaged by this operation as low as possible.

Finally, another problem in gillnetting has to be mentioned. This is the loading of large quantities of gillnets on board a vessel. Gillnets can be set and hauled over the stern but, in general, they are set from the stern of a vessel and are hauled over the side of the forepart of the vessel. That means that the hauled nets, before being re-set, have to be transported from the forepart of the vessel to the stern. This has to be done by hand, which involves a great amount of manpower. The simplest way to mechanize this work is to use a plastic tube and to tow the nets through it smoothly from one place to another. The tube has a funnel on the side from which the nets are hauled. A rope with a stone on its end is thrown through the tube, and the end of the first net is fixed on this line before one net after

Fig 691 Chinese gillnetter of the Pescadores Islands, Taiwan, with transport tube for gillnets. (1978).

the other is towed through the tube from the hauling place to the setting place. This simple method is practised by the Chinese fishermen of the Pescadores Islands (Penghu) in the Formosa Strait (*Fig 691*) as well as by the Danish fishermen in Hvide Sande (*Fig 692*). Also, the Japanese have a system of transferring the nets with an open channel (*Fig 693*), sometimes combined with a moving belt, as used for hauling tuna longlines onboard a vessel.

Fig 692 Danish gillnetter in Hvide Sande with movable tube for the transportation of gillnets for cod. (*Photo: H Mohr, 1979.*)

Fig 693 Japanese gillnetter for salmon fishing with open channel for the transfer of the gear. (*Photo: Hayashi Kamakura.*)

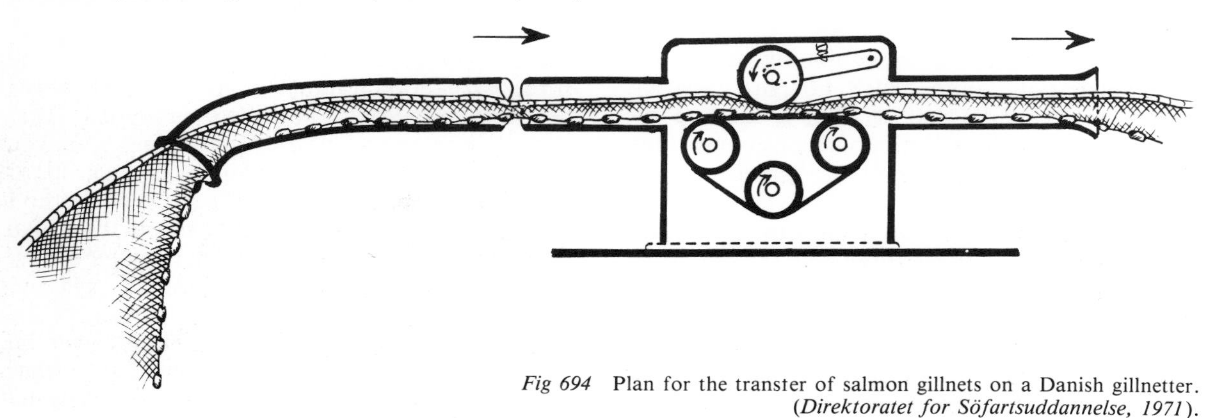

Fig 694 Plan for the transter of salmon gillnets on a Danish gillnetter. (*Direktoratet for Söfartsuddannelse, 1971*).

Chapter thirty

Entangling nets

Around the middle of the last century a weed (*Elodea canadensis*) became so abundant in European waters that it was called 'the water plague'. All of these plants were said to have originated from a single specimen brought from America to Ireland in 1836. Soon, however, that mass development and spread declined for reasons that were never quite clear. Some talked of 'water fatigue' as being responsible in a way similar to the phenomenon of soil fatigue that is known to occur in fields that have been subject to continuous monoculture. Although the mass spread of that weed hampered fishing and shipping, it was welcomed by some people harvesting the rich quantities of submerged plants for feeding animals or fertilizing their gardens and fields. Moreover, the dense areas of this plant did create hiding places for young fish of all varieties and some clever people had the idea of catching fish fry by twisting the plants together. So there is found this account: 'Not far from the beach, where the weed is growing exuberantly, in winter time a hole is made in the ice, two stakes or a fork-shaped branch are put into the thick weed and carefully turned round, so that the weed is towed from afar and turned into a thick cylindrical rope, which is gradually dragged from below the ice, including rather considerable amounts of fish, naturally consisting mainly of great masses of young fish.[30] For that reason, protests were made against such a method of catching young fish indiscriminately by entangling them in plants. The decline of the 'water plague', however, automatically finished that strange fishing method. Nevertheless, at the beginning of this century one of the first German fishery biologists, Paulus Schiemenz, lamented the loss of small water animals important for growing fish by the harvesting of submerged water plants for feeding pigs.[550]

In stormy seas, masses of floating weed drift around and can make even sport fishing with pole and line impossible. In such a case some people recommend abandoning fishing and going home, but it has been said that it can be pleasant to clear the trace and to find an entangled fish underneath the rubbish.[249] The idea of catching small fish by entangling them in water plants is not known only in Europe. It is related, for example, that in the flood fisheries of former Rhodesia, women cut the grass in the water with a hoe and then, turning the grass over, they remove the entangled fish.[234] Pond fishermen know that fish fry can be lost by entangling themselves in bushes of algae. This incident comes as a reminder of a joke a professor of the former German University in Königsberg had with some young fishery students during some excursions in the cutter fishery. He presented them with a brush-like mop and said it was a kind of fishing gear. The idea was laughed at by the older students. In the fringes of that mop, he said, fish would entangle themselves! But note this: a writer in Viet Nam, when reporting on a curious fishery of Madagascar, declared that the tassel-like end of a cow's tail was useful for catching the tiniest fish 'not larger than a clove'.[422] As can be seen in the next section the professor of Königsberg was not quite so wrong after all with his humorous reference to 'mop' fishery!

30.1 'Mopping'

In the last section a doubtful fishing method was mentioned which can be called 'mopping' – that means, catching something by entangling, maybe by towing a mop-like instrument over the ground. Indeed, 'mopping' is known as a catching method for starfish. For cleaning mussel cultures, mop-like gears made of cotton are dragged over oyster banks. Starfish will be entangled by the small rays and pincer-like structures that cover their bodies.[355] The method of dragging twines or net webbing over the bottom and catching animals entangled in that material is successfully employed by fishermen gathering precious corals. The Italian 'ingegno per la pesca del corallo' (*Fig 695*) is a weighted wooden cross from the arms of which bundles of net webbing are suspended.[38] If these are dragged slowly through colonies of corals, the fine branches of corals become entangled in the netting, break off,

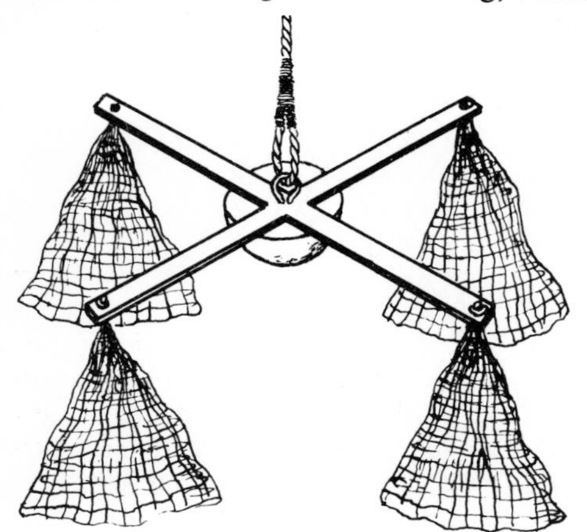

Fig 695 Italian coral net. (*Bertuccioli, 1955*).

and are hauled to the surface. Similar 'coral nets' are known in the fisheries of the Far East for the same purpose – to gather white and red corals. The Pescadores Islands (Penghu) in the Formosa Strait are considered one of the world centres for coral fishing. For 'fishing' the corals, according to an originally Japanese method, bunches of netting are towed over the ground in up to 200 metres of water where corals are expected to be. To do this, about four bunches of netting are tied on a line with a heavy egg-shaped stone (about 30kg) at the end (*Fig 696*). For entangling the corals in the netting, the local water currents are utilized. By towing the stone with the current, the netting floats before the stone, entangling the corals before they are broken from their base by the following stone (*Fig 697*). But also other tactics are known like towing the stone against the current. In this case the stone breaks the corals first which then become entangled by the following netting. Each vessel tows six, twelve or even more lines. Larger vessels are not only fishing near Taiwan but also in deeper waters up to 600 metres around Hawaii. The same principle of fishing is used by Mediterranean fishermen who catch sea urchins by using small pieces of netting tied onto the end of a stick. With the help of this implement the urchins hidden in holes are entangled and can be taken out.

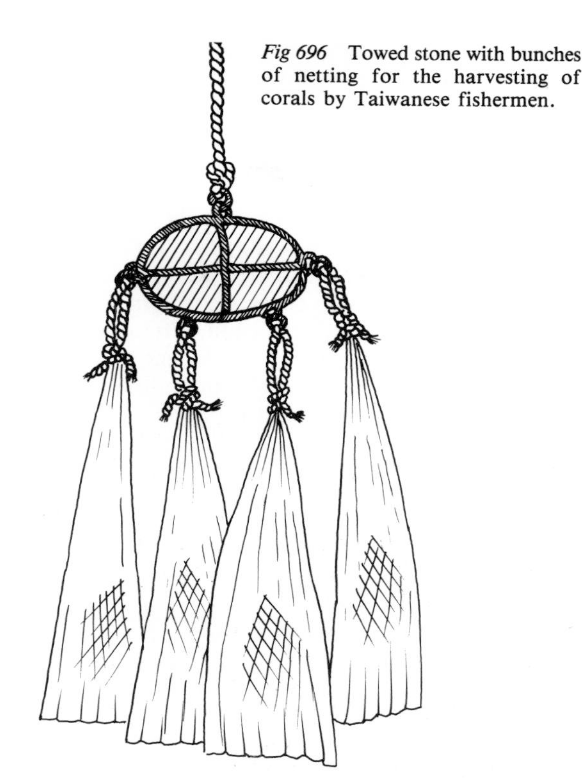

Fig 696 Towed stone with bunches of netting for the harvesting of corals by Taiwanese fishermen.

Fig 697 Method of breaking and collecting coral stocks: first entangling the netting with the corals by towing the stone with the current, then breaking the coral from the ground by towing the following stone down-current. (1978).

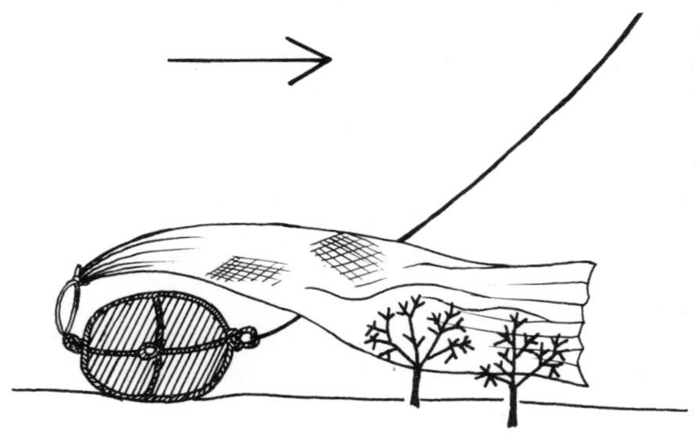

30.2 Single-walled tangle nets

In connection with gillnets, we have already seen that fish with a circumference smaller than the meshes can swim through the nets. But fish whose greatest circumference slightly exceeds the mesh size can become meshed and entangled in the neighbouring netting by their violent struggling. This can even occur with rather large fish, which may have just pushed the tip of their nose into a mesh and yet become entangled in the netting by violently trying to escape. The same is also true for fish which have hard fins and many spines, like perches. They are mostly caught not by gilling but by becoming entangled, even in typical gillnets. Many fish may be caught with single-walled tangle nets but this gear is most important for use in catching crustaceans. Lobsters, spiny lobsters, king crabs, and various other species of crabs are caught in them. These bulky animals, which are frequently equipped with spines and long legs, become more entangled in the nets the more they struggle to get free. Such nets, however, are very soon worn out, and the fishery is only worthwhile if large quantities of valuable crustaceans can be caught, as in the king crab fishery in the North Pacific. Lobsters were formerly caught by the fishermen of Heligoland with netting which was spread horizontally on the bottom of the sea and ballasted. These nets were also worn out very soon. Nevertheless, the catch is highly priced and therefore this method is also used in other parts of the world. Spiny lobsters are caught on the southwest coast of Sri Lanka by using old gillnets of suitable mesh size also exposed horizontally over the bottom. In this case the nets are also baited to attract spiny lobsters which then are lifted, with the netting, by means of ropes attached to surface floats. By this method the crustaceans which are not already entangled on the bottom, are entangled during hauling.[548]

Better known are single-walled tangle nets which are operated in a vertical position like gillnets, either as bottom nets, or anchored and floating, or free drifting. Their efficiency can be increased by the type of mounting, especially when hung very slack. This can be achieved by having floatlines longer than the ground-lines (*Fig 698*). This can also be achieved by making the side lines of the net much shorter. Moreover, especially with driftnets, the leadline is omitted to give the netting better flexibility for entangling *eg* to catch Spanish mackerel and salmon (*Fig 699 E*). This is also achieved to some extent by fixing a small amount of weight only to the ground-rope.

For the reasons mentioned, it is scarcely correct (as is often done) to describe these single-walled nets as gillnets. That certainly cannot be correct of nets for sturgeons (*Figs 700* and *701*). The nets used for them are simple wide-meshed net walls into which the usually pointed fish push and get stuck because of their barbed spines being directed backwards from the mouth opening. The fish is then caught in the net by its own struggles. Also many large fish like tuna, salmon, ray and shark are caught in the sea by single-walled entangling nets. The nets used in South Africa and Australia to protect the beaches against shark attacks are also single-walled entangling nets.[126] In freshwater fishing, too, some of the larger predatory species of fish are caught by being entangled in finer nets set for gilling smaller fish.

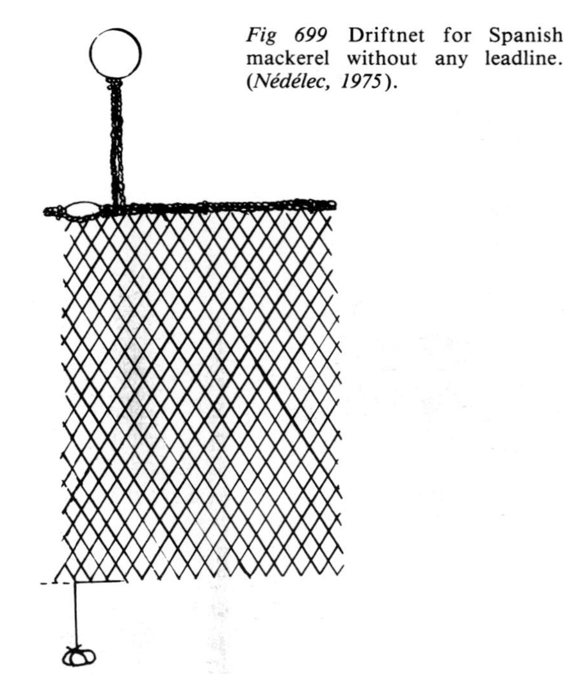

Fig 699 Driftnet for Spanish mackerel without any leadline. (*Nédélec, 1975*).

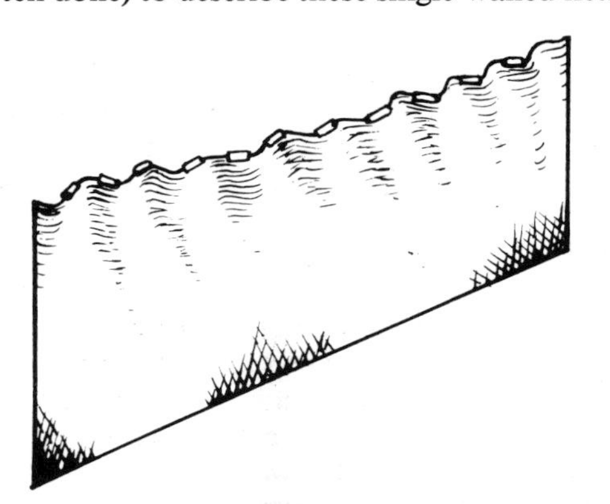

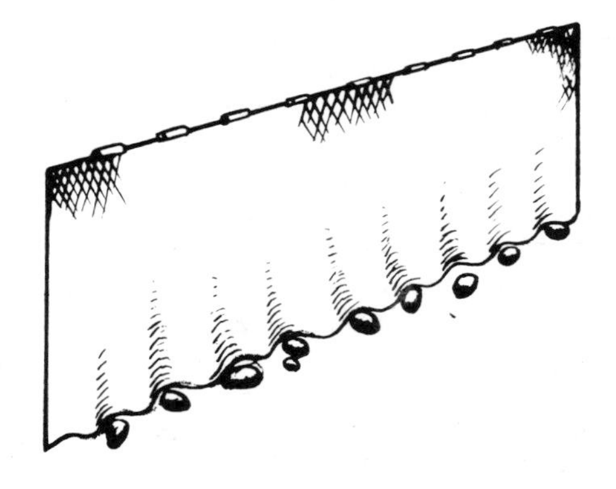

Fig 698 Net construction and entangling: longer floatline increases the possibility of entangling; longer leadline gives a better connection of the gear with the bottom on rough ground.

Fig 700 Iranian fishermen hauling sturgeon nets off the southern coast of the Caspian Sea. (1970).

Fig 701 Fisherman hauling a sturgeon entangled in a one-walled net off the Turkish Black Sea coast. (1971).

What has been said of single-walled netting for fish applies even more so for catching crustaceans. The nets are again set vertically, like normal gillnets, but often, as the French do when fishing for 'langouste verde' off the Mauritanian coast, they are set in such a manner that they stay more sloping than vertical to assist entangling. This can be said also for the Japanese nets set to catch king crab in the northern Pacific (*Fig 702*).[537] Catching king crab with entangling nets is not only done by the Japanese but also by the Russians and Koreans in a large-scale fishery. The nets must be set quite soft and slack, but on the other hand the current must not press them on to the bottom. Because entangling nets have no selectivity they have been forbidden in the USA since 1955.

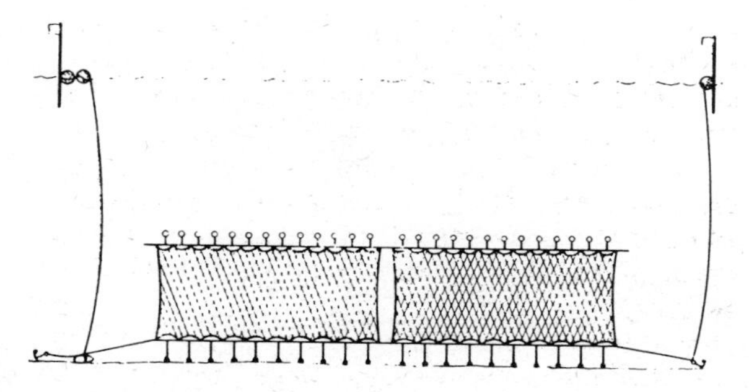

Fig 702 Japanese entangling net for king crab.

The Japanese king crab fishery with single-walled tangle nets is a good example of a large-scale industrial fishery with a fleet of different vessels. A large factory vessel for the processing of the crabs, and the maintenance of the fleet, is accompanied by two or three middle-sized vessels used for searching for the fishing places and for setting the nets. These boats usually stay at sea for five or six days. Moreover, eight to ten catcher boats accompany the fleet to haul the nets, maybe 2,500 to 3,000 a day. On these vessels the crabs caught are taken out of the netting and transported to the factory ship. Here the entangled nets will be freed, cleaned and mended wherever necessary. The crabs are processed and tinned ready for the market. Some hundreds of people are needed for catching, processing and navigation. Such a fleet can have 15,000 to 30,000 nets in operation.

One-walled tangle nets are not only used in large-scale fisheries but also in small-scale fisheries, even in the subsistance fisheries. The Japanese use very small types of gear for catching crustaceans by entangling. *Figure 703* shows such a mini gear, set in a shape of a tube and held by floats around a bait. The gear looks like a fishing pot, but the principle of catching is entangling. A special type of entangling net is the Japanese bottom driftnet, which is used in coastal bays to catch shrimp (*Penaeus japonicus*) and also other crustaceans and cephalopods. These are nets with the lower edge turned up to form a pocket into which the shrimp fall when jumping up and are entangled. The nets, maybe eight or more, drift in the current, held by a boat on the one end and a float on the other, gliding with their lower rim with the pockets over the ground. The fishing ground must be smooth and not rocky. Also the driftnet has more of a lying position than a vertical one.[474] Recently a new type of bottom driftnet with entangling pockets was demonstrated by the Japanese. This net has pockets with arch-shaped openings at the bottom, allowing the shrimps to enter the pocket of the netting as it

Fig 703 Japanese entangling net for crab. (1960).

sweeps along the bottom (*Fig 704*).

Not only fish and crustaceans are caught in single-walled tangle nets. Turtles can be caught with this gear, and since recently also squids in drifting 'gillnets'. Even sea mammals like seals, porpoises and whales can be caught with single-walled entangling nets. Nets in whaling are used particularly for catching small mammals like porpoises. Formerly, however, the catching of even large whales with nets was practised in north and east Asia and in the Arctic. To manufacture these necessarily strong nets, strips of skin cut from walrus hide, baleen from whales, and other stout materials were used. The people of Kamchatka stretched such nets in river estuaries. Once the whales got into the nets they became entangled and drowned.[35] Even today newspapers sometimes report that a whale has been found somewhere entangled in a fishing net and drowned.

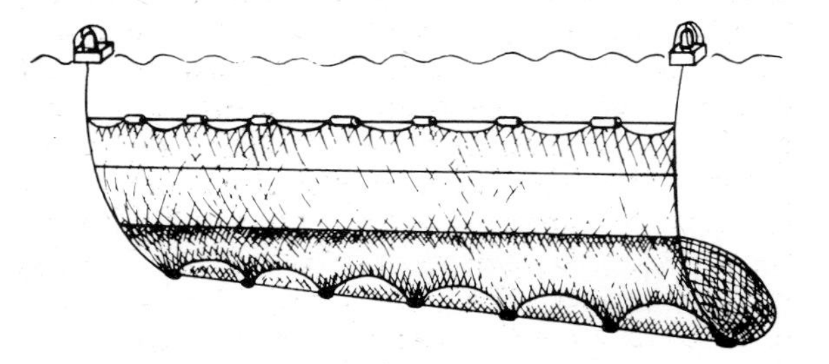

Fig 704 Japanese bottom driftnet with open pockets. (*Yamaha Fishery Journal 2, 1978).*

30.3 Tangle nets with snoods or frames

It has been mentioned already that entangling in a net is more likely to occur with a slack net, and that this can be caused by using side lines which are shorter than the depth of the netting. There are other means of increasing the slack of a net. One of them is to connect the floatline and leadline with connecting lines (snoods) rather shorter than the depth of the net (*Fig 705*). These are usually placed in pairs at either side of the net wall but sometimes connecting lines are used at one side only. Nets of this type are set in rivers with the snoods facing the current, so that the gear forms a series of semi-circles like a netbag.[7] Single connecting lines can be also strung through each mesh. The distance of the lines may be half a metre and their length can be 50% of that of the netting. This results in the netting having a high degree of slackness and will help much in entangling fish trying to swim through it. Gillnets with vertical snoods can have the disadvantage that the loose netting tends to accumulate at the leadline and to wind around it.

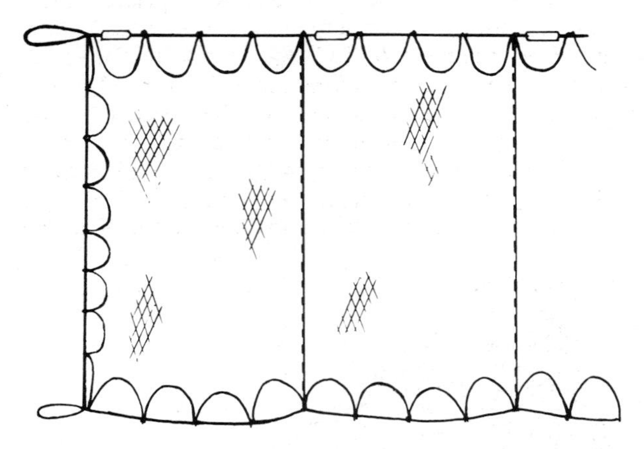

Fig 705 Entangling net with vertical connection lines.

This is why, in spite of better catches, these nets have not become very popular.[7] To overcome the gathering of loose netting at the leadline, the Finns fix to the vertical snoods two additional horizontal lines, one in the middle of the gear, the other near the ground line (*Fig 706*).[219] The loose netting is tied on the horizontal lines and the massing together of the netting at the ground line is prevented. Moreover, the netting is held some distance from the leadline that it cannot touch the bottom where it may be damaged.

The idea of fixing the loose netting by vertical

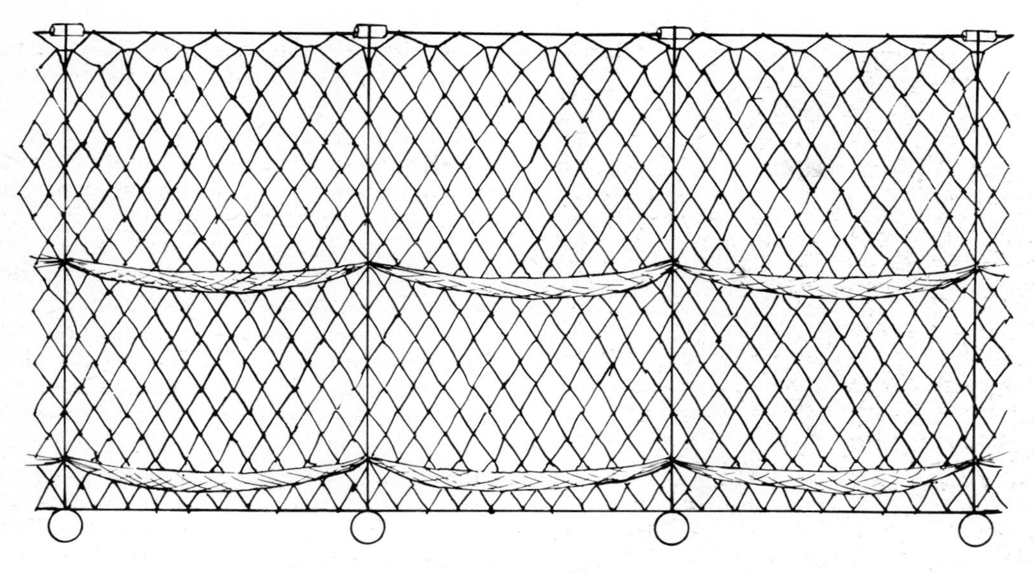

Fig 706 Slack in a Finnish entangling net. (*Halme and Aalberg, 1959*).

and horizontal lines is known from the so-called 'framed' nets, in some countries better known than the entangle nets with vertical snoods. As can be seen in *Figure 707*, these nets are divided into many small catching sections. The shorter vertical lines and the longer horizontal lines cross each other, building 'frames' or 'windows' one metre or so square. The lines are strung through the meshes and fixed only to each other and the netting at the crossing points. With this arrangement the loose netting cannot slide down and accumulate in a heap at the leadline as with the nets with vertical lines only. To show how much slack of netting can be

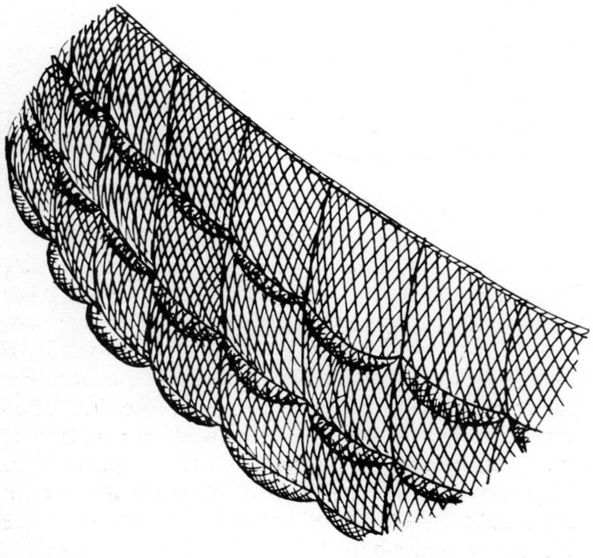

Fig 707 Chinese framed netting. (*Kasuga, 1975*).

in a frame of one metre square, it may be said that in an example of 14 × 14 meshes it has been found that each stretched mesh had a length of 150mm; that means that the length of the frame line is 50 per cent of the netting ($14 \times 0{\cdot}15 = 2{\cdot}1$m), or, in other words, the hanging is 50 per cent[417]. Framed nets are operated in fresh waters of India, China and the USSR. In India they are used to catch carp and catfish. It may be that these nets originated in China where they are still used today in the mainland fishery[289]. In the USSR they are especially known in Siberian rivers. There they are considered more effective than simple single-walled entangling nets[7].

30.4 Trammelnets

The entangling nets described so far have been in the form of single-walled nets similar to gillnets. But there is still another type of net that is more distinctly used to catch fish by entangling them and that is the trammelnet, which differs in its construction very much from the one-walled gillnets. It is supposed that the name 'trammelnet' is of French origin – derived from 'trois mailles', which means 'three meshes' – according to the construction of this gear. Trammelnets are not single-walled but are triple-walled (*Fig 708*). Between the two wide-mesh stretched outer walls, a rather loose interior netting with smaller meshes is inserted. This small-meshed inner sheet of netting (named the lint or linnet) has plenty of slack because it is two to three times as deep as the rigged gear. When a fish swims through the large outer meshes it encounters and pushes against the loose interior

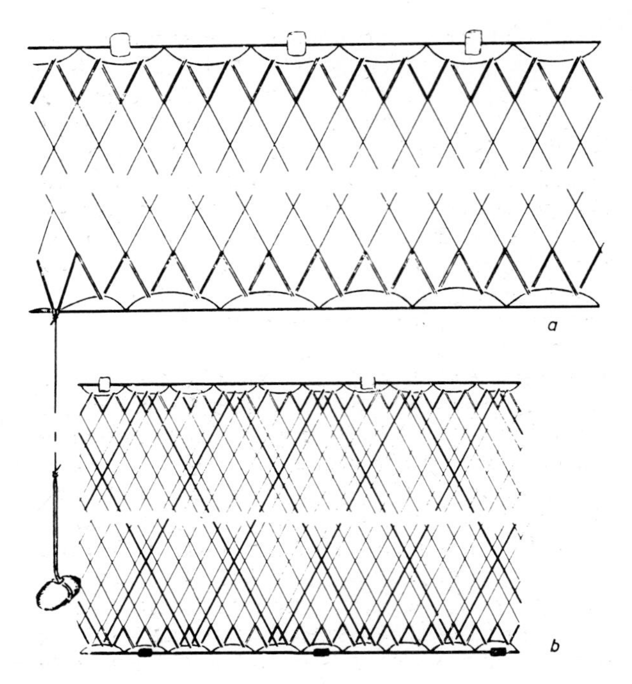

Fig 708 Turkish sturgeon nets: (*a*) single walled; (*b*) trammelnet.

net so that a pocket is formed around the fish in which it becomes entrapped (*Fig 709*). To be successful, the large meshes of the two outer walls must be exactly opposite each other so that the pocket will not be prevented from developing. In German speaking countries the trammelnets are therefore also called 'Spiegelnetz', which means 'mirror net'. The outer meshes are of rhombic shape as in other net walls. There are, however, trammelnets, the outer walls of which have meshes in a square shape (*Fig 710*). This type was considered more effective in trout fisheries. Mostly this net had no floats but was fixed on rings drawn on a stick held over fishing waters, especially streams in the mountains. Trammel nets are operated in the freshwater and inshore fishery mostly as stationary gear. These can be used also in wintertime for fishing under ice. In sea fisheries trammelnets are used for catching bottom fish like flatfish (*Fig 711*), in some cases also for cod. Even cuttlefish can be caught in trammelnets as the Italian fishermen do in the Adriatic Sea.

It is understandable that because of the great visibility presented by triple net walls, even when made of monofilaments, often fish do not actively swim into the net, but instead are frightened into it. That implies the use of noise and such fishing methods as already described in the drive-in fishery (Chapter 26), where certain areas of *eg* reed are

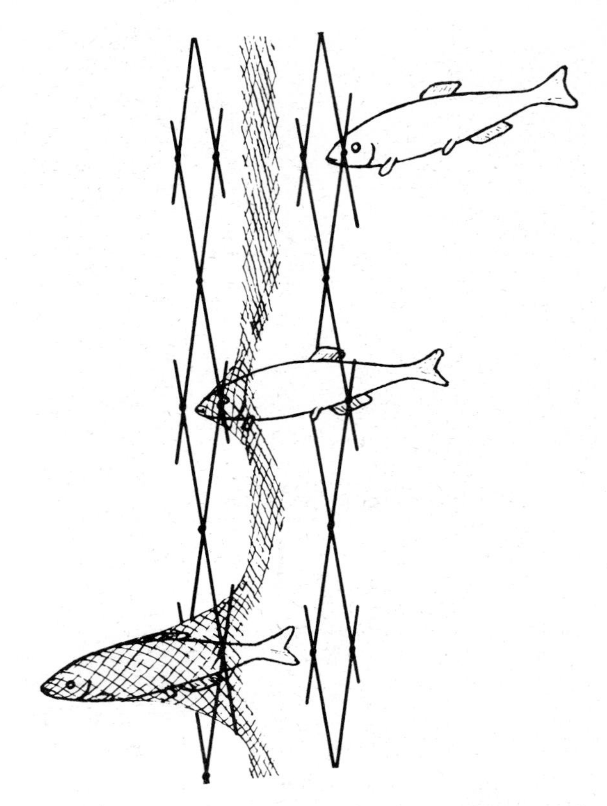

Fig 709 How a trammelnet operates: the fish entangle themselves by forming a pocket of the small-meshed webbing between the two big-meshed walls.

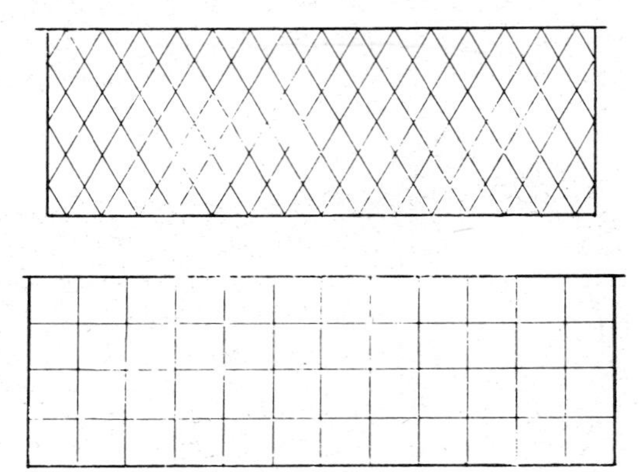

Fig 710 Different forms of hanging the outer walls of a trammel net: (*a*) rhombic (*b*) quadrangular.

surrounded by trammelnets (*Fig 597*). Nowadays this catching method of drive-in fishery is also used to catch eels with trammelnets.[181] Trammelnets are more familiar as stationary gear, but they can also be used as driftnets and can even be towed. The so-called 'Kurrennet' of the fishermen of the Curishes Haff were trammelnets several hundred metres in length and were towed by two sailing boats.[30] It

Fig 711 Fishermen preparing trammelnets in the fishing port of Istanbul for catching flatfish off the west coast of the Black Sea.

seems that formerly trammelnets were more often used like seine nets (*Fig 712*). A German fishery dictionary of 1936[420] mentioned that seine nets without a bag (Chapter 24) could be made of single or triple sheets of netting. In this manner three-walled seine nets are operated in southern Germany and in Switzerland.[265] Here must be added the so-called 'sweeping' trammelnets of the Japanese fishery. This is a real trammelnet operated in a special manner. One end of the net is fixed by an anchor and the other end is pulled by a boat in a circle around this fixed point.[475]

In a few cases trammelnets are also operated as driftnets. These are used in Great Britain in the River Dee[98, 279] and also for catching salmon in northwest Europe. Moreover, drifting trammelnets are also known in Rumania.[147] Trammelnets are also sometimes used as a part of another gear *eg* within liftnets (Chapter 27), to entangle the fish and to prevent them jumping from the lifted gear or for entangling fish caught in lantern nets (Chapter 28). A very specialized gear made with trammel netting is the so-called 'trandadaia' (*Figs 713* and *714*) operated in Rumania. This gear is made of a wooden triangle, looking like a skimming net, with a base of about two metres. The two ends are connected with an iron chain four metres in length. Between the two legs of the gear a net bag made of trammel netting is mounted (*Fig 714*). This gear

Fig 712 Fishing with a towed trammelnet for 'Huchen' in the Bavarian Forest in southern Germany. (*Photo: Graf v. Mandelsloh.*)

Fig 713 Dragged 'trandadaia' in the lower River Danube, Rumania. (1976).

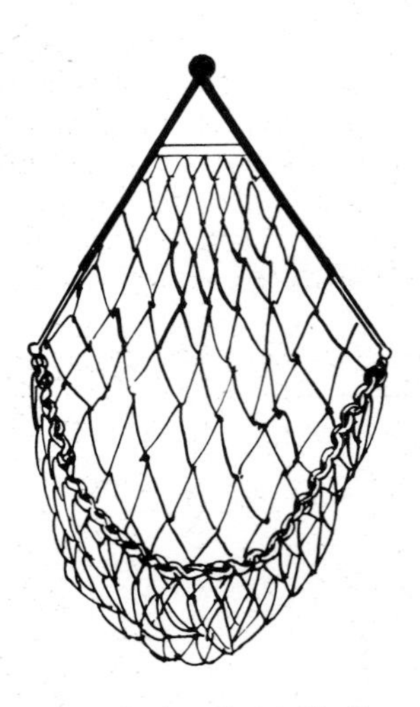

Fig 714 Construction of a 'trandadaia' in Rumania. The bagnet is made of trammel netting.

is towed in the River Danube, from a rowing boat, with the current, especially for catching large fish hidden in pits on the bottom.[19] The towing line between fisherman and gear is also used as a feeler line to know when a carp, perch or pike is entangled in the netting. It seems that the fisheries in the inundation area of the river Danube are well experienced with trammelnets: it has been reported that the Rumanians operate trammelnets horizontally under ice by lowering them over a school of fish which will be entangled when trying to escape.

30.5 Double-walled entangling nets

Trammelnets are made of two large-meshed outside sheets of netting and one small-meshed inside netting. When a fish tries to swim through this three-walled gear, no matter from which side, the inside netting, with plenty of slack, forms a bag through one of the outside large meshes in which the fish will entangle itself (*Fig 709*). Where the fish always come from the same side of the gear, as in the drive-in fishery, or wherever fish swim against the current, a two-walled gear with the small meshed netting at the side from which the fish is expected to come, would have the same effect as the three-walled one. Indeed, it is mentioned in an older Russian publication, that two-walled netting was operated in such a manner that the bags for entangling the fish were not made by the fish swimming through the netting but were made in advance by the fisherman.[333]

Two-walled driftnets have been known since olden times in Russia.[333, 343] The catching method has been described as being like that given for trammelnets, but there may be some doubt if this is right. When there are two walls only, the fish must come from the small meshed side, forming a pocket through one of the large meshes. But this is not always so. Two-walled nets can be used in another way. A traveller visiting Russia at the end of the eighteenth century[484] explained that this double-walled gear was operated by the Cossacks as a driftnet floating with the current, in quite another manner for catching sturgeon. A shorter large-meshed netting drifts before the bag made of a deeper small-meshed netting. The sturgeon, swimming against the current, comes from the large-meshed side and has no difficulty in passing through the very large meshes but will be entangled in the following bag of small-meshed netting. This description is in agreement with a later observation made of the Turkish double-walled tangle nets known in the Black Sea fishery.[384] In this case the two-walled nets are used for encircling fish shoals, always in such a manner that the netting with the large mesh is inside the circle. The frightened fish, trying to escape, swim through a large mesh, push against the small meshed netting and in attempting to escape into the depth the fish become entangled, (*Fig 715*). Two-walled nets are always set in such a manner that the large meshed netting is on the side from which the fish is expected, therefore the oncoming direction of the fish must be known. Double-walled nets are operated today in Russia in Siberian rivers,[7] as well as in southeastern Europe. It seems that formerly two-walled nets were also operated in the Baltic.[237] They are also known in Japan, to a small extent only.

Fig 715 Principle of catching in two-walled netting. (*T Mengi, 1977*).

30.6 Combined entangling and gilling nets

Trammelnets and gillnets can also be combined and used together. In this case, the upper part of the net consists of one wall and the lower part of three walls of netting (*Fig 716*). The lower trammel section of the nets acts by entangling the larger fish near the bottom. The upper gillnet is designed to catch smaller pelagic fish.[63] Nets combined in this way are used in the Mediterranean (Spain, Morocco, France,[417] Malta, and Greece) and it is somewhat remarkable that the Japanese have also developed and employed such combined nets (*Fig 717*). It is scarcely to be supposed that the knowledge has been communicated directly but, as in other cases, the same solution would seem to have

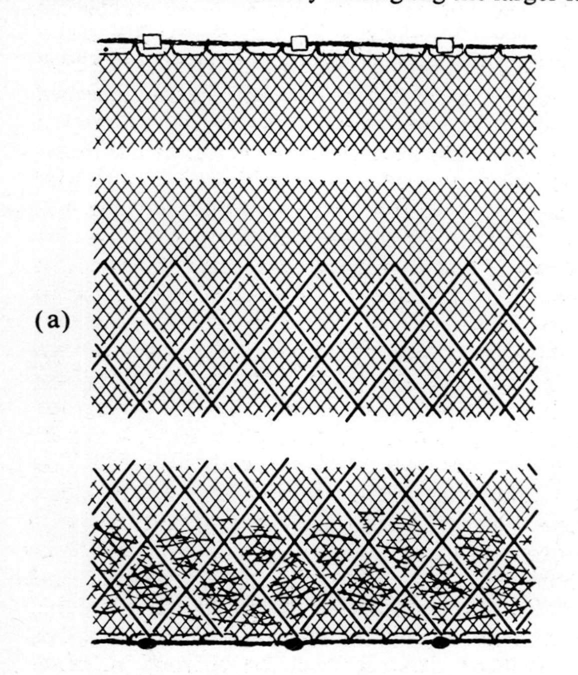

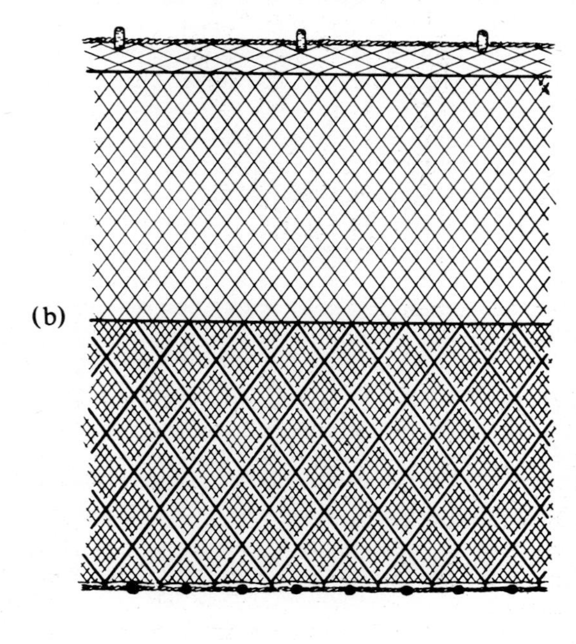

Fig 716 Some combined nets: (*a*) from Molivos, Lesbos (Greece): (*b*) from southern France (*Gourret, 1934*).

Fig 717 A gillnet combined with a trammelnet as used in Japan.

been found to the same problem, although the areas concerned are so far apart. In both cases bottom fish as well as pelagic fish are caught. According to a Japanese explanation (Dr Nomura; by letter), when fishing in some strong currents a gear made completely of trammel netting has a high resistance in the water. This causes it to stay more or less diagonally – maybe nearly horizontally. To prevent this, half of the gear is made of one-walled netting which stays vertical due to its lower resistance, and guides the fish into the trammelnet below the gillnet. This means the upper single-walled part is more a guiding section than a catching one.

Turkish fishermen in the Black Sea also combine trammelnets with double-walled nets. In this case two upper trammel nets are combined with two double-walled nets below. The lower part of the double-walled nets is provided with a broad strip of rough netting as a selvage. This strip is not, as a rule, combined with the netting mesh by mesh, but both parts are mounted together on a common line. As can be seen in *Figure 715*, with two-walled nets the small-meshed netting has to build a bag to entangle the fish. For this reason the small meshed netting has a high degree of slack. To prevent this bag gathering near the leadline and contacting the bottom, the aforementioned broad selvage is added under this netting. Of course, this strip of netting also helps in handling the gear. By such combinations, very deep gear can be constructed (up to 30 metres and more) suitable for catching bottom as well as pelagic fish.

30.7 Future trends

A disadvantage of entangling nets is that they have low selectivity, and this greatly hinders the management of fish populations. There are a few cases only where entangling nets are operated in large quantities. This can happen in sea fisheries, such as when single-walled nets are used for salmon, Spanish mackerel *etc*, or when trammelnets are used for flatfish such as sole and halibut. Entangling nets are also successful in tropical waters where different species of fish of different sizes are caught. In fresh-waters and coastal waters trammelnets can be helpful for drive-in fisheries as can be double-walled nets. On the other hand, trammelnets as well as double walled nets, are sometimes considered too complicated in their construction, too difficult to repair, and also more labour-intensive.

Mechanization of the operation of entangling nets (*Fig 718*) can be similar to that of gillnets (last section of Chapter 30). In some cases entangling nets have participated in the progress made for gillnets. Monofilament fibres are now used for the netting of both types of fishing gear with great success. The same can be said for the mechanization of the operation of entangling nets, especially for hauling mechanisms. Entangling nets, especially one-walled ones, are, like gillnets, cheap fishing gear with low costs of maintenance and handling but, like gillnets, they will become labour-intensive and may be uneconomic when operated in large numbers in industrial bulk fishing, especially when high priced products like salmon, sturgeon, tuna do not form a high proportion of the catch. Nevertheless, in view of an extended artisanal fishery under the new national economic zones, entangling nets, like gillnets, may have an increasing importance in fishery development, not least because both types of fishing gear belong to those methods of catching having a low consumption of energy.

Fig 718 Simple hand-driven hauling device for trammelnets on a Greek vessel of Crete, fishing off Denia, Cyrenaica. (*Photo: J Schärfe, 1961.*)

Chapter thirty-one

Fishing systems and harvesting machines

In the first chapter some of the impulses which may have led to the development of fishing gear and fishing methods for subsistence fishing, small-scale artisanal fisheries and nowadays to large-scale commercial fisheries were mentioned. This development began in prehistoric times and will continue in the future. The universal gear for hunting in general was replaced by specialized gear for catching fish and other water prey. Wooden gear was replaced by gear partly or entirely made of netting; fisheries in shallow waters were extended to deeper waters; smaller gear was replaced by larger; the manpower needed for the operation of the larger gears was reduced by mechanization; fishing spread from the coast to more distant areas, combining catching with fish searching; electronic gear for fish finding brought with it the ability to control the catch and the gear more effectively during fishing. Most important of all, increasing observation of fishing methods and the need to combine these observations and handling methods before, during and after the catch (this includes the bringing of the catch aboard), are leading to the development of an integrated fishing system. This system will be steered by computers being used to collect and to evaluate data, and to apply fully automatic fishing methods combining searching, catching and processing, so bringing the optimum of success. All this can be realized only on the assumption that the new Exclusive Economic Zones (EEZs), and new ideas about the protection of nature, or the increasing price of energy, does not stop or change the direction of fisheries development.

Concerning the combination of searching, catching and processing, there have been proposals for such a system, especially in trawling (Chapters 21 and 22). However, limited large-scale trawling opportunities and the need to conserve fuel due to the increasing price of oil, may complicate the development of fishing systems in the future. Nevertheless, there are some beginnings of further developments in fishing systems, not only in trawling but also in purse seining and longlining. These new ideas range from hunting a single fish to the management of large fish populations and their harvesting in an economic manner. To some extent the well known fishing methods have to be varied or even replaced by newer harvesting methods. Originally electrical fishing was considered to be the beginning of a new way of netless fishing, but it was discovered that this method could not meet the needs of the large-scale sea fisheries for reasons mentioned earlier (Chapter 5). Nevertheless, electrical fishing is repeatedly recommended with new fishing systems. One such system proposed catching coastal pelagic fish from unused oil rig platforms[567] – the fish being concentrated first with floating or submerged stationary objects, sometimes with lights, electrical current, sound lures or even smells. The proposal envisages the catch being taken automatically onto the platform (or aboard the vessel) which may incorporate a fish processing system. There are some beginnings in this direction for catching fish and also for dredging mussels and harvesting the different types of seaweed. These completely new forms of fishing methods are comparable with the agricultural combine-harvesters which reap and thresh the grain and pack the corn into bags. Such machines are generally known as 'harvesting machines', a term which will be used also in this chapter. Fishing with harvesting machines, sometimes with pumps and conveyors, with or without filtration devices, can be considered as the final step in the development of fishing gear.

31.1 Pump fishing

Suction pumps are mostly known in fisheries for 'fish pumping', that means transferring a catch of fish or other prey from a gear into the hold of the vessel. The catch may also be pumped from the vessel in harbour directly to a fish processing factory. Fish pumping is done especially in purse seining instead of brailing with scoop nets (*Figs 577* and *585*). Some attempts have been made at continuous trawling by pumping the catch out of the gear during fishing. This chapter does not discuss this form of 'fish pumping' but looks instead at the use of suction pumps to catch fish, shrimp, squid, krill or plankton without the use of nets. This so-called 'pump fishing' is mostly done with light and electricity. There are two problems to face in pumping fish: first, the size of the fish in relation to the diameter of the hose, and secondly the rate of damage to the fish. The diameter of the hose used for pumping must be limited, therefore only small fish can be pumped. If the fish are to be used for the production of fish meal and not for human consumption, the rate of damage is not important. The difficulties of pumping fish diminish with the decreasing size of the fish. Up till now pumps have been used to catch small fish to be used for bait or other commercial use without nets or any other gear. It is predicted that there will be a trend towards the greater use of smaller, that means of lower trophic level, fish.[106] If this is right, pumps will have an increasing application as a form of fishing gear. To operate pumps economically in fishing, without any other gear, needs a high concentration of prey near the water surface. Moreover, the concentrated prey must not be frightened by the water current caused by the suction of the pump. This should be achieved by a widely published proposal demonstrated in *Figure 719*. The fish are attracted by light from the depths to the area of the pump, and are there concentrated and narcotized by electric currents. Thereafter the fish are taken on board the fishing vessel by means of a suction pump. According to some over-optimistic newspaper reports, pump fishing should become a permanent fishing method by vessels anchored in the midst of the oceans. The fact that the area of light attraction, and the stunning effect of an electric field, are both limited is overlooked. As correctly demonstrated in *Figure 719 (III)* the outer area of the electrical field has a frightening effect on the fish; only the fish inside a small area are attracted and stunned. Therefore this method cannot be used as simply as many people expected.

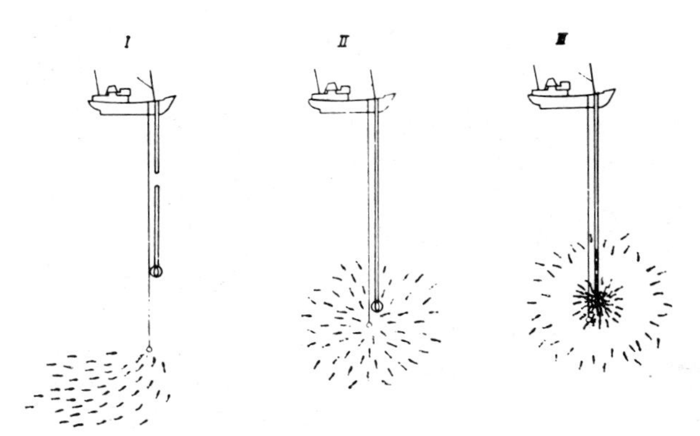

Fig 719 Diagram showing the principle of fishing for sardine with electric light, electricity and pump. The fishes are attracted by light, stupefied by electricity, and pumped out of the water.

Pump fishing without electricity became successful for small types of clupeid fishes. In the Soviet area of the Caspian Sea, fishery in this way has been developed on a commercial scale.[425] The fish, a sardine-like species found by echo-sounder, are attracted by light and pumped on board the vessel while the suction nozzle, with two lamps of 1,500 Watts, is moved up and down (*Fig 720*).

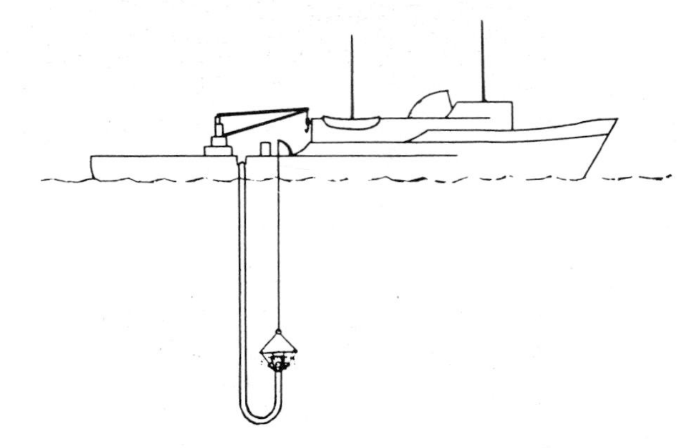

Fig 720 Pump fishing with light in the Caspian Sea.

Originally, rotary fish pumps were used and the suction hose was handled by a crane. Nowadays, instead of a pump system, an airlift principle has been adopted and the hoses, as well as the pipe for the compressed air and the cable for electrical current, are stored on reels.[449] The fish can be pumped from depths of up to 110 metres. The hose has an inside diameter of 20cm. On the vessel a separator (*Fig 721*) removes the water and most of the fish scales. There are other ideas for combining pump fishing with electricity,[426] and especially for overcoming the frightening effect of the suction intake. More may be known about this method of combining light attraction and electrolysis in the near future (*Fig 722*).[5, 31, 32, 364, 462]

Pump fishing became successful in the squid fishery. Off the Californian coast, squid were attracted by light from an anchored vessel. Originally, Chinese fishermen used torches hanging from the bow of their skiffs to light the water. At the beginning of this century squid were caught with lampara nets brought from Italy. This method has

Fig 721 Pump and separator for 'kilka' fishing on the Russian vessel *Lenkoram*, fishing in the Caspian Sea.

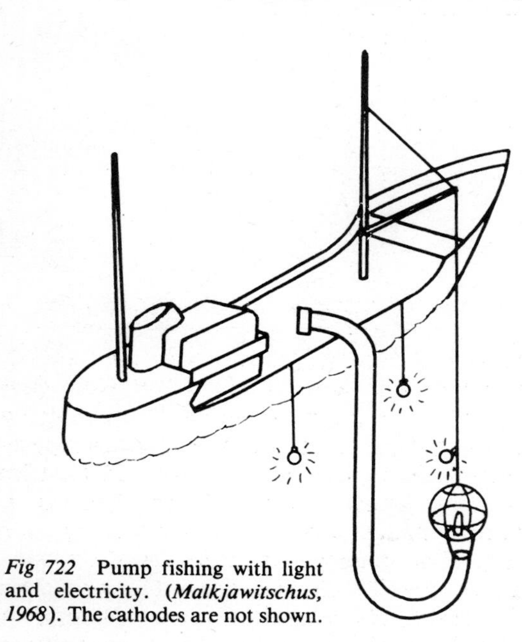

Fig 722 Pump fishing with light and electricity. (*Malkjawitschus, 1968*). The cathodes are not shown.

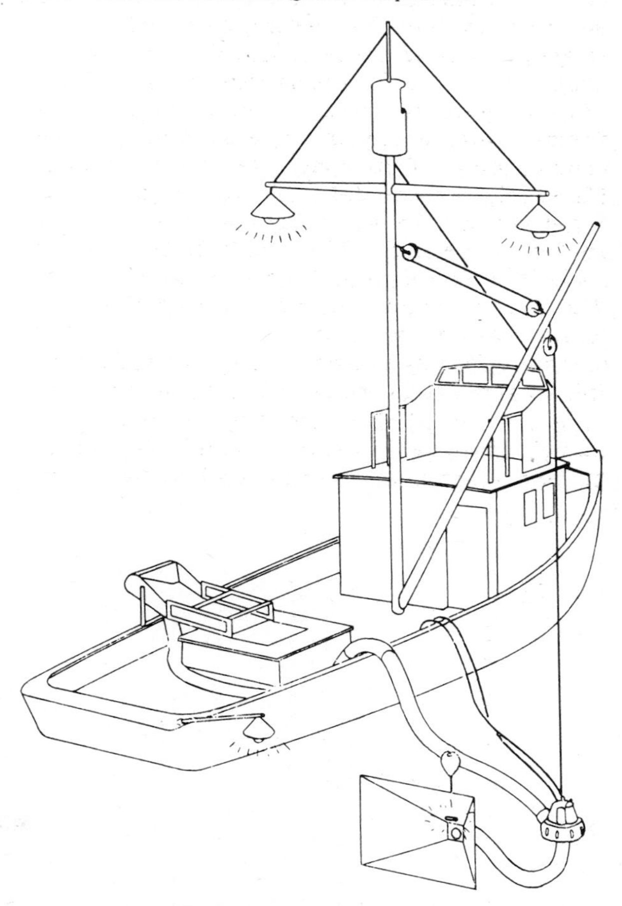

Fig 723 Pump fishing with light for squid off the Californian coast. (*By courtesy Susumu Kato, National Marine Fisheries Service, La Jolla, California.*)

now been improved by attracting the squid with strong artificial lights. Until now, when enough squid had gathered under the lights they were captured by powered or hand-operated brails. The attracting system remains unchanged but today the basic fishing unit is a pump with a large funnel with another light inside (*Fig 723*). The pump carries the squid to a separator on board which leads to a fish hold by means of an adjustable chute.[291, 450] There have been some ideas for using pumps for fishing krill, but up till now they have been used for 'fish pumping' only; that means they are used to transfer the caught krill from the trawl to the vessel.[255]

Pumps have been used very successfully for collecting mussel shells for lime burning, chicken food *etc.*[633] This form of exploitation of the sea is considered as a form of fishing; also this is true 'pump fishing'.

31.2 Hydraulic dredges with pumps and/or conveyors

As mentioned in Chapters 7 and 20, hand-operated and hydraulic jet dredges are used to dig and to wash out mussels that have buried themselves in the seabed. This system is also used to stir up shrimps grown in ponds, as is done in Japan with the so-called 'pump net'.[573] This is a type of dredge with a net bag towed by a motor boat equipped with a water pump. Similar to that shown in *Figure 92b,* the supply pipe receives compressed water through a hose from the pump on the boat. The water jet stirs up the bottom sand together with the shrimp, which are trapped in the bag of the dragged dredge. The shrimp are taken out of the gear by frequent haulings.

Some of the dredges are so improved that the prey is not only dug out, or stirred up and collected in a bag, but is also conveyed on board the vessel by the same gear. This was an important step forward. Therefore this gear, combining digging and hauling, can be considered a harvesting machine as explained in the first section of this chapter. This is especially true in cases where mechanical shellfish diggers are combined with suction pumps, escalators or conveyors. *Figure 724* shows a schematic drawing of a cockle suction dredge. In this case the dredge is combined with an air lift pump, lifting the mussels to the separator on board, from where the clean washed cockles are delivered by a chute to the hold.[451] Such shellfish harvesters are especially valuable when the mussel density is too thin to make hand-digging

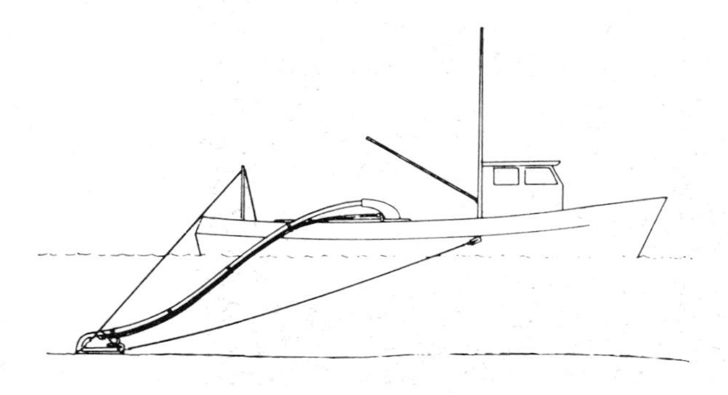

Fig 724 British cockle dredger with suction pump. (*NN, 1970*).

economical. The dredge is lowered from a small gallows and towed by a single warp. Two pipes run to the dredge as can be seen in *Figure 725.* The smaller one is a high pressure PVC hose directing the water, under pressure, into the large pipe by means of an internal jet. Suction is created in the larger pipe on the Venturi principle. It is this suction which picks up water and cockles and forces them into the boat.[447]

Fig 725 Dredge with high pressure hose and larger suction pipe of a British cockle dredger. (*Photo: Meixner.*)

Another way of bringing the washed-out shells on board the dredging vessel is to work with 'mechanical escalator harvesters'. In this case the shells are hauled with the help of a conveyor. A disadvantage of this system is that more sand is transported by the belt as compared with a suction pump. Hydraulic escalator dredges became of interest for harvesting soft shell clams (*Mya arenaria*). The basic design of such elevator dredges can be seen in two schematic drawings (*Figs 726* and *727*) showing the essential parts and the operation of the Maryland hydraulic escalator dredge which was invented and introduced about 1951 (*Fig 728*). The digging equipment is forced into the seabed by the boat. In front of the scoop is a manifold with water jets to loosen the sediment in its path. Behind is a conveyor with an endless belt which brings the shellfish up to the boat on the surface.[132, 451] The incidental mortality rate for this harvester (like that

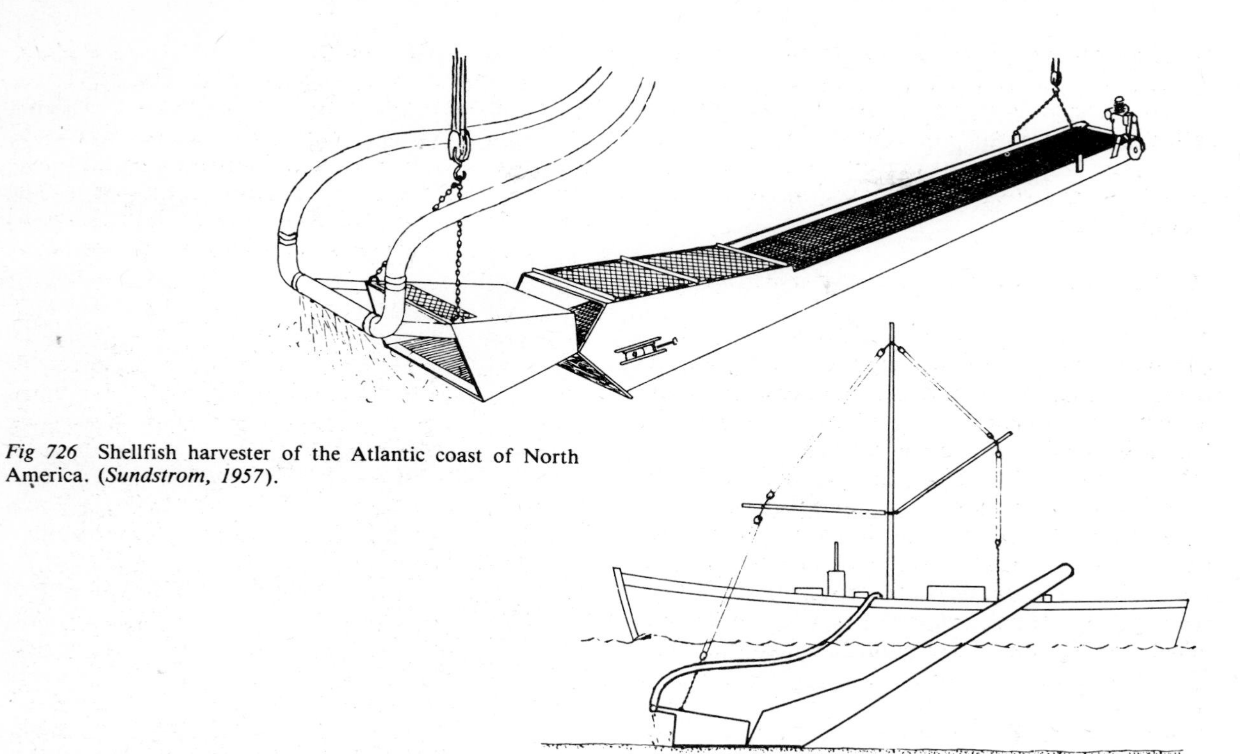

Fig 726 Shellfish harvester of the Atlantic coast of North America. (*Sundstrom, 1957*).

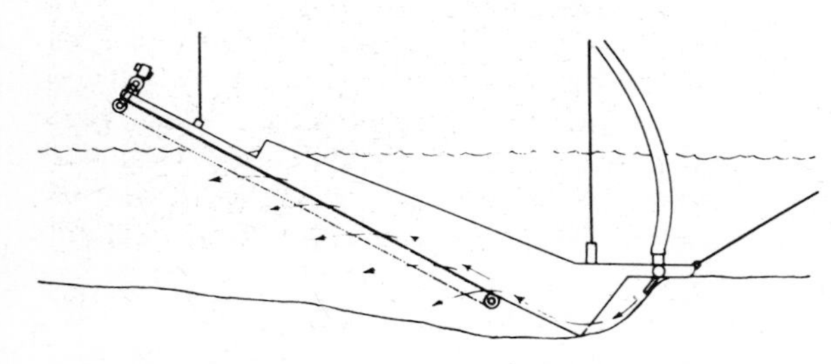

Left. Fig 727 Schematic drawing of a shellfish harvester for soft-shell clam (*Leaflet 3, 1965 of Atlantic States Marine Fisheries Commission, Florida*).

Fig 728 Mechanical clam digger at work. (*Dickie and MacPhail, 1957*).

for hydraulic rakes mentioned in Chapter 7) is less than 5 per cent.[378] This design was later improved and modified to harvest oysters and hard clams. Revolving spring-loaded teeth, attached to two drums, pull or rake oysters from the bottom. Horizontal water jets and the action of the revolving teeth lift the oysters onto a conveyor belt which carries them to the boat.

There are problems involved in shell dredging in tidal areas, such as in Brittany on the French Atlantic coast. There it was necessary for boats to go to the fishing places or mussel beds during high tide, work there during low water and then wait for high tide again in order to return. The problem was solved with an 'amphibious mussel harvester'. This vehicle can be operated like a boat to reach the fishing place, work there as a wheeled craft in the low water, and drive back into deep water to return to port as boat. Four and three-wheeled models are available.[470] Wheeled harvesting machines to replace boats are not new to fisheries. In British Columbia an eight-wheeled clam digging machine has been operated. This machine washes out razor clams with powerful jets and immediately picks them up with a large scoop net. A conveyor belt carries the clams up to separators in the vehicle's working area.[455]

31.3 Harvesting machines for aquatic weeds

Aquatic plants in fresh waters and sea waters can be harvested for commercial use and also as a form of plant control with the object of destroying floating plants like *Eichhornia crassipes* or submerged ones such as *Myriophillum, Elodea* and others which are a nuisance. Although much more progress has been made in the mechanical control of water plants,[351] there is some related development in commercial harvesting of seaweeds like laver, undaria, kelp *etc* as foodstuff for human needs, for feeding animals, as raw material for fertilizer and for the needs of chemical industries.[566]. It is only the commercial harvesting of useful aquatic plants that is considered in this section.

Originally, the methods used for collecting aquatic plants were very simple. As can be seen in Chapter 2, sometimes fishermen only gathered the kelp that was washed ashore as a result of storms (*Fig 3*). Large quantities were lost by this method. Simple gear like sickles and scythes were also used for cutting and collecting aquatic plants. Some of this gear has already been mentioned in Chapter 7, *eg* rakes and wrenching gear, and in Chapter 20 when dredging was discussed. In some cases this gear has been mechanized and a few have formed the basis for the development of harvesting machines which not only cut the seaweed under water, collect it, and lift it aboard, but can also transport large quantities and discharge the material on the shore. Some of these harvesting machines can also chop, press and de-water the material, so that a wet pulverised weed is the final product.[351, 359]

Most projected harvesters have been based on the idea of a large flexible tube with a rotating cutter at one end, the cut weed then being drawn up with a pump. Kelp harvesters are like giant seagoing reaping machines or lawn-mowers (*Fig 729*). The barge-like harvesting machines will be moved back and forth over the designated harvesting area. The kelp is cut by the large cutting racks at the rear of the vessel and conveyor belts haul the cut seaweed aboard. In addition to such giant machines, there are smaller and simpler types that can do the work of collecting algae. In Chapter 7, (*Figs 90* and *91*) some wrenching gear for harvesting aquatic plants were described. This original gear was turned by hand to entangle the required plants. This can also be done in the same way with a mechanized gear. *Figure 730* shows a Russian design for the mechanized harvesting of sea weed – in this case *Laminaria*. These machines operate with a crane turning a wrenching gear to wind up the kelp and bring it aboard. The French operate a similar gear

Fig 729 Modern Californian kelp harvester.

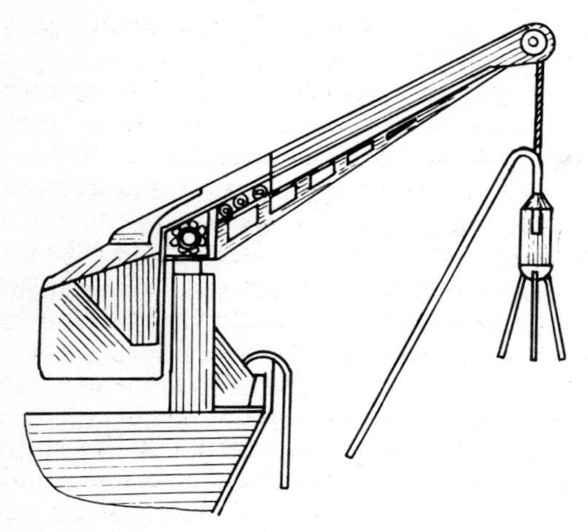

Fig 730 Russian crane with turning implement for harvesting *Laminaria*. (*Lunin, 1980*).

in Brittany, also for harvesting *Laminaria*[500]. There a small crane is mounted on the vessel with a spiral for twisting together and tearing out the seaweed (*Fig 731*). The Frenchmen call this arrangement 'scoubidou', which means nothing more than 'what's-its-name?', a term used in France for many other things when the exact name is not known. The crane is also used to unload the harvested seaweed

Fig 731 French harvesting machine for algae; so-called 'scoubidou'; near Brest. (1977).

from the vessel onto a truck on shore. For this purpose the crane is fitted with grabs (*Fig 732*).

31.4 Fishing systems in the future

There is no doubt that in the future, due to the high cost of manpower and energy, the importance of fully mechanized and computerized harvesting machines will increase. Some trends towards the development of such sophisticated arrangements as 'integrated fishing systems' are apparent. Such a system includes not only the computerized operation of the vessel's engine, and of the fish

Fig 732 French harvesting machine for algae, also used for unloading seaweed from the vessel or to a truck in the harbour, near Brest. (1977).

processing plant on board, but includes also fish searching, fish identification, and the selection of the catch. The system also includes all the navigation required to bring the vessel and gear into the best position in relation to the prey desired to be caught. Computers will calculate the right time to shoot the gear, in order to control the catching process and the quantity of fish caught. Finally, the system includes automatic hauling of the gear and the handling of the catch for processing. During the second Fishing Gear Congress of FAO in London in 1963, a captain mentioned that he would like to go fishing with a large vessel and his family only. An engineer answered that there are no technical problems to prevent realization of this dream, but he had some doubt if any one would pay the price, for the development of such a system! In the meantime, fishing units have become more expensive, and the number of people willing to work in fisheries steadily decreases. With the help of space research and other technological developments the problems of computerizing complicated systems can be solved. Overcoming the difficulties of greater automatic control in fisheries is under discussion in many parts of the world. No predictions can be made at this time for the future development of fishing technology. It may be that unexpected events like changes in fishing rights, political measures, variations in the needs of the international markets, and increasing costs of labour and fuel, may retard or even prevent such new developments – in which case simpler methods will prevail. Fishing is very vulnerable to outside events. Periods of rapid development, such as after World War II, alternate with periods of hardly any innovation. This underlines the widespread belief that fisheries are very conservative. It may be that such a period of little progress will come again.

Appendix

Classification of catching methods

This book deals with 'catching methods' in fisheries. Most people will consider this to be identical with 'fishing methods' or quite simply 'fishing gear'. Strictly speaking this is not quite correct. The 'fishing gear' is the tool of the fisherman, sometimes operated in different ways and combined with different tactics – that means some gear can be operated in several different 'catching methods'. But as we have seen in various chapters, there are some fishing methods which use no gear in the general sense, such as fish poisoning, catching by hand, or with the help of animals. Therefore, the term 'catching method' has been used as a term for fishing activities with and without gear. This must not be forgotten when dealing with the classification of these methods.

It was not until the eighteenth century that encyclopaedic books were printed dealing with fishes, fisheries and fishing gear. Artistic drawings showed the gear and its operation. Some grouping of the gear was done, mostly according to artistic points or in connection with the objects to be caught. Many of these illustrations of the early encyclopaedists, especially in France, have been made in such a nice and correct manner that they have been reprinted in modern books (*Figs 36* and *424*). At the end of the last century scientists, especially zoologists and physicians of different countries, became interested in fishing problems, and in their publications descriptions of fishing gear have been concentrated in a few groups. This grouping can be considered as the beginning of a classification of catching methods.

A.1 Principles of classification

A classification of catching methods will vary markedly according to the purpose for which the classification is needed. There can be a high concentration on a few groups only on the one hand; or on the other there can be a grouping down to the last individual gear with some variations according to the personal ideas of the individual fisherman. In this article a classification is given which tries to include all catching methods of the world in sea and freshwater fisheries, in commercial and sports fisheries and regardless of the 'importance' of the methods varying with the different fishing areas.

The basis for the classification is the *principle* of how the fish are caught. This manner of capture is not identical with the method by which the fish is removed from the water. Decisive for the catching method is the fact that the prey is held in a condition in which its chances of escape are negligible.[92] In fishing with purse seines, for example, the pursing is decisive and not the brailing with scoop nets or fish pumps. These are accessory devices only, just as is a landing net when used by sports fishermen fishing with flies.

With the help of the principle of how the fish is caught, some main groups of catching methods have been known in fisheries for a long time. The difficulty is that there is not always the same grouping according to the viewpoints of the different authors and the local importance of a fishing gear. As has been mentioned before, the 'importance' of a fishing method, from whatever viewpoint, should be ignored. Considered generally, a fishing method of no interest today can, in an improved form, become a successful one tomorrow. Similarly, a catching method not of interest for a certain fishing place can become the basis of the prosperity of another one. Another problem is the fact that very often in literature, and especially in fishery statistics, different catching methods are summarized under a few headings *eg* active and passive gear, fishing gear made of netting or other materials, and so on. Especially in statistics, many catching methods are catalogued under 'Miscellaneous' or simply as 'Others'! Such meaningless groupings have no place in this book. Each method is given the same careful consideration and each subdivision has been created with specific reasons – namely to demonstrate how the basic catching method is achieved in practice. This can be done in different ways according to the type of gear; consequently subdivisions may be based on factors like the following:

(*a*) *Material* Many fishing gears have been made originally of wood, including branches, bast *etc*. In contrast to these wooden gears are those made of fibres, natural or synthetic, sometimes also wire. Moreover, there are some fishing gears made completely or partially of iron or steel, or moulded out of plastic.
(*b*) *Construction* Any principle of catching can be realized by different constructions. Constructional differences include also items like the size of the gear (*eg* fyke nets and pound nets catch fish on the same principle, but they are considered as types of different sub-groups for many reasons).
(*c*) *Method of operation* For different reasons it may be necessary to mention if a gear is set on the bottom, dragged, pushed, cast, lifted, floating or drifting. It is of interest if a gear is operated by hand or is mechanized so as to need special arrangements (*eg* gallows), and/or if a raft or vessel is needed or not.

This means that sub-groups of the different groups of catching methods are based on different principles. It is not possible to follow a special scheme for the sub-groups as has been done with the main groups. This may lead to some objections because, as for naturalistic classifications, a grouping in classes, families, species and sub-species according to constant facts is needed, as in zoology and botany.[406]

A.2 Main groups of catching methods

In literature, most classifications of fishing gear are limited to a country, a small area, or to the methods used to catch a special type of fish. All-embracing, world-wide classifications are seldom used and are mostly made by ethnologists.[344, 406] Nevertheless, there are some main groups mentioned by most of them. These are the following:

Wounding (piercing, transfixing) gear like harpoons spears *etc*.
Lines (hooks) like handlines and longlines
Traps like pots, fyke nets, weirs and pound nets
Trawls like bottom and mid-water trawls
Seine nets like beach seines, boat seines and Danish seines
Surrounding nets like lampara nets, purse seines and ring nets
Liftnets
Gillnets, set and drifting
Trammelnets

These generally-accepted main groups will cover most of the catching methods used in the different parts of the world. But some well known catching techniques are missing, such as stow nets, scoop nets, cast nets, cover pots and also all modern developments for harvesting the living products of the water. Moreover, such catching methods as poisoning, stupefying or collecting by hand *etc* are not included. That means that more groups have to be added to the generally accepted list of fishing methods.

The groupings given above are mentioned by the author in a different order than others have done. When studied in detail it can be found that there are not only courses of development but also some relationship between the different groups. There is no linear development which includes all catching methods. According to different relationships only a two-dimensional or maybe a three-dimensional representation would give the right impression.[287] This is not possible for practical and technical reasons. Therefore each arrangement in the classification of catching methods needs benevolent acceptance.

Such acceptance is also necessary to overcome some serious differences, which can be found in the classifications when different authors are compared. Very often, for example, seine nets and trawls are placed in the same group. Both can be towed over the bottom, but there is a strong difference in their operation. Trawls can fish like dredges on an unlimited area; therefore the yield is calculated in catch per hour of towing. Seine nets are used to fish a fixed area only, and this is limited by the size of the gear and the method of shooting, so the yield is calculated in catch per set (Chapter 24). There are some methods of seining with some dragging (fly dragging), but this can be done in a limited manner only. On the other hand, some people like to mix seine nets with purse seines. The English name is very tempting. Both are surrounding the expected prey, but the purse seines surround not only from the side but also from below. They are a pelagic fishing gear. Seine nets can be operated in this manner as surface floating gear or when hauled like a liftnet, but these are exceptions and not in accord with their original construction.

Very often gillnets and entangling nets (one-walled, double- or triple-walled) are brought together because they are operated in the same manner. But when the *manner of capture* is decisive they are seen to work quite differently. It may happen that some fish with hard fins and spines are also entangled in gillnets or large fish entangle themselves in small-meshed gillnets. Nevertheless, the main manner of capture is gilling. On the other hand, single-walled entangling nets can never gill sturgeons or crabs. They are entangled. This is especially true for trammelnets.

In the classification of Far Eastern countries, scoop nets are included in the group of lift- or dipnets. But in contrast to scoop nets all types of liftnets make vertical movements up and down only. Therefore it may be more justified to include the different types of scoop nets in the same group as gape and stow nets. These stow nets are also combined with traps. The manner of capture is nearly the same. But stow nets need water current and are limited to catching fish swimming with the current. Therefore it may be permitted to separate these framed net bags from the traps, even when they have funnels and chambers like traps and often the end is completed by a basket or fyke net.

As mentioned before, the manner of catching is decisive for the main groups. How the prey is brought, or comes, into relationship with the gear can be dealt with in different ways even with the same gear. Therefore this cannot be an item of grouping. The prey can be lured by chemical (bait), optical (light), acoustical (noise) or electrical means. Therefore 'light fishing' is not a valid main group for classification. Some people do not mention 'electrical fishing' as a special fishing method. But there are some cases where stupefying by electricity is an essential part of the method, and the gear used (a small scoop net) is without worth when used without electricity. In this case it is not a fishing gear electrified to increase its efficiency only, but it is a manner of capture and has to be included as a catching method.

A similar situation exists with the drive-in fishery. Fish can be driven into many different gears, but there are some types of gear which are especially made for this purpose and do not work otherwise. Therefore also these gears have to be mentioned in a special group of fishing methods.

Most authors make sub-classifications in such a manner that simple gear is mentioned before more complicated ones. This does not mean that a gear with an apparently more complicated construction has been developed from simpler ones.[639]

A.3 Revised classification

For the first Fishing Gear Congress held in Hamburg in 1957, a classification was submitted which inspired many translations and revised proposals in different languages. As mentioned before, such a classification needs benevolent acceptance and should be, more or less, a framework allowing for summarizing and enlargement.

Because of new developments, and the author's own personal experiences, the original classification, published first in German in 1952 (*Protokolle zur Fischereitechnik*, Vol 2, No 6) and in English in 1957 (*Modern Fishing Gear of the World: 1,* London, 1959) and revised in 1964 (*Fish Catching Methods of the World,* London 1964) and again in 1972 in the second edition of this book, a few alterations (sometimes only by a better wording) became necessary for this third edition of *Fish Catching Methods of the World.* Also, some enlargement of the classification became necessary. This was brought about by the inclusion of 'wrenching gear' in the second group (grappling and wounding gear) of this classification, (thanks to the help of Professor Kwan So Ko of the National Fisheries University of Busan, Korea); by a new arrangement of the sub-group of ripping hooks in group 4 (lines); by including the pursed cast nets in group 13 (falling gear) (thanks to Prof. Dr T Mengi, University of Istanbul, Turkey); by including dragged gillnets in group 14 (gillnets) (thanks to Professor V Angelescu, Instituto Biologia Marina, Mar del Plata, Argentina); and by the new grouping of group 15 (tangle nets) (with thanks for the help of Professor Dr Bacalbasa-Dobrovici in Galati, Rumania and Prof. Dr T Mengi in Elazik, Turkey). The result is the following proposal for a classification of catching methods used in fisheries. In brackets are given the numbers of figures in this book, which illustrate the fishing methods listed.

It has to be mentioned that for technical reasons the order of succession in the following classification is not always in agreement with the descriptions of fishing gear and methods given in the chapters.

1. Without gear

Fishes and other prey are collected by hand or with the help of more or less trained animals (dogs, otters, cormorants and others). Hand-picking can be done along the shore, in shallow water by wading fishermen, or in deeper water by divers with or without diving suits. Only small tools are needed; more important are baskets and bags for the carrying of the collected material.

1.1. grasping by hand (*Fig 7*)
1.2. by diving (*Figs 14, 15* and *18*)
1.3. with hunting animals (*Figs 26* and *29*)

2. Grappling and wounding gear

As in hunting, man has extended the range of his arm by using long-handled implements which can be pushed, thrown or shot. The prey is taken by grappling, squeezing, piercing, transfixing, or wounding. Barbs prevent efforts to escape. Clamps, tongs and raking devices are types within this group but so also are spears, harpoons, arrows, and other missiles.

2.1. taken without wounding
- 2.1.1. wrenching gear (*Figs 90* and *91*)
- 2.1.2. clamps (*Figs 78* to *80* and *86*)
- 2.1.3. raking devices (*Fig 89*)
- 2.1.4. tongs (*Figs 83* to *85*)

2.2. taken by a wounding method *eg* with sharp projectiles
- 2.2.1. spears and lances (pushed or thrown) (*Figs 39* to *41*)
- 2.2.2. fish plummets (*Figs 45* to *48*)
- 2.2.3. fish combs (*Figs 49* and *50*)
- 2.2.4. arrows and similar missiles, (shot by bows, crossbows, catapults, rifles *etc.*) (*Figs 51* to *54*)
- 2.2.5. harpoons (pushed or thrown) (*Figs 55* to *59, 60* to *66, 72* and *73*)
- 2.2.6. blow guns (*Figs 74* to *76*)
- 2.2.7. rifles

3. Stupefying devices

The manner of capture of this group is to prevent fish from escaping by stupefying or stunning them. This can be achieved in various ways.

3.1. mechanical stupefying
- 3.1.1. striking gear (thrown stones, fish clubs, wooden or iron hammers)
- 3.1.2. explosives *eg* dynamite, hand grenades or bombs (*Fig 30*)

3.2. chemical stupefying (fish poisoning)
- 3.2.1. ichthyotoxic plants (*Figs 31* and *32*)
- 3.2.2. animal poisons
- 3.2.3. chemicals (like burnt lime, copper vitriol, *etc*)
- 3.2.4. deoxygenation (by stirring up the mud in shallow waters)

3.3. electrical stupefying (electrical fishing) (*Figs 33* to *35*)

4. Lines

In this case the manner of capture is for the fish to be offered a real or supposed bait which is presented in such a manner that it is difficult for the fish to let it go once it is taken. This is complicated by gorges or hooks. Hooks also allow the capture of fish by active ripping when they come within their range. Most methods are known in commercial fisheries as well as in sports fishing.

4.1. without hook (bobbing) (*Figs 93* to *97*)

4.2. with gorges or hooks (single, double or triple hooks; also three or more single hooks fixed with each other) (*Figs 98* to *101; 106* to *108*)
- 4.2.1. handlines (including pole lines operated in commercial and sport fisheries as well as vertical longlines) (*Fig 117*)
- 4.2.2. set lines (including bottom or near bottom longlines) (*Figs 129* to *133*)
- 4.2.3. drift lines (including drifting longlines) (*Fig 142*)
- 4.2.4. troll lines (including spin fishing in sport fisheries) (*Figs 148, 150* to *158* and *173*)

4.3. with rip hooks (foul hooking)
- 4.3.1. pole hooks (gaffs) (*Fig 189*)
- 4.3.2. pilks or jigs (*Fig 194*)
- 4.3.3. squid hooks (*Figs 208* to *210*)
- 4.3.4. set rip lines (*eg* for sturgeon) (*Figs 201, 202* and *215*)
- 4.3.5. dragged bottom rip hooks (single hooks, fish harrows or towed longlines) (*Figs 191* to *193*)

5. Traps

These are implements in which the fish enters voluntarily but is hampered from coming out. Usually in these traps there are one or more chambers which will be closed when the prey enters or which have a retarding device like a gorge or a funnel. Smaller types are completely closed except for the entrance *ie* they are three-dimensional. Larger types operate in two dimensions only.

5.1. hiding places
- 5.1.1. brush traps (*Figs 223* to *227*)
- 5.1.2. eel tubes (*Fig 228*)
- 5.1.3. octopus pots (*Figs 229* to *231*)

5.2. barriers
- 5.2.1. walls or dams (stone, wood, netting *etc* often in tidal areas (*Figs 256, 257* and *383*)
- 5.2.2. fences (fish screens, labyrinth traps) (*Figs 260* and *280*)
- 5.2.3. gratings (*Figs 262* to *268*)
- 5.2.4. watched chambers (closed by fishermen after entrance of the fish) (*Figs 271* to *279*)

5.3. mechanical traps (closed mechanically by a mechanism released by the prey)
- 5.3.1. gravity traps or box traps (*Figs 232* to *239*)
- 5.3.2. bent rod traps (whipping bough traps) (*Figs 240* to *246*)
- 5.3.3. torsion traps (*Fig 248*)

5.3.4. snares (*Figs 249* to *252*)
5.4. tubular traps (narrow funnel-like or hose-like gear without gorges)
5.4.1. genuine tubular traps (the fish is pressed in the funnel-shaped gear by the current) (*Figs 282* to *285*)
5.4.2. smooth tubular traps (the fish is held on the hose-like gear made of netting by its own fins) (*Fig 286*)
5.4.3. thorn lined traps (the fish cannot escape from the narrow funnel-shaped gear because of thorns) (*Fig 287*)
5.5. baskets, mostly small traps, 3-dimensional, with retarding devices
5.5.1. pots (made of wood or wire or plastic, mostly without wings and leaders) (*Fig 309*)
5.5.2. conical and drum like traps (made of netting with hoops and frames; mostly with wings and leaders; sometimes many fyke nets are combined in a catching system) (*Figs 330* and *350*)
5.5.3. box-like traps (made of strong, mostly iron, frames) (*Figs 335* to *338*)
5.6. trapping gear, mostly large traps, 2-dimensional, with retarding devices, fixed on sticks or anchors, set or floating, can have wings and/or leaders
5.6.1. simple forms made of fences or netting (*Figs 292* to *303*)
5.6.2. weirs, predominately made of wood (*Figs 347* and *348*)
5.6.3. pound nets, predominately made of netting (*Figs 349* and *352* to *356*)

6. Aerial traps

Some fish, shrimps or even squid, when in danger or opposite an obstacle, jump out of the water. Because they cannot steer their gliding flight they can be caught easily. The manner of capturing jumping fish is based on the possibility of stirring them up so as to catch them in the air by special devices obstructing their glide.

6.1. box traps (*Fig 360*)
6.2. raft traps (*Fig 362*)
6.3. boat traps (*Figs 363* to *370*)
6.4. verandah nets (*Figs 371* to *378*)
6.5. scoop nets for jumping fish (*Figs 379* to *380*)

Here can be included a special trap for fishes migrating over land:

6.6. pitfall traps

7. Bagnets

These are bags of netting (originally also wood) which are kept open vertically by a frame on the opening side and extended horizontally by the current. Smaller types, like scoop nets, are moved through the water for the same reason. The fish or other prey entering, more or less voluntarily, are caught by filtering.

7.1. scoop baskets and nets (small hand-operated gear)
7.1.1. landing nets (with a more or less round frame; mostly an accessory in sport fishing, but also used for fishing directly) (*Figs 398* to *403* and *404* to *409*)
7.1.2. skimming nets (with two crossing sticks) (*Figs 408c* and *419* to *422*)
7.1.3. push nets (with triangular or semi-circular frame) (*Figs 408d* and *415*)
7.1.4. dragged scoop nets (with a rectangular frame, identically with dredges) (*Figs 424* and *425*)
7.1.5. brail nets (large scoop nets with purse line for closing the under side) (*Fig 418*)
7.2. scrape nets (small ones operated by hand, larger ones mostly mechanically operated; stationary on the shore or on a vessel) (*Figs 427* and *429*)
7.3. gape nets without wings (large framed gear with retarding device)
7.3.1. stow nets on stakes (*Figs 434* and *435*)
7.3.2. stow nets on anchors (with or without vessel) (*Figs 438* to *445*)
7.4. gape nets with wings (large gear without framed opening, with retarding device)
7.4.1. winged stow nets on stakes (*Fig 446a*)
7.4.2. winged stow nets on anchors (*Fig 446b*)
7.4.3. winged stow nets with otter boards (*Fig 447*)
7.5. closable bagnets (*Figs 448* to *450*)

8. Dragged gear

This group contains all bagnets or net walls which are towed through the water on or near the bottom or even pelagically for an unlimited time. The manner of capture is by filtering the passive prey by the active moved gear.

8.1. sweep nets (towed sheets of netting, single- or triple-walled; overlapping with 14.3 and 15.4) (*Fig 712*)
8.2. runner nets (two frames shaped like the runners of a sledge and covered with netting (*Fig 733*); the frames joined at a narrow angle; the gear towed along the bottom by two persons while steered by a third. Once a fish is felt in the netting, the gear is closed on the fish and brought ashore).

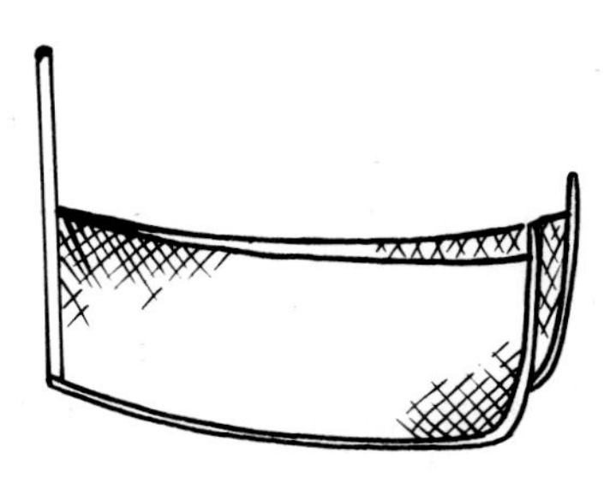

Fig 733 Runner net as formerly operated in the freshwater fisheries of northeastern Europe. (Benecke, 1881)

8.3. dredges
  8.3.1. hand dredges (with handle; scratcher) (*Figs 451* to *453*)
  8.3.2. boat dredges (*Figs 455* to *460*)
  8.3.3. mechanical dredges (*Figs 463* to *465*)
8.4. bottom trawls
  8.4.1. with one boat broadside sailing (*Fig 477*)
  8.4.2. with two boats, pair trawling (*Fig 501*)
  8.4.3. beam trawls (*Figs 467* to *476*)
  8.4.4. otter trawls (including semi-pelagic trawls with otter boards on the bottom) (*Figs 479* to *482* and *484* and *504b* and *c*)
8.5. mid-water trawls (pelagic trawls including surface trawls)
  8.5.1. one-boat otter trawls (*Figs 504a, 511* and *512*)
  8.5.2. two-boat trawls (*Figs 508, 509* and *516*)

9. Seine nets

This is a gear with very long wings and towing warps with or without bag or bags. The mode of capturing is by surrounding a certain area and towing the gear over this area with both ends to a fixed point on the shore or on a vessel.

9.1. double stick nets (a more or less small sheet of netting mostly without bag held between two sticks) (*Fig 531*)
9.2. genuine seine net (without, and with one or more bags; equi-winged or non-equi-winged; with towing lines of equal or non-equal length) (*Fig 528*)
  9.2.1. beach seines (on sea coast or in fresh waters, also under ice; the gear is hauled with or without vessels on the beach) (*Figs 539* to *542*)
  9.2.2. boat seines (the gear is hauled in the deep water in a boat) (Bottom *Fig 543,* surface *Fig 541* and pelagic type *Fig 536*)

10. Surrounding nets

The manner of capture is to surround the fish not only from the side but also from beneath, thus permitting the capture of fish over very deep waters by preventing their escape into the depths.

10.1. lampara-like nets (without pursing device) (*Figs 553* to *555a,* and *556* and *557*)
10.2. purse seines (with pursing device)
  10.2.1. one-boat system (with or without auxiliary skiff) (*Figs 555b* and *560*)
  10.2.2. two-boat system (*Figs 563* and *565*)
10.3. ring nets (hybrid type between lampara nets and purse seines, with pursing device) (*Fig 555c*)
10.4. 'Chiromila' purse net (*Fig 571*)

11. Drive-in nets

Fish can be caught by driving them into a fishing gear of any type. Most of them are caught also without driving, but in smaller quantities. There are some constructions of stationary gear which catch *only* when the fish are driven into them among other methods by swimming or diving fishermen, or by frightening lines. These are mentioned in the following:

11.1. dustpan-like stationary gear (*Figs 592* to *595*)
11.2. trawl-like gear, more or less stationary (*Figs 589* and *591*)
11.3. gillnets set in a circle around a fish school, or in a spiral (*Fig 596*)

There are some more methods which are often used in this fishery by driving fishes into blankets, in scoop nets (*Fig 598*) and some push nets (*Figs 599* to *601*)

12. Liftnets

The manner of capture with lift or dipnets is to bring the prey over a flat or more or less bag-like netting. They are then caught by lifting the gear. Smaller types have special devices to keep the netting spread. Larger types need mechanical arrangements for lifting; originally by levers, later by beams and winches.

12.1. hand liftnets (portable; including hoop nets) (*Figs 602* to *608*)
12.2. mechanized liftnets (shore or boat installed)
  12.2.1. lever liftnets (*Figs 612* to *614*)
  12.2.2. gallows liftnets (*Figs 615* to *618*)
12.3. blanket nets
  12.3.1. held by beams from the shore (*Figs 619* to *622*)
  12.3.2. with stationary buildings (*Figs 623* to *627*)
  12.3.3. mounted on vessels (*Figs 628* to *630* and *632* to *637*)
12.4. fish wheels (*Figs 638* to *643*)

13. Falling gear

The manner of capture is to cover the fish with a gear. This can be done without difficulty in shallow waters; with some difficulty in deeper waters.

13.1. cover pots
- 13.1.1. wooden cover pots (*Figs 644* to *647*) and newer variations (*Figs 648* and *649*)
- 13.1.2. lantern nets (wooden frame with netting) (*Figs 650* to *652*)
- 13.1.3. cover nets (*Figs 653* to *656*)

13.2. cast nets, with or without pockets
- 13.2.1. hand thrown cast nets (*Figs 657* to *661*)
- 13.2.2. cast nets with gallows (*Fig 664*)
- 13.2.3. cast nets for boats (drive cast nets) (*Fig 665*)

13.3. cast nets with purse line (*Figs 662* and *663*)

13.4. jerk nets (a rectangular net under tension between two sticks is pushed forward) (*Fig 667*)

14. Gillnets

These are single-walled nets, with a mesh opening of such a size that the wanted fish can gill themselves in the netting. This is a passive gear,but fish can also be driven into the gillnets. The nets are used singly or in large 'fleets'.

14.1. set gillnets (anchored on the bottom, sometimes floating) (*Figs 671* to *673*)

14.2. driftnets (with or without vessel) (*Fig 674*)

14.3. dragged gillnets (*Fig 679*)

14.4. encircling gillnets (fishes are driven into the encircling gillnets mostly by noises, see 11.3.)

15. Tangle nets

The manner of capture of the tangle (entangling) nets is that the fish or crabs entangle themselves in the netting by coming into the single-, double- or triple-walled (trammel) nets voluntarily or by being driven.

15.1. entangling gear (different types for corals, starfish, crabs *etc*) (*Figs 695* to *697*)

15.2. single-walled tangle nets, sometimes with vertical snoods or as frame nets (*Figs 698* to *702* and *705* to *707*)

15.3. double-walled nets (*Fig 715*)

15.4. trammel nets (triple-walled) (*Figs 708* to *712*)

Tangle nets can be combined with gillnets; also different types of gillnets can be incorporated in one gear as well as different types of tangle nets (*Figs 716* to *717*)

16. Harvesting machines

In this group all fishing gear is mentioned which takes the prey out of the water and also transports it on board the vessel by various methods.

16.1. hand-operated venturi dredges and washout nozzles (*Fig 20*)

16.2. harvesting machines (with conveyor belts) (*Figs 726* to *729*)

16.3. fish pumps (for pump fishing) (*Figs 719* to *725*)

16.4. collector for algae with crane and wrenching gear (*Figs 730* and *731*)

16.5. other harvesting and transporting systems which are in development and which may require classification at some point in the future.

Bibliography

1. ABERDEIN, C. The harvesting of seaweed. *Fish. News Int.* 7 (2), 24-28, 1968.
2. ABU BAKAR ABD. RAHMAN. *Belat-belat di Johor.* Bil. **53**, 1977, (in Malayan).
3. ALBERT-PETIT, G *et al. La Pêche moderne.* Paris, 1933.
4. ALDINGER, H. *Der erfolgreiche Spinn-, Schlepp- und Zockangler.* Stuttgart, 1974.
5. ALEKSEEV, A P (*ed*). *Fish behaviour and fishing techniques.* Israel Program for Scientific Translations. Jerusalem, 1971.
6. ALVERSON, D L and WILIMOVSKY, N J. Prospective developments in the harvesting of marine fishes. *Modern Fishing Gear of the World* **2**, 583-589, London, 1964.
7. ANDREEV, N. *Handbook of fishing gear and its rigging.* Israel Program for Scientific Translations. Jerusalem, 1966.
8. ANDRESKA, J. Archäologische Funde von Fischfanggeräten in Mikulčice in der Tschechoslowakei. *In: Studien zur europäischen traditionellen Fischerei.* Solymos, E (*ed*). Bajai Dolgozatok 3, 89-94, Baja, 1976.
9. ANELL, B. *Contribution to the history of fishing in southern seas.* Upsala, 1955.
10. ANELL, B. Hunting and trapping methods in Australia and Oceania. *Studia Ethnographica Upsaliensia* **XVIII**, Lund, 1960.
11. DE ANGELIS, R. Fishing installations in saline lagoons. *GFCM Studies and Reviews,* No. 7, 1959.
12. ANGOT, M. *Vie et économie des mers tropicales.* Paris, 1961.
13. ANTIPA, GR. *Pescăria si pescuitul in România.* Bucharest, 1916, (in Rumanian).
14. APOSTOLSKI, K. Fishing by means of 'Naseki' in Dojran Lake. *Izdanija* **II** (5), 83-101, 1958.
15. APOSTOLSKI, K and MATVEJEV, S. Fischfang in Umzäunungen mit Hilfe von Vögeln am Dojran-See. *Izdanija* **I** (3), 1955.
16. AUGUR, C H. Fishnets. *Bull. US Fish. Comm.* **13**, 1894.
17. AU LAI-SHING. The long-line fisheries of Hong Kong. Part 1: Golden-thread long-lining. *Fish. Bull.* **1**, 5-18. Hong Kong, 1970.
18. BACALBAŞA, N. Cors de tehnica pescuitului. *Pescuitul ind,* Bucharest, 1965, (in Rumanian).
19. BACALBAŞA, N. Die Fischerei in der Donau in der Zone des jetzigen Stausees 'Eisernes Tor', als Basis zur Organisierung der Stauseefischerei. *Hydrobiologica* **15**, 337-349. Bucharest, 1977.
20. BACALBAŞA, N and PECTU, A. Pescuitul cu sacovistea in zona viitorului lac de acumulare de la Portile de Fier. *Hydrobiologica* **10**, 151-161. Bucharest, 1969, (in Rumanian).
21. BACALBAŞA, N and PECTU, A. Pescuitul cu vîrsele în zona viitorului lac de acumulare 'Portile de Fier'. *Lucrări* Ştiinţifice, Vol. IV, 419-431, 1970, (in Rumanian).
22. BAHRAM, E G, TAGUCHI, W K and REILEY, S B. Porpoise rescue methods in the yellowfin purse seine fishery and the importance of Medina panel mesh size. *Mar. Fish. Rev.* **39** (5), 1-10, 1977.
23. BALASUBRAMANYAN, R, SATYANARAYANA, A V V and SARDAUDAN, K A. A preliminary account of the experimental rock-lobster fishing *etc. Indian J. of Fish.* **VII**, 407-422, 1960.
24. BALDAQUE DA SILVA, A A. *Estado actuel das pesca em Portugal.* Lisbon, 1891/92, (in Portuguese).
25. BARTZ, F. Fischgründe und Fischereiwirtschaft an der Westküste Nordamerikas. *Schriften des Geogr. Inst. der Uni. Kiel* **XII**, 1942.
26. BARTZ, F. *Alaska,* Stuttgart, 1950.
27. BARTZ, F. Bevölkerungsgruppen mit besonderer gesellschaftlicher Stellung unter den Küstenbewohnern und Fischern des Fernen Ostens. Erdkunde, *Arch.f. wiss. Geographie,* **XIII** Slg. 4, 1959.
28. BARTZ, F. *Die grossen Fischräume der Welt* I-III. Wiesbaden, 1964-74.
29. DE BEAUCLAIR, I. Field notes on Lan Yü (Botel Tobago). *Bull. Inst. Ethnology, Academia Sinica,* No. 3, 1957.
30. BENECKE, B. *Fische, Fischerei und Fischzucht in Ost- und Westpreussen.* Königsberg Pr., 1881.
31. BEN-YAMI, M. Fishing with light. *World Fish.* **23** (8), 46-48, 1974.
32. BEN-YAMI, M. *Fishing with Light.* Fishing News Books Ltd, Farnham, 1976.
33. BEN-YAMI, M. Sailkite's value proved in model tests. *World Fish.* **28** (9), 77-79, 1979.
34. BEN-YAMI, M. (*ed*). *Tuna fishing with pole and line.* Fishing News Books Ltd, Farnham, 1980.
35. BERGER, A. *Die Jagd aller Völker im Wandel der Zeiten.* Berlin, 1928.
36. BERGSTRAND, E and CORDONE, A J. Exploratory bottom trawling in Lake Victoria. *Afr. J. Trop. Hydrobiol. Fish.* **1** (1), 13-23, 1971.
37. BERT, P. Pêches et pêcheries de l'Annam. *La Nature,* 1886.
38. BERTUCCIOLI, U. *Il primo libro del pescatore.* Venice, 1955.
39. BEST, E. *Fishing methods and devices of the Maori.* Wellington, 1977.
40. BEUN, J. Garnaalvissers te paard. *Bachtn te Kupe* **11** (4), 73-81, 1969 (in Flemish).
41. BEURMANN, A. *Der Aberglaube der Jäger.* Hamburg, 1961.
42. BICKERDYKE, J. *Sea Fishing.* London, 1895. (With reference to Holdsworth, *Deep Sea Fishing and Fishing Boats.* London, 1874.)

43. BJORDA, A. *Engineering and fish reaction aspects of long-lining – a review.* ICES C. M. 1981/B:35, Fish capture committee, 1981.
44. BLACHE, J and MITON, F. *Première contribution à la connaissance de la pêche dans le bassin hydrographique Logone-Chari Lac Tchad.* ORSTOM, Paris, 1962.
45. BLAIR, C H and ANSEL, W D. *A guide to fishing boats and fishing gear.* 1968.
46. BLOTT, A J. A preliminary study of timed release mechanisms for lobster traps. *Mar. Fish. Rev.* **40** (5-6), 44-49, 1978.
47. BOBZIN, W and FINNERN, D. *Vollmatrose der Hochseefischerei: Fangtechnik.* Berlin, 1975.
48. BOECK, J A. *Die nasse Weyd.* Vienna, 1972.
49. BÖCKING, W. *Lachsfang mit der Salmenwage.* Heimatkalender des Kreises Rees, 158-162, Wesel, 1967.
50. BÖCKING, W. Ursprung und Herkunft der Fanggeräte: Hamenwage und Salmwippe Die Heimat. *Zeitschrift für niederheinische Kultur- u. Heimatpflege* **47**, 119-124, 1976.
51. BÖCKING, R L. So fischte man am Rhein. *Die Heimat* **49**, 54-60. Krefeld, 1978.
52. DE BOER, E J. Beam trawling. *Afdeling technish onderzoek Directie van de Visserijen,* 1970 (in Dutch).
53. BOLLORÉ, G-A. *Guide du pêcheur à pied.* Paris, 1960.
54. BOMBACE, G. Pots, baits and live fish tanks in Sicily. *GFCM* **8**, 83-94, 1967.
55. BOONSTRA, G P. Onderzoek naar de mogelijkheden van toepassing van elekrische visserij op garnalen en platvis 1968-1978. *Visserij* **32** (2), 107-121, 1979 (in Dutch).
56. V D BORNE, M and QUINT, W. *Die Angelfischerei.* Hamburg/Berlin, 1974.
57. BOUDAREL, N. *Les richesses de la mer.* Paris, 1948.
58. BRABANT, M. and PORTIER, M. 16-metre mesh trawl. *World Fish.* **28** (5) 40-43, 1979.
59. V BRANDT, A. Scherbretter in der Schleppangelfischerei. *Der Kescher* 2, 220-232, 1952.
60. V BRANDT, A. Fischerei zu Fuss. Bilder aus der bretonischen Fischerei. *Die Fischwirtschaft* 8, 132-133, 1956.
61. V BRANDT, A. Fang des Weissen Thuns an der französischen Atlantikküste. *Fischereiwelt* **8**, 55-56, 1956.
62. V BRANDT, A. *Fischnetzknoten.* Berlin, 1957.
63. V BRANDT, A. Bemerkenswerte Fangmethoden und Geräte in der griechischen Fischerei. *Protok. Fischereitech.* **6**, 327-365, 1960.
64. V BRANDT, A. Fishing methods in world sardine fisheries. *Proc. of the World Scientific Meeting on the Biology of Sardines and Related Species.* FAO, Vol. II, 563-623, 1960.
65. V BRANDT, A. Madagaskar, fischereiliche Reisenotizen. *Protok. Fischereitech.* **IX** (41), 148-196, 1964.
66. V BRANDT, A. Die Fanggeräte der Kutter- und Küstenfischerei. *Schriftenreihe der AID,* No. 113, 1966.
67. V BRANDT, A. Die Fischerei der Maltesischen Inseln. *Protok. Fischereitech.* **10**, 166-212, 1966.
68. V BRANDT, A. Fishing methods for univalve and bivalve molluscs. *Proc. Symposium on Molluscs III,* 857-867, 1968.
69. V BRANDT, A. Störfischerei an der türkischen Schwarzmeerküste. *Protok. Fischereitech.* **11**, 353-384, 1969.
70. V BRANDT, A. Zur Konservierung von Fischnetzen I. *Mikrobielle Schädigung, Material und Organismen* 4 (4), 297-337, 1969. II. *Widerstand von Netzgarnen, Material und Organismen* **5** (1), 1-18, 1970.
71. V BRANDT, A. Vor- und frühgeschichtliches Netzwerk. *Protok. Fischereitech.* **12**, 107-128, 1970.
72. V BRANDT, A. Baumkurren für die Fischerei auf Wellhornschnecken. *Protok. Fischereitech.* **12**, 129-137, 1970.
73. V BRANDT, A. Treibanker und Treibsegel in der Fischerei. *Protok. Fischereitech.* **12**, 160-163, 1970.
74. V BRANDT, A. Spermwalfang in der Küstenfischerei der Azoren. *Arch. f. Fischereiwissenschaft* **24** (1-3), 41-50, 1973.
75. V BRANDT, A. *Enmeshing nets: gillnets and entangling nets, the theory of their efficiency.* FAO EIFAC/74/I/Symp. -9, 1974.
76. V BRANDT, A. *Fischfang.* Zur Geschichte der fischereilichen Fangtechnik. Innsbruck/Frankfurt, 1975.
77. V BRANDT, A. The use of new methods for locating fish over large areas. *Appl. Sci. and Dev.* **7**, 112-124, 1976.
78. V BRANDT, A. Trawling from the past, at the present, and in the future. *Dep. Fish. Tech.* **8**, 4-18, 1979. Taiwan Prov. College of Marine Science and Technology, Keelung.
79. V BRANDT, A and KAULIN, M. Zur Mechanisierung der Zugnetzfischerei. *Fischwirt* **16**, 231-235, 1966.
80. V BRANDT, A and KAULIN, M. *Netze knüpfen – Netze schneiden.* Berlin, 1971.
81. V BRANDT, A and STEINBERG, R. Fischereimethoden der Kap Verden. *Protok. Fischereitech.* **IX**, 63-80, 1964.
82. BRELSFJORD, W V. *Fishermen of the Bangweulu Swamps;* a study of fishing activities of the Unga tribe. The Rhodes-Livingstone Papers No. 12. The Rhodes-Livingstone Institute, Livingstone, Northern Rhodesia, 1946.
83. BRIET, R. *La pêche en lagune Ebrié.* Abidjan, 1961.
84. BRINKMANN, A. Hansen's basill og Nielsen's basill to bergenske opptagelser. *Naturen,* **88**, 275-288, Bergen, 1964 (in Norwegian).
85. BROBAK, K. *Fartøy og redskap.* Oslo, 1952 (in Norwegian).
86. BROCK, F. Der Köder als fischereibiologisches Problem. *Arch. Fischereiwiss.* **2**, 74-78, 1950.
87. BRÜHL. Der Fischfang mit Giften am Kongo. *Fischerbote* **V**, 100-102, 1913.
88. BRUNELLI, G *et al.* La laguna di Venezia. *Monografia* Vol. III, parte VI, Tomo Venezia, 1940 (in Italian).
89. BRUSCHEK, E. Huchenfang mit dem 'Hucheneisen' am unteren Inn. *Öst. Fischerei* **15**, 138-140, 1962.
90. BUCKINGHAM, H. A new approach to seine netting. *World Fish.* **24** (6), 22, 1975.
91. BUESA MAS, R J. *La nasa antillana.* Contribución No. 15 del Centro de Investigaciónes Pesqueres. Havana, 1962 (in Spanish).
92. BURDON, T W. A consideration of the classification of fishing gear and methods. *Proc. Indo-Pac. Fisheries Council,* Sect. II/21, Madras, 1951.
93. BURDON, T W. The fishing methods of Singapore. *J. Malay. Br. Royal Asiatic Soc.* **22** (2), 5-76, 1954.
94. BURDON, T W. *A report on the fishing industry of Malta.* 1956.
95. BURGESS, J. *Handlining and trolling.* Bridport, 1971.
96. BURGESS, J. *Longlining.* Bridport, 1973.
97. BURGESS, J. *Shellfish trapping.* Bridport, 1973.
98. BURGESS, J. *Trammel netting.* Bridport, 1973.
99. BURGOON, D W. The use of fishpumps in USA. *Modern Fishing Gear of the World,* 414-417, 1959.
100. BUSCHAN, G. *Die Völker Asiens, Australiens und der Südseeinseln.* Berlin, (nd).
101. BUSNEL, R-G. Symbolic relationship between man and dolphins. *Trans. NY Acad. Sci.* **35** (2), 112-131, 1973.
102. CAPCO, S R and MANACOP, P R. The abuyan, an improved type of goby fishing gear, used in Laguna de Bay. *Philipp. J. Fish.* **3**, 65-84, 1955.
103. CARLISLE, J G, TURNER, C H and EBERT, E E. Artificial habitat in the marine environment. *Fish. Bull.* **124**, California, 1964.
104. CARTER, P. Bushman fishing, as depicted in rock

paintings. *Sci. S. Africa,* 578-581, 1965.
105. CARVER, A. Australian fishermen could learn from islanders' tuna techniques. *Australian Fisheries* **39** (7), 18-19, 1980.
106. CHAPMAN, W M. Implications of space research to fishery development. *In: Oceans from space,* 202-216, Houston/Texas, 1969.
107. CHAREMPHOL, S. Indigenous marine fishing gear of Thailand. *Proc. Indo-Pac. Fish. Council* Sect. II and III, 99-123, 1951.
108. CHEN, C. T. [*A survey of fishing gear used in the coastal fishery of Taiwan.*] Taipei, 1960 (in Chinese).
109. CHEN, M-T. [*Fishing gear and methods in Taiwan.*] Spec. publication No. 11 of The Joint Commission on Rural Reconstruction. Taipei, 1973 (in Chinese).
110. CHEN, T P. *Aquaculture practices in Taiwan.* Farnham, 1976.
111. CLARK, G. *The stone age hunters.* Library of early civilisation. London, 1971.
112. CLÉBERT, J-P. *Das Volk der Zigeuner.* Stuttgart, 1964.
113. COGGINS, J. *Nets overboard! The story of the fishing fleets.* London, 1967.
114. CONRAD, C R. Lachsfang und Lachsschiessen. *Dtsch. Jägerzeitung* **46**, 751-53, 1905/06.
115. CONTAG, D. Die Fischerei im Hochrhein, *Z.f.Fischerei, NF* **VI**, 103-108, 1957.
116. CORDINI, J M. *Rio Parana, sus peces mas comunes pesca commercial.* Ministerio de Agricultura y Ganaderia. Publicacion miscelanea No 410. Buenos Aires, 1955 (in Spanish).
117. CORDINI, J M. *La pesca en el Mar Argentino,* Direction General de Pesca y Conservacion de la Fauna. 1962 (in Spanish).
118. CORNWALL, I W. *Prehistoric animals and their hunters.* London, 1968.
119. DA COSTA, M. *Métodos e apetrechos de pesca.* Moçambique Publicaçoes Serie B, Divulgaçao No. 32, 1967 (in Portuguese).
120. COURT, W. Japan's squid fishing industry. *Marine Fish Rev.* **42** (7/8), 1-9, 1980.
121. COUSTEAU, Y. *Die schweigende Welt.* Berlin, 1953.
122. DE LA CUEVA SANZ, M S. *Artes y aparejos, tecnologia pesquera.* Madrid, 1974 (in Spanish).
123. DAHM, E. Erfolgreiche Schleppnetzfischerei in der Möhnetalsperre. *Inf. Fischwirtsch.* **20** (4/5), 128-130, 1974.
124. DAHM, E. *Importance of active fishing gear in the management of waters for recreational fishing.* EIFAC Techn. Consultation on the Allocation of Fishery Resources. Vichy. EIFAC/AFR/80/EP 14, 1980.
125. DAUBRÉE, M L. *Pêche fluviale en France. Principaux engins et modes de pêche autorisés ou interdits.* Paris, 1900.
126. DAVIES, D H. *About shark and shark attack.* Durban, 1964.
127. DAVIS, F M. *An account of fishing gear of England and Wales.* Fishery Investigations Ser. II, Vol. 21, No. 8, 1958.
128. DEMANDT, E. Die Fischerei der Samoaner. *Mitteilungen des Museums für Völkerkunde,* Hamburg III, **1**, 1912.
129. DEMBINSKY, W and CHMIELEWSKI, A. *A new approach to the electrification of seine nets.* FAO/EIFAC Consultation on eel fishing gear and techniques. Hamburg, 1970.
130. DIACONESCU, I. Geräte und Methoden der volkstümlich-bäuerischen Fischerei im Südwesten Rumäniens. *In: Studien zur europäischen traditionellen Fischerei.* Solymos E. (*ed*). Bajai Dolgozatok 3, 73-87, Baja, 1976.
131. DICKIE, L M and MCPHAIL, J S. Mechanical shellfish digger developed. *World Fishing* **5** (11), 40-51. 1957.
132. DICKIE, L M and MCPHAIL, J S. An experimental mechanical shellfish digger. Progress report and reports of the Atlantic coast stations. *Fish. Res. Bd. of Can.* No. **66**, 3-8, 1957.
133. DIDEROT, M D and D'ALEMBERT, J L. Pêches, pêche de mer, *etc. In: L'encyclopédie.* Paris, 1751-1782.
134. DIEUZEIDE, R and NOVALLA, M. La matérial de pêche maritime utilisé en Algire. *Documents et Reseignements Agricoles,* Bull. 179, 1953.
135. Direktorat for Söfartsuddennelse: Fiskerilaere, Section E: *Laksfiskeri med drivgarn.* Esbjerg, 1971 (in Danish).
136. Direktorat Jenderal Perikanan, Departemen Pertanian: Ketentuan Kerja Pengumpulan, Pengolahan, Danpenyajian Data Statistik Perikaban Buku 1: Standard Statistik Perikanan. Jakarta, 1975 (in Indonesian).
137. DITTON, R B, *et al.* Access to and usage of offshore Liberty ship reefs in Texas. *Mar. Fish. Rev.* **41** (9) 25-31, 1979.
138. Division of Training and Extension (*ed*). Alat-alat menangrap ikan dimalaysia, [*Gear for catching fish in Malaysia*]. Poster for information centers. Division of Fisheries together with the Publication Unit of the Ministry of Agriculture and Rural Development, Kuala Lumpur.
139. DOOGUE, R. Odd methods of catching fish. *In:* J. Pollard (*ed*) *The scream of the wheel: Deep-sea, beach, estuary and inland angling in Australian and New Zealand waters.* 366-379, Wellington, 1977.
140. DOOGUE, R. *Hook, line and sinker.* Wellington, 1974.
141. DOW, R L. Sea scallop fishery. In Firth, F E (*ed*): *The encyclopedia of marine resources,* 616-623, New York, 1969.
142. DUGE, P, HENKING, H and WILHELMS, O. Bericht über die Int. Fischerei-Ausstellung in St. Petersburg 1902. Berlin, 1902.
143. DUHAMEL DU MONCEAU, H L. Traité général des pêches maritimes de rivières et des étangs *etc.* Paris, 1769/82.
144. DUHAMEL DU MONCEAU, H L and DE LA MARR, L H. *Traité des pêches, et histoire des poissons* Neuchâtel 1776-1779.
145. DUMONT, H and SUNDSTROM, G T. *Commercial fishing gear of the United States.* Fish and Wildlife Circular 109, 1961.
146. DURKIN, J T and PARK, D L. A coarse seine for sampling juvenile salmonids. *Prog. Fish Culturist* **29**, 56-59, 1967.
147. DRENNIÈRE, P Y and NÉDÉLEC, C. Données sur les bateaux et engins de pêche en Mediterranée. *FAO/CGPM Etudes et Revues* No. 56, 1977.
148. EDDIE, C G. The engineer's contribution to fisheries development. *Fish. News Int.* **12** (4) 20-26, 1973.
149. EDWARDS, E. *The edible crab and its fishery in British waters.* Farnham, 1978.
150. v EHRENKREUZ. *Das Ganze der Angelfischerei und ihre Geheimnisse.* Quedlinburg/Leipzig, 1852.
151. EIGENMANN, C H and ALLEN, E R. *Fishes of Western South America.* Kentucky, 1942.
152. EILERS, A. *Westkarolinen.* Ergebnisse der Sudsee-Expedition 1908-1910. Vol. 9, Hamburg, 1935.
153. EIPELTAUER, N. *Streamerfischen.* Hamburg, 1980.
154. v EITZEN, J H C. *Schleppnetze in der Hochseefischerei.* Berlin, 1960.
155. E K R. (Roscher). Süberkrub-Scherbretter für die Hochseefischerei. *Fischwoche* **16**, 103/106, 1947.
156. ELLIOT, F E. On the status of electric fishing. *Oceanology International '69.* Brighton, 1969.
157. ELSTER, H-J. Einige Beobachtungen über die Binnenfischerei Ägyptens. *Fischwirt* **9**, 345-356, 1959.
158. ENDAL, A. Energy consumption in various Norwegian fisheries. *In:* Fuel challenge soaring costs pose problems

for fishing. *Fish. News. Int.* **18** (7), 24/25, 1979.
159. EUZIERE, J. *La pêche du thon et des thonidés en Méditerranée.* L'Olivette. n.d.
160. FAO (SCHÄRFE, J (*ed*)). *FAO catalogue of fishing gear designs.* Farnham, 1972/1978.
161. FAO. *Report of the expert consultation on selective shrimp trawls.* FAO Fisheries Reports No. 139, 1973.
162. FAO. *Otter board design and performance.* FAO Fishing Manuals, Rome, 1974.
163. FAO. Contributed papers submitted to the expert consultation of fishing for squid and other cephalopods. FAO Fisheries Reports No. 170, Sppl. 1, Rome, 1976.
164. FELBERMAYER, F. *Sagen und Überlieferungen der Osterinsel.* Nürnberg, 1971.
165. FELDHAUS, F M. *Die Technik Lexikon der Vorzeit der geschichtlichen Zeit und der Naturvölker.* Munich, 1970.
166. FERGUSON, R G and REGIER, H. Selectivity of four trawl cod ends towards smelt. *Trans. Amer. Fish. Soc.* **92**, 125-131, 1963.
167. FILY, M and D'AUBENTON, F. Report on fisheries technology in the Great Lake and the Tonle Sap. Rep. of France, Ministry of Foreign affairs, Department of Technical Co-operation, National Museum of Natural History. Paris, 1965.
168. FIRTH, F E (*ed*). *The encyclopedia of marine resources.* New York, 1969.
169. FISCHER, J E. Ruttenfang mit dem Ofenrohr. *Allg. Fischereizeitung* **84**, 53-54, 1959.
170. FISCUS, C H and MARQUETTE, W M. National marine fisheries service field studies relating to the bowhead whale harvest in Alaska, 1974. Northwest Fisheries Center processed report, 1975.
171. FLEURY, G. *La pêche à pied.* Les dossiers des éditions du pen-duick. Paris, 1981.
172. FLOYD, H M. *Castnets constructed of machine-made netting.* USA Bureau of Commercial Fisheries. Leaflet 579, 1965.
173. FODERA, U. The Sicilian tuna trap. *FAO GFCM Studies and Reviews* **15**, 1961.
174. FORBES, M. Fishing with kite and spider web. *Natural History* **56**, 488-489, 1946.
175. FOSNAES, T. Newfoundland cod war over use of gillnets. *Fish. News Int.* **14** (6), 40 and 43, 1975.
176. FOSTER, J J. Two new trawls from Aberdeen lab. *World Fish.* **24** (10), 28-30, 1975. (See also *Aquatic Sci. & Fish. Abst.* **6** (5) 201, No. 5575, 1976.)
177. FRAZER, J E. Kuwait. *Nat. Geogr.* 135 (5), 336-365, 1969.
178. FRECHET, J. Discussion on gillnetting, longlining *etc.* Kristjonsson, H (*ed*) *In: Modern Fishing Gear of the World* **2**, 291. London, 1964.
179. FREY, H W (*ed*). *California's living marine resources and their utilization.* State of California, Department for Fish and Game, 1971.
180. FREYTAG, G, HORN, W and STEINBERG, R. Erfolgreiche Weiterentwicklung binnenfischereilicher Schleppnetze durch Elektrifizierung. *Protok. Fischereitech.* **12** (58), 417-426, 1971.
181. FREYTAG, G and MOHR, H. Untersuchungen über die Pulsfischerei auf Aale. *Protok. Fischereitech.* **XIII**, 60, 82-106, 1973.
182. v FRISCH, K. Zur Psychologie des Fischschwarmes. *Naturwissenschaften* **26**, 601-606, 1938.
183. FULTON, G. Drum stern trawling. *Fish. News Int.* **8** (4), 24-27, 1969.
184. GABRIEL, O and KAROW, M. Entwicklung neuer Scherkörper für die pelagische Schleppnetzfischerei. *Seewirtschaft* **9** (5), 282-286, 1977.
185. GABRIEL, O and SCHUMACHER, W. Windkanaluntersuchungen zur Verbesserung der hydrodinamischen Eigenschaften pelagischer Scherkörper. *Fischerei-forschung* **15** (1), 59-75, 1977.
186. GARAU, V-F. *Traité de pêche maritime pratique illustré et des industries secondaires en Algerie.* Algir, 1909.
187. GARRET, W E and JEFFERY, D. Burma's leg sowers and floating farms. *Nat. Geogr.* **145** (6) 826-845, 1974.
188. GARNER, J. *How to make and set nets.* London, 1962.
189. GARNER, J. Salmon trap fishing in Scotland. *Fish. News Int.* **15**, (1) 26-27, 1976.
190. GARNER, J. Sweep nets for salmon catching. *Fish. News Int.* **15** (2), 26-27, 1976.
191. GARNER, J. *Modern deep sea trawling gear.* Farnham, 1977.
192. GEORGE, V C. *An account of the inland fishing gear and methods of India.* Central Institute of Fisheries Technology. Special Publ. 1 Ernaculam, 1971.
193. GEUENICH, E. Moderne Knebelangeln in Frankreich. *Monatshefte für Fischerei* **8**, 96, 1940.
194. GHIGI, A. *La pesca.* Turin, 1966 (in Italian).
195. GLANVILLE, A. The Larsen midwater-trawl. *FAO Fisheries Bull. IX*, 113-129, 1956.
196. GLIEWE, S. Am Dojransee in Macedonien. *Allg. Fischerei Ztg.* (Fischwaid) **101** (7), 352-353, Munich, 1976.
197. GOURRET, R. *Les pêcheries et les poissons de la Méditerranée.* Paris, 1934.
198. GRIGG, R W. Precious corals. Hawaii's deep-sea jewels. *Nat. Geog.* **155** (5), 719-132, 1979.
199. GROSSKOPF, B C. Bemerkenswerte Netzkonstruktionen. *Monatshefte für Fischerei* **10**, 151-153, 1942.
200. GRUVEL, A. *L'Indo-Chine, ses richesses marines et fluviales.* Paris, 1925.
201. GRUVEL, A. *La pêche de la préhistoire, dans l'antiqité et chez le peuples primitives.* Paris, 1928.
202. GUDGER, E W. Dogs as fishermen. *Nat. Hist.* **23** (6), 559-568, 1923.
203. GUDGER, E W. Fishing with the cormorant. I. In China. *Amer. Nat.* **60**, 5-41, 1926.
204. GUDGER, E W. Fishing with the otter. *Amer. Nat.* **61**, 193-225, 1927.
205. GUDGER, E W. Fishing with the cormorant in Japan. *Sci. Mon.* **29**, 5-37, 1929.
206. GUDGER, E W. Fooling the fishes. Fishing with the bateau and the white varnished board in China and with similar devices in other parts of the world. *Sci. Mon.* **44**, 295-306, 1937.
207. GUDGER, E W. The perils and romance of swordfishing. The pursuit of *Xiphias gladius* with the trident in the Strait of Messina. *Sci. Mon.* **51**, 36-38, 1940.
208. GUDGER, E W. Canine fishermen. Accounts of some dogs that went a-fishing. *Nat. Hist. Mag.* **47**, 140-148, 1941.
209. GUDGER, E W. Swordfishing with the harpoon in New England water. *Sci. Mon.* **54**, 418-430 and 499-512, 1942.
210. GUDGER, E W. The origin of fly-fishing. *Salmon and Trout Mag.* **121**, 237-240, 1947.
211. GUDGER, E W. La pêche à la main en Europe. *La Nature* No. 3190, 1951.
212. GUDGER, E W. Fishing with the hand in certain Asiatic countries. *J. Zool. Soc. India* **3**, 357-363, 1952.
213. GUNDA, B. *Fish poisoning in the Carpathian area and in the Balkan peninsula.* The Kroeber anthropological society papers. Spec. Publication No. 1, 1967.
214. GUNDA, B. Beziehungen zwischen den naturbedingten Faktoren und der Fischerei in den Karpaten. *Acta Ethnographica Slovaca* I, 111-121, 1974.
215. GUSINDE, M. *Urmenschen in Feuerland.* Berlin, 1946.

216. Guthrie, J F. The channel net for shrimp in North Carolina. *Comm. Fish. Rev.* **28** (11), 24-27, 1966.
217. Haasteren, L M van. Elektrisch vissen in Nederland. *Visserij* **30** (2), 63-74, 1977 (In Dutch).
218. v Habsburg-Lothringen, L S. *Die Balearen,* 1897. (Los Baleares II, La pesca; Palma de Mallorca, 1956.)
219. Halme, E and Aalberg, A F. Parhaita kalanpyydyksiä [*Best fishing gear and how to make it*] Helsinki, 1959 (in Finnish).
220. Halsband, E and I. Einführung in die Elektrofischerei. *Schriften der Bundesforschungsanstalt für Fischerei* **7**, Berlin, 1975.
221. Halsband, E. Die stoffwechsel- und nervenphysiologischen Gesetzmässigkeiten der Elektrofischerei in mit 'Abwassergiften' belasteten Gewässern und deren Anwendung für die Praxis der Elektrofischerei. *Fischwirt,* **27** (4), 20-22, 1977.
222. Hamuro, C. Studies on automation of fishing with otter trawls, Danish seines, midwater trawls and purse seines. *In: Modern Fishing Gear of the World* Vol. **3**, 504-508, London, 1971.
223. Han, H *et al. Korean fishing gear and illustrations,* 3. Pusan 1968/70.
224. Hardy, D. *Scallops and the diver-fisherman.* Fishing News Books Ltd. Farnham, 1981.
225. Harrer, H. *Geister und Dämonen, Magische Erlebnisse in fernen Ländern.* Berlin, 1969.
226. Hart, D V. *Securing aquatic products in Siaton municipality, Negros Oriental Province, Philippines.* Monograph of the Institute of Science and Technology, No. 4, Manila, 1956.
227. Harvey, W H. *The sea-side book.* London, 1857.
228. Hashimoto, T and Maniwa, Y. Research on the luring of fish schools by underwater sound. *Modern Fishing Gear of the World,* **3**, 501-503. London, 1971.
229. Hass, G. Der Kleinwalfang in Norwegen. *Dtsch. Norweg. Wirtschafts-Zeitschr,* **3**, 213-217, 1943.
230. Hattop, W H and Predel, G. Die Anwendung elektrischer Schleppnetze in den Binnengewässern der DDR. *Z.Fischerei NF* **17**, 216-226, 1969.
231. Haven, D S, Whitcomb, J P and Davis, Q R. A mechanical escalator harvester for live oyster and shell. *Mar. Fish. Rev.* **41** (12), 17-20, 1979.
232. Hayer, F and Halsband, E. Elektrische Befischung grösserer Gewässer mit einer kombinierten Scheuch-Fangmethods. *Fischwirt* **15**, 10-14, 1965.
233. Heintz, K. *Der Angelsport im Süsswasser.* Munich/Berlin, 1903.
234. Heidrich, G. Wahrnehmungen auf einer Studienreise in die Vereinigten Staaten *Mitt. des Dtsch. Seefischerei-Vereins* **21**, 443-475, 1905.
235. Heitman, K E. *Die Urzeitjäger im technischen Paradies.* Düsseldorf, 1962.
236. Helgeland, G (*ed*). *Archery world's complete guide to bowhunting.* Englewood Cliffs, 1975.
237. Henking, H and Fischer, E. *Die Ostsee-Fischerei in ihrer jetzigen Lage.* Public. de Circomstance No. 13B des Cons. Perm. Int. pour l'Exploration de la Mer. Copenhagen, 1905.
238. Henking, H. Die Ostseefischerei. *Handbuch der Seefischerei Nordeuropas V,* Stuttgart, 1929.
239. Herman, O. *Die Forschungsreisen des Grafen Eugen Zichy in Asien.* Dritte Reise Bd. 1 Recension. Budapest, 1900.
240. Herter, K. *Die Fischdressuren und ihre sinnesphysiologischen Grundlagen.* Berlin, 1953.
241. Hester, F J. Application of drum seining in the Californian wetfish fishery. *Modern Fishing Gear of the World* **3**, 228-290, London, 1971.
242. Hester, F J. Some considerations of the problems associated with the use of live bait for catching tunas in the tropical Pacific Ocean. *Mar. Fish. Rev.* **36** (5), 1-12, 1974.
243. Heyde, G. Motorisierung der Zugentzfischerei. *Allg. Fischerei-Ztg.* **42**, Neudamm, 1939.
244. Hickling, F C. *Tropical inland fisheries.* London, 1961.
245. High, W L. Pudget Sound drum seining. *Mar. Fish. Rev.* **36** (12), 5-11, 1974.
246. Hildebrand, O. Nochmals Hechtfang am Bodensee: über das Schleppfischen mit mehreren Schnüren. *Allg. Fischerei-Ztg.* **78** (3), 45-46, 1953.
247. Hochheimer, H. *Die Geschichte der grossen Ströme.* Köln, 1954.
248. Hokusai. *Manga VI*, 1816. (See also J A Michener, *The Hokusai sketch books.* Tokyo, 1959.)
249. Holden, J. *Shorefishing.* London, 1979.
250. Holdsworth, E W H. *Deep-sea fishing and fishing boats.* London, 1874.
251. Holttum, R E. *Plant life in Malaya.* London, 1973.
252. Hood, D W (*ed*). *Impingement of man on the oceans.* New York, 1971.
253. Horn, W. Rationalisierung der Seezungenfischerei durch Einsatz elektrifizierter Baumkurren. Information für die Fischwirtschaft 23, 1, 20-22, 1976.
254. Horn, W. Weitere Ergebnisse von Untersuchungen an elektrifizierten Baumkurren für den Seezungenfang. *Information für die Fischwirtschaft* **24**, 6, 226-228, 1977.
255. Horn, W. Versuche zum Einsatz einer Netzpumpe in der Krill-Fischerei Erforschung und wirtschaftliche Erschliessung der Krillbestände und Nutzfische in der Antarktis, Bericht II, 1978 (see *Fish. News Int.* **18** (6) 13, 1979).
256. Horn, W. Modellversuche mit Schersegeln bei Tauwerknetzen. *Informationen für die Fischwirtschaft* **26** (6), 189-193, 1979.
257. Horn, W and Mohr, H. Modellversuche zur Weiterentwicklung des Kugelkappen-Scherbretts. *Information für die Fischwirtschaft des Auslandes* **26** (2), 66-70, 1979.
258. Hornell, J. Survivals of the use of oculi in modern boats. *J. Roy. Anth. Inst. G.B. Ire.* **LIII**, 289-321, 1923.
259. Hornell, J. Boat oculi survivals: additional records. *J. Roy. Anth. Inst. G.B. Ire.* **LXVIII**, 339-348, 1938.
260. Hornell, J. *Water transport, origins and early evolution.* Cambridge, 1946.
261. Hornell, J. *Fishing in many waters.* Cambridge, 1950.
262. Hosaka, E Y. *Shore fishing in Hawaii.* Hawaii, 1973.
263. Houser, A and Dunn, J E. Estimating the size of threadfin shad population in Bull Shoal Reservoir from midwater trawl catches. *Trans. Amer. Fish. Soc.* **96** (2), 176-184, 1967.
264. Hu, L C. Diving lines for tuna. *World Fish.* **23** (7), 1974.
265. Huber, A. Gerätschaften und Fangmethoden der Berufsfischer. *In: Fisch und Fischerei,* 167-182, Winterthur, 1952.
266. Hughes, W D. *Australian lobster fishery: gear and methods.* Australian Fisheries Paper No. 7 (revised).
267. Hunter, J R and Mitchell, C T. Association of fishes with flotsam in the offshore waters of Central America. *US Fish. & Wild. Serv. Fish. Bull.* **66**, 9-20, 1966.
268. Hunter, J R and Mitchell, C T. Design and use of a miniature purse seine. *Prog. Fish Cult.* **28**, 175-179, 1966.

269. HUNZIKER, H. *ABC für Sportfischer*. Zürich, 1950.
270. HURLBURT, C G and S W. Blue gold, mariculture of the edible blue mussels, (*Mytilus edulis*). *Mar. Fish. Rev.* **37** (10), 10-18, 1975.
271. HURUM, H J. *A history of the fish hook and the story of Mustad, the hook maker*. London, 1977.
272. HUTZFELD, H H. Wattwurmsuche mit Aussenbordmotor. *Fisch und Fang* **18** (10), 744, 1977.
273. IDYLL, C P. Grunion, the fish that spawns on land. *Nat. Geogr.* 135 (5), 714-723, 1969.
274. ISO: International Standard 1107. *Fishing nets – netting – basic terms and definitions*. Geneva, 1974.
275. ISO: International Standard 1531: *Fishing Nets – hanging of netting – basic terms and definitions*, 1973.
276. IVANOVIC, V. *Modern spearfishing*. London, 1954.
277. IWASHITA, M *et al*. A basic study on mechanization of pole and line fishing for skipjack and albacore 2. *J. Coll. Mar. Sci. and Tech.* No. 2, Tokai University, 1967.
278. JANKÓ, J. *Herkunft der magyarischen Fischerei*. Budapest/Leipzig, 1900.
279. JENKINS, J G. *Nets and coracles*. Newton Abbot, 1974.
280. JENSEN, A E. *Mythus und Kult bei Naturvölkern*. Wiesbaden, 1960.
281. JOHNSON, R G and SIMS, C W. Purse seining for juvenile salmon and trout in Columbia River estuary. *Trans. Amer. Fish. Soc.* **102**, 341-345, 1973.
282. JOSEPH, K M and NARAYANAN, K P. Fishing gear and methods of the river Brahmaputra in Assam. *Fish. Tech.* **2** (2), 205-219, 1965.
283. JOYNER, I. Resources exploitation – Living. *In: Impingement of man on the oceans*. Hood, D W (*ed*). 529-551. New York, 1971.
284. JOYNER, T, MAHNKEN, C V W and CLARK, R C. Salmon, future harvest from the Antarctic Ocean? *Mar. Fish. Rev.* **36** (5), 20-28, 1974.
285. JUYNBOLL, H H. *Java, Katalog des Ethnographischen Reichsmuseums* **IX**. Leiden, 1914.
286. KAHLKE, H D. Die Kormoranfischerei in Lutschou. *Natur und Museum* **94**, 131-138, 1964.
287. KAJEWSKI, G. Gedanken zür Systematik der fischereilichen Fanggeräte. *Zeits. f. Fisch.* **VI** 397-403, 1957.
288. KANO, T and SEGAWA, K. *An illustrated ethnography of Formosan aborigines. 1: The Yami*. Tokyo, 1956.
289. KASUGA, OSAKA, L. (*ed*). *Catálogo de artes y métodos de pesca artesanales de la República Popular China*. Instituto Nacional de Pesca, México, 1975 (in Spanish).
290. KATCH, H. [*Fishery with closable octopus pots*] n.d. (in Japanese).
291. KATO, S. Catching squid by the ton with pumps. *Nat. Fish.* June 1970.
292. KATO, S. Sea urchins: a new fishing develops in California. *Mar. Fish. Rev.* **34** (9/10), 23-30, 1972.
293. KATO, S. *The California squid fishery*. FAO Fisheries Report 170, Spl. 1: Contributed papers submitted to the expert consultation of fishing for squid and other cephalopods. 107-127, Rome, 1976.
294. KATSUKI, J (*ed*). [*Illustration of fishing gear*] Otaru/Hokkaido, 1951 (in Japanese).
295. KAULIN, M. Holeinrichtungen für Setznetze. *Fischerblatt* **17**, 265-69, 1969.
296. KAULIN, M. Eine Langleine mit Hechtfallen von der Insel Gotland. *Fischwirt* **19** (12), 280-282, 1969.
297. KAUSCH, K. Makrelenfang mit Schleppangeln. *Fischwaid* **13**, 240-241, 1958.
298. KAWAGUSHI, K. Handline and longline fishing explorations for snapper and related species in the Caribbean and adjacent waters. *Mar. Fish. Rev.* **36** (9), 8-31, 1974.
299. KESTEVEN, G L (*ed*). *Malayan fisheries*. Singapore, 1949.
300. KIENER, A. *Poissons, pêche et pisciculture à Madagascar*. Noyent-sur-Marne (Seine), 1963.
301. KIRCHHOFF, A. *Mensch und Erde*. Reihe aus Wissenschaft und Geisteswelt No. 31. Leipzig, 1901.
302. KISHINOUGE, K. Prehistoric fishing in Japan. *J. Coll. Agric. Imp. Univ. Tokyo* **II**, 327-382, 1941.
303. KLIMA, E F. The automated fishing platform. *Modern Fishing Gear of the World* **3**, 498-501. London, 1971.
304. KLOPFENSTEIN, D and I. Fishing the big white sturgeon along the Columbia River. *Fish. News Int.* **16** (1), 95-97, 1977.
305. KLUNZINGER, C B. *Bodenseefische, deren Pflege und Fang*. Stuttgart, 1892.
306. KLUST, G. Wurfnetze in der Elbfischerei. *Fischwirt* **9**, 176-177, 1959.
307. KLUST, G. Bundgarn *In: FAO catalogue of fishing gear designs*. Rome, 1965.
308. KLUST, G. Zur Aalreusenfischerei in grossen Fliessgewässern. *Allg. Fischerei Ztg.* (10), 319-323, 1969.
309. KLUST, G. *Eel Stownets in German rivers*. FAO/EIFAC Technical paper No. 14. EIFAC consultation on eel fishing gear and techniques McGrath, C J (*ed*). 39-56, Rome, 1971.
310. KLUST, G. *Netting materials for fishing gear*. FAO Fishing Manuals, Fishing News Books Ltd. Farnham, 1982.
311. KNAKE, B O, MURDOCK, J F and CATING, J P. *Double-rig shrimp trawling in the Gulf of Mexico*. US Fish and Wildlife Service, Fishery Leaflet 470, 1958/1969.
312. KWAN SOH KO, PROFESSOR. National Fisheries University, Busan, S-Korea: by letter.
313. KOCH, G. *Die materielle Kultur der Ellice-Inseln*. Veröff. des Museums für Völkerkunde, Berlin NF3, Berlin, 1965.
314. KOCH, G. *Materielle Kultur der Gilbert-Inseln*. Veröff. des Museums für Völkerkunde Berlin NF6, Berlin, 1965.
315. KOCH, G. *Die materielle Kultur der Santa Cruz-Inseln*. Veröff. des Museums für Völkerkunde, Berlin NF. 21, Berlin 1971.
316. KOCH, G. Völkerkundemuseum Berlin-Dahlem: (by letter).
317. KOENIG, O. Urmotiv Auge. Neuentdeckte Grundzüge menschlichen Verhaltens. Munich/Zürich, 1975.
318. KOLLMANNSPERGER, F. *Die Seefischerei in der Manggarai, Westflores, Indonesia*. (Unpublished report) 1972.
319. KÖTHKE, H and KLUST, G. Der Scherbretthamen. *Arch. Fischereiwiss* **7**, 93-119, 1956.
320. KOZLOV, V V. [Trawl boards for medium tonnage ships] (In Russian). *Rybnoe Khozyajstov* **5**, 55-959. (Engl. summary in *World Fish.* **24**, 8, 60-61, 1975.)
321. KRAMER, H and MATSCHCHOSS, O. *Farben in Kultur und Leben*. Stuttgart, 1963.
322. KRAUSE, E. Vorgeschichtliche Fischereigeräte und neuere Vergleichsstücke. *Zeits. f. Fischerei.* **11**, 133-300, 1904.
323. KRICKEBERG, W. Amerika. *In: Die grosse Völkerkunde* **III**. Bernatzik, H A (*ed*). 18-367, 1939.
324. KRISTJÁNSSON, L. *Islenzkir Sjávarhaettir*. Vol. 1, Reykjavik, 1980 (In Icelandic).
325. KRISTJONSSON, H (*ed*). *Techniques of finding and catching shrimp in commercial fishing*. FAO Fish. Rep. 57 (2), 125-192, 1968.
326. KRISTJONSSON, H. *A desk study of needs and opportunities for a regional approach to development of artisanal/small-scale fisheries in Lake Tanganyika*. Report to the Swedish International Development Authority, FAO, Rome, 1974.
327. KRISTOF, E. The last US whale hunters. *Nat. Geog.* **143** (3), 34, 1973.
328. KROEBER, A L and BARRETT, S A. Fishing among the Indians of northwestern California. *Anthropological Records* **21**, 1. Los Angeles, 1960.

329. KRUMBIEGEL, J. *Von Haustieren und ihrer Geschichte.* Stuttgart, 1947.
330. KÜHL, H. Studien über die Sandklaffmuschel *Mya arenaria. Arch. Fischereiwiss.* **2**, 25-39, 1950.
331. KUHN, G. *Die Fischerei im Oberrhein.* Hohenheimer Arbeiten 83, Agraroekonomie, Stuttgart, 1976.
332. KUNICKE, H. Der Fisch als Fruchtbarkeitssymbol bei den Waldindianern Südamerikas. *Anthropos* **VII**, 206-229, 1912.
333. KUSNETZOW, J. *Fischerei und Thiererbeutung in den Gewässern Russlands.* St. Petersburg, 1898.
334. KUZNETZOW, Y A. The behaviour of fish in the zone affected by a curtain of air bubbles. *In: Fish behaviour and fishing techniques,* Alekseev, A P (*ed*). 103-110. Jerusalem, 1971.
335. LAGERCRANTZ, S. *Fish-hooks in Africa and their distribution.* Ryksmuseets Ethnografiska Avddelning, Nr. 12, 1934.
336. LAGLER, K F. Capture, sampling and examination of fishes. 7-40 (45) *In: Methods of assessment of fish production in fresh waters,* Ricker, W E (*ed*). IBP Handbook 3. London, 1968.
337. LANE, F W. *Kingdom of the octopus.* New York, 1960.
338. LANE, P. Eels and their utilization. *Mar. Fish. Rev.* **40** (4), 1-20, 1978.
339. LANGE, K. *German experiments with spherical otter-boards.* ICES, C M 1976/B:40, Gear and Behaviour Committee, 1976.
340. LARSEN, K. *Amator fiskeri i havet.* Copenhagen, 1968 (in Danish).
341. LE FEVRE, I. Australian fisheries; in Firth, F E (*ed*). *The encyclopedia of marine resources,* 41-47, New York, 1969.
342. LEHTONEN, J U E. Kansanomainen ravustus ja rapujen hyväksikäytto Suomessa. [*The popular methods to catch crayfish and their use in Finland.*] Helsinki, 1975 (in Finnish).
343. LEONHARDT, E E. Die Entwicklung der Fischerei und ihrer Geräte. *Zeit. f. Fischerei* **XIII**, 87-171, 1908.
344. LEROI-GOURHAN, A. *Milieu et techniques. Sciences d'aujourdhui.* Paris, 1945.
345. LIGERS, Z. *La cueillette, las chasse et la pêche en Lettonie.* Paris, 1953.
346. LIGRECI, F. Brevi notize e documentazione iconografica sul settore peschreccio in Sicilia. *Revista della Pesca* **VIII**, 4, 1045-1093, 1967 (in Italian).
347. LINDBLOM, G. Fischfang mit einem weissen Brett in China und ähnliche Methoden aus anderen Teilen der Welt. *Ethnos* **3**, 115-132, 1943.
348. LINEHAM, E J and CURTSINGER, B. The trouble with the dolphins. *Nat. Geogr.* 155 (4), 506-541, 1979.
349. LIPS, J. *Fallensysteme der Naturvölker.* Leipzig, 1927.
350. LIPS, J E. *Vom Urspung der Dinge.* Darmstadt, 1961.
351. LITTLE, E C S. *Handbook of utilization of aquatic plants.* FAO Fish. Technical Paper No. 187. Rome, 1979.
352. LIU, C L. [*Mackerel lining in Su-ao.*] Fishery Survey 8, Taiwan, 1956 (in Chinese).
353. LIU, S Y. The fishing industries of Hong Kong. A general survey Part V. Description of gear and methods. *Hong Kong Fish. Res. Stat. J.* **1** (2), 107-135, 1940.
354. LOEBELL, R. *So Fängt man Aale.* Hamburg, 1966.
355. LOOSANOFF, V L. *The American or eastern oyster.* US Department of the Interior. Bureau of Comm. Fisheries, Circular 205. Washington, 1965.
356. DE LUNA, J C. *Peces de los litorales Ibérico y Morroqui y su pesca.* Madrid, 1948, (in Spanish).
357. LUNDBECK, J. Fanggeräte der Haff- und Seefischerei an der Preussischen Bucht. *Protok. Fischereitech.* **3**, 14-30, 1954.
358. LUNDBECK, J. Die Fischerei von den Naturvölkern bis zur modernen Technik und Wirtschaft: Fangverfahren und-Geräte der Fischerei. *Mitteilungen des Instituts für Seefischerei* **13**, 37-142, 1972
359. LUNIN, V I. Piscevaja Promyslennost. [The methods of the fishing industry] Moscow, 1980 (in Russian).
360. LUX, F E, UZMANN, J R and LIND, H F. Strandings of shortfin squid, *Ilex illecebrosius,* in New England in fall 1976. *Mar. Fish. Rev.* **40** (1), 21-26, 1978.
361. MACLAREN, P J R. *The fishing devices of central and southern Africa.* The occasional papers of the Rhodes-Livingstone Museum. Livingstone, Northern Rhodesia, 1958.
362. MACPHAIL, J S and MEDCOF, J C. A new digger for soft-shell clams. 'Trade News' of the Department of Fisheries of Canada, March 1963.
363. MÄKI, T V and PITKÄNEN, H. *Kalastajan tietokirja* [*Fishermen's encyclopedia*], Helsinki, 1969 (in Finnish).
364. MALKJAWITSCHUS, S K. [La pêche du poisson en mer sans filet, ses perspectives de developpement], *Rybnoje Chosjaistvo* **44**, (10), 44-46, 1968 (in Russian).
365. MANACOP, P R and CAPCO, S R. The goby dredge-trawl fishery of Laguna de Bay. *Philipp. J. Fish.* **2**, 125-160, 1953.
366. MARCOTTI, T. *Bogen und Pfeile.* Munich, 1958.
367. MARGETTS, A R. Some conclusions from underwater observation of trawl behaviour. *World Fish.* **1** (5), 161-165, 1952.
368. MARIN, P-H and GILLES, P-M. *Pêche en mer à voile.* Paris, 1978.
369. MARSHALL, W. Die Erforschung des Meeres. *In: Weltall und Menschheit* **IV**, Kramer, H (*ed*). 245-382, (1904).
370. MAS, R. and BUESA, J. *La nasa Antillana.* Centro de Investigatiomes Pesqueros, Cuba, Contribucion No. 15, 1962 (in Spanish).
371. MASSUTI, M. Resultados de la pruebas experimentales effectuadas en aguas de Mallorca para la pesca con nasas de las gambas de profundidad. *Publicationes Tecnicas de la Junta de Estudios de Pesca,* No. 6, Madrid, 1967 (in Spanish).
372. MATHESON, C. *Wales and the sea fisheries.* Cardiff, 1929.
373. MATSUMOTO, W M, KAZAMA, T K and AASTED, D C. Anchored fish aggregating devices in Hawaiian waters. *Mar. Fish. Rev.* **43** (9) 1-13, 1981.
374. MATTHEWS, L H (*ed*). *The whale.* London, 1968.
375. MATUZAKI, M. *Angling in Japan.* Tourist Library: 32. Tokyo, 1940.
376. MCNEELY, R L. Purse seine revolution in tuna fishing. *Pac. Fisherman* **59** (7), 27-58, 1961.
377. MCRAE, E D and FRENCH, L E. An experiment in electrical fishing with an electric field used as an adjunct to an otter-trawl net. *Comm. Fish. Rev.* **27** (6), 1-11, 1965.
378. MEDCOF, J C. Effect of hydraulic escalator harvester on under-sized soft-shell clams. *Proc. Nat. Shellfish. Ass.* **50,** 1961.
379. MEDWAY, LORD. *The wild mammals of Malaya* (penninsular Malaysia) and Singapore. Kuala Lumpur, 1978.
380. MEISSNER, R. *Der Königsspiegel. Konungsskuggsjà.* Halle/Saale, 1944.
381. MENDEZ-AROCHA, A. *La pesca en Margarita.* (La pesca en la isla de Margarita, Venezuela), Caracas, 1963.
382. MENGI, T. Der Beykoz-Dalyan. *Protok. Fischereitech.* **10**, 351-415, 1967.
383. MENGI, T. Türkiyéde mersin baligi yakalama âletleri (1).

Balik ve Balikçilik **16** (10), 1-10, 1968 (in Turkish).
384. MENGI, T. *Balikçilik teknigi* (fishing techniques, Black Sea, Marmara Sea and some special forms of fishing gear). Istanbul, 1977 (in Turkish).
385. MENZEBACH, F. Eitel und Rutten kurzhalten. *Allg. Fischereizeitung* **83**, 41-43, 1958.
386. MENZEBACH, F. Gerätekunde. *In: Handbuch für den Sportfischer,* 256-302 and 370-377, Munich, 1979.
387. MENZIES, R J. Improved techniques for benthic trawling at depths greater than 2000 meters. *Biology of the Antarctic Seas. Antarctic Research Series Vol. 1,* 93-109, (nd).
388. MESCHKAT, A. Neues über die Schleppangel. *Fischereiwelt* **2**, 152-153, 1950.
389. MESCHKAT, A. Fischtreiben mit Vögeln und andere absonderliche Fischereimethoden auf dem Dojran-See in Jugoslavien. *Fischwirt* **7**, 113-121, 1957.
390. MEYER-WAARDEN, P F. *Electrical fishing.* FAO Fisheries Study 7, Rome, 1957.
391. MEYER-WAARDEN, P F. *Beobachtungen und Versuche an Fischen, die durch reflektions-seismische Messungen verletzt bzw. getötet wurden.* Veröffentlichungen des Instituts für Küsten und Binnenfischerei No. 37, Hamburg, 1966.
392. MEYER-WAARDEN, E and HALSBAND, I. Einführung in die Elektrofischerei. *Schriften der Bundesforschungsanstelt für Fisherei* Vol. 7, Berlin, 1975.
393. MILLER, R C. *The sea.* London, 1966.
394. MILLOT. Le troisième Coelacantha. *Le Naturaliste Malgache.* Prem. Suppl. 1954.
395. MILNE, J D and GODFREY, H. The Chinook and Coko salmon fisheries of British Columbia. *Fish. Res. Bd. Can. Bull.* **142**, 1964.
396. Ministerium der Staatl. Besitztümer. *Zeichnungen zur Forschung der Fisch- und Tierausbeute im Kaspischen Meer.* St. Petersburg, 1861.
397. MITCHELL, C T and HUNTER, J R. Fishes associated with drifting kelp off the coast of Southern and Northern Baja California. *California Fish and Game.* **56** (4), 288-297, 1970.
398. MITZKA, W. *Deutsche Fischervolkskunde.* Neumünster. 1940.
399. MOHR, H. Das Verhalten der Fische gegenüber Fanggeräten. *Protok. Fischereitech.* **6**, 296-326, 1960.
400. MOHR, H. Aquarienversuche über die Scheuchwirkung eines Vorhanges aus Luftblasen bei einigen Süsswasserfischen, besonders bei Aalen. *Protok. Fischereitech.* **7**, 121-129, 1960.
401. MOHR, H. Eel traps made of plastic. *In: Modern Fishing Gear of the World* **2**, 277-279, London, 1964.
402. MOHR, H. Behaviour patterns of different herring stocks in relation to ship and midwater trawl. *In: Modern Fishing Gear of the World,* **3**, 368-371. London, 1971.
403. MOHR, H. Auswirkungen der Erdgas- und Erdölförderung auf die Fischerei in der Nordsee. *Inf. Fischwirtsch.* **23** (1), 23-25, 1976.
404. MOHSIN, A K M. Some aquarium and food fishes of Malaysia. *In: The Livestock industry in Malaysia,* 53-70. Faculty of Veterinary and Animal Science, Universiti Pertanian Malaysian, Serdang/Selangor, 1978.
405. MONOD, T. *L'industrie de pêche au Cameroun.* Paris, 1928.
406. MONOD, T. Contribution à l'établissement d'une classification fonctionelle des engins de pêche. *Bull. du Muséum Nat. d'Histoire Naturelle,* 3e série, No. 156 Ecologie général 12, 1973.
407. MONTILLA, J R, HILARIO, C A and ESQUIERES, P G. *Various fishing gear used in the Philippines.* Technolog. services sect. Marine Fisheries Division, December 1959.
408. MORGAN, H. *World sea fisheries.* London, 1956.
409. MORGAN, R. Harvesting krill as food. *Hydrospace* **3** (2), 39-40/43, 1970.
410. MÜLLER, W. Yap. *Ergebnisse der Südsee-Expedition 1908-1910,* IIB 2a. Hamburg, 1917.
411. MÜNSTER, H. Mit dem Pödder auf den Aal. *Fischwaid* **104** (3), 135, 1979.
412. MÜNZING, J. *Die Jagd auf den Wal. Schleswig-Holsteins und Hamburgs Grönlandfahrt.* Heide, 1978.
413. NACHTIGALL, H. Indianische Fischer, Feldbauer und Viehzüchter. Beiträge zur peruanischen Völkerkunde. *Marburger Studien zur Völkerkund* **2**. Berlin, 1966.
414. NACHTIGALL, H. Völkerkunde, von Herodot bis Che Guevara. Naturvölker werden Entwicklungsländer. Stuttgart, 1972.
415. NADAUD, J (*ed*). *La pêche.* Paris, 1979.
416. NAINTRE, L, ADDENIO, C J and BRUNAND, T. *La pêche en mer.* Collection l'escapade. 1967.
417. NÉDÉLEC, C. (*ed*). *FAO catalogue of small scale fishing gear.* Farnham 1975.
418. NÉDÉLEC, C and LIBERT, L. Etude du chalut. *Revue des Reavaux* **XXIII** 2 et 3, **XXIV** 4, **XXV** 4, 1962.
419. NELSON, W R and BOUSSU, M F. *Evaluation of trawls for monitoring and harvesting fish populations in Oahe Reservoir, South Dakota.* Fish and Wildlife Service Techn. Paper 76, 1974.
420. NEUMANN-NEUDAMM, J. (*ed*). *Illustriertes Fischerei-Lexicon.* Neudamm, 1936.
421. NEVERMANN, H. Admiralitätsinseln. *Ergebnisse der Südsee-Expedition 1908-1910,* IIA. Hamburg, 1934.
422. VAN NHIEM, R. *Des poissons et des hommes.* 1956.
423. NICOLAS, M. *Poissons et pêche en Turquie.* Paris, 1974.
424. NIKOLSKI, G H. *Spezielle Fischkunde.* Berlin, 1957.
425. NIKONOROV, I V. The basic principles of fishing for the Caspian Kilka by underwater light. *In: Modern Fishing Gear of the World* **1**, 559-566, London, 1959.
426. NIKONOROV, I V. *In:* Pump fishing with light and electric current. *In: Modern Fishing Gear of the World* **2**, 577-579. London, 1964.
427. NISHIMURA, A. Primitive fishing methods. *Ryukyuan Culture and Society,* 67-77, 1964.
428. NISHIMURA, A. Living fossils of oldest fishing gear in Japan. *VIIIth Int. Congress of Anthropological and Ethnological Sciences.* Tokyo and Kyoto, 1968.
429. NISHIMURA, A. The most primitive means of transportation in Southeast and East Asia. *Asian Folklore Studies,* **XXVII**-2, 1-93, 1969.
430. NISHIMURA, A. Ishihiki, the oldest fishing gear, its morphology and function. *Studia ethnographica and folkloristica in honorem Béla Gunda,* 619-629, 1971.
431. NISHIMURA, A. Cultural and social change in the modes of ownership of stone tidal weirs. *In: Maritime adaptations of the Pacific;* Casteel, R H and Quimbi, G J (*eds*). 77-88. The Hague, 1975
432. NIYAZAKI, CH and YAMAGUCHI, Y. Effects of throwing stone to drive the fish into gillnet. *Bull. Tokai Reg. Fish. Res. Lab.* **50**, 31-39, 1967.
433. NN. *Onomatologia forestalis-piscatorio-venatoria oder vollständiges Forst-, Fisch- und Jagdlexikon.* Frankfurt/Leipzig, 1772.
434. NN. *Zur Erforschung der Fisch- und Tierausbeute im Weissen-und Eis-Meer.* (*ed*) Ministerium für Staatl. Besitztümer. St. Petersburg, 1871.
435. NN. [*Handbook of fishing gear in Siam.*] Bangkok, 1907 (in Thai).
436. NN. *La pêche aux colonies.* Paris, 1926.
437. NN. *Wales and sea fisheries.* 1929.
438. NN. Die mechanische Gewinnung der Klaffmuschel. *Die*

Fischwoche **3** (7/8), 53, 1948.
439. NN. *Aquatic resources of the Ryukyu-Area.* Fish and Wildlife Service. Fishery Leaflet 333, 1949.
440. NN. [*Fishing gear of the Caspian Sea.*] (*ed*). Ministry of Fisheries, Moscow 1951, (in Russian).
441. NN. [*Fishing gear in the Azov Sea and in the Black Sea*] (*ed*). Ministry of Fisheries. Moscow, 1952 (in Russian).
442. NN. [*Handbook of fishing gear in Siam.*] Bangkok, 1953 (in Thai).
443. NN. *The commercial fisheries of Maryland.* Educ. Series No. 30, 1953.
444. NN. [*History of the fishery for cormorants.*] Tokyo, 1957 (in Japanese).
445. NN. *Illustrations of Japanese fishing boat and fishing gear.* Tokyo, 1959/65.
446. NN. Modern North Pacific halibut gear. *Pac. Fisherman* **61** (10), 23-25, 1963.
447. NN. High productivity dredging. *World Fish.* **16** (7), 60-61/64, 1967.
448. NN. *Korean fishing gear and illustrations.* Vol. **3**. Pusan, 1968/70.
449. NN. Tide-line shrimping new style. *World Fish.* **18** (4), 43, 1969.
450. NN. California squid boats try fishing with pump. *Fish. News Int.* **9** (5), 73, 1970.
451. NN. Purpose-built cockle dredger. *World Fish.* **19** (5), 26-27, 1970.
452. NN. Australia tests electronic shark shield. *Aust. Fish.* **29** (5), 16-17, 1970.
453. NN. Mechanization of longline fishing. A complete system for handling all operations. *World Fish.* **24** (12), 73-75, 1971.
454. NN. Diving for abalone in Australia. *Fish. News Int.* **11** (4), 39, 1972.
455. NN. Eight-wheeled clam catcher works Canadian beach. *Fish. News Int.* **11** (8), 18, 1972.
456. NN. Purse seining by net drum. *Fish. News Int.* **11** (8), 43-49, 1972.
457. NN. Dutch fishery developments — boats and gear. *World Fish.* **23**, 1/2, 33/35, 1974.
458. NN. Luring fish. *World Fish.* **23**, 1-2, 54, 64, 1974.
459. NN. New Zealand seminar presents hard facts on squid fishing. *World Fish.* **24** (11), 57, 1975.
460. NN. Dip net fishery is revived on Columbia river. *Fish. News Int.* **14** (9), 95-96, 1975.
461. NN. Beach seine power hauler. *Fish. News Int.* **16** (3), 69, 1977.
462. NN. Fish pump survey. *World Fish.* **26** (5), 47/49/51, 1977.
463. NN. *Mechanized beach seining.* Leaflet of the Ministry of Agriculture, Fisheries Technology Unit. Haifa, 1977.
464. NN. UK 'Carousel' longlining system proved. *World Fish.* **27** (10), 37/39/43, 1978.
465. NN. Trawl boards. *World Fish.* **28**, (6), 83, 87, 1979.
466. NN. Performance and efficiency of otter board designs. *World Fish.* **28**, (7), 57, 59, 61, 65, 1979.
467. NN. 'Autoclip' small boat longlining system proven on WFA trials. *World Fish.* **28** (11), 27/28, 30, 32, 1979.
468. NN. Developments from French trawl and gear research. *World Fish.* **29** (5), 85/89/93, 1980.
469. NN. Twin trawls for pair trawling. *World Fish.* **29** (5), 95, 1980.
470. NN. The boat on wheels. *Fish. News Int.* **19** (5), 46, 1980.
471. NOEL, H S (*ed*). *Fisherman's manual.* London, 1976.
472. NOEL, H S and BEN-YAMI, M. *Pair trawling with small boats.* FAO Training Series 1. FAO, Rome, 1980.
473. NOMURA, M. Stick-held dip net fishery in Japan. *Protok. Fischereitech.* **7**, 330-348, 1962.
474. NOMURA, M. *Outline of fishing gear and method.* Kanagawa Int. Fisheries Training Centre. Nagai, Kanagawa-ken, 1978.
475. NOMURA, M and YAMAZAKI, T. *Fishing techniques.* Compilation of transcripts of lectures presented at the Training Department SEAFDEC. Tokyo, 1975.
476. NORDHOFF, C. Notes on the off-shore fishing of the Society Islands. *J. Polynes. Soc.* Vol **XXXIX**, 2-3 Wellington NZ, 1930.
477. Norink Tokai Japan Association of Agriculture and Forestry. Illustrations of Japanese fishing boat and fishing gear. Tokyo, 1965.
478. OLAUS MAGNUS. *De gentibus septentrionalibus.* Rome, 1555.
479. OKAZAKI, A. *Seaweeds and their uses in Japan.* Tokyo, 1971.
480. OKLADNIKOW, A P. *Der Hirsch mit dem goldenen Geweih, vorgeschichtliche Felsbilder Sibiriens.* Wiesbaden, 1972.
481. OLSEN, S and BELTESTAD, A K. Russian hexagon mesh is proved in Norway. *World Fish.* **29** (2), 47-50, 1980.
482. OPPIAN. *Halieutica.* Loeb Classical Library. Harvard, (nd).
483. ORMSTAD, O and ROM, K. *Isfiske.* Oslo, 1972 (in Norwegian).
484. PALLAS, P S. *Reise durch verschiedene Provinzen des russischen Reichs.* St. Petersburg, 1801.
485. PARKER JR, R O, STONE, R B and BUCHANAN, C C. Artificial reefs off Murrells Inlet, South Carolina. *Mar. Fish. Rev.* **41** (9) 12-24, 1979.
486. PARKINSON, R. *Dreissig Jahre in der Südsee.* Stuttgart, 1907.
487. PARRY, M L. The fishing methods of Kelantan and Trengganu. *J. Malay. Br. R. Asiat. Soc.* **27**, Sect. 2, 77-144, 1954.
488. PEARSON, J. Fishing appliances of Ceylon. *Bull. Ceylon Fish.* **1**, 65-134, 1922.
489. PEESCH, R. *Die Fischerkommünen auf Rügen und Hiddensee.* Berlin, 1961.
490. PEESCH, A. *Holz-Gerät in seinen Urformen.* Berlin, 1966.
491. VAN PEL, H. De Beoefening van de Majang Zeevischerij langs de Noordkust van Java. Inst. voor de Zeevischerij te Batavia. *Mededeeling* **28**, 101-113, 1938 (in Dutch).
492. PENNINGTON, F. The Japanese have many ways to catch the giant octopus. *Fish. News Int.* **18** (11) 56/57, 1979.
493. PEROSINO, S. *La pesca.* Navara, 1963 (in Italian).
494. PERRIN, W F. The porpoise and the tuna. *Sea Front.* **14** (3), 166-174, 1968.
495. PETERS, J A. Scallops and their utilization. *Mar. Fish. Rev.* **40**, (11), 1-9, 1978.
496. PETERS, N. Angeln. *Handbuch der Seefischerei Nordeuropas* **4**, 1935.
497. PETIT, G. *L'industrie des pêches à Madagaskar.* Paris, 1930.
498. PESSON-MAISSONNEUVE, M. *Manuel du pêcheur.* Paris, 1834.
499. PHILLIPS, W J. *Maori life and custom.* Sidney, 1966.
500. PIBOUBES, P. *Pêche et conchyliculture en Bretagne-Nord.* (2 Vol.) Biarritz, 1973/74.
501. DU PLESSIS, C G. Fishing with South African pursed lampara. *In: Modern Fishing Gear of the World,* 391-393, 1959.
502. PLOMANN, J. Das pflanzliche Gift 'Rotenon' und seine Bedeutung für die Fischerei. *Dtsch. Fischerei-Ztg.* **5**, 22-25, 1958.
503. POLL, M. *Exploration hydrobiologique du Lac Tanganika (1946-1947).* **1**, 103-165, Les vertébrés. Brussels, 1952.
504. POWNALL, P. Fisheries of Papua New Guinea. *Aust. Fish.*

31 (9) 2-13, 1972.

505. POWNALL, P. Ducks help Danau Panggang fishermen to catch fish. *Aust. Fish.* **34** (2), 29, 1975.
506. POWNALL, P. *Fisheries of Australia.* Farnham, 1979.
507. QUAYL, D B. Pacific oyster culture in British Columbia. *Fish. Res. B. Can. Bull.* 169, 1969.
508. QUEDENS, G. Aalpödderei. *Fischwaid,* 211-212, 1963.
509. RADCLIFFE, W. *Fishing from the earliest times.* New York, 1921/1969.
510. RASALAN, S B. The development of the Philippine bagnet (Basnig) for increased sufficiency. *In: Modern Fishing Gear of the World,* 418-421, London, 1959.
511. RASMUSSEN, H. Vodfiskeri. *In: Dansk fiskeri før industrialisieringen.* Lundbaek, M (*ed*). Nationalmuseet, Copenhagen, 1975, (in Danish).
512. RASMUSSEN, K. *Die grosse Schlittenreise.* Essen, 1946.
513. RASSOW, M. *Fischersprache und Brauchtum im Lande zwischen dem Darss.* Berlin, 1958.
514. RATHCLIFFE, C. Commercial small craft pair trawling trials: Lake Chilwa, Malawi 1971. *Afr. J. Trop. Hydrobiol. Fish.* **3** (1), 61-78, 1974.
515. RAU, C. Prehistoric fishing in Europe and North America. *Smithsonian Contributions of Knowledge* **XXV**, Article I. Washington, 1884.
516. RAUCHFUSS, W. Schlickschlitten an der Nordseeküste. *Jahrbuch der Männer vom Morgenstern* **54**, 279-311, 1974.
517. RAUCHFUSS, W. Schlickschlitten als Mehrzweck-Transportgerät an der Nordseeküste. *Jahrbuch Heimatbund Männer vom Morgenstern* **57**, 255-277, 1978.
518. RAUSING, G. The bow. Some notes on its origin and development. *Acta Archaeol. Lundensia,* Ser. 8, 6. Bonn/Lund, 1967.
519. REECE, N C. *The cultured pearl.* Tokyo, 1959.
520. RENARD, M. *La pêche à pied au bord de la mer.* Paris, 1955.
521. RENAULT, R. *L'anguile, ses moeurs, ses pêche.* Paris, 1978.
522. RICCIUTI, E R. *Menschenhai und Mördermuschel* (Killers of the seas) Hannover, 1973.
523. RICHTER, G. Im Kolumbianischen Küstengebiet um Santa Marta. *Nat. Mu.* **96**, 74-83, 1966.
524. RICKER, W E. *Methods for assessment of fish production in fresh waters.* Oxford/Edinburgh, 1968.
525. ROBERTS, P A. Developing a lake fishery in Northern Kenya. *Fish. News Int.* **14** (2), 21-25, 1975.
526. ROBIN, B. *Survive à la dérive.* Paris, 1977.
527. DE ROHAN-CSERMAK, G. *Sturgeon hooks of Eurasia.* Chicago, 1963.
528. ROSTLUND, E. *Freshwater fish and fishing in native North America.* Los Angeles, 1952.
529. ROUGHLEY, T C. *Fish and Fisheries of Australia.* Sydney, 1968.
530. ROUMRUK, S and CHAROEN, S. *Illustration of sea fishing gear for the coast of Indian Ocean.* Bangkok, 1951 (in Thai).
531. ROYCE, W F. *Introduction to the fishery sciences.* New York/London, 1972.
532. RUBIÓ, M. *Pescas con paradas con nasas de plastico y de junco.* Publicaciones Tecnicas de la Junta de Estudios de Pesca No. 7 Madrid, 1968, (in Spanish).
533. RUDAU, B. *Die Flussperlmuschel im Vogtland in Vergangenheit und Gegenwart.* Museumreihe H.23, Plauen i. Vogtl, 1961.
534. RUSSEL, F S and YONGE, C M. *The seas.* London, 1949.
535. SAHRHAGE, D. Die Seefischerei in der Republik Guinea und einige Möglichkeiten zu ihrer Intensivierung. *Arch. Fischereiwiss.* **12**, 38-74, 1961.
536. SAINSBURY, J C. *Commercial fishing methods, an introduction to vessels and gear.* London, 1971.
537. SAITO, I. Pelagic fisheries. Fishery Science Series Vol. 4 [*King crab fishery*] 252-277. Tokyo, 1960 (in Japanese).
538. SAMS, M. Southeastern Pacific aircraft assisted purse seining. *In: Modern Fishing Gear of the World* **3**, London, 1971.
539. SANCHEZ, P M. *Breve reseña sobre las principales artes de pesca usadas en Mexico.* Mexico, 1959 (in Spanish).
540. SATTLER, W. Beiträge zur Kentnis von Lebensweise und Körperbau der Larve und Puppe von Hydropsyche mit besonderer Berücksichtigung des Netzbaues. *Z.Morph. und Ökol. Tiere* **47**, 115-192, 1958.
541. SCHAFF, W E. Status of the Gulf and Atlantic menhaden fisheries and implications for resource management. *Mar. Fish. Rev.* **37** (9), 1-9, 1975.
542. SCHÄRFE, J. Über die Verwendung künstlichen Lichtes in der Fischerei. *Protok. Fischereitech.* **2**, 81-109, 1953.
543. SCHÄRFE, J. A new method for 'aimed' one-boat trawling in mid-water and on the bottom. *Stud. and Rev.* **13**, 1960.
544. SCHÄRFE, J. Improvements and trends of developments in marine fishing methods and gear. *In: The Better Use of the World's Fauna for Food,* 105-107. London, 1963.
545. SCHÄRFE, J. Neue Versuche mit Elektrofischerei im Meer. *Allg. Fischwirtschafts-Ztg.* **17** (28/29), 12-16, 1965.
546. SCHÄRFE, J. The German one-boat midwater trawl (development since 1959 to the beginning of 1960). *Protok. Fischereitech.* **12** (54), 1-75, 1969.
547. SCHÄRFE, J (*ed*). *FAO Catalogue of fishing gear designs.* Farnham, 1978.
548. SCHÄRFE, J. *The role of fishing technology in fisheries development.* FAO 70P/TF-REM/33 (NOR)/78/11. FAO/Norway workshop on fishery resources of the North Arabian Sea. 1978.
549. SCHÄRFE, J. Fishing technology for developing countries. *Oceanus* **22** (1), 54-59, 1979.
550. SCHIEMENZ, P. Die Verwertung der Fische, anderer Süsswassertiere und Süsswasserpflanzen. *Katalog: Brandenburgische Fischerei-Ausstellung,* 88-96. Berlin, 1903.
551. v SCHMID, L. Der Fischfang mit der sogenannten Otter. *In:* v. Ehrenkreutz *J. f. Fischerei* **2**, 73-76, 1855.
552. SCHMIDT, G. Karpfenfang mit dem Stuker. *Dtsch. Fischerei-Ztg.* **3**, 106-108, 1956.
553. SCHMIDT, P G. The Puretic power block and its effect on modern purse seining. *In: Modern Fishing Gear of the World* 400-413. London, 1959.
554. SCHNAKENBECK, W. Schleppnetze, Waden. *Handbuch der Seefischerei Nordeuropas* **4**, Stuttgart, 1942.
555. SCHNAKENBECK, W. Stehende Geräte. *Handbuch der Seefischerei Nordeuropas* **4**. Stuttgart, 1942.
556. SCHNAKENBECK, W. *Die deutsche Seefischerei in Nordsee und Nordmeer.* Hamburg, 1953.
557. SCHREBER, D G. Allgemeine Abhandlungen von den Fischereien und Geschichte der Fische von Duhamel du Monceau und de la Marre. *In: Schauplatz der Künste und Handwerke* Vol. **11**. Leipzig/Königsberg, 1772.
558. SCHRECKENBACH, K. Die Erleichterung der Eisfischerei durch Einsatz von Magneten. *Dtsch. Fischerei-Ztg.* **13** (3), 67-72, 1966.
559. SCHUBERT, K. Der Walfang der Gegenwart. *Handbuch der Seefischerei Nordeuropas* **11**, No. 6, 1955.
560. SCHWABE, G H. Über Mariscos und Mariscofischerei. *Zeits. Fischerei.* **39**, 313-347, 1951.
561. SCOFIELD, J, KRISTOF, E and LITTLEHALES, B. The lower keys, Florida's 'Out Islands'. *Nat. Geog.* **139** (1), 72-93, 1971.

562. SCOFIELD, W L. Drift and set line fishing gear in California. *Fish. Bull.* No. **66**, 1947.
563. SCOFIELD, W L. Trawling gear in California. *Fish. Bull.* No. **72**, 1948.
564. SCOFIELD, W L. Purse seines and other roundhaul nets in California. *Fish. Bull.* No. **81**, 1951.
565. SCOFIELD, W L. Trolling gear in California. *Fish. Bull.* No. **103**, 1956.
566. SCOFIELD, W L. History of kelp harvesting in California. *Cal. Fish and Game* **45** (3), 135-157, 1959.
567. SEIDEL, W R and VANSELOUS, T M. Automated unmanned fishing system to harvest coastal pelagic fish. *Mar. Fish. Rev.* **38** (2), 21-26, 1976.
568. SEIDEL, W R and WATSON, JR J W. The trawl design: Employing electricity to selectively capture shrimps. *Mar. Fish. Rev.* **40** (9), 21-23, 1978. (*Fish. News Int.* **18** (4), 22-23, 1979.)
569. SELIGO, A. *Die Fischerei in den Fliessen, Seen und Strandgewässern Mitteleuropas.* Stuttgart, 1925.
570. SERÈNE, M M R., Nguyen-Chan and Nyuyen-Trong-Hien: Ètudes sur les techniques des pêches au Viet-Nam. *Hai Hoc Vien* **13**, Natrang, 1956.
571. SHAW SPARROW, W. *Angling in British art.* London, 1923.
572. SHEMANSKY, Y A. [*Modern sportfishing in sea water.*] Leningrad, 1966 (in Russian).
573. SHIGUENO, K. *Shrimp culture in Japan.* Tokyo, 1974.
574. SHIMOZAKI, Y, YAJIMA, S and KOYAMA, T *et al.* Studies on the developing of reel system longline fishing method. *Bull. Tokai Reg. Fish. Res. Lab.* **48**, 1-27, 1966.
575. SHRESTHA, T K. Technique of fishing in Nepal. I: Innovation and development of loop line snaring. *Journal of Nat. Hist. Mus.* **3** (4), 121-138, 1979.
576. SHRESTHA, T K. *Wildlife of Nepal. A study of renewable resources of Nepal Himalayas.* Katmandu, 1981.
577. SINSOILLIEZ, R. *La pêche à pied, coquillages et crustacés.* Paris, 1968.
578. SINSOILLIEZ, R. *La pêche à pied, des poissons de mer.* Paris, 1970.
579. SIOLI, PROF. DR H. Plön; (verbal information).
580. SIRELIUS, U T. *Über die Sperrfischerei bei den finnischugrischen Völkern.* Helsingfors, 1906.
581. SIRELIUS, U T. Jagd und Fischerei in Finland. *Die Volkskultur Finnlands* Vol. **1**. Berlin, 1934.
582. SMITH, K. Facing up to the challenges of multi-purpose vessels. *World Fish.* **26** (6) 39, 1979.
583. SMOLOWITZ, R J. Trap design and ghost fishing; an overview. *Mar. Fish. Rev.* **40** (5/6), 2-8, 1978.
584. SMOLOWITZ, R J (*ed*). Lobster, *Homorus americanus,* trap designs and ghost fishing. *Mar. Fish. Rev.* **40** (5/6), 1-77, 1978.
585. DE SOLA, C R. The fisherman fish of the West Indies. *Bull. NY Zool. Soc.* **35**, 75-85, 1932.
586. SOLJAN, T. *Projet d'un classement des bateaux et des engins de pêche maritime et des méthodes correspondantes en vue de leur étude dans la Méditerranée. GFCM* 21/1. Istanbul, 1956.
587. SOLYMOS, E. A borító halászszerszámok fejlödése Magyarországon. [*The development of cover gear in Hungaria*]. *Etnographia LXIII*, 468-469, 1957 (in Hungarian).
588. SOLYMOS, E. Dunai halászat [*Artisanal fishery in the Hungarian part of the river Danube*] Budapest, 1965, (in Hungarian).
589. SOLYMOS, E (*ed*). *Studien zur europäischen traditionellen Fischerei. Baja Dolgozatok* **3**, Baja, 1976.
590. SOLYMOS, E. Die südslawischen Beziehungen der ungarischen Donaufischerei. *In: Studien zur traditionellen europäischen Fischerei.* Solymos, E (*ed*). *Bajai Dolgozatok* **3**, 65-72. Baja, 1976.
591. South Pacific Commission Publications Bureau. A handbook for fishermen, *Bêche-de-mer of the South Pacific Islands.* Haymarket/Australia. (nd).
592. SPAKOV, G T. [*Some problems about the mechanization of laminar harvesting*] *Rybn. Hozjajstvo* 5, 63-65, 1977 (in Russian).
593. STEINBERG, R. Unterwassergeräusche und Fischerei. *Protok. Fischereitech.* **4**, 216-249, 1957.
594. STEINBERG, R. Die Fängigkeit von Kiemennetzen für Barsch und Plötze in Abhängigkeit von den Eigenschaften des Netzmaterials etc. *Arch. Fischereiwiss.* **12**, 173-230, 1961.
595. STEINBERG, R. Entwicklung und gegenwärtiger Stand der pelagischen Schleppnetzfischerei der deutschen Kombilogger. *Protok. Fischereitech.* **10** (47), 213-318, 1967.
596. STEINBERG, R. Neue Entwicklungen auf dem Gebiet der Schleppnetzfischerei Arbeiten des *Dtsch. Fischerei-Verb.* **17**, 52-65, 1975.
597. STEINBERG, R. Erprobung eines modifizierten 4-Laschen – Tauwerk-Schleppnetzes (see: Steinberg, R and Dahm, E. *German experiments with a modified four panel rope trawl.* ICES, CM 1976/8:39) 1977.
598. STEINBERG, R. Versuchsfischerei mit zwei deutschen Fischkuttern im Seegebiet der Seychellen. *Das Fischerblatt* **29** (10) 263-266, 1981.
599. STEINBERG, R and DAHM, E. *The use of two-boat bottom and mid-water trawls in inland waters:* experiences in the German fishery. EIFAC/T 23 (Suppl. 1), 1, 23-35, 1975.
600. STELZNER, H. *Tauchertechnik.* Lübeck, 1943.
601. STEUBEN, K S and KREFFT, G. *Die Haie der Sieben Meere.* Arten. Lebensweise und sportlicher Fang. Hamburg/Berlin, 1978.
602. STEWART, P A M. Comparative fishing for flatfish using a beam trawl fitted with electric ticklers. Scottish Fisheries Research Report No. 11, 1978.
603. SÜBERKRUB, F. Praktische Erfahrungen mit neuen Schrebrettern. *Schiff und Werft* **19**, 282-294, 1943.
604. SÜBERKRÜB, F. Otterboards for pelagic trawling. *In: Modern Fishing Gear of the World* **1**, 359-360, London, 1959.
605. SUNDER LAL HORA. Crab-fishing at Uttarbhag, Lower Bengal. *Curr. Sci.* **III**, 11, 543-546, 1935.
606. SUNDSTROM, G T. *Commercial fishing vessels and gear.* US Fish and Wildlife Service, Circ. 48. Washington, 1957.
607. SVENDSEN, L. *Tun, fiskeri og tunfisk.* Kopenhagen, 1949 (in Danish).
608. TERUNI, N I. [*Mechanization of marine fishing with beach-seine.*] *Rbyn. Khoz.* 40 (1), 64-69, 1964 (in Russian).
609. TESCH, F W and GREENWOOD, P H. *The eel: Biology and management of anguillid eels.* London, 1977.
610. THIEL, H. Merkwürdige Fischfanganlagen. *Kosmos* **45**, 481-485, 1949.
611. THIEL, J F (*ed*). Haus (der) Völker und Kulturen, Führer 1977: Afrika, Neuguinea, Christl. Kunst. St. Augustin/Bonn, 1977.
612. THIENEMANN, A. Bilder aus der Binnenfischerei auf Java und Sumatra. *Arch. Hydrobiol.* Suppl. Vol. 29, 529-618, 1951.
613. DE THIERSANT, P D. *Le pisciculture et la pêche en Chine.* Paris, 1872.
614. THOMAS, H J. *A comparison of some methods used in lobster and crab fishing.* Marine Laboratory, Aberdeen (nd).
615. THOMAZI, A. *Histoire de la pêche.* Paris, 1947.
616. THOMSON, D B. *Seine fishing; bottom fishing with rope*

warps and wing trawls. Fishing News Books Ltd. Farnham, 1981.

617. THOMSON, D B. *Pair trawling and pair seining; the technology of two-boat seining*. Fishing News Books Ltd. Farnham, 1978.
618. THOMPSON, L G. *History of the fisheries of New South Wales*. Sidney, 1893.
619. THORSTEINSSON, G. Fangmethoden in der Kabeljaufischerei. *Protok. Fischereitech.* **IX**, 43, 288-381, 1965.
620. THORSTEINSSON, G. Fiskveidar og Veidarfaeri [*Fisheries and fishing gear*] Reykjavik, 1980 (in Icelandic).
621. TIEWS, K and MINNEMANN, K. Report on the fisheries of Ceylon *etc*, Sessional paper No. **XX**. Colombo, 1963.
622. TINLEY, K L. Fishing methods of the Thonga tribe in northeastern Zululand and southern Mocambique. *The Lammergeyer* **III** (1) 9-39, 1964.
623. TODD, P. Wairewa Maoris stick by old eeling methods. *Catch* **5** (2) 24, 1978.
624. TODD, P. Wanganui lamprey fisher. *Catch* **79**, Freshwater Suppl. 2, 19-20, 1979.
625. TREIDE, D. Die Organisierung des indianischen Lachsfanges im westlichen Nordamerika. *Veröff. des Museum für Völkerkunde zu Leipzig* **14**, Berlin, 1965.
626. TRENCH, C C. *A history of angling*. London, 1974.
627. VAN TRIE, T. Essai de Pêche comparative entre les filets en nylon et en ramie. Contribution No. 108, *Int. Fishing Gear Congress,* Hamburg, 1957.
628. TRYBORN, F and WOLLEBRAEK, A. Die Ostseefischerei und ihre jetzige Lage. *Pub. de Circonstance* 13A, 1904.
629. TURNER, C H and SEXSMITH, J C. *Marine baits of California,* 1964.
630. UMALI, A F. *Guide to the classification of fishing gear in the Philippines.* Fish and Wildlife Service, Research Report 17, Washington, 1950.
631. UMALI, A F. Plants used in fishing in the Philippines. *Proc.* of the Eight Pacific Science Congress **IV**, 309-336, 1957.
632. UNDERHILL, R. *Indians of the Pacific Northwest.* Washington, 1944.
633. URSINUS, P. Schillgewinnung mit Muschelsauger. *Protok. Fischereitech.* **11**, 385-389, 1969.
634. VAMBEZ, L DE. Nouméa, New Caledonia, verbal information.
635. VANSELOUS, T M. Fishery engineering advancements: A 5-year SEFC progress report. *Mar. Fish. Rev.* **39** (4) 12-24, 1977.
636. VARE, A and HARDY, A E. *The sea angler's first handbook.* London, 1980.
637. VERHEIJEN, F J. The mechanisms of the trapping effect of artificial light sources upon animals. *Arch. néerl. de Zool.* **13**, 1-107, 1958.
638. VIBERT, R. *Fishing with electricity, its application to biology and management.* FAO/EIFAC, London, 1967.
639. VILKUNA, K. Unternehmen Lachsfang. Die Geschichte der Lachsfischerei in Kemijoki. Studia Fennica. *Rev. of Finnish linguistics and ethnology* No. **19**. Helsinki, 1975.
640. VILLADOLID, D V. Methods and gear used in fishing in Lake Taal and the Pansipit river. *Philipp. Agric.* **20**, 571-579, 1932.
641. VOSS, G L. *Cephalopod resources of the world.* FAO Fisheries Circular 149, 1973.
642. VOSS, G L. *Cephalopod resources of the world.* FAO Fisheries Reports 170. Rome, 1975.
643. WALKER, B W. A guide to the Grunion. *Calif. Fish and Game* **38**, 409-420, 1952.
644. WALTER, E. *Der Flussaal.* Neudamm, 1910.
645. WALTON, I. *The compleat angler.* London, 1950.
646. WARD, B. *Freshwater fishing.* London, 1980.
647. WARLEN, S M. Night stalking flounder in the ocean surf. *Mar. Fish. Rev.* **37** (9), 27-30, 1975.
648. WATSON JR, J W and MCVEA JR, C. Development of a selective shrimp trawl for the southeastern United States Penaeid shrimp fisheries. *Mar. Fish. Rev.* **39**, (10), 18-24, 1977.
649. WEBER, A. Die Jagd auf Wale. *In: Der neue deutsche Walfang,* Peters, N (*ed*). 142-152, Hamburg, 1938.
650. WELCHERT, H H. *Der unsterbliche Angler.* Hamburg, 1963.
651. WELCOMME, R L. Les moyens de pêche dans les eaux continentales du Dahomey. *Études Dahoméennes NS* No. **17**. 5-35, 1970.
652. WELCOMME, R L. A description of certain indigenous fishing methods from southern Dahomey. *Afr. J. Trop. Hydrobiol. Fish* Vol. **1** No. 2, 129-140, 1971.
653. WELCOMME, R L. An evaluation of the acadja method of fishing as practised in the coastal lagoons of Dahomey (West Africa) *J. Fish. Biol.* **4**, 39-55, 1972.
654. WELCOMME, R L. *Fisheries ecology of floodplain rivers.* London, 1979.
655. WENBAN-SMITH, H B. The coastal fisheries near Dar es Saláam. *Tanganyika Notes and Records,* 165-174, 1963.
656. WENT, A E J. The Galway fishery. *Proc. Royal Irish Academy,* **XLIX**, Sect. C. No. 5, 187-219, 1944.
657. WENT, A E J. The pursuit of salmon in Ireland. *Proc. Royal Irish Academy* 63, Sect. C., No. 6, 191-244, 1964.
658. WESTENBERG, J. Acoustical aspects of some Indonesian fisheries. *J. du Cons.* **18**, 311-325, 1953.
659. WESTPHAL-HELLBUSCH, S. Berufs-Kasten im Irak. *Umschau* **60** (24), 755-758, 1960.
660. WEULE, K. *Kulturelemente der Menschheit.* Stuttgart, 1911.
661. WEULE, K. *Die Anfänge der Naturbeherrschung I.* Stuttgart, 1921.
662. WEULE, K. Chem. Technologie der Naturvölker. *Anfänge der Naturbeherrschung* **2**, Stuttgart, 1922.
663. WEYER, E. *Primitive Völker heute.* Gütersloh, 1959.
664. WFA (White Fish Authority). *Net drums.* Data Sheet No. 1 (nd).
665. WFA (White Fish Authority). *Storage of seine ropes below deck.* Data sheet No. 7 (nd).
666. WHITE, C M N. The role of hunting and fishing in Luvale society. *Afric. Stud.* **15** (2), 75-86, 1956.
667. WICKHAM, D A and SEIDEL, W R. A self-contained subsurface light source system for fish attraction. *Mar. Fish. Rev.* **35** (10), 14-19, 1973.
668. WIEBALK, R. Von den Rechten der Wurster im Wattenmeer. *Männer im Morgenstern* **XVIII**, 108-115, 1917.
669. WILBERT, J. Problematica de algunos métodos da pesca de los indios sudamerica as. *Memorias de la Sociedad de ciencias Naturales de Salle.* **15**, 41, Caracas 1955 (in Spanish).
670. WILCOCKS, J C. *The sea-fisherman.* London, 1875.
671. WILKE, H. Krebssteine ein grosser Erfolg. *Allg. Fischerei-Ztg.* **105** (8). 458, 1980.
672. WILKINSON, W A. Tuna aggregation system boosts catch. *World Fish.* **27** (11), 29, 1978.
673. WILKINSON, W A. Tonga – the spirit fishery. *Fish. News Int.* **19** (2) 17, 1980.
674. WILIMOVSKY, N J and ALVERSON, D L. The future of fisheries. *In: Modern Fishing Gear of the World* **3**, 509-513, 1971.
675. WILLER, A. Ostpreussen, Lettland, Finnland, eine

fischereiliche Betrachtung. *Mitt. Dtsch. Seefischerei,* Ver. 45, 151-173, 1929.

676. WILLER, A. Stinthengst oder Lachskönig? *Fischereizeitung,* **37** Neudamm, 1934.

677. WINTERHOFF, E. *Walfang in der Antarktis.* Oldenburg/Hamburg, 1974.

678. WOLF, R S and CHISLETT, G R. Trap fishing explorations for snapper and related species in the Caribbean and adjacent waters. *Mar. Res. Fish. Rev.* **36** (9), 49-61, 1974.

679. WOOD, E J F and JOHANNES, R E. *Tropical marine pollution.* Amsterdam, 1975.

680. WRIGHT, H. Purse seining with a drum. *Fish. News Int.* **18** (6), 36-39, 1979.

681. YAJIMA, S and MITSUGI, S. *Japanese squid jigging gear.* FAO Fisheries Report No. 170 Suppl. 1, 85-88, Rome, 1976.

682. YAMAMOTO, I. *Ketentuan Kerja Buku I, Standard Statistik Perikanan.* Jakarta, 1975 (in Indonesian).

683. YAMASHITA, Y. *The octopus fishery of Hokkaido.* FAO Fisheries Report No. 170, Suppl. 1, 142-147, Rome, 1976.

684. v YHLEN, G. Die Seefischerei an der Westküste Schwedens. Int. Fischereiausstellung Berlin 1880. Amtliche Berichte. Berlin, 1881.

685. YUEN, H S H. Response of skipjack tuna (*Katsuwonus pelamis*) to experimental changes in pole-and-line fishing operations. *Proc* FAO Conference on Fish Behaviour in Relation to Fishing Techniques and Tactics. *FAO Fisheries Report* No. **62**, 607-618, 1969.

686. ZERRIES, O. Wild- und Buschgeister in Südamerika. *Studien zur Kulturkunde* **XI**. Wiesbaden, 1954.

687. ZEUNER, F. *Geschichte der Haustiere.* Munich, 1967.

688. ZIMMERMANN, W F A. Die Inseln des indischen und stillen Meeres. Berlin, 1865.

689. ZNAMIEROWSKA-PRÜFFEROWA, M. Rybackie Narzedzia Kolne w Police i w Krajach Sasiedhich. *Studia Soc. Sc. Torunensis.* Suppl. 4, 1957 (in Polish).

690. ZNAMIEROWSKA-PRÜFFEROWA, M. Bemerkungen zur traditionellen Fischerei in Polen *In: Studien zur europäischen traditionellen Fischerei.* Solymos, E. (*ed*) *Bajai Dolgozatok* **3**, 17-34, 1976.

Subject index

Species and product index

Geographical index